Prealgebra

A JOURNEY TO COLLEGE MATHEMATICS

MEGAN CAVANAH
CHARLES P. MCKEAGUE

xyztextbooks

Prealgebra
A Journey to College Mathematics

Megan Cavanah
Charles P. McKeague

Publisher: XYZ Textbooks
Editorial Team: Anne Scanlan-Rohrer
and Buddy Galletti
Proofreader: Jana Mooney
Composition: Tessa Avila
Design: Katherine Heistand Shields
Cover Photo: © istock.com/ franckreporter

ISBN-13: 978-1-63098-157-0 / ISBN-10: 1-63098-157-5

For product information and technology assistance, contact us at
XYZ Textbooks, 1-877-745-3499

For permission to use material from this text or product,
e-mail: **info@mathtv.com**

XYZ Textbooks
1339 Marsh Street
San Luis Obispo, CA 93401
USA

Printed in the United States of America

For your course and learning solutions, visit **www.xyztextbooks.com**

A JOURNEY TO COLLEGE MATHEMATICS

MEGAN CAVANAH
CHARLES P. MCKEAGUE

Brief Contents

Contents

Preface

A NOTE TO INSTRUCTORS

Description

Prealgebra is a one-semester college mathematics book that introduces students to negative numbers and equations early in the course. Negative numbers are in the second chapter, and equations are in the third chapter. Students are also introduced to evaluating algebraic expressions and solving algebraic equations early on in the text. These problems are found in subsequent chapters as new concepts are introduced.

The common sequence of topics is enriched with applications, study skills, and other features as detailed below. We suggest encouraging your students to make regular use of these features—our objective is to help students build a foundation of successful studying practices that will benefit them in their future courses.

This textbook includes more than just the book itself. While many students still prefer to use the printed book in their studies, the eBook extends the reach of the book, giving students and instructors access to a wide array of supporting tools. Some key features include:

- The eBook includes free digital access to the *Prealgebra* text, plus over 20 eBooks covering eight math courses.
- The text and eBook include free access to over 10,000 MathTV videos, with multiple tutorials for every example found in the text.
- Additionally, QR codes printed in each section provide students quick and easy connection to videos for those examples.

Textbook Features

Every section has been written so that it can be discussed in a single class session. A clean layout and conversational style are used by the authors to make it easy for students to read. Important information, such as definitions and properties, is also highlighted so that it can easily be located and referenced by students. "Paying Attention to Instructions" exercises highlight the importance of carefully reading the directions for exercises.

In addition, the following features provide both instructors and students a vast array of resources that can be used to enrich the learning environment and promote student success.

Connecting Print and Digital We want students to get the most out of their course materials, which is why we think of the textbook as a "toolbox" for students. QR codes are integrated throughout the textbook, to connect the printed version to the digital assets easily. As students read their printed book, support material is quickly and conveniently available via one scan of the accompanying QR code. We find that this direct link to additional support is a comfortable level of technology for all students taking this course; it integrates technology without being overwhelming.

Spotlight on Success This feature offers students a variety of strategies from many different sources and highlights both the challenges and triumphs common to students taking mathematics courses. Students and instructors share their unique approaches to learning and suggestions for success in a math course. Many of the spotlights feature the same relatable peer tutors that students will see on the MathTV videos that accompany the text.

"How To" and "Summary" Segments   Many sections include a "How To" or "Summary" segment that outlines the steps in the method or process used to solve certain types of problems. We have emphasized these segments within each section so that students are aware that they are key concepts. They also help students internalize the particular problem-solving strategy introduced in that section.

HOW TO   Strategy for Solving Linear Equations in One Variable

Step 1a: Use the distributive property to separate terms, if necessary.

1b: If fractions are present, consider multiplying both sides by the LCD to eliminate the fractions.

1c: Combine like terms on each side of the equation.

Step 2: Use the addition or subtraction property of equality to get all variable terms on one side of the equation and all constant terms on the other side. A variable term is a term that contains the variable. A constant term is a term that does not contain the variable.

Step 3: Use the multiplication or division property of equality to get x

Facts from Geometry   Concepts from geometry have been incorporated throughout the text. These topics apply the concepts of the section and help solidify abstract concepts. They also provide additional opportunities to apply concepts in a geometry context.

FACTS FROM GEOMETRY

Pythagorean Theorem

A **right triangle** is a triangle that contains a 90° (or right) angle. The longest side in a right triangle is called the **hypotenuse**, and we use the letter c to denote it. The two shorter sides are denoted by the letters a and b. The Pythagorean theorem states that the sum of the squares of the two legs of a right triangle equals the square of the hypotenuse. In symbols, we have

$$a^2 + b^2 = c^2$$

Using the rules of algebra, we could derive and then use the following

Application Problems   From our experience, we have found that students do better in their math course when they see an application to real-world problems. That's why we've included as many applied problems as we can. We hope students can relate to the context of these problems. Additionally, we hope these questions give students a greater mathematical sense of the topics covered in that section.

Improving Your Quantitative Literacy

79. **Super Bowl Viewers** The chart shows the number of people who have watched the Super Bowl over a ten-year Use the information to answer the following questions.

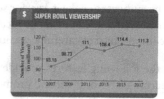

$ SUPER BOWL VIEWERSHIP

a. If the trend from 2013 to 2015 had continued, what would the viewership have been in 2017?

Key Concept Review   At the end of each section you will find conceptual questions under the heading "Key Concept Review." These open-ended problems encompass the key concepts of the section. Students should be able to articulate the answers to these questions after reading the section or attending class. These problems can also be used as classroom assessment tools to collect just-in-time feedback on student understanding. For example, they could be utilized as an entry or exit "ticket" to class or as discussion topics for review among students.

KEY CONCEPT REVIEW

After reading through the preceding section, respond in your own words and in complete sentences.

A. When we translate a sentence such as "What number is 15% of 63?" into symbols, what does each of the following translate to?

a. is   **b.** of   **c.** what number

B. Using Example 1 in your text as a guide, answer the question below.

The number 9.45 is what percent of 63?

C. Show that the answer to the question below is the same as the answer to the question in Example 2 of your text.

The number 21 is what percent of 42?

Getting Ready for the Next Section When students finish a section, they can feel a great sense of accomplishment. We want to help maintain their momentum as much as possible, which is why we offer a brief preview of the next stop in their mathematical journey. A small set of "Getting Ready for the Next Section" problems appear near the end of every problem set. These are similar problems that students will see when they read through the next section of the text.

Getting Ready for the Next Section

Multiply.

99. $2 \cdot 2 \cdot 3 \cdot 3 \cdot 3$ **100.** $2^2 \cdot 3^3$ **101.** $2^2 \cdot 3 \cdot 5$ **102.** $2 \cdot 3^2 \cdot 5$

Divide.

103. $12 \div 3$ **104.** $15 \div 3$ **105.** $20 \div 4$ **106.** $24 \div 4$

107. $42 \div 6$ **108.** $72 \div 8$ **109.** $102 \div 2$ **110.** $105 \div 7$

Landmark Review These review boxes are strategically placed in each chapter. They capture key concepts that have already been covered in the chapter.

LANDMARK REVIEW: CHECKING YOUR PROGRESS

Write each percent as a fraction with denominator 100.

1. 15%   **2.** 27%   **3.** 14%   **4.** 89%

Change each percent to a decimal.

5. 17%   **6.** 28%   **7.** 5%   **8.** 6.37%

Change each decimal to a percent.

9. 0.38   **10.** 0.98   **11.** 0.09   **12.** 4.87

Change each fraction or mixed number to a percent. Round to the nearest tenth of a percent if necessary

13. $\frac{1}{}$ **14.** $\frac{1}{}$ **15.** $\frac{1}{}$ **16.** $3\frac{1}{}$

Navigation Skills The Navigation Skills are designed to support students in a college math course. Some include study strategies while others are more reflective, helping students reframe their mindset for success.

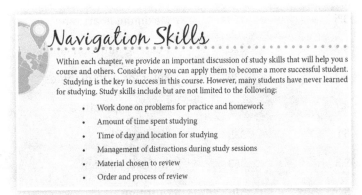

Navigation Skills

Within each chapter, we provide an important discussion of study skills that will help you s course and others. Consider how you can apply them to become a more successful student.

Studying is the key to success in this course. However, many students have never learned for studying. Study skills include but are not limited to the following:

- Work done on problems for practice and homework
- Amount of time spent studying
- Time of day and location for studying
- Management of distractions during study sessions
- Material chosen to review
- Order and process of review

Chapter Summaries and Tests Every chapter concludes with a chapter summary and chapter test. The chapter summary lists the main properties and definitions found in the chapter, with examples given in the margin. The chapter test provides a representative sample of the various types of problems students have encountered in the chapter. These features are valuable assets to students in preparing for exams or refreshing their skills with previously learned concepts.

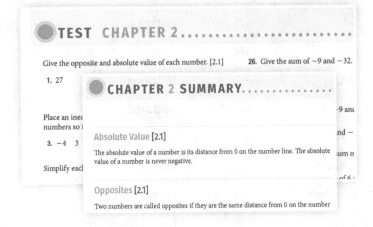

TEST CHAPTER 2

Give the opposite and absolute value of each number. [2.1]   **26.** Give the sum of -9 and -32.

1. 27

Place an ineq -9 an
numbers so

3. -4 3

Simplify eac

CHAPTER 2 SUMMARY

Absolute Value [2.1]

The absolute value of a number is its distance from 0 on the number line. The absolute value of a number is never negative.

Opposites [2.1]

Two numbers are called opposites if they are the same distance from 0 on the number

Medical and Health Sciences Applications

Many students in this course may be considering careers in the medical field or health sciences. Throughout the text, students can find applications in these areas to help them better understand the usefulness of mathematics and how the concepts in this course are related to these careers and others. These applications also show all students the applicability of mathematics to everyday life.

SECTION	PAGE	APPLICATION	EXERCISE/EXAMPLE
1.4	39	Caffeine content	Example 8
1.4	42	Calories burned during exercise	#67
1.4	42	Calories in fast food	#68
1.5	51	Reading nutrition labels	Example 12
1.5	52	Calories burned during exercise	Example 13
1.5	60	Exercise and calories	#112–117
1.6	70	Fitness walking	#79
1.6	71	Nutrition	#87–88
1.7	79	Reading nutrition labels	#85–88
1.7	79	Calories in fast food	#89–90
3.5	185	Maximum heart rate	#51–52
4.2	228	Reading nutrition labels	#59–62
4.3	239	Veterans with diabetes	#72
4.7	282	Body temperature	#56
5.1	335	Nutrition	#65–66
5.3	353	Caffeine content	#70
5.5	376	Nutrition	#63–64
6.1	418	Alcohol–water solution	Example 5
6.1	421	Nutrition	#28
6.4	438	Alcohol–water solution	Example 3
6.4	440	Nutrition	#6
6.4	441	Nutrition	#15–16, 18
6.4	441	Drug dosage: nursing	#21–24
6 Review	463	Nutrition	#47
6 Review	463	Drug dosage: nursing	#50–51
6 Test	465	Drug dosage: nursing	#13–14

SECTION	PAGE	APPLICATION	EXERCISE/EXAMPLE
7.1	470	Hydrocortisone percent	Example 4
7.1	476	Physiology	#71
7.1	477	Nutrition	#75
7.2	479	Painkiller	Chapter opening
7.2	482	Nutrition	Example 7
7.2	487	Nutrition	#45–48
7.3	491	Alcohol–water solution	#3
8.1	542	DNA	#46
8.2	554	Blood plasma	#59
8.2	554	Lung capacity	#60
8.2	554	Heart volume	#61
8.2	554	Red blood cells	#62–63
8.3	558	Vitamin grams	Example 4
8.3	561	Fish oil	#31–32
8.3	561	B-complex	#33–34
8.3	561	Aspirin	#35–36
8.3	561	Brain mass	#39–40
8.4	567	Flu temperature	Example 7
8.4	570	Body temperature	#45
8.4	571	Caffeine	#65–66
8.4	571	Ibuprofen	#67
8 Review	585	Red blood cells	#66
8 Review	585	Brain mass	#67
9.1	599	Heart beats	#106
9.2	613	Cell radius	#112

Supplements for the Instructor

Please contact your sales representative—or see xyztextbooks.com/instructors for more info.

MathTV.com   Every example in every XYZ Textbook is worked on video by multiple student instructors. Students benefit from seeing multiple approaches and gain confidence in learning from their peers. These videos can be used to supplement class time or for alternative instruction, such as a flipped classroom approach.

eBook   Through the website, instructors can access the eBook for this course as well as other texts. Using the My Bookshelf feature, you can view the text as well as the resources available to both you and the student.

Complete Solutions Manual   Available online, this manual contains complete solutions to all the exercises in the problem sets.

Printable Test Items   Instructors can choose from a bank of pre-created tests. These are provided in an editable format so that they can be tailored to your teaching style and testing preferences.

Computerized Test Bank   The testing system enables the instructor to choose questions either manually or randomly by section, question type, and other criteria. You can find a link to download the program and the testbank at http://www.xyztextbooks.com/instructors/

Matched Problems Worksheets   These worksheets integrate the textbook content and MathTV videos in order to check student progress or provide an alternative to classroom instruction.

PowerPoint Presentations   We have provided presentations that can be opened in PowerPoint, Apple Keynote or Google Slides as a template for classroom lectures. Instructors can add examples that they want to use in class or use these to supplement their presentation of the material.

Customization   This title can also be customized to meet the needs of your institution, students, and department.

Supplements for the Student

eBook   Students who purchase the textbook have one year of free access to the eBook. Students can also choose to purchase the eBook instead of the printed text. The eBook has videos and practice problems for every example in the book.

Student Solutions Manual   The student solutions manual contains complete solutions to all the odd-numbered exercises in the text. It is available for purchase separately.

QR Code   QR codes quickly and easily connect the textbook to digital resources. By scanning the QR code located in each section, students will be taken directly to the accompanying MathTV videos for the examples in that section.

MathTV.com   Students have access to math instruction 24 hours a day, seven days a week. Within a few clicks or a scan of the QR code in the textbook, students can access multiple videos that correspond to each example in the text. Many of the video examples are also presented by Spanish-speaking instructors.

Reviewers

Reviews from the following instructors were much appreciated.

Monica Hennessy, *University of Cincinnati Blue Ash*

R. Warren Lemerich, *Laramie County Community College*

Vochita Mihai, *Medaille College*

Susan Twigg, *Wor-Wic Community College*

Gowribalan A. Vamadeva, *University of Cincinnati Blue Ash*

Alexsis Venter, *Arapahoe Community College*

Angela Wayne, *Los Angeles City College*

The following instructors participated in online focus groups for an earlier, alternate version of this text.

Dr. Mohammed Abella, *Washtenaw Community College*

Darrell Abney, *Maysville Community & Technical College*

Ignacio Alarcon, *Santa Barbara City College*

Lisa Allai-Stop, *Eastern Michigan University*

Karen Anglin, *Tyler Junior College*

Sandra Arman, *Motlow State Community College*

Anna Bakman, *LA Trade-Tech*

Lee Barnhill, *Wenatchee Valley College*

Jamie Baughman, *Wilburton School*

Michelle Beard, *Ventura College*

Rosanne B. Benn, *Prince George's Community College*

Fatemah Bicksler, *Delgado Community College*

Tammy Bishop, *Wayne Community College*

Nick Bykov, *San Joaquin Delta College*

Shawna M. Bynum, *Napa Valley College*

Susan D. Caire, *Delgado Community College*

Elizabeth Cannis, *Pasadena City College*

Nemie Capacia, *Grossmont College*

Carl Clark, *Indian River State College*

Thomas J. Close, *North Central State College*

Julane B. Crabtree, *Johnson County Community College*

Dr. Scott Demsky, *Broward College*

Robert Diaz, *Fullerton College*

Tia L. Doyle, *Kirkwood Community College*

Dale Duke, *Oklahoma City Community College*

Christopher Dyer, *West Valley College*

J. Robson Eby, *Blinn College—Bryan Campus*

Sipra Eko, *Muscatine Community College*

Mike Everett, *Santa Ana College*

Scott Fallstrom, *MiraCosta College*

Dawnnel Francis, *Garden City Community College*

David French, *Tidewater Community College*

Linda Fuqua, *North Central Texas College*

Abel Gage, *Skagit Valley College*

Jaime Garces, *Palo Alto College*

David W. Gilbert, *Santa Barbara City College*

Frank Gonzalez, *Saddleback College*

Margery C. Grammer, *Lone Star College*

Judith M. Graves, *Butte-Glenn Community College*

Dean Greve, *Gateway Technical College*

Susanna Gunther, *Solano College*

Lourdes Gutierrez, *Shoreline Community College*

Keven Hansen, *Southwestern Illinois College*

Mark Harbison, *Sacramento City College*

Andy Henley, *Guilford Technical Community College*

Elizabeth A. Hentges, *Century College*

Todd Hoff, *Wisconsin Indianhead Technical College*

Ken Hoffmann, *Century Community and Technical College*

Karen Horn, *Red Rocks Community College*

Jo Beth Horney, *South Plains College*

Lorie Hughes, *Snow College*

June Hundley, *Rowan–Cabarrus Community College*

Linda D. Hunt, Ed.D, *Shawnee State University*

Sarah K. Jackson, *Pratt Community College*

Charles Jaronek, *Oklahoma City Community College*

Jeffrey Jones, *County College of Morris*

Kanetra H. Jones, *Baton Rouge Community College*

Thomas W. Judge, *Ohlone College*

Sally Keely, *Clark College*

Donna Ens Kessler, *Moberly Area Community College*

Harriet Higgins Kiser, *Georgia Highlands College*

Daniel Kleinfelter, *College of the Desert*

Constance Kuchar, *Jefferson College*

Debra Lackey, *Odessa College*

Patricia M. Lambdin, *Chesapeake College*

John Leamy, *Columbia College*

Mary Margarita Legner, *Riverside City College*

Jeanine M. Lewis, *Aims Community College*

Ivan Loy, *Front Range Community College/LC*

Sherry McCormack, *Hopkinsville Community College*

RD McDaniel, Jr., *Rowan–Cabarrus Community College*

Shyla G. McGill, *New Mexico Junior College*

Robbie McKelvy, *Cossatot Community College—UA*

Sharon M. McPherson, *Pikes Peak Community College*

Susan C. Metzger, *North Central Michigan College*

Julie Mihalcik, *Fulton Montgomery Community College*

Pam Miller, *Phoenix College*

Derek S. Milton, *Santa Barbara City College*

Becky A. Moening, *Ivy Tech Community College—Northeast*

Kathy Moore, *Santiago Canyon College*

James Christian Morgan, *Holyoke Community College*

Donna E. Nordstrom, *Pasadena City College*

Rodney Null, *Rhodes State College*

Jon Odell, *Richland Community College*

Louise Olshan, *County College of Morris*

David Olson, *Aims Community College*

Louise W. Pack, *Rowan–Cabarrus Community College*

Dr. Shelly Ray Parsons, *Aims Community College*

Mari M. Peddycoart, *Lone Star College*

Kathy Perino, *Foothill College*

Nancy Pevey, *Pellissippi State Community College*

Professor Mark W. Pierce, LtCol, USAF,(ret), *Georgia Military College*

David Radcliffe, *Inver Hills Community College*

Jayanthy Ramakrishnan, *Lansing Community College*

Stacy Reagan, *Caldwell Community College and Technical Institute*

Tammy S Reilley, *North Central Michigan College*

Stacey Reynolds, *Front Range Community College*

Lucia Riderer, *Citrus College*

Kathy Rigdon, *Metropolitan Community College*

Donald Roach, *El Camino College—Compton Center*

Hazel Ross, *Monterey Peninsula College*

Jan Roy, *Montcalm Community College*

Kathy Ryan, *Front Range Community College*

Farid Sadeghipour, *Mesa College in San Diego*

Nancy J. Sattler, Ph.D., *Terra Community College*

Sue Sensenbaugh-Padgett, *Northwestern Michigan College*

Patty Jean Shelton, *Cuyahoga Community College*

Kathleen Shepherd, *Monroe County Community College*

David F. Sherrill, *Sandhills Community College*

Mike Shirazi, *Germanna Community College*

Diana Snyder, *Community College of Philadelphia*

Jayne A. Spears, *Murray State College*

Alan Spirlet, *Bristol Community College*

Marie St. James, *St. Clair County Community College*

Bryan Stewart, *Tarrant County College*

Connie Stocker, *St. Louis Community College—Meramec*

Jane D. Tanner, *Onondaga Community College*

Janet E. Teeguarden, *Ivy Tech Community College—Indianapolis*

Rose Toering, *Kilian Community College*

Julie Turnbow, *Collin College—Preston Ridge*

Norine L Turner, *Weatherford College*

Svitlana Tyson, *HACC—York Campus*

Diane Valade, *Piedmont Virginia Community College*

Alexsis Venter, *Arapahoe Community College*

Dave Vinson, *Pellissippi State Community College*

Thomas Virgin, *Des Moines Area Community College—Urban Campus*

Melinda S. Wall, *Southwestern Michigan College*

Ken S. Wagman, *Gavilan College*

Jan Weis, *Scott Community College*

Christine V. Wetzel-Ulrich, *Northampton Community College*

Karen White, *Northwest Vista*

Tammy Widmer, *Lake Region State College*

Patricia Wilder, *Ivy Tech Community College*

Marissa Wolfe, *Yavapai College*

Sharón Lynn Wyeth, *Alamo Community College*

Ronald W. Yates, *College of Southern Nevada*

 # Preface

A NOTE TO STUDENTS

We want you to succeed.

Welcome to the XYZ Textbooks/MathTV community! We are dedicated to your success in this course. As you will see as you progress through this book, and access the other tools we have for you, we are different from other publishers.

Our authors are experienced teachers.   We believe the best textbooks are written by experienced instructors. These individuals can draw on their background teaching in the classroom and online learning environments and incorporate that expertise into our textbooks. Our objective is to provide the best instruction students can get in written form, produced by award-winning, experienced instructors.

Innovative products.   The foundation of our products is the textbook, which is also a source of tools that you will need to do well in your math course. These include eBooks, videos, worksheets, and a variety of ways to access these resources, from QR codes built into our books to our MathTV Mobile site.

Peer tutors.   Learning mathematics can be a challenge. Sometimes your class time and textbook are not enough. We understand that, which is why we created MathTV, providing you with a set of instructional videos by students just like you, who have found a way to master the same material you are studying. Since these videos are available on the internet, you can access them whenever and wherever you may be studying. You'll also get to see how your peers solve each problem, sometimes offering a different view from how an instructor solves the problem, and other times, solving the problem in the same way your instructor does, giving you confidence that that is the way the problem can be solved.

Fair prices.   We're small, independently owned and independently run. Why does that matter to you? Because we do not have the overhead and expenses that the larger publishers have. Yes, we want to be a profitable business, but we believe that we can keep our prices reasonable and still give you everything you need to be successful. Also, we want you to use this book, and the best way to make sure that happens is to make it affordable.

Unlimited access.   When you purchase one of our products, we give you access to all of our products. Why? Because everything you need to know about math is not contained in one book. Suppose you need to review a topic from a math course you completed previously? No problem. Suppose you want to see an alternate approach? It's all yours. As a member of our XYZ Textbooks/MathTV community, you have access to everything we produce, including all our eBooks.

We know you can do it.

We believe in you.   We have seen students with all varieties of backgrounds and levels in mathematics do well in the courses where we supply books and materials. In fact, we have never run across a student who could not be successful in algebra. Where that carries over to you: We believe in you. We believe you can be successful in whatever math class you are taking. Our job is to supply you with the tools you can use to attain success—you supply the drive and ambition.

We know college can be difficult.   It is not always the material you are studying that makes college difficult. We know that many of you are working, some part time, some full time. We know many of you have families to support or look after. We understand that your time can be limited. We take all this to heart when we create the materials we think you will need. For example, we make our videos available on your smartphone, tablet, and on the internet. That way, no matter where you are, you will have access to help when you get stuck on a problem.

We believe in what we do.   We are confident that you will see the value in the text and resources we have created. That's why the first chapter in every one of our eBooks is free, and so are all the resources that come with it. We want you to try us out for free. See what you think. We wouldn't do that if we didn't believe in what we do here.

How to Be Successful in Mathematics

Mathematics is a challenging subject. Often, it includes abstract concepts that require critical thinking. Concepts also build on one another, requiring that you maintain skills and retain knowledge that you learned in the past. As a result, learning a topic in mathematics isn't always accomplished the first time through the material. If you don't understand a topic the first time you see it, that's perfectly normal. Our advice, though, is to stick with it! Understanding mathematics takes time. You may find that you need to read over new material a number of times before you can begin to work problems. The process of understanding requires reading the book, studying the examples, working problems, and getting your questions answered.

Here are some additional suggestions that will help you succeed in mathematics.

1. **If you have a class meeting time, be sure to attend all class sessions on time.**   You simply will not know exactly what went on in class unless you were there. Missing class and then expecting to find out what went on from someone else is not a good strategy. Make the time to be there—and to be attentive.

2. **Read the book.**   It is best to read the section that will be covered in class beforehand. It's OK if you don't fully understand everything you read! Reading in advance at least gives you a sense of what will be discussed, which puts you in a good position when you get to class.

3. **Work problems every day and check your answers.**   One secret to success in mathematics is working problems. The more problems you work, the better you will perform. It's really that simple. The answers to the odd-numbered problems in each section are given in the back of the book. When you have finished an assignment, be sure to compare your answers with those in the book. If you have made a mistake, find out what it is, and try to correct it.

4. **Do it on your own.**   Having someone else show you how to work a problem is not the same as working the problem yourself. It is absolutely OK to get help when you are stuck. As a matter of fact, it is a good idea. Just be sure you do the work yourself. After all, when it's test time, it's all you! Get confident in every problem type, and you will do well.

5. **Review every day.**   After you have finished the problems your instructor has assigned, take another 15 minutes and review a section you have already completed. This simple trick works wonders. Studies have shown, the more you review, the longer you will retain the material you have learned. Since math topics build upon one another, this will help you throughout the term.

6. **Don't expect to understand every new topic the first time you see it.**   Sometimes it will come easy and sometimes it won't. Don't beat yourself up over it—this is perfectly normal. Expecting to understand each new topic the first time you see it can lead to disappointment and frustration. The process of understanding takes time and practice. It requires that you read the book, work problems, and get your questions answered.

7. **Spend as much time as it takes for you to master the material.**   What's the exact amount of time you need to spend on mathematics to master it? There's no way to know except to do it. You will find out as you go what is or isn't enough time for you. Some sections may take less time, and some may take more. If you end up spending 2 or more hours on each section, OK. Then that's how much time it takes; trying to get by with less will not work.

8. **Know what resources are available to you.**   We have provided a multitude of resources within this text to help you succeed in this course. There are probably also resources at your college to help you as well. Does your instructor have time set aside to help students? Does your campus have a tutoring center with tutors? We want to make sure you have all the resources you need to be successful in your math course.

9. **Relax. It's probably not as difficult as you think.**   You might get stuck at points. That's OK, everyone does. Take a break if you need to. Seek some outside help. Watch a MathTV video of the problem. There is a solution, and you will find it—even if it takes a while.

WHOLE NUMBERS

1

V isitors to Athens, Greece can visit one of the most iconic temples of Ancient Greece, the Parthenon. Construction on the Parthenon began in 447 BC at the height of the Athenian Empire. Its architecture style is post and lintel construction, which is also seen in other temples in the region. The temple also features almost 70 columns. Although the building was dedicated to Athena, the goddess of wisdom and war, its primary function was a treasury at the time it was built. Later, in the sixth century AD, it was used as a Christian church. Then, in the 1460s, it was turned into a mosque after the Ottoman conquest.

228 feet

101 feet

Suppose you are visiting the Parthenon and you decided to walk around the exterior of the temple. In mathematics, we call this distance the perimeter. After examining the illustration above, we can see that the length of the temple is 228 feet and the width is 101 feet. We can then use these measurements to calculate the total perimeter. In this chapter, we will work problems similar to this one.

YOU ARE HERE

1.1 PLACE VALUE AND NAMES WITH NUMBERS

OBJECTIVES

A Identify the place value for digits.

B Write numbers in expanded form.

C Write numbers in words.

KEY WORDS

place value

expanded form

standard form

set

counting numbers

whole numbers

number line

VIDEO EXAMPLES

SECTION 1.1

Each year, cities across the world host International Pillow Fight Day in early April. In 2010, the 5th Pillow Fight NYC took place in Union Square, New York City. People from all over the city filled the square and wielded pillows. When the fight began, people swung their pillows from side to side, hoping it would land on the nearest victim before getting hit themselves. The city's inaugural pillow fight took place in 2006 and had 500 participants. By 2010, the event garnered at least 5,000 people.

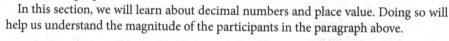

In this section, we will learn about decimal numbers and place value. Doing so will help us understand the magnitude of the participants in the paragraph above.

A Place Value

We write all numbers in our number system using the digits 0, 1, 2, 3, 4, 5, 6, 7, 8, and 9. Because there are 10 of these digits, our number system is called a **base 10** number system. The positions of the digits in a number determine the values of the digits. For example, the 5 in the number 251 has a different value from the 5 in the number 542. We will see the difference in these two values when we discuss expanded form.

The **place values** in our number system are as follows: The first digit on the right is in the ones column. The next digit to the left of the ones column is in the tens column. The next digit to the left is in the hundreds column. For a number like 542, the digit 5 is in the hundreds column, the 4 is in the tens column, and the 2 is in the ones column.

If we keep moving to the left, the columns increase in value. The following table shows the name and value of each of the first seven columns in our number system. Also, notice how the number 1 is located in the appropriate place value column.

Table 1

Millions Column	Hundred Thousands Column	Ten Thousands Column	Thousands Column	Hundreds Column	Tens Column	Ones Column
1,000,000	100,000	10,000	1,000	100	10	1

Example 1   Give the place value of each digit in the number 305,964.

Solution   Starting with the digit at the left, we have 3 in the hundred thousands column, 0 in the ten thousands column, 5 in the thousands column, 9 in the hundreds column, 6 in the tens column, and 4 in the ones column.

Practice Problems

1. Give the place value of each digit in the number 17,045.

Large Numbers

Often we need to be able to understand and perform computations with larger numbers. For example, later in this section, we will see application problems in science, salaries, and sales that involve large numbers. In astronomy, distances to objects are given in light-years—the distance light travels in a year. If we assume light travels 186,000 miles in one second, then a light-year is 5,865,696,000,000 miles; that is,

5 trillion, 865 billion, 696 million miles

To find the place value of digits in large numbers, we can use Table 2. Note how the ones, thousands, millions, billions, and trillions categories are each broken into ones, tens, and hundreds. Note also that we have written the digits for our light-year in the last row of the table.

Note   When writing numbers with four or more digits, we use a comma to separate every three digits, starting from the ones column. We always place the comma by counting from right to left.

Table 2

Trillions			Billions			Millions			Thousands			Ones		
Hundred	Ten	One	Hundred	Ten	One	Hundred	Ten	One	Hundred	Ten	One	Hundred	Ten	One
		5	8	6	5	6	9	6	0	0	0	0	0	0

Example 2   Give the place value of each digit in the number 73,890,672,540.

Solution   The following diagram shows the place value of each digit.

Ten Billions, Billions, Hundred Millions, Ten Millions, Millions, Hundred Thousands, Ten Thousands, Thousands, Hundreds, Tens, Ones

7 3, 8 9 0, 6 7 2, 5 4 0

2. Give the place value of each digit in the number 4,572,106,890.

B Expanded Form

We can use the idea of place value to write numbers in **expanded form**. For example, the number 542 is written in condensed or **standard form**. We can also write it in expanded form as

$$542 = 500 + 40 + 2$$

because the 5 is in the hundreds column, the 4 is in the tens column, and the 2 is in the ones column. Similarly, 251 can be written in expanded form as

$$251 = 200 + 50 + 1$$

We now see that the value of the 5 in 542 is different from the value in 251.

Answer

1. 1 = ten thousands, 7 = thousands, 0 = hundreds, 4 = tens, 5 = ones

Billions, Hundred Millions, Ten Millions, Millions, Hundred Thousands, Ten Thousands, Thousands, Hundreds, Tens, Ones

2. 4, 5 7 2, 1 0 6, 8 9 0

Here are more examples of numbers written in expanded form:

3. Write 23,187 in expanded form.

Example 3   Write 5,478 in expanded form.

Solution $5,478 = 5,000 + 400 + 70 + 8$

We can use money to make the results from Example 3 more intuitive. Suppose you have $5,478 in cash as follows:

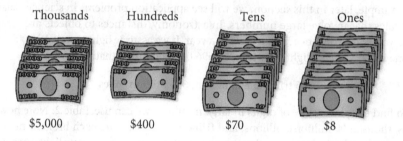

Thousands	Hundreds	Tens	Ones
$5,000	$400	$70	$8

Using this diagram as a guide, we can write

$$\$5,478 = \$5,000 + \$400 + \$70 + \$8$$

which shows us that our work writing numbers in expanded form is consistent with our intuitive understanding of the different denominations of money.

4. Write 1,049,580 in expanded form.

Example 4   Write 56,094 in expanded form.

Solution   Notice that there is a 0 in the hundreds column. This means we have 0 hundreds. In expanded form, we have

$$56,094 = 50,000 + 6,000 + 90 + 4$$
$$\uparrow$$

Note that we don't have
to include the 0 hundreds.

Now let's reverse the process. In the next two examples, we will take an expression in expanded form and condense it back to standard form.

5. Write $60,000 + 8,000 + 700 + 90 + 3$ in standard form.

Example 5   Write $10,000 + 7,000 + 500 + 60 + 9$ in standard form.

Solution $10,000 + 7,000 + 500 + 60 + 9 = 17,569$

6. Write $4,000,000 + 200,000 + 6,000 + 40 + 5$ in standard form.

Example 6   Write $5,000,000 + 70,000 + 600 + 3$ in standard form.

Solution   Notice that the expanded form does not include values for the hundred thousands place, thousands place, or tens place. Therefore, we will use a 0 in the standard form: 5,070,603.

C Writing Numbers in Words

The idea of place value and expanded form can be used to help write the names for numbers. Naming numbers and writing them in words takes some practice. Let's begin by looking at the names of some two-digit numbers. Table 3 lists a few. Notice that the two-digit numbers that are greater than twenty and do not end in 0 have two parts. These parts are separated by a hyphen.

Answers
3. $20,000 + 3,000 + 100 + 80 + 7$
4. $1,000,000 + 40,000 + 9,000 + 500 + 80$
5. 68,793
6. 4,206,045

Table 3

Number	In English	Number	In English
25	Twenty-five	30	Thirty
47	Forty-seven	62	Sixty-two
93	Ninety-three	77	Seventy-seven
88	Eighty-eight	50	Fifty

Notice, in mathematics we do not use the term "and" when writing numbers in words. Also, we use a hyphen between the tens digit and the ones digit when writing out twenty-one (21) through ninety-nine (99).

The following examples give the names for some larger numbers. In each case, the names are written according to the place values given in Table 2.

Example 7   Write each number in words.

a. 452   **b.** 397   **c.** 608

Solution

a. Four hundred fifty-two

b. Three hundred ninety-seven

c. Six hundred eight

Example 8   Write each number in words.

a. 3,561   **b.** 53,662   **c.** 547,801

Solution

a. Three thousand, five hundred sixty-one

> Notice how the comma separates the thousands from the hundreds. We will always use a comma here. Later, we will also use a comma after millions, billions, trillions, etc.

b. Fifty-three thousand, six hundred sixty-two

c. Five hundred forty-seven thousand, eight hundred one

Because there is a zero in the tens place, we omit this place when writing the number in words.

In Example 7c, we wrote 608 as six hundred eight. Because there was a 0 in the tens digit, we omitted this value. This is also true for larger place values. For example, 602,000 in words is six hundred two thousand.

Example 9   Write each number in words.

a. 507,034,005   **b.** 739,600,075   **c.** 5,003,007,006

Solution

a. Five hundred seven million, thirty-four thousand, five

b. Seven hundred thirty-nine million, six hundred thousand, seventy-five

c. Five billion, three million, seven thousand, six

7. Write each number in words.
   a. 940
   b. 386
   c. 507

8. Write each number in words.
   a. 4,865
   b. 1,759
   c. 408,623

9. Write each number in words.
   a. 406,058,210
   b. 3,200,486,404

Answers

7. **a.** Nine hundred forty
   b. Three hundred eighty-six
   c. Five hundred seven
8. **a.** Four thousand, eight hundred sixty-five.
   b. One thousand, seven hundred fifty-nine.
   c. Four hundred eight thousand, six hundred twenty-three.
9. **a.** Four hundred six million, fifty-eight thousand, two hundred ten.
   b. Three billion, two hundred million, four hundred eighty-six thousand, four hundred four.

The next examples show how we write a number given in words as a number written with digits.

10. Write eight thousand, two hundred thirty-nine using digits instead of words.

Example 10   Write five thousand, six hundred forty-two, using digits instead of words.

Solution   Five thousand, six hundred forty-two

$$5 \qquad 6 \qquad 42 \qquad \rightarrow \qquad 5{,}642$$

11. Write each number using digits instead of words.
    a. Seven million, forty-two thousand, six hundred.
    b. Twelve million, four hundred.
    c. Six hundred thousand, eight.

Example 11   Write each number using digits instead of words.
a. Three million, fifty-one thousand, seven hundred
b. Two billion, five
c. Seven million, seven hundred seven

Solution

a. 3,051,700

b. 2,000,000,005

c. 7,000,707

Sets and the Number Line

In mathematics, a collection of numbers is called a **set.** In this chapter, we have been working with the set of **counting numbers** (also called natural numbers) and the set of **whole numbers,** which are defined as follows:

$$\text{Counting numbers} = \{1, 2, 3, \ldots\}$$
$$\text{Whole numbers} = \{0, 1, 2, 3, \ldots\}$$

The dots mean "and so on," and the braces { } are used to group the numbers in the set together.

Another way to visualize the whole numbers is with a **number line.** To draw a number line, we simply draw a straight line and mark off equally spaced points along the line, as shown in Figure 1. We label the point at the left with 0 and the rest of the points, in order, with the numbers 1, 2, 3, 4, 5, and so on.

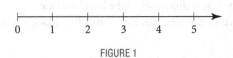

FIGURE 1

The arrow on the right indicates that the number line can continue in that direction forever, just as the dots in the braces above.

> ● **KEY CONCEPT REVIEW** · · · · · · · · · · · · · · · · · ·
>
> *After reading through the preceding section, respond in your own words and in complete sentences.*
>
> **A.** Give the place value of the 9 in the number 305,964.
>
> **B.** Write the number 742 in expanded form.
>
> **C.** Place a comma and a hyphen in the appropriate place so that the number 2,345 is written correctly in words below:
>
>   Two thousand three hundred forty five
>
> **D.** Is there a largest whole number?

Answers

10. 8,239

11. a. 7,042,600   b. 12,000,400
    c. 600,008

EXERCISE SET 1.1 •

VOCABULARY REVIEW •

Choose the correct words to fill in the blanks below.

comma   expanded form   counting numbers   standard form
place value   whole numbers   hyphen   set

1. _____ is the value of a digit in a number determined by its position.

2. The number 619 is written in _____ , but is written in _____
   when it appears as 600 + 10 + 9.

3. The name of a two-digit number that is greater then twenty and does not end in 0 has two parts
   separated by a _____.

4. When writing a number with four or more digits, use a _____ to separate
   every three digits.

5. A collection of numbers is called a _____.

6. The set of _____ is defined as {1, 2, 3,...}.

7. The set of _____ is defined as {0, 1, 2, 3,...}.

Problems

A Give the place value of each digit in the following numbers.

1. 78   **2.** 93   **3.** 45   **4.** 79

5. 348   **6.** 789   **7.** 608   **8.** 450

9. 2,378   **10.** 6,481   **11.** 273,569   **12.** 768,253

Give the place value of the 5 in each of the following numbers.

13. 458,992   **14.** 75,003,782   **15.** 507,994,787   **16.** 320,906,050

17. 267,894,335   **18.** 234,345,678,789 **19.** 4,569,000   **20.** 50,000

B Write each of the following numbers in expanded form.

21. 658   **22.** 479   **23.** 68   **24.** 71

25. 4,587   **26.** 3,762   **27.** 32,674   **28.** 54,883

29. 3,462,577

30. 5,673,524

31. 407

32. 508

33. 30,068

34. 50,905

35. 3,004,008

36. 20,088,060

Write each of the following numbers in standard form.

37. 500 + 40 + 7

38. 900 + 60 + 5

39. 6,000 + 300 + 20 + 3

40. 5,000 + 700 + 90 + 9

41. 20,000 + 7,000 + 30 + 5

42. 40,000 + 8,000 + 40 + 9

43. 70,000 + 900 + 7

44. 90,000 + 700 + 4

45. 100,000 + 80,000 + 600 + 40 + 3

46. 700,000 + 40,000 + 7,000 + 50 + 7

47. 400,000 + 6,000 + 8

48. 700,000 + 40 + 5

C Write each of the following numbers in words.

49. 29

50. 75

51. 40

52. 90

53. 573

54. 895

55. 707

56. 405

57. 770

58. 450

59. 23,540

60. 56,708

61. 3,004

62. 5,008

63. 3,040

64. 5,080

65. 104,065,780

66. 637,008,500

67. 5,003,040,008

68. 7,050,800,001

69. 2,546,731

70. 6,998,454

71. 20,432,000

72. 300,508,100

Write each of the following numbers with digits instead of words.

73. Three hundred twenty-five

74. Forty-eight

75. Five thousand, four hundred thirty-two

76. One hundred twenty-three thousand, sixty-one

77. Eighty-six thousand, seven hundred sixty-two

78. One hundred million, two hundred thousand, three hundred

79. Two million, two hundred

80. Two million, two

81. Two million, two thousand, two hundred

82. Two billion, two hundred thousand, two hundred two

Applying the Concepts

83. Hot Air Balloon The first successful crossing of the Atlantic in a hot air balloon was made in August 1978 by Maxie Anderson, Ben Abruzzo, and Larry Newman of the United States. The 3,100-mile trip took approximately 140 hours. What is the place value of the 3 in the distance covered by the balloon?

84. Seating Arrangements The number of different ways in which 10 people can be seated at a table with 10 places is 3,628,800. What is the place value of the 3 in this number?

85. Record Attendance The Rose Bowl in Pasadena, CA, had a record attendance of 106,869. Write this number in expanded form.

86. Astronomy The average distance from the sun to the earth is 92,897,416 miles. Write this number in expanded form.

87. Baseball Salaries Assume a Major League Baseball player's salary was $3,014,572, an increase of 0.6% from the previous season's wages. Write 3,014,572 in words.

88. Top Disney Movies The illustration shows the average income for some of Disney's classic movies.

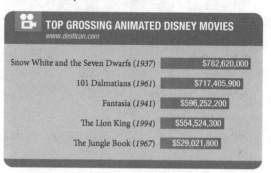

TOP GROSSING ANIMATED DISNEY MOVIES
www.destican.com

Snow White and the Seven Dwarfs (*1937*)	$782,620,000
101 Dalmatians (*1961*)	$717,405,900
Fantasia (*1941*)	$596,252,200
The Lion King (*1994*)	$554,524,300
The Jungle Book (*1967*)	$529,021,800

From the chart, write the following gross incomes in words.

a. Snow White and the Seven Dwarfs

b. The Jungle Book

Extending the Concepts

Many of the problem sets in this book will end with a few problems like the ones below. These problems challenge you to extend your knowledge of the material in the problem set. In most cases, there are no examples in the text similar to these problems. You should approach these problems with a positive point of view; even though you may not always work them correctly, just the process of attempting them will increase your knowledge and ability in mathematics.

The numbers on the number line below are each 1 inch apart. As with all number lines, the arrow indicates that the number line continues to the right indefinitely. Use this number line to answer the following questions.

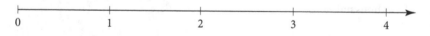

89. How far apart are the numbers 1 and 4?

90. How far apart are the numbers 2 and 5?

91. How far apart are the numbers 0 and 5?

92. How far apart are the numbers 0 and 10?

93. What number is 4 inches to the right of 2?

94. What number is 4 inches to the right of 3?

95. What number is 4 inches to the left of 7?

96. What number is 4 inches to the left of 12?

97. If 1 foot is 12 inches in length, what number is 1 foot to the right of 0?

98. What number is 2 feet to the right of 0?

FIND THE MISTAKE

Each sentence below contains a mistake. Circle the mistake and write the correct word(s) or number(s) on the line provided.

1. The place value of the 7 in the number 562,472 is hundreds. _____

2. The number 12,789 written in expanded form is 1,200 + 700 + 80 + 9. _____

3. The number 9,023,627,003 written in words is nine and twenty-three million, six and twenty-seven thousand, three. _____

4. Writing forty million, three hundred forty-eight thousand, thirteen in digits gives 4,034,813. _____

Navigation Skills

Within each chapter, we provide an important discussion of study skills that will help you succeed in this course and others. Consider how you can apply them to become a more successful student.

Studying is the key to success in this course. However, many students have never learned effective skills for studying. Study skills include but are not limited to the following:

- Work done on problems for practice and homework
- Amount of time spent studying
- Time of day and location for studying
- Management of distractions during study sessions
- Material chosen to review
- Order and process of review

Let's begin our discussion with the topic of homework. The rule of thumb is that students should spend two hours on homework for every hour they are scheduled to attend class. This has become the standard suggestion because students who dedicate this amount of time to the course tend to be more successful. Following this rule, if you attend class three hours a week, you would spend about six hours doing homework or studying for the course. To help visualize this commitment, map out a weekly schedule that includes your classes, work shifts, extracurriculars, and any additional obligations. Fill in the hours you intend to devote to completing assignments and studying for this class. Post this schedule at home and keep a copy with your study materials to remind you of your commitment to success.

1.2

 ADDITION WITH WHOLE NUMBERS, AND PERIMETER

The type of camera lens used depends on the subject that's being photographed. Selecting the size and shape of a lens depends on what you want to photograph. For example, a longer lens is usually better for taking action shots like a soccer player kicking a ball during a game. On the other hand, a shorter lens tends to be better for taking landscape or nature photos. Say a company sells camera lenses for $99. If you wanted to buy two, you would need to add 99 and 99 to find out how much you will pay (before sales tax). In this section, we will learn how to do addition with whole numbers, such as adding 99 and 99. Let's begin by visualizing addition on the number line.

Facts of Addition

Using lengths to visualize addition can be very helpful. In mathematics, we generally do so by using the number line. For example, we add 3 and 5 on the number line like this: start at 0 and move to 3, as shown in Figure 1. From 3, move 5 more units to the right. This brings us to 8. Therefore, $3 + 5 = 8$.

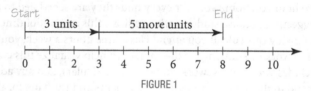

FIGURE 1

If we do this kind of addition on the number line with all combinations of the numbers 0 through 9, we get the results summarized in Table 1.

We call the information in Table 1 our basic addition facts. Your success with the examples and problems in this section depends on knowing the basic addition facts.

Note Table 1 is a summary of the addition facts. Knowing these facts will help you make a successful start in your study of basic mathematics. Also, being both fast and accurate when recalling these facts is extremely helpful.

Table 1

Addition Table

	0	1	2	3	4	5	6	7	8	9
0	0	1	2	3	4	5	6	7	8	9
1	1	2	3	4	5	6	7	8	9	10
2	2	3	4	5	6	7	8	9	10	11
3	3	4	5	6	7	8	9	10	11	12
4	4	5	6	7	8	9	10	11	12	13
5	5	6	7	8	9	10	11	12	13	14
6	6	7	8	9	10	11	12	13	14	15
7	7	8	9	10	11	12	13	14	15	16
8	8	9	10	11	12	13	14	15	16	17
9	9	10	11	12	13	14	15	16	17	18

Suppose we want to use the Table 1 to find the answer to $3 + 5$. We locate the 3 in the column on the left and the 5 in the row at the top. We read *across* from the 3 and *down* from the 5. The entry in the table that is across from 3 and below 5 is 8.

Vocabulary

The word we use to indicate addition is **sum.** If we say "the sum of 3 and 5 is 8," what we mean is $3 + 5 = 8$. The word sum always indicates addition. We can state this fact in symbols by using the letters a and b to represent numbers.

DEFINITION sum

If a and b are any two numbers, then the **sum** of a and b is $a + b$. To find the sum of two numbers, we add them.

Table 2 gives some phrases and sentences in English and their mathematical equivalents written in symbols.

Note When mathematics is used to solve everyday problems, the problems are almost always stated in words. The translation of English to symbols is a very important part of mathematics.

Table 2

In English	In Symbols
The sum of 4 and 1	$4 + 1$
4 added to 1	$1 + 4$
8 more than m	$m + 8$
x increased by 5	$x + 5$
The sum of x and y	$x + y$
The sum of 2 and 4 is 6.	$2 + 4 = 6$

A Adding Whole Numbers

To add whole numbers, we add digits with the same place value. First we add the digits in the ones place, then the tens place, then the hundreds place, and so on.

Example 1   Add: 43 + 52

Solution   This type of addition is best done vertically—aligning the digits with the same place value. First, we add the digits in the ones place.

$$
\begin{array}{r}
43 \\
+\,52 \\
\hline
5
\end{array}
$$

Then we add the digits in the tens place.

$$
\begin{array}{r}
43 \\
+\,52 \\
\hline
95
\end{array}
$$

We will now add larger numbers. The procedure will be very similar, aligning the digits with the same place value and adding from right to left.

Example 2   Add: 165 + 801

Solution   Writing the sum vertically, and adding from right to left, we have

$$
\begin{array}{r}
165 \\
+\,801 \\
\hline
966
\end{array}
$$

— Add ones place.
— Add tens place.
— Add hundreds place.

B Adding Whole Numbers with Carrying

In Examples 1 and 2, the sums of the digits with the same place value were always 9 or less. There are many times when the sum of the digits with the same place value will be a number larger than 9. In these cases, we have to do what is called **carrying** in addition. The following examples illustrate this process.

Example 3   Add: 197 + 213 + 324

Solution   We write the sum vertically and add digits with the same place value.

$$
\begin{array}{r}
\overset{1}{1}97 \\
213 \\
+\,324 \\
\hline
4
\end{array}
$$

When we add the ones, we get $7 + 3 + 4 = 14$. We write the 4 and carry the 1 to the tens column.

$$
\begin{array}{r}
\overset{1\,1}{1}97 \\
213 \\
+\,324 \\
\hline
34
\end{array}
$$

We add the tens, including the 1 that was carried over from the last step. We get 13, so we write the 3 and carry the 1 to the hundreds column.

$$
\begin{array}{r}
\overset{1\,1}{1}97 \\
213 \\
+\,324 \\
\hline
734
\end{array}
$$

We add the hundreds, including the 1 that was carried over from the last step.

Practice Problems

1. Add: 23 + 45

Note To show *why* we add digits with the same place value, we can write each number showing the place value of the digits:

$$
\begin{array}{r}
43 = 4\text{ tens} + 3\text{ ones} \\
+\,52 = 5\text{ tens} + 2\text{ ones} \\
\hline
9\text{ tens} + 5\text{ ones}
\end{array}
$$

2. Add: 243 + 526

3. Add: 238 + 432 + 186

Answers

1. 68
2. 769
3. 856

Example 4   Add: 46,789 + 2,490 + 864

Solution   We write the sum vertically and then use the shorthand form of addition.

4. Add: 17,386 + 5,978 + 468

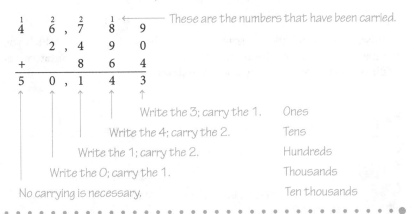

$$
\begin{array}{r}
\overset{1}{4}\ \overset{2}{6}\ ,\ \overset{2}{7}\ \overset{1}{8}\ 9 \\
2\ ,\ 4\ 9\ 0 \\
+\quad\ 8\ 6\ 4 \\
\hline
5\ 0\ ,\ 1\ 4\ 3
\end{array}
$$

These are the numbers that have been carried.

Write the 3; carry the 1.   Ones
Write the 4; carry the 2.   Tens
Write the 1; carry the 2.   Hundreds
Write the 0; carry the 1.   Thousands
No carrying is necessary.   Ten thousands

Adding numbers as we are doing here takes some practice. Often people don't make mistakes in carrying. Most mistakes in addition are made in adding the numbers in the columns. That is why it is so important to maintain accuracy with the basic addition facts given in this chapter.

C Properties of Addition

Once we become familiar with addition, we may notice some facts about addition that are true regardless of the numbers involved. The first of these facts involves the number zero (0).

Whenever we add zero to a number, the result is the original number. For example,

$$7 + 0 = 7 \quad \text{and} \quad 0 + 3 = 3$$

Because this fact is true no matter what number we add to zero, we call it a property of zero.

PROPERTY Addition Property of Zero

If we let a represent any number, then it is always true that

$$a + 0 = a \qquad \text{and} \qquad 0 + a = a$$

In words: Adding zero to any number leaves that number unchanged.

When we stated the addition property of zero, we used the letter a to represent an unknown number. We do this frequently in mathematics. When letters are used like this, we call them **variables** because the values they take on can vary. For example, both $8 + 0 = 8$ and $11 + 0 = 11$ are true. We use the variables in the definitions and properties because they are true for all numbers that you will encounter in this book.

Answer

4. 23,832

A second property we notice by becoming familiar with addition is that the order of two numbers in a sum can be changed without changing the result.

$$3 + 5 = 8 \quad \text{and} \quad 5 + 3 = 8$$
$$4 + 9 = 13 \quad \text{and} \quad 9 + 4 = 13$$

This fact about addition is true for *all* numbers. The order in which you add two numbers doesn't affect the result. We call this fact the **commutative property of addition,** and we write it in symbols as follows:

PROPERTY   Commutative Property of Addition

If a and b are any two numbers, then it is always true that

$$a + b = b + a$$

In words: Changing the order of two numbers in a sum doesn't change the result.

5. Use the commutative property of addition to rewrite each sum.
   a. $5 + 9$
   b. $12 + 13$
   c. $17 + 0$
   d. $x + 3$

Example 5   Use the commutative property of addition to rewrite each sum.
a. $4 + 6$ **b.** $5 + 9$ **c.** $3 + 0$ **d.** $7 + n$

Solution   The commutative property of addition indicates that we can change the order of the numbers in a sum without changing the result. Applying this property we have

a. $4 + 6 = 6 + 4$

b. $5 + 9 = 9 + 5$

c. $3 + 0 = 0 + 3$

d. $7 + n = n + 7$

Notice that we did not actually add any of the numbers. The instructions were to use the commutative property, which involves only the order of the numbers in a sum.

• •

Note   This discussion is here to show why we write the next property the way we do. Sometimes it is helpful to look ahead to the property itself (in this case, the associative property of addition) to see what it is that is being justified.

The last property of addition we will consider here has to do with sums of more than two numbers. Suppose we want to find the sum of 2, 3, and 4. We could add 2 and 3 first, and then add 4 to what we get.

$$(2 + 3) + 4 = 5 + 4 = 9$$

Or, we could add the 3 and 4 together first and then add the 2.

$$2 + (3 + 4) = 2 + 7 = 9$$

The result in both cases is the same. If we try this with any other numbers, the same thing happens. We call this fact about addition the **associative property of addition,** and we write it in symbols as follows:

PROPERTY   Associative Property of Addition

If a, b, and c represent any three numbers, then

$$(a + b) + c = a + (b + c)$$

In words: Changing the grouping of three or more numbers in a sum doesn't change the result.

Example 6 Use the associative property of addition to rewrite each sum.

a. $(5 + 6) + 7$ **b.** $(3 + 9) + 1$ **c.** $6 + (8 + 2)$ **d.** $4 + (9 + n)$

Solution The associative property of addition indicates that we are free to regroup the numbers in a sum without changing the result.

a. $(5 + 6) + 7 = 5 + (6 + 7)$

b. $(3 + 9) + 1 = 3 + (9 + 1)$

c. $6 + (8 + 2) = (6 + 8) + 2$

d. $4 + (9 + n) = (4 + 9) + n$

The commutative and associative properties of addition tell us that when adding whole numbers, we can use any order and grouping. When adding several numbers, it is sometimes easier to look for pairs of numbers whose sums are 10, 20, and so on.

Example 7 Add: $9 + 3 + 2 + 7 + 1$

Solution

$$
\begin{aligned}
9 + 3 + 2 + 7 + 1 &= (9 + 1) + (3 + 7) + 2 &&\text{Associative property of addition}\\
&= 10 + 10 + 2 &&\text{Add.}\\
&= 22
\end{aligned}
$$

D Solving Equations

We can use the addition table to help solve equations. If n is used to represent a number, then the equation

$$n + 3 = 5$$

will be true if n is 2. The number 2 is therefore called a **solution** to the **equation,** because, when we replace n with 2, the equation becomes a true statement.

$$2 + 3 = 5$$

Equations like this are really just puzzles, or questions. When we say, "Solve the equation $n + 3 = 5$," we are asking the question, "What number do we add to 3 to get 5?"

When we solve equations by reading the equation to ourselves and then stating the solution, as we did with the equation above, we are solving the equation by **inspection.**

Example 8 Find the solution to each equation by inspection.

a. $n + 5 = 9$ **b.** $n + 6 = 12$ **c.** $4 + n = 5$ **d.** $13 = n + 8$

Solution We find the solution to each equation by using the addition facts given in Table 1.

a. The solution to $n + 5 = 9$ is 4 because $4 + 5 = 9$.

b. The solution to $n + 6 = 12$ is 6 because $6 + 6 = 12$.

c. The solution to $4 + n = 5$ is 1 because $4 + 1 = 5$.

d. The solution to $13 = n + 8$ is 5 because $13 = 5 + 8$.

6. Use the associative property of addition to rewrite each sum.
   a. $(2 + 5) + 6$
   b. $(x + 3) + 5$
   c. $5 + (4 + 7)$
   d. $11 + (8 + n)$

7. Add: $8 + 2 + 7 + 3 + 6$

Note The letter n as we are using it here is a **variable** that is a solution to an equation. We will do more work with equations later in the book.

8. Find the solution to each equation by inspection.
   a. $n + 4 = 9$
   b. $n + 7 = 15$
   c. $3 + n = 12$
   d. $15 = n + 6$

Answers
6. **a.** $2 + (5 + 6)$
   b. $x + (3 + 5)$
   c. $(5 + 4) + 7$
   d. $(11 + 8) + n$
7. 26
8. **a.** 5 **b.** 8 **c.** 9 **d.** 9

E Perimeter

We end this section with an introduction to perimeter. Let's start with the definition of a polygon.

DEFINITION   polygon

A **polygon** is a closed geometric figure, with at least three sides, in which each side is a straight line segment.

 FACTS FROM GEOMETRY • • • • • • • • • • • • • • • • • •

Perimeter

The most common polygons are squares, rectangles, and triangles. Examples of these are shown in Figure 2.

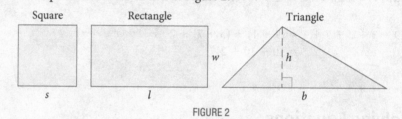

FIGURE 2

In the square, s is the length of the side, and each side has the same length. In the rectangle, l stands for the length, and w stands for the width. The width is usually the lesser of the two. In the triangle, h stands for height, and b stands for the length of the base.

DEFINITION   perimeter

The **perimeter** of any polygon is the sum of the lengths of the sides, and it is denoted with the letter P. To find the perimeter of a polygon, we add all the lengths of the sides together.

Example 9   Find the perimeter of each geometric figure.

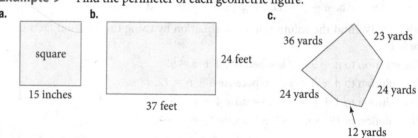

Solution   In each case, we find the perimeter by adding the lengths of all the sides.

a. The figure is a square. Because the length of each side in the square is the same, the perimeter is

$$P = 15 \text{ in.} + 15 \text{ in.} + 15 \text{ in.} + 15 \text{ in.} = 60 \text{ inches}$$

b. In the rectangle, two of the sides are 24 feet long, and the other two are 37 feet long. The perimeter is the sum of the lengths of the sides.

$$P = 24 \text{ ft} + 24 \text{ ft} + 37 \text{ ft} + 37 \text{ ft} = 122 \text{ feet}$$

Note Often we use abbreviations for units. Here are some common units and their abbreviations:

inches (in.)

feet (ft)

yards (yd)

centimeters (cm)

meters (m)

---

9. Find the perimeter of each geometric figure.

a.

9 inches

b.

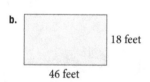

18 feet

46 feet

c.

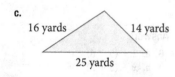

16 yards   14 yards

25 yards

Answers

9. a. 36 inches **b.** 128 feet
  c. 55 yards

c. For this polygon, we add the lengths of the sides together. The result is the perimeter.

$$P = 36 \text{ yd} + 23 \text{ yd} + 24 \text{ yd} + 12 \text{ yd} + 24 \text{ yd} = 119 \text{ yards}$$

KEY CONCEPT REVIEW

After reading through the preceding section, respond in your own words and in complete sentences.

A. What number is the sum of 6 and 8?

B. Make up an addition problem using the number 456 that involves carrying from the ones column to the tens column only.

C. Explain the difference between the commutative property of addition and the associative property of addition.

D. What is the perimeter of a polygon?

Spotlight on Success

SHELBY, student instructor

The price of success is hard work, dedication to the job at hand, and the determination that whether we win or lose, we have applied the best of ourselves to the task at hand.

~ Vince Lombardi

I have never been naturally gifted at math, but I enjoy a challenge. I wouldn't allow my setbacks to stop me from succeeding in my classes. As a high school freshman I struggled in my geometry class, and as a senior, I thrived in my AP Calculus class. The difference in those short four years was the effort I put in, as well as having great teachers, who provided the necessary knowledge and support along the way.

However, to continue to thrive in math, I had to realize that my success wasn't solely in the hands of the teacher. I saw students fail classes taught by some of the best teachers on campus. It all stemmed from the personal goals each student held. There were multiple times when I told myself, "You can do this. You can learn the concepts." I'm not sure I would have moved past prealgebra without those personal words of encouragement.

Having confidence in yourself is necessary to be successful in all aspects of life. It's easy to give up on something that doesn't come naturally, but the reward of achieving something you thought to be impossible is worth the hardship.

VOCABULARY REVIEW ·

Choose the correct words to fill in the blanks below.

sum	associative	inspection	commutative	carrying
zero	variable	solution	perimeter	

1. If the sum of the digits with the same place value is larger than 9, use the process called
_____ to complete the problem.

2. The _____ of *a* and *b* is *a* + *b* if *a* and *b* are any two numbers.

3. The addition property of _____ states that adding zero to any number leaves
that number unchanged.

4. The _____ property of addition states that changing the order of two
numbers in a sum doesn't change the result.

5. The _____ property of addition states that changing the grouping of three
numbers in a sum doesn't change the result.

6. When we solve equations by reading the equation to ourselves and then stating the
_____ , we are solving the equation by _____ .

7. To find the _____ of a polygon, we add all the lengths of the sides
together.

8. A letter that is used to represent a number is called a _____ .

Problems

A Find each of the following sums. (Add.)

1. $3 + 5 + 7$ **2.** $2 + 8 + 6$ **3.** $1 + 4 + 9$ **4.** $2 + 8 + 3$

5. $5 + 9 + 4 + 6$ **6.** $8 + 1 + 6 + 2$ **7.** $1 + 2 + 3 + 4 + 5$ **8.** $5 + 6 + 7 + 8 + 9$

9. $9 + 1 + 8 + 2$ **10.** $7 + 3 + 6 + 4$

Add each of the following. (There is no carrying involved in these problems.)

11. $\begin{array}{r} 43 \\ +25 \\ \hline \end{array}$ **12.** $\begin{array}{r} 56 \\ +23 \\ \hline \end{array}$ **13.** $\begin{array}{r} 81 \\ +17 \\ \hline \end{array}$

14. $\begin{array}{r} 37 \\ +22 \\ \hline \end{array}$ **15.** $\begin{array}{r} 4,281 \\ +3,016 \\ \hline \end{array}$ **16.** $\begin{array}{r} 2,749 \\ +1,250 \\ \hline \end{array}$

17.   3,482
   + 3,005

18.   2,496
   +7,503

19.   32
    21
   +43

20.   521
    340
   +135

21.   6,245
     203
   + 1,001

22.   27
   4,510
   +   342

B   Add each of the following. (All problems involve carrying in at least one column.)

23.   49
   +16

24.   85
   +29

25.   74
   +28

26.   36
   +46

27.   682
   +193

28.   439
   +270

29.   638
   +191

30.   444
   +595

31.   4,963
   +5,428

32.   8,291
   +7,489

33.   6,205
   +9,999

34.   8,888
   +9,999

35.   56,789
   +98,765

36.   45,678
   +87,654

37.   52,468
   +58,642

38.   13,579
   +97,531

39.   4,296
    8,720
   +4,375

40.   5,637
     481
   +7,899

41.   4,994
     449
   +9,449

42.   6,824
     371
   +4,857

43.   12
    34
    56
   +78

44.   21
    43
    65
   +87

45.   999
    444
    555
   +222

46.   646
    464
    525
   +252

47.   9,245
     672
   8,341
   +   27

48.   45
   9,876
      54
   + 6,789

49.   123
    469
     87
   +   95

50.   835
     84
    107
   +   98

51.   5,894
     256
   + 1,045

52.   8,265
     648
   + 2,384

Complete the following tables.

53.

First Number a	Second Number b	Their Sum $a + b$
61	38	
63	36	
65	34	
67	32	

54.

First Number a	Second Number b	Their Sum $a + b$
10	45	
20	35	
30	25	
40	15	

55.

First Number a	Second Number b	Their Sum $a + b$
9	16	
36	64	
81	144	
144	256	

56.

First Number a	Second Number b	Their Sum $a + b$
25	75	
24	76	
23	77	
22	78	

C Rewrite each of the following using the commutative property of addition.

57. $5 + 9$ **58.** $2 + 1$ **59.** $3 + 8$ **60.** $9 + 2$ **61.** $6 + 4$ **62.** $1 + 7$

Rewrite each of the following using the associative property of addition.

63. $(1 + 2) + 3$ **64.** $(4 + 5) + 9$ **65.** $(2 + 1) + 6$ **66.** $(2 + 3) + 8$

67. $1 + (9 + 1)$ **68.** $2 + (8 + 2)$ **69.** $(4 + n) + 1$ **70.** $(n + 8) + 1$

D Find a solution for each equation by inspection.

71. $n + 6 = 10$ **72.** $n + 4 = 7$ **73.** $n + 8 = 13$ **74.** $n + 6 = 15$

75. $4 + n = 12$ **76.** $5 + n = 7$ **77.** $17 = n + 9$ **78.** $13 = n + 5$

79. $15 = n + 6$ **80.** $23 = n + 14$ **81.** $16 = 12 + n$ **82.** $24 = 16 + n$

Write each of the following expressions in words. Use the word *sum* in each case.

83. 4 + 9

84. 9 + 4

85. 8 + 1

86. 9 + 9

87. 2 + 3 = 5

88. 8 + 2 = 10

Write each of the following in symbols.

89. a. The sum of 5 and 2

  b. 3 added to 8

90. a. The sum of *a* and 4

  b. 6 more than *x*

91. a. *m* increased by 1

  b. The sum of *m* and *n*

92. a. The sum of 4 and 8 is 12.

  b. The sum of *a* and *b* is 6.

E Find the perimeter of each figure. The first four figures are squares.

93.

3 in.

94.

8 in.

95.

4 ft

96.

2 ft

97.
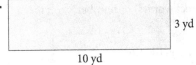
3 yd
10 yd

98.
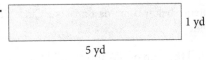
1 yd
5 yd

99.
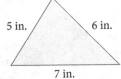
5 in.   6 in.
7 in.

100.
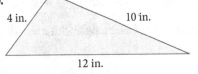
4 in.   10 in.
12 in.

101.
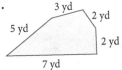
3 yd
2 yd
5 yd
2 yd
7 yd

102.
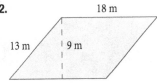
18 m
13 m   9 m

Applying the Concepts

The application problems that follow are related to addition of whole numbers. Read each problem carefully to determine exactly what you are being asked to find. Don't assume that just because a number appears in a problem you have to use it to solve the problem. Sometimes you do, and sometimes you don't.

103. Gallons of Gasoline Tim bought gas for his economy car twice last month. The first time he bought 18 gallons and the second time he bought 16 gallons. What was the total amount of gasoline Tim bought last month?

104. Perimeter In the chapter opener, we discussed the Parthenon in Athens, Greece. The length of the temple is 228 feet and the width is 101 feet. If you walk the perimeter, what is the total distance you walked?

105. Account Balance On Monday, Bob had a balance of $241 in his checking account. On Tuesday, he made a deposit of $108, and on Thursday, he purchased something for $24. What was the balance in his account on Wednesday?

106. Number of Passengers A plane flying from Los Angeles to New York left Los Angeles with 67 passengers on board. The plane stopped in Bakersfield and picked up 28 passengers, and then it stopped again in Dallas where 57 more passengers came on board. How many passengers were on the plane when it landed in New York?

FIND THE MISTAKE •

Each sentence below contains a mistake. Circle the mistake and write the correct word(s) or number(s) on the line provided.

1. To find the sum of 786 and 49, add the ones place by writing the 1 and carrying the 5.

   _____

2. The problem $(12 + 7) + 3 = 12 + (7 + 3)$ uses the commutative property of addition.

   _____

3. The solution for the equation $47 = x + 29$ is $x = 8$. _____

4. The perimeter of a rectangle with a length of 35 inches and a width of 15 inches is 50 inches.

   _____

SUBTRACTION WITH WHOLE NUMBERS

The island of Saint John in the US Virgin Islands is approximately 60% national park. At Trunk Bay, one of the most popular beaches on the island, visitors can sit on the pristine beach or borrow equipment for snorkeling, kayaking, and paddle boarding. One of the most unique features of this beach is the underwater snorkel trail. Similar to a guided hiking trail, snorkelers can swim along a path and read plaques that point out different types of coral and fish in the reef.
If you rent snorkel gear at Trunk Bay, there is a $50 fee to ensure that you return the equipment. If you are asked to pay $72 at the time you rented a snorkel and fins, and you will receive your $50 when you return them, how much did you spend on the rental? To answer this question, we need to understand a little more about subtraction. Subtraction is the opposite of addition.

OBJECTIVES

A Use vocabulary for subtraction.

B Subtract whole numbers without borrowing.

C Subtract whole numbers with borrowing.

D Solve subtraction equations.

KEY WORDS

difference

borrowing

estimation

VIDEO EXAMPLES

SECTION 1.3

A Vocabulary

The word **difference** always indicates subtraction. We can state this in symbols by letting the letters a and b represent numbers.

DEFINITION difference

The **difference** of two numbers a and b is

$$a - b$$

Table 1 gives some word statements involving subtraction and their mathematical equivalents written in symbols.

Table 1

In English	In Symbols
The difference of 9 and 1	$9 - 1$
The difference of 1 and 9	$1 - 9$
The difference of x and y	$x - y$
3 subtracted from 8	$8 - 3$
2 subtracted from t	$t - 2$
The difference of 9 and 3 is 6.	$9 - 3 = 6$

B The Meaning of Subtraction

When we want to subtract 3 from 8, we write

$$8 - 3, \qquad 8 \text{ subtract } 3, \qquad \text{or} \qquad 8 \text{ minus } 3$$

The number we are looking for here is the difference between 8 and 3, or the number we add to 3 to get 8; that is,

$$8 - 3 = ? \qquad \text{is the same as} \qquad ? + 3 = 8$$

In both cases, we are looking for the number we add to 3 to get 8. The number we are looking for is 5. We have two ways to write the same statement:

Subtraction		Addition
$8 - 3 = 5$	or	$5 + 3 = 8$

For every subtraction problem, there is an equivalent addition problem. Table 2 lists some examples.

Table 2

Subtraction		Addition
$7 - 3 = 4$	because	$4 + 3 = 7$
$9 - 7 = 2$	because	$2 + 7 = 9$
$10 - 4 = 6$	because	$6 + 4 = 10$
$15 - 8 = 7$	because	$7 + 8 = 15$

To subtract numbers with two or more digits, we align the numbers vertically and subtract in columns from right to left.

Example 1 Subtract: $376 - 241$

Solution We write the problem vertically, aligning digits with the same place value. Then we subtract in columns.

$$
\begin{array}{r}
376 \\
- 241 \\
\hline
135
\end{array}
$$
← Subtract the bottom number in each column from the number above it.

$$
\begin{array}{ccc}
 & 3 & 7 & 6 \\
- & 2 & 4 & 1 \\
\hline
 & 1 & 3 & 5
\end{array}
$$

$6 - 1 = 5$ Ones
$7 - 4 = 3$ Tens
$3 - 2 = 1$ Hundreds

We can visualize Example 1 using money.

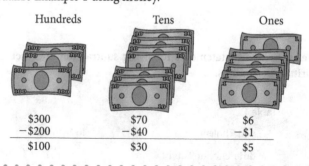

Hundreds	Tens	Ones
$300	$70	$6
−$200	−$40	−$1
$100	$30	$5

Practice Problems

1. Subtract: $485 - 123$

Answer

1. 362

Example 2   Subtract 503 from 7,835.

Solution   In symbols, this statement is equivalent to

$$7{,}835 - 503$$

To subtract, we write 503 below 7,835 and then subtract in columns.

$$
\begin{array}{r}
7835 \\
-\ 503 \\
\hline
7332
\end{array}
$$

2. Subtract 320 from 1,865.

As you can see, subtraction problems like the ones in Examples 1 and 2 are very similar to the addition problems we solved earlier in the chapter. We write the problem vertically, lining up the digits with the same place value, and subtract in columns. We always subtract the bottom number from the top number.

C Subtraction with Borrowing

Subtraction must involve **borrowing** when the bottom digit in any column is larger than the digit above it. In one sense, borrowing is the reverse of the carrying we did in addition.

Example 3   Subtract: $92 - 45$

Solution   We write the problem vertically with the place values of the digits showing.

$$
\begin{array}{l}
92 = 9 \text{ tens } 2 \text{ ones} \\
-\ 45 = 4 \text{ tens } 5 \text{ ones}
\end{array}
$$

Look at the ones column. We cannot subtract immediately, because 5 is larger than 2. Instead, we borrow 1 ten from the 9 tens in the tens column and regroup that 1 ten with the 2 ones. We can rewrite the number 92 as

$$
\begin{array}{l}
9 \text{ tens } + 2 \text{ ones} \\
= 8 \text{ tens } + 1 \text{ ten } + 2 \text{ ones} \\
= 8 \text{ tens } + 12 \text{ ones}
\end{array}
$$

3. Subtract: $87 - 29$

> *Note* The discussion here shows why borrowing is necessary and how we go about it. To understand borrowing, you should pay close attention to this discussion.

Now we are in a position to subtract.

$$
\begin{array}{l}
92 = 9 \text{ tens } 2 \text{ ones} = 8 \text{ tens } 12 \text{ ones} \\
-\ 45 = 4 \text{ tens } 5 \text{ ones} = 4 \text{ tens } 5 \text{ ones} \\
\hline
\phantom{-\ 45 = 4 \text{ tens } 5 \text{ ones} = } 4 \text{ tens } 7 \text{ ones}
\end{array}
$$

The result is 4 tens + 7 ones, which can be written in standard form as 47.

Writing the problem out in this way is more trouble than is actually necessary. The shorthand form of the same problem looks like this:

$$
\begin{array}{r}
\overset{8}{\cancel{9}}\ \overset{12}{\cancel{2}} \\
-\ 4\ 5 \\
\hline
4\ 7
\end{array}
$$

This shows we have borrowed 1 ten to go with the 2 ones.

$12 - 5 = 7$ Ones

$8 - 4 = 4$ Tens

This shortcut form shows all the necessary work involved in subtraction with borrowing. We will use it from now on.

The borrowing that changed 9 tens + 2 ones into 8 tens + 12 ones can be visualized with money.

Tens   Ones   Tens   Ones

=

$90 $2 $80 $12

> **Note**
> 1 ten = 10 ones
> 1 hundred = 10 tens

4. Find the difference of 268 and 179.

Example 4   Find the difference of 549 and 187.

Solution   In symbols, the difference of 549 and 187 is written

$$549 - 187$$

Writing the problem vertically so that the digits with the same place value are aligned, we have

$$\begin{array}{r} 549 \\ -\ 187 \end{array}$$

The top number in the tens column is smaller than the number below it. This means that we will have to borrow from the next larger column.

$$\begin{array}{r} \overset{4}{\cancel{5}}\ \overset{14}{\cancel{4}}\ 9 \\ -\ 1\ 8\ 7 \\ \hline 3\ 6\ 2 \end{array}$$

← Borrow 1 hundred to go with the 4 tens.

$9 - 7 = 2$ Ones
$14 - 8 = 6$ Tens
$4 - 1 = 3$ Hundreds

The actual work we did in borrowing looks like this:

5 hundreds + 4 tens + 9 ones

= 4 hundreds + 1 hundred + 4 tens + 9 ones

= 4 hundreds + 14 tens + 9 ones

5. Joshua has $615 in his checking account. If he writes a check for $289 to make his car payment, how much is left?

Example 5   Jo Ann has $742 in her checking account. If she writes a check for $615 to pay the rent, how much is left in her checking account?

Solution   To find the amount left in the account after she has written the rent check, we subtract.

$$\begin{array}{r} \$7\ \overset{3}{\cancel{4}}\ \overset{12}{\cancel{2}} \\ -\ 6\ 1\ 5 \\ \hline \$1\ 2\ 7 \end{array}$$

She has $127 left in her account after writing a check for the rent.

Answers
4. 89
5. $326

D Solving Equations

We can solve equations involving subtraction as we did with addition, by inspection. For example, the equation

$$n - 4 = 8$$

has a solution of 12, since $12 - 4 = 8$. Later, we will learn other methods for solving these equations.

Example 6 Find the solution to each equation by inspection.

a. $n - 3 = 7$ **b.** $n - 4 = 9$ **c.** $12 - n = 5$ **d.** $7 = 18 - n$

Solution

a. The solution to $n - 3 = 7$ is 10, because $10 - 3 = 7$.

b. The solution to $n - 4 = 9$ is 13, because $13 - 4 = 9$.

c. The solution to $12 - n = 5$ is 7, because $12 - 7 = 5$.

d. The solution to $7 = 18 - n$ is 11, because $7 = 18 - 11$.

6. Find the solution to each equation by inspection.
   a. $n - 5 = 9$
   b. $n - 1 = 7$
   c. $19 - n = 15$
   d. $4 = 12 - n$

Estimating

One way to **estimate** the answer to the problem shown in Example 5 is to round 742 to 700 and 615 to 600 and then subtract 600 from 700 to obtain 100, which is an estimate of the difference. Making a mental estimate in this manner will help you catch some of the errors that will occur if you press the wrong buttons on your calculator. We will cover estimating and rounding more thoroughly in the next section.

 KEY CONCEPT REVIEW

After reading through the preceding section, respond in your own words and in complete sentences.

A. Which sentence below describes the problem in Example 1?

   a. The difference of 241 and 376 is 135.

   b. The difference of 376 and 241 is 135.

B. Write a subtraction problem using the number 234 that involves borrowing from the tens column to the ones column.

C. Write a subtraction problem using the number 234 in which the answer is 111.

D. Describe how you would subtract the number 56 from the number 93.

Answers
6. a. $n = 14$ **b.** $n = 8$
   c. $n = 4$ **d.** $n = 8$

EXERCISE SET 1.3 ....

Problems

A Perform the indicated operation.

1. Subtract 24 from 56.

2. Subtract 71 from 89.

3. Subtract 23 from 45.

4. Subtract 97 from 98.

5. Find the difference of 29 and 19.

6. Find the difference of 37 and 27.

7. Find the difference of 126 and 15.

8. Find the difference of 348 and 32.

Write each of the following expressions in words. Use the word *difference* in each case.

9. $10 - 2$

10. $9 - 5$

11. $a - 6$

12. $7 - x$

13. $8 - 2 = 6$

14. $m - 1 = 4$

Write each of the following expressions in symbols.

15. The difference of 8 and 3

16. The difference of x and 2

17. 9 subtracted from y

18. a subtracted from b

19. The difference of 3 and 2 is 1.

20. The difference of 10 and y is 5.

B Work each of the following subtraction problems.

21. $\begin{array}{r} 975 \\ -\ 663 \\ \hline \end{array}$

22. $\begin{array}{r} 480 \\ -\ 260 \\ \hline \end{array}$

23. $\begin{array}{r} 904 \\ -\ 501 \\ \hline \end{array}$

24. $\begin{array}{r} 657 \\ -\ 507 \\ \hline \end{array}$

25. $\begin{array}{r} 9,876 \\ -\ 8,765 \\ \hline \end{array}$

26. $\begin{array}{r} 5,008 \\ -\ 3,002 \\ \hline \end{array}$

27. $\begin{array}{r} 7,976 \\ -\ 3,432 \\ \hline \end{array}$

28. $\begin{array}{r} 6,980 \\ -\ 470 \\ \hline \end{array}$

C Find the difference in each case. (These problems all involve borrowing.)

29. 52 − 37

30. 65 − 48

31. 70 − 37

32. 90 − 21

33. 74 − 69

34. 31 − 28

35. 51 − 18

36. 64 − 58

37. 329 − 234

38. 518 − 492

39. 348 − 196

40. 759 − 661

41.
$$\begin{array}{r} 932 \\ -\ 658 \\ \hline \end{array}$$

42.
$$\begin{array}{r} 895 \\ -\ 597 \\ \hline \end{array}$$

43.
$$\begin{array}{r} 647 \\ -\ 159 \\ \hline \end{array}$$

44.
$$\begin{array}{r} 842 \\ -\ 199 \\ \hline \end{array}$$

45.
$$\begin{array}{r} 905 \\ -\ 367 \\ \hline \end{array}$$

46.
$$\begin{array}{r} 804 \\ -\ 238 \\ \hline \end{array}$$

47.
$$\begin{array}{r} 600 \\ -\ 437 \\ \hline \end{array}$$

48.
$$\begin{array}{r} 800 \\ -\ 342 \\ \hline \end{array}$$

49.
$$\begin{array}{r} 4{,}583 \\ -\ 2{,}973 \\ \hline \end{array}$$

50.
$$\begin{array}{r} 7{,}849 \\ -\ 2{,}957 \\ \hline \end{array}$$

51.
$$\begin{array}{r} 79{,}040 \\ -\ 32{,}957 \\ \hline \end{array}$$

52.
$$\begin{array}{r} 86{,}492 \\ -\ 78{,}506 \\ \hline \end{array}$$

Complete the following tables.

53.

First Number a	Second Number b	The Difference of a and b $a - b$
25	15	
24	16	
23	17	
22	18	

54.

First Number a	Second Number b	The Difference of a and b $a - b$
90	79	
80	69	
70	59	
60	49	

55.

First Number a	Second Number b	The Difference of a and b $a - b$
400	256	
400	144	
225	144	
225	81	

56.

First Number a	Second Number b	The Difference of a and b $a - b$
100	36	
100	64	
25	16	
25	9	

D Find the solution to each equation by inspection.

57. $n - 1 = 5$

58. $n - 4 = 11$

59. $n - 5 = 14$

60. $n - 6 = 9$

61. $12 - n = 3$ **62.** $15 - n = 10$ **63.** $20 - n = 7$ **64.** $25 - n = 24$

65. $10 = n - 15$ **66.** $12 = n - 5$ **67.** $8 = n - 3$ **68.** $10 = n - 4$

69. $5 = 14 - n$ **70.** $4 = 20 - n$ **71.** $5 = 6 - n$ **72.** $8 = 12 - n$

Applying the Concepts

Not all of the following application problems involve only subtraction. Some involve addition as well. Be sure to read each problem carefully.

73. Account Balance Diane has $504 in her checking account. If she makes five transactions that total $249, how much does she have left in her account?

74. Account Balance Larry has $763 in his checking account. If he pays each of the three bills listed, how much will he have left in his account?

Item	Amount
Car Payment	$418
Gas	$25
Insurance	$117

75. Tallest Mountain The world's tallest mountain is Mount Everest. On May 5, 1999, it was found to be 7 feet taller than it was previously thought to be. Before this date, Everest was thought to be 29,028 feet high. That height was determined by B. L. Gulatee in 1954. The first measurement of Everest was in 1856. At that time, the height was thought to be 29,002 feet. What is the difference between the current height of Everest and the height measured in 1856?

76. Home Prices In 2005, Mr. Hicks paid $137,500 for his home. He sold it in 2015 for $260,600. What is the difference between what he sold it for and what he bought it for?

77. Enrollment Six years ago, there were 567 students attending Smith Elementary School. Today the same school has an enrollment of 399 students. How much of a decrease in enrollment has there been in the last six years at Smith School?

78. Oil Spills In March 1977, an oil tanker hit a reef off Taiwan and spilled 3,134,500 gallons of oil. In April 2010, an explosion on an oil rig in the Gulf of Mexico spilled 210,000,000 gallons of oil. How much more oil was spilled in the 2010 disaster?

Account Balance On Monday, Gil has a balance of $425 in his account. On Tuesday, he deposits $149 into the account. On Wednesday, he spends $37, and on Friday he spends $188. Use this information to answer the following problems.

79. Find Gil's balance after he makes the deposit on Tuesday.

80. What is his balance after he makes the purchase on Wednesday?

81. Smartphone Users The bar chart shows the approximate number of smartphone users in the U. S. from 2014 to 2016.

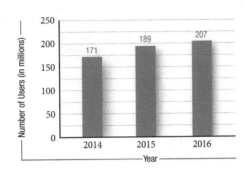

Year	Number of Users (Millions)
2014	
2015	
	207

Source: statista.com

a. Use the information in the bar chart to fill in the missing entries in the table.

b. What is the difference in the number of smartphone users between 2014 and 2016?

82. Projected Smartphone Users The bar chart shows the projected number of smartphone users in the U. S.

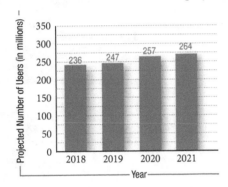

Year	Projected Users (Millions)
2018	
2019	
	257
	264

Source: statista.com

a. Use the chart to fill in the missing entries in the table.

b. What is the difference in projected number of smartphone users between 2019 and 2021?

FIND THE MISTAKE ·

Each sentence below contains a mistake. Circle the mistake and write the correct word(s) or number(s) on the line provided.

83. Translating "The difference of 22 and 3 is 19" into symbols gives us $3 - 22 = 19$. _____

84. To subtract 50 from 290, vertically align the tens column of the first number with the hundreds column of the second number. _____

85. To find the difference of 85 and 27, begin by subtracting 7 from 5. _____
_____

86. The solution for the equation $108 = 130 - y$ is $y = 238$. _____

LANDMARK REVIEW: CHECKING YOUR PROGRESS • • • • • • • • • • •

This feature is intended as a review of key skills from the preceding sections in the chapter. Each review will give you the opportunity to utilize important concepts and check your progress as you practice problems of different types. Take note of any problems in this review that you find difficult. There is no better time than now to revisit and master those difficult concepts in preparation for any upcoming exams or subsequent chapters.

Write each of the following numbers in expanded form.

1. 549   **2.** 1,493   **3.** 60,243   **4.** 30,403,005

Perform the indicated operations.

5. $4 + 2 + 12$ **6.** $4 + 3 + 8 + 9 + 5 + 2$ **7.**
$$\begin{array}{r} 52 \\ +\ 65 \end{array}$$

8.
$$\begin{array}{r} 2{,}435 \\ +\ 5{,}215 \end{array}$$
      9.
$$\begin{array}{r} 14{,}253 \\ 25{,}489 \\ 53{,}503 \\ +\ 10{,}456 \end{array}$$
      10.
$$\begin{array}{r} 145{,}358 \\ 256{,}789 \\ +\ \ \ \ \ 15 \end{array}$$

11.
$$\begin{array}{r} 957 \\ -\ 427 \end{array}$$
      12.
$$\begin{array}{r} 6{,}492 \\ -\ 5{,}257 \end{array}$$
      13. Subtract 15 from 32.

14. Subtract 5 from 27.   **15.** Find the difference of 37 and 25.   **16.** Find the difference of 142 and 40.

Find a solution for each equation by inspection.

17. $5 + x = 10$ **18.** $1 + n = 15$ **19.** $12 = 5 + a$ **20.** $29 = y + 9$

21. $x - 1 = 15$ **22.** $7 - n = 3$ **23.** $10 - y = 5$ **24.** $34 - x = 33$

ROUNDING NUMBERS, ESTIMATING ANSWERS, AND DISPLAYING INFORMATION

1.4

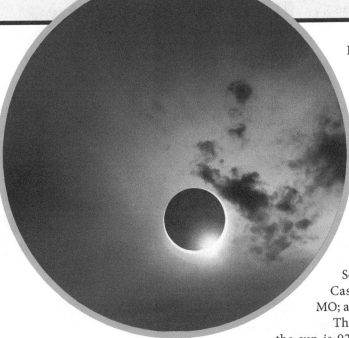

In August of 2017, people across the United States were able to view a complete solar eclipse, where the sun disappears behind the moon, causing a state of twilight in the middle of the day. People traveled to various locations that were close to the center of the path to get the best view of this phenomena. Some of these cities included Casper, WY; Jefferson City, MO; and Columbia, SC.

The distance from Earth to the sun is 92,955,807 miles, although scientists don't usually state this. Often they use estimation and rounding skills to say that Earth is approximately 93,000,000 miles from the sun. In this section, we will learn how to round numbers to a specific place and then apply that skill to estimating answers for math problems. First, let's consider another example that uses rounded numbers.

When we talk about numbers, it is sometimes helpful to use numbers that have been *rounded off*, rather than exact numbers. For example, the city where I live has a population of 45,119. But when I tell people how large the city is, I usually say, "The population is about 45,000." The number 45,000 is the original number rounded to the nearest thousand. The number 45,119 is closer to 45,000 than it is to 46,000, so it is rounded to 45,000. We can visualize this situation on the number line.

OBJECTIVES

A Round numbers to specified place values.

B Estimate sums and differences.

C Read graphs and bar charts.

KEY WORDS

round

estimate

bar chart

horizontal axis

vertical axis

VIDEO EXAMPLES

SECTION 1.4

A Rounding Numbers

The steps used in rounding numbers are given below.

HOW TO **Steps for Rounding Whole Numbers**

1. Find the place you want to round to and locate the digit just to the right of it.

2. If that digit is less than 5, replace it and all digits to its right with zeros. This is called rounding down.

3. If that digit is 5 or more, replace it and all digits to its right with zeros, and add 1 to the digit to its left. This is called rounding up.

Note After you have used the steps listed here to work a few problems, you will find that the procedure becomes almost automatic.

35

1. Round 2,849 to the nearest hundred.

You can see from these steps that in order to round a number you must be told what place value to round to.

Example 1   Round 5,382 to the nearest hundred.

Solution   The 3 is in the hundreds column. We look at the digit just to its right, which is 8. Because 8 is greater than 5, we add 1 to the 3, and we replace the digits to the right with zeros.

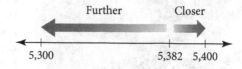

5,382   is   5,400   to the nearest hundred

Greater than 5   Add 1 to get 4.   Put zeros here.

The number 5,382 is closer to 5,400 than it is to 5,300. We can visualize this on the number line.

Further   Closer

5,300   5,382   5,400

2. Round 1,427 to the nearest ten.

Example 2   Round 94 to the nearest ten.

Solution   The 9 is in the tens column. To its right is 4. Because 4 is less than 5, we replace it with 0.

94   is   90   to the nearest ten

Less than 5   Replaced with zero

3. Round 955 to the nearest hundred.

Example 3   Round 973 to the nearest hundred.

Solution   We have a 9 in the hundreds column. To its right is 7, which is greater than 5. We add 1 to 9 to get 10, and then replace the digits to the right with zeros.

973   is   1,000   to the nearest hundred

Greater than 5   Add 1 to get 10.   Put zeros here.

4. Round 479,580 to nearest thousand.

Example 4   Round 47,256,344 to the nearest million.

Solution   We have 7 in the millions column. To its right is 2, which is less than 5. We simply replace all the digits to the right of 7 with zeros to get

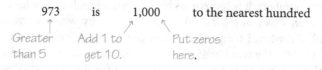

47,256,344   is   47,000,000   to the nearest million

Less than 5   Leave as is.   Replaced with zeros

Table 1 gives more examples of rounding.

Table 1			
		Rounded to the Nearest	
Original Number	Ten	Hundred	Thousand
6,914	6,910	6,900	7,000
8,485	8,490	8,500	8,000
5,555	5,560	5,600	6,000
1,234	1,230	1,200	1,000

RULE Calculating and Rounding

If we are doing calculations and are asked to round our answer, we do all our arithmetic first and then round the result. That is, the last step is to round the answer; we don't round the numbers first and then do the arithmetic.

Example 5 The pie chart below shows how an individual earning $36,913 a year spends his money.

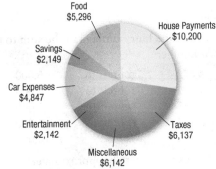

Food $5,296

House Payments $10,200

Savings $2,149

Car Expenses $4,847

Entertainment $2,142

Taxes $6,137

Miscellaneous $6,142

a. To the nearest hundred dollars, what is the total amount spent on food and entertainment?

b. To the nearest thousand dollars, how much of his income is spent on items other than taxes and savings?

Solution In each case, we add the numbers in question and then round the sum to the indicated place.

a. We add the amounts spent on food and entertainment and then round that result to the nearest hundred dollars.

Food	$5,296
Entertainment	+ 2,142
Total	$7,438 = $7,400 to the nearest hundred dollars

b. We add the numbers for all items except taxes and savings.

House payments	$10,200
Food	5,296
Car expenses	4,847
Entertainment	2,142
Miscellaneous	+ 6,142
Total	$28,627 = $29,000 to the nearest thousand dollars

5. Using the pie chart from Example 5, answer the following questions.
  a. To the nearest hundred dollars, what is the total amount spent on taxes and house payments?
  b. To the nearest thousand dollars, how much of his income is spent on items other than house payments?

Answers
5. a. $16,300 **b.** $27,000

B Estimating Sums and Differences

When we **estimate** the answer to a problem, we simplify the problem so that an approximate answer can be found quickly. There are a number of ways of doing this. One common method is to use rounded numbers to simplify the arithmetic necessary to arrive at an approximate answer, as our next example shows.

6. Estimate the answer to the following addition problem by rounding each number to the nearest thousand.

$$
\begin{array}{r}
15{,}465 \\
1{,}564 \\
893 \\
+\ 11{,}989 \\
\hline
\end{array}
$$

Example 6   Estimate the answer to the following addition problem by rounding each number to the nearest thousand.

$$
\begin{array}{r}
4{,}872 \\
1{,}691 \\
777 \\
+\ 6{,}124 \\
\hline
\end{array}
$$

Solution   We round each of the four numbers in the sum to the nearest thousand. Then we add the rounded numbers.

4,872	rounds to	5,000
1,691	rounds to	2,000
777	rounds to	1,000
+ 6,124	rounds to	+ 6,000
		14,000

We estimate the answer to this problem to be approximately 14,000. The actual answer, found by adding the original unrounded numbers, is 13,464. Estimating gives us relatively inaccurate answers but allows us to make computations quickly.

7. Estimate the answer to the following subtraction problem by rounding each number to the nearest hundred.

$$
12{,}487 - 5{,}806
$$

Example 7   Estimate the answer to the following subtraction problem by rounding each number to the nearest hundred.

$$
5{,}423 - 1{,}856
$$

Solution   Round each number to the nearest hundred, then subtract.

5,432	rounds to	5,400
− 1,856	rounds to	− 1,900
		3,500

We estimate the answer to be approximately 3,500. The actual answer, found by subtracting the original numbers, is 3,567.

Note   Rounding involves writing an exact answer in approximate form. Estimating involves rounding each number and then performing the computations.

The method used in Examples 6 and 7 above does not conflict with the rule we stated before Example 5. In Examples 6 and 7, we are asked to *estimate* an answer, so it is okay to round the numbers in the problem before adding them. In Example 5, we are asked for a rounded answer, meaning that we are to find the exact answer to the problem and then round to the indicated place. In this case, we must not round the numbers in the problem before adding.

RULE   **Rounding and Estimating**

If we are doing calculations and are asked to round our answer, we do all our arithmetic first and then round the result. That is, the last step is to round the answer. When we want to find an estimate, we round each of the numbers in the problem so that we can find an approximate answer quickly. Then we perform the computations.

Answers

6. 30,000
7. 6,700

C Bar Charts

 DESCRIPTIVE STATISTICS

Below are two representations for the amount of caffeine in five different drinks, one numeric and one visual.

Table 2

Beverage (6-Ounce Cup)	Caffeine (In Milligrams)
Brewed Coffee	100
Instant Coffee	70
Tea	50
Cocoa	5
Decaffeinated Coffee	4

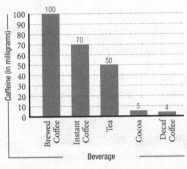

FIGURE 1

The diagram in Figure 1 is called a **bar chart**. The horizontal line below which the drinks are listed is called the **horizontal axis,** while the vertical line that is labeled from 0 to 100 is called the **vertical axis.**

Example 8   Refer to the bar chart shown in Figure 1. How many milligrams of caffeine are consumed in one serving of instant coffee?

Solution   Find the instant coffee bar on the horizontal axis and read its corresponding value from the vertical axis. The amount of caffeine in one serving of instant coffee is 70 milligrams.

8. Using Figure 1, how much caffeine is consumed in one serving of decaffeinated coffee?

 KEY CONCEPT REVIEW

After reading through the preceding section, respond in your own words and in complete sentences.

A. Describe the process you would use to round 5,382 to the nearest thousand.

B. Describe the process you would use to round 47,256,344 to the nearest ten thousand.

C. Find a number not containing the digit 7 that will round to 700 when rounded to the nearest hundred.

D. Describe a scenario in your day-to-day life in which estimating could be useful.

Answers

8. 4 milligrams

Choose the correct words to fill in the blanks below.

more   round   estimate
less   horizontal axis   vertical axis

1. When asked to _____ your answer, do all calculations first then round the result.

2. When rounding numbers, if the digit to the right of the place you are to round to is _____ than 5, replace it and all digits to its right with zeros.

3. When rounding numbers, if the digit to the right of the place you are to round to is 5 or _____, replace it and all digits to its right with zeros, and add 1 to the digit to its left.

4. The horizontal line below the bars of a bar chart is called the _____, whereas the vertical line to the left of the bars is called the _____.

5. When asked to _____ your answer, use rounded numbers to arrive at an approximate answer.

Problems

A Round each of the numbers to the nearest ten.

1. 42	**2.** 44	**3.** 46	**4.** 48	**5.** 45	**6.** 73
7. 77	**8.** 75	**9.** 458	**10.** 455	**11.** 471	**12.** 680
13. 56,782	**14.** 32,807	**15.** 4,504	**16.** 3,897	**17.** 1,195	**18.** 10,998

Round each of the numbers to the nearest hundred.

19. 549	**20.** 954	**21.** 833	**22.** 604	**23.** 899	**24.** 988
25. 1090	**26.** 6,778	**27.** 5,044	**28.** 56,990	**29.** 39,603	**30.** 31,999

Round each of the numbers to the nearest thousand.

31. 4,670	**32.** 9,054	**33.** 9,760	**34.** 4,444
35. 978	**36.** 567	**37.** 657,892	**38.** 688,909
39. 608,433	**40.** 3,789,345	**41.** 5,744,500	**42.** 509,905

Complete the following table by rounding the numbers on the left as indicated by the headings in the table.

Original Number	Rounded to the Nearest		
	Ten	Hundred	Thousand
43. 7,821			
44. 5,945			
45. 5,999			
46. 4,353			
47. 10,985			
48. 11,108			
49. 99,999			
50. 95,505			

Business Expenses The pie chart shows one year's worth of expenses for a small business. Use the chart to answer the following problems.

51. To the nearest hundred dollars, how much was spent on postage and supplies?

52. Find the total amount spent, to the nearest hundred dollars, on rent, utilities, and car expenses.

53. To the nearest thousand dollars, how much was spent on items other than salaries, rent, and utilities?

54. To the nearest thousand dollars, how much was spent on items other than postage, supplies, and car expenses?

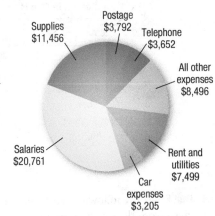

Supplies $11,456
Postage $3,792
Telephone $3,652
All other expenses $8,496
Salaries $20,761
Rent and utilities $7,499
Car expenses $3,205

B Estimate the answer to each of the following addition problems by rounding each number to the indicated place value and then adding.

55. Hundred
  750
  275
+ 120

56. Thousand
  1,891
    765
+ 3,223

57. Hundred
  472
  422
  536
+511

58. Hundred
  399
  601
  744
+ 298

59. Thousand
  25,399
   7,601
  18,744
+ 6,298

60. Thousand
  9,999
  8,888
  7,777
+ 6,666

Estimate the answer to the following problems by rounding each number to the indicated place value and then subtracting.

61. Hundred
17,487 − 5,640

62. Hundred
986 − 249

63. Thousand
8,946 − 3,815

64. Thousand
18,955 − 12,049

65. Thousand
204,489 − 107,815

66. Thousand
49,899 − 29,846

C Working with Bar Charts

67. Exercise The following table lists the number of calories burned in 1 hour of exercise by a person who weighs 150 pounds. Construct a bar chart from the information in the table.

Calories Burned by a 150-Pound Person in One Hour	
Activity	**Calories**
Bicycling	374
Bowling	265
Handball	680
Yoga	300
Jogging	680
Skiing	544

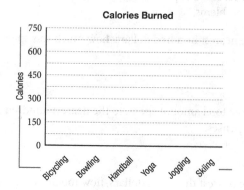

68. Fast Food The following table lists the number of calories consumed by eating some popular fast foods. Construct a bar chart from the information in the table.

Calories in Fast Food	
Food	**Calories**
McDonald's hamburger	270
Burger King hamburger	260
Jack in the Box hamburger	280
McDonald's Big Mac	510
Burger King Whopper	630
Jack in the Box Colossus burger	940

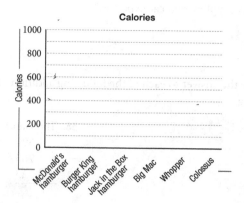

69. Tablet Sales The bar chart shows the projected sales of a new tablet over three years.

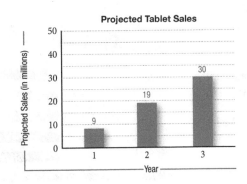

Projected Tablet Sales

Year	Projected Sales (Millions)
1	
2	
	30

a. Use the information in the bar chart to fill in the missing entries in the table.

b. What is the difference in projected tablet sales between the third year and the first year?

70. Mobile Gaming Revenues The bar chart shows the projected revenue for paid mobile games.

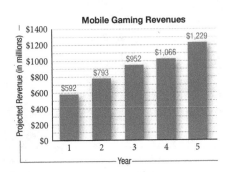

Mobile Gaming Revenues

Year	Projected Revenue (Millions)
1	
2	
	$952
4	
	$1,229

a. Use the chart to fill in the missing entries in the table.

b. What is the difference in projected revenue between the fourth year and the first year?

Applying the Concepts

71. Average Salary Assume a major league baseball's average player's salary for a season was $3,014,572, representing an increase of 0.6% over the previous season's average. Round the average player salary to the nearest hundred thousand.

72. Tallest Mountain The world's tallest mountain is Mount Everest. On May 5, 1999, it was found to be 7 feet taller than it was previously thought to be. Before this date, Everest was thought to be 29,028 feet high. That height was determined by B. L. Gulatee in 1954. The first measurement of Everest was in 1856. At that time the height was given as 29,002 feet. Round the 1999 height, the 1954 height, and the 1856 height of Mount Everest to the nearest thousand.

TV Ratings The chart shows the number of viewers watching different primetime shows on a popular network in one week. Use the information to answer Problems 73-76.

73. What is the number of viewers watching these shows during the week?

74. Using your answer from the previous problem, is the statement "About 27 million viewers watched these shows" correct?

75. To the nearest hundred thousand, how many people watched the competition talent show during the week?

76. To the nearest ten thousand, how many people watched the game show during the week?

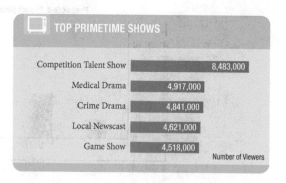

Improving Your Quantitative Literacy

77. Olympic Venues The bar chart below shows the seating capacity for several venues at a recent Winter Olympics.

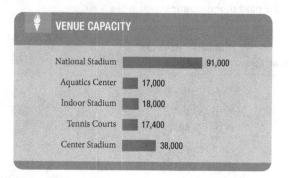

Venue	Capacity
National Stadium	
Aquatics Center	
	18,000
Tennis Courts	
	38,000

a. Use the information in the bar chart to fill in the missing entries in the table.

b. How many more people can attend a competition in the National Stadium than in the Aquatics Center?

FIND THE MISTAKE •

Each sentence below contains a mistake. Circle the mistake and write the correct word(s) or number(s) on the line provided.

1. Rounding 12,456 to the nearest hundred gives us 12,400. _____

2. To round 102,673 to the nearest ten, replace the 3 with a zero and add 1 to the 7. _____

3. To estimate the sum of 14,256 and 2,789 by rounding to the nearest hundred, add 14,200 and 2,800. _____

4. Using the bar chart below, Student C's home is 13 more miles from school than Student A's home. _____

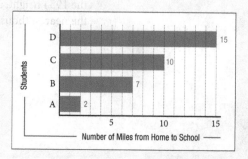

MULTIPLICATION WITH WHOLE NUMBERS, AND AREA

1.5

The Eiffel Tower in Paris, France, is visited by almost seven million people each year, making it an iconic symbol of the country and one of the most popular monuments in the world. Every night after sundown the tower lights up and sparkles for ten minutes every hour, on the hour. Because each of the 20,000 light bulbs on the tower uses 29 kilowatts of electricity a year, the city is exploring alternative means of powering the tower.

Considering this information, how many total kilowatts of electricity are used by the Eiffel Tower each year? To answer this problem, we need to understand multiplication with whole numbers, which we will cover in this section.

OBJECTIVES

A Multiply numbers by using repeated addition.

B Use terminology and properties of multiplication.

C Multiply numbers involving carrying and place value.

D Solve application problems, including area.

E Solve multiplication equations by inspection.

KEY WORDS

product

factors

distributive property

multiplication property of zero

identity property of multiplication

commutative property of mutiplication

associative property of multiplication

area

A Multiplication as Repeated Addition

To begin, we can think of multiplication as shorthand for repeated addition. That is, multiplying 3 times 4 can be thought of this way:

$$3 \text{ times } 4 = 4 + 4 + 4 = 12$$

Multiplying 3 times 4 means to add three 4s. We can write 3 times 4 as 3×4, or $3 \cdot 4$.

Example 1   Multiply $4 \cdot 400$ using repeated addition.

Solution   Using the definition of multiplication as repeated addition, we have

$$4 \cdot 400 = 400 + 400 + 400 + 400$$
$$= 1,600$$

One way to visualize this process is to think about a 4 by 400 meter relay team where each individual runs 400 meters.

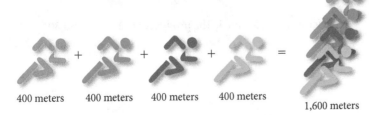

400 meters   400 meters   400 meters   400 meters   1,600 meters

Notice that if we had multiplied 4 and 4 to get 16 and then attached two zeros on the right, the result would have been the same.

Practice Problems

1. Multiply $5 \cdot 400$ using repeated addition.

Answer

1. 2,000

45

Note The kind of notation we will use to indicate multiplication will depend on the situation. For example, when we are solving equations that involve letters, it is not a good idea to indicate multiplication with the symbol ×, since it could be confused with the variable *x*.

B Vocabulary and Properties

There are many ways to indicate multiplication. All the following statements are equivalent. They all indicate multiplication with the numbers 3 and 4.

$$3 \cdot 4, \quad 3 \times 4, \quad 3(4), \quad (3)4, \quad (3)(4), \quad \begin{array}{r} 4 \\ \times 3 \\ \hline \end{array}$$

If one or both of the numbers we are multiplying are represented by variables, we may also use the following notation:

$5n$	means	5 times n
ab	means	a times b

We use the word **product** to indicate multiplication. If we say, "The product of 3 and 4 is 12," then we mean

$$3 \cdot 4 = 12$$

Both $3 \cdot 4$ and 12 are called the products of 3 and 4. The 3 and 4 are called **factors.**

DEFINITION factors

A **factor** of a is a number that can be multiplied by another number to get a.

Table 1 gives some word statements involving multiplication and their mathematical equivalents written in symbols.

Table 1

In English	In Symbols
The product of 2 and 5	$2 \cdot 5$
The product of 5 and 2	$5 \cdot 2$
The product of 4 and n	$4n$
The product of x and y	xy
The product of 9 and 6 is 54.	$9 \cdot 6 = 54$
The product of 2 and 8 is 16.	$2 \cdot 8 = 16$

2. Identify the products and factors in the statement $5 \cdot 7 = 35$.

Example 2 Identify the products and factors in the statement
$$9 \cdot 8 = 72$$

Solution The factors are 9 and 8, and the products are $9 \cdot 8$ and 72.

• •

3. Identify the products and factors in the statement $2 \cdot 5 \cdot 11 = 110$.

Example 3 Identify the products and factors in the statement
$$30 = 2 \cdot 3 \cdot 5$$

Solution The factors are 2, 3, and 5. The products are $2 \cdot 3 \cdot 5$ and 30.

• •

Answers

2. Factors: 5, 7
  Products: $5 \cdot 7$, 35
3. Factors: 2, 5, 11
  Products: $2 \cdot 5 \cdot 11$, 110

Distributive Property

To develop an efficient method of multiplication, we need to use what is called the **distributive property.** To begin, consider the following two problems:

Problem 1	Problem 2
$3(4 + 5)$	$3(4) + 3(5)$
$= 3(9)$	$= 12 + 15$
$= 27$	$= 27$

The result in both cases is the same number, 27. This indicates that the original two expressions must have been equal also; that is,

$$3(4 + 5) = 3(4) + 3(5)$$

This is an example of the distributive property. We say that multiplication *distributes* over addition.

$$3(4 + 5) = 3(4) + 3(5)$$

We can write this property in symbols using the letters a, b, and c to represent any three numbers.

PROPERTY   Distributive Property

If a, b, and c represent any three numbers, then

$$a(b + c) = a(b) + a(c)$$

The distributive property also works for subtraction:

$$a(b - c) = a(b) - a(c)$$

> **Note**   When using the distributive property, we multiply $a(b)$ and $a(c)$ before adding their products together because of a rule called order of operations. Part of this rule states that we multiply and then we add. We will study this rule more later on in this chapter.

Example 4   Use the distributive property to rewrite each expression, then simplify.

a. $2(5 + 6)$

b. $3(x + 2)$

Solution

a. $2(5 + 6) = 2(5) + 2(6)$
$= 10 + 12$
$= 22$

b. $3(x + 2) = 3(x) + 3(2)$
$= 3x + 6$

4. Apply the distributive property, then simplify.
a. $4(10 + 6)$
b. $5(x + 8)$

Answers

4. a. 64   **b.** $5x + 40$

More Properties of Multiplication

PROPERTY Multiplication Property of 0

If a represents any number, then

$$a \cdot 0 = 0 \quad \text{and} \quad 0 \cdot a = 0$$

In words: Multiplication by zero always results in zero.

PROPERTY Identity Property of Multiplication

If a represents any number, then

$$a \cdot 1 = a \quad \text{and} \quad 1 \cdot a = a$$

In words: Multiplying any number by one leaves that number unchanged.

PROPERTY Commutative Property of Multiplication

If a and b are any two numbers, then

$$ab = ba$$

In words: The order of the numbers in a product does not affect the result.

PROPERTY Associative Property of Multiplication

If a, b, and c represent any three numbers, then

$$(ab)c = a(bc)$$

In words: We can change the grouping of the numbers in a product without changing the result.

$Note$ The root word of commutative is commute, and the root word of associative is associate. These root words can be helpful for learning and recalling each property.

To visualize the commutative property, we can think of a dining room with 8 guests.

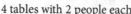

4 tables with 2 people each   =   2 tables with 4 people each

5. Use the commutative property of multiplication to rewrite each product.
a. $5 \cdot 12$
b. $6(x + y)$

Example 5   Use the commutative property of multiplication to rewrite each of the following products.
a. $7 \cdot 9$ **b.** $4(6)$

Solution   Applying the commutative property to each expression, we have
a. $7 \cdot 9 = 9 \cdot 7$
b. $4(6) = 6(4)$

Example 6   Use the associative property of multiplication to rewrite each of the following products.

a. $(2 \cdot 7) \cdot 9$ **b.** $3 \cdot (8 \cdot 2)$

Solution   Applying the associative property of multiplication, we regroup as follows:

a. $(2 \cdot 7) \cdot 9 = 2 \cdot (7 \cdot 9)$

b. $3 \cdot (8 \cdot 2) = (3 \cdot 8) \cdot 2$

C Multiplication with Whole Numbers

Suppose we want to find the product 7(65). By writing 65 as $60 + 5$ and applying the distributive property, we have

$$7(65) = 7(60 + 5) \qquad 65 = 60 + 5$$

$$= 7(60) + 7(5) \qquad \text{Distributive property}$$

$$= 420 + 35 \qquad \text{Multiply first, then add.}$$

$$= 455$$

We can write the same problem vertically like this:

$$
\begin{array}{r}
60 + 5 \\
\times\ 7 \\
\hline
35 \\
+420 \\
\hline
455
\end{array}
\begin{array}{l}
\leftarrow\ 7(5) = 35 \\
\leftarrow\ 7(60) = 420
\end{array}
$$

To save space in writing, we use the following steps. We will show each step here and then show the condensed form that we will use in the future.

$$
\begin{array}{r}
\overset{3}{6}5 \\
\times\ 7 \\
\hline
5
\end{array}
\quad \leftarrow
\begin{array}{l}
\text{Step 1: } 7(5) = 35; \text{ write the 5} \\
\text{in the ones column, and then carry} \\
\text{the 3 to the tens column.}
\end{array}
$$

$$
\begin{array}{r}
\overset{3}{6}5 \\
\times\ 7 \\
\hline
455
\end{array}
\quad \leftarrow
\begin{array}{l}
\text{Step 2: } 7(6) = 42; \text{ add the 3 we} \\
\text{carried to 42 to get 45.}
\end{array}
$$

This notation takes some practice.

Example 7   Multiply: 9(43).

Solution

$$
\begin{array}{l}
\text{Step 2: } 9(4) = 36; \text{ add the 2} \longrightarrow \\
\text{we carried to 36 to get 38.}
\end{array}
\begin{array}{r}
\overset{2}{4}3 \\
\times\ 9 \\
\hline
387
\end{array}
\begin{array}{l}
\text{Step 1: } 9(3) = 27; \text{ write the 7} \\
\leftarrow \text{in the ones column, and then carry} \\
\text{the 2 to the tens column.}
\end{array}
$$

Example 8   Multiply: 52(37)

Solution   First we will find the product using the distributive property. Then we will use an alternative notation. Notice 52(37) is the same as 52(30 + 7) and by the distributive property.

$$52(30) + 52(7)$$

$$
\begin{array}{r}
\overset{1}{5}2 \\
\times\ 30 \\
\hline
1{,}560
\end{array}
\qquad
\begin{array}{r}
52 \\
\times\ 7 \\
\hline
364
\end{array}
$$

6. Use the associative property of multiplication to rewrite each product.
a. $(5 \cdot 8) \cdot 3$
b. $3 \cdot (7 \cdot n)$

Note   Notice, finding 7(60) is the equivalent of multiplying 7 and 6 and adding a zero. This applies to all multiples of 10. The concept can be extended to multiples of 100, 1,000, etc. For example, 8(900) is the product of 8 and 9 and adding two zeroes. Thus, 8(900) = 7,200.

7. Multiply: 7(59)

8. Multiply: 67(45)

Answers

6. a. $5 \cdot (8 \cdot 3)$ **b.** $(3 \cdot 7) \cdot n$
7. 413
8. 3,015

The sum of these two numbers is $1{,}560 + 364 = 1{,}924$. Here is a summary of what we have so far:

$$52(37) = 52(30 + 7) \qquad 37 = 30 + 7$$
$$= 52(30) + 52(7) \qquad \text{Distributive property}$$
$$= 1{,}560 + 364 \qquad \text{Multiply first, then add.}$$
$$= 1{,}924$$

Like we've done previously, we will show each step and then in the future we will use a condensed form.

$$
\begin{array}{r}
\overset{1}{5}2 \\
\times\ 37 \\
\hline
4
\end{array}
$$
$\longleftarrow$ Step 1: 7(2) = 14; write the 4 in the ones column, and then carry the 1 to the tens column.

$$
\begin{array}{r}
\overset{1}{5}2 \\
\times\ 37 \\
\hline
364
\end{array}
$$
$\longleftarrow$ Step 2: 7(5) = 35; add the 1 to get 36.

$$
\begin{array}{r}
52 \\
\times\ 37 \\
\hline
364 \\
0
\end{array}
$$
$\longleftarrow$ Step 3: Add a 0 in the ones column of the next line.

$$
\begin{array}{r}
52 \\
\times\ 37 \\
\hline
364 \\
60
\end{array}
$$
$\longleftarrow$ Step 4: 3(2) = 6

$$
\begin{array}{r}
52 \\
\times\ 37 \\
\hline
364 \\
1560
\end{array}
$$
$\longleftarrow$ Step 5: 3(5) = 15

$$
\begin{array}{r}
52 \\
\times\ 37 \\
\hline
364 \\
+\ 1560 \\
\hline
1924
\end{array}
$$
$\longleftarrow$ Step 6: 364 + 1,560 = 1,924

From now on, we will only show the last step.

9. Multiply: 124(375)

$\mathcal{Note}$ To check our work, we could estimate the answer to Example 9 by rounding each number to the nearest hundred and then multiplying.

$$300\,(400) = 120{,}000$$

Our estimate is 120,000, which is close to the actual answer, 119,412.

Example 9 Find the product of 279 and 428.

Solution We want to multiply.

$$
\begin{array}{r}
279 \\
\times\ \ 428 \\
\hline
2{,}232 \\
5{,}580 \\
+\ 111{,}600 \\
\hline
119{,}412
\end{array}
$$

$\longleftarrow$ 8(279) = 2,232
$\longleftarrow$ 20(279) = 5,580
$\longleftarrow$ 400(279) = 111,600

Answer

9. 46,500

D Applications

Example 10   A supermarket orders 35 cases of a certain soft drink. If each case contains 12 cans of the drink, then how many cans were ordered?

Solution   We have 35 cases and each case has 12 cans. The total number of cans is the product of 35 and 12, which is 35(12).

$$
\begin{array}{r}
12 \\
\times\ 35 \\
\hline
60 \\
+\ 360 \\
\hline
420
\end{array}
$$

$\longleftarrow\quad 5(12) = 60$

$\longleftarrow\quad 30(12) = 360$

There is a total of 420 cans of the soft drink.

10. A restaurant orders 45 cases of drinking glasses. If each case contains 24 glasses, how many were ordered?

Example 11   Shirley earns $12 an hour for the first 40 hours she works each week. If she has $109 deducted from her weekly check for taxes and retirement, how much money will she take home if she works 38 hours this week?

Solution   To find the amount of money she earned for the week, we multiply 12 and 38. From that total we subtract 109. The result is her take-home pay. Without showing all the work involved in the calculations, here is the solution:

$38(\$12) = \$456$ *Her total weekly earnings*

$\$456 - \$109 = \$347$ *Her take-home pay*

11. Rodrigo earns $9 per hour at his tutoring job. If he works 35 hours and has $42 deducted for taxes, how much will his paycheck be for the week?

Example 12   In 1993, the government standardized the way in which nutrition information is presented on the labels of most packaged food products and has revised the graphic over the years. Figure 1 shows the 1993 standardized food label. It is from a box of original Cheez-It™ baked snack crackers. Approximately how many crackers are in the box, and what is the total number of calories consumed if all the crackers in the box are eaten?

Solution   Reading toward the top of the label, we see that there are about 27 crackers in one serving, and approximately 9 servings in the box. Therefore, the total number of crackers in the box is

$9(27) = 243$ crackers

This is an approximate number, because each serving is approximately 27 crackers. Reading further we find that each serving contains 150 calories. Therefore, the total number of calories consumed by eating all the crackers in the box is

$9(150) = 1{,}350$ calories

As we progress through the book, we will study more of the information in nutrition labels.

12. From Example 12, how many calories from fat will you consume if you eat the entire box of crackers?

Nutrition Facts

Serving Size 30 g. (About 27 crackers)
Servings Per Container: 9

Amount Per Serving

| **Calories** 150 | Calories from fat 70 |

	% Daily Value*
Total Fat 8g	**12%**
Saturated Fat 2g	**10%**

FIGURE 1

Answers

10. 1,080

11. $273

12. 630 calories from fat

13. Using the chart from Example 13 suppose a 150-pound person bicycles for 3 hours and goes jogging for 2 hours in a week. How many calories did that person burn in a that time?

> *Note*   The letter g that is shown after some of the numbers in the nutrition label in Figure 1 stands for grams, a unit used to measure weight. The unit mg stands for milligrams, another smaller unit of weight. We will have more to say about these units later in the book.

Example 13   The table below lists the number of calories burned in 1 hour of exercise by a person who weighs 150 pounds. Suppose a 150-pound person goes bowling for 2 hours after having eaten the box of crackers mentioned in the previous example. Will he or she burn all the calories consumed from the crackers?

Activity	Calories Burned in 1 Hour by a 150-Pound Person
Bicycling	374
Bowling	265
Handball	680
Yoga	300
Jogging	680
Skiing	544

Solution   Each hour of bowling burns 265 calories. If the person bowls for 2 hours, he or she will burn a total of

$$2(265) = 530 \text{ calories}$$

Because the box of crackers contained 1,350 calories, not all of them have been burned with 2 hours of bowling.

• •

Area

To understand some of the notation we use for area, we need to talk about exponents. The 2 in the expression 3^2 is an exponent. The expression 3^2 is read "3 to the second power," or "3 squared," and it is defined this way:

$$3^2 = 3 \cdot 3 = 9$$

As you can see, the exponent 2 in the expression 3^2 tells us to multiply two 3s together. Here are some additional expressions containing the exponent 2.

$$4^2 = 4 \cdot 4 = 16$$

$$5^2 = 5 \cdot 5 = 25$$

$$11^2 = 11 \cdot 11 = 121$$

We will cover exponents in more detail later in this chapter.

DEFINITION   area

The **area** of a flat object is a measure of the amount of surface the object has.

The rectangle in Figure 2 below has an area of 6 square inches, because that is the number of squares (each of which is 1 inch long and 1 inch wide) it takes to cover the rectangle.

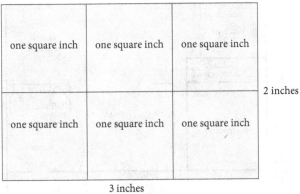

FIGURE 2

It is no coincidence that the area of the rectangle in Figure 2 and the product of the length and the width are the same number. We can calculate the area of the rectangle in Figure 2 by simply multiplying the length and the width together.

$$
\begin{aligned}
\text{Area} &= (\text{length}) \cdot (\text{width}) \\
&= (3 \text{ inches}) \cdot (2 \text{ inches}) \\
&= (3 \cdot 2) \cdot (\text{inches} \cdot \text{inches}) \\
&= 6 \text{ square inches}
\end{aligned}
$$

The unit **square inches** can be abbreviated as *sq. in.* or *in²*.

FACTS FROM GEOMETRY ·

Area

Figure 3 shows two common geometric figures along with the formulas for their areas.

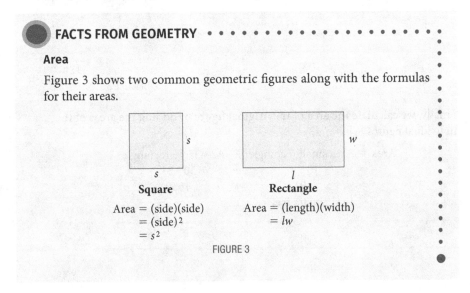

Square

$$
\begin{aligned}
\text{Area} &= (\text{side})(\text{side}) \\
&= (\text{side})^2 \\
&= s^2
\end{aligned}
$$

Rectangle

$$
\begin{aligned}
\text{Area} &= (\text{length})(\text{width}) \\
&= lw
\end{aligned}
$$

FIGURE 3

14. From the figure in Example 14, find the area of the two bedrooms.

Example 14 Find the total area of the house and deck shown in Figure 4.

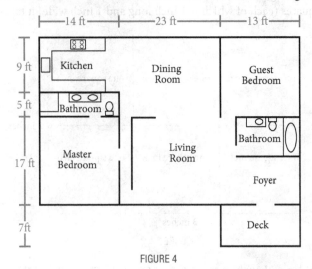

FIGURE 4

Solution We begin by drawing an additional line (see Figure 5) so that the original figure is now composed of two rectangles. Next, we fill in the missing dimensions on the two rectangles (Figure 6).

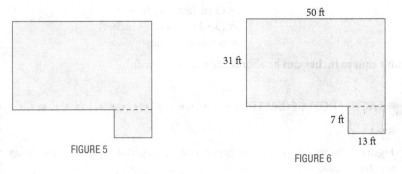

FIGURE 5   FIGURE 6

Finally, we calculate the area of the original figure by adding the areas of the individual figures.

$$\begin{aligned}
\text{Area} &= \text{Area small rectangle} + \text{Area large rectangle} \\
&= \qquad 13 \cdot 7 \qquad + \qquad 50 \cdot 31 \\
&= \qquad 91 \qquad\quad + \qquad 1550 \\
&= 1641 \text{ square feet}
\end{aligned}$$

Answer

14. 420 square feet

E Solving Equations

If n is used to represent a number, then the equation

$$4 \cdot n = 12$$

is read "4 times n is 12," or "The product of 4 and n is 12." This means that we are looking for the number we multiply by 4 to get 12. Using inspection, we can see that the number is 3. Because the equation becomes a true statement if n is 3, we say that 3 is the solution to the equation.

Example 15　Find the solution to each of the following equations by inspection.

a. $6 \cdot n = 24$　　**b.** $4 \cdot n = 36$　　**c.** $15 = 3 \cdot n$　　**d.** $21 = 3 \cdot n$

Solution

a. The solution to $6 \cdot n = 24$ is 4, because $6 \cdot 4 = 24$.

b. The solution to $4 \cdot n = 36$ is 9, because $4 \cdot 9 = 36$.

c. The solution to $15 = 3 \cdot n$ is 5, because $15 = 3 \cdot 5$.

d. The solution to $21 = 3 \cdot n$ is 7, because $21 = 3 \cdot 7$.

15. Find the solution to each of the following equations by inspection.
 a. $5 \cdot n = 30$
 b. $7 \cdot n = 56$
 c. $24 = 4 \cdot n$
 d. $33 = 3 \cdot n$

● **KEY CONCEPT REVIEW** · · · · · · · · · · · · · · ·

After reading through the preceding section, respond in your own words and in complete sentences.

A. Explain how multiplication is shorthand for repeated addition.

B. Use the variables a, b, and c to explain the distribution property.

C. Explain how you would find the area of a flat object.

D. What is the difference between the commutative property of multiplication and the associative property of multiplication?

EXERCISE SET 1.5 ....

VOCABULARY REVIEW •

Choose the correct words to fill in the blanks below.

associative	addition	distributive	multiplication property of zero
area	commutative	factors	identity property of multiplication

1. Multiplication is repeated _____.

2. _____ are numbers that when multiplied together give a product.

3. The _____ property states that $a(b + c) = a(b) + a(c)$.

4. The _____ states that multiplication by 0 always results in 0.

5. The _____ property of multiplication states that the order of the numbers in a product doesn't affect the result.

6. The _____ property of multiplication states that $(ab)c = a(bc)$.

7. The _____ of a flat object is a measure of the amount of surface the object has.

8. The _____ states that $a \cdot 1 = a$, for any number a.

Problems

A Multiply each of the following using repeated addition.

1. $3 \cdot 100$ **2.** $7 \cdot 100$ **3.** $3 \cdot 200$ **4.** $4 \cdot 200$

5. $6 \cdot 500$ **6.** $8 \cdot 400$ **7.** $5 \cdot 1,000$ **8.** $8 \cdot 1,000$

9. $3 \cdot 7,000$ **10.** $6 \cdot 7,000$ **11.** $9 \cdot 9,000$ **12.** $7 \cdot 7,000$

B Write each of the following expressions in words, using the word *product*.

13. $6 \cdot 7$ **14.** $9(4)$ **15.** $2 \cdot n$

16. $5 \cdot x$ **17.** $9 \cdot 7 = 63$ **18.** $(5)(6) = 30$

Write each of the following in symbols.

19. The product of 7 and n **20.** The product of 9 and x **21.** The product of 6 and 7 is 42.

22. The product of 8 and 9 is 72.   **23.** The product of 0 and 6 is 0.   **24.** The product of 1 and 6 is 6.

Identify the products in each statement.

25. $9 \cdot 7 = 63$ **26.** $2(6) = 12$ **27.** $4(4) = 16$ **28.** $5 \cdot 5 = 25$

Identify the factors in each statement.

29. $2 \cdot 3 \cdot 4 = 24$ **30.** $6 \cdot 1 \cdot 5 = 30$ **31.** $12 = 2 \cdot 2 \cdot 3$ **32.** $42 = 2 \cdot 3 \cdot 7$

Rewrite each of the following using the commutative property of multiplication.

33. $5(9)$ **34.** $4(3)$ **35.** $6 \cdot 7$ **36.** $8 \cdot 3$

Rewrite each of the following using the associative property of multiplication.

37. $2 \cdot (7 \cdot 6)$ **38.** $4 \cdot (8 \cdot 5)$ **39.** $3 \times (9 \times 1)$ **40.** $5 \times (8 \times 2)$

Use the distributive property to rewrite each expression, then simplify.

41. $7(2 + 3)$ **42.** $4(5 + 8)$ **43.** $9(4 + 7)$ **44.** $6(9 + 5)$

45. $3(x - 1)$ **46.** $5(x - 8)$ **47.** $2(x - 5)$ **48.** $4(x - 3)$

C Find each of the following products (multiply). In each case, use the shortcut method.

49. $\begin{array}{r} 25 \\ \times\ 4 \\ \hline \end{array}$ **50.** $\begin{array}{r} 43 \\ \times\ 9 \\ \hline \end{array}$ **51.** $\begin{array}{r} 38 \\ \times\ 6 \\ \hline \end{array}$ **52.** $\begin{array}{r} 45 \\ \times\ 7 \\ \hline \end{array}$

53. $\begin{array}{r} 18 \\ \times\ 2 \\ \hline \end{array}$ **54.** $\begin{array}{r} 29 \\ \times\ 3 \\ \hline \end{array}$ **55.** $\begin{array}{r} 72 \\ \times\ 20 \\ \hline \end{array}$ **56.** $\begin{array}{r} 68 \\ \times\ 30 \\ \hline \end{array}$

57. $\begin{array}{r} 19 \\ \times\ 50 \\ \hline \end{array}$ **58.** $\begin{array}{r} 24 \\ \times\ 40 \\ \hline \end{array}$ **59.** $\begin{array}{r} 69 \\ \times\ 25 \\ \hline \end{array}$ **60.** $\begin{array}{r} 27 \\ \times\ 36 \\ \hline \end{array}$

61. $\begin{array}{r} 11 \\ \times\ 11 \\ \hline \end{array}$ **62.** $\begin{array}{r} 12 \\ \times\ 21 \\ \hline \end{array}$ **63.** $\begin{array}{r} 97 \\ \times\ 16 \\ \hline \end{array}$ **64.** $\begin{array}{r} 24 \\ \times\ 39 \\ \hline \end{array}$

65. 168
     × 25

66. 452
     × 34

67. 728
     × 91

68. 680
     × 76

69. 698
     × 400

70. 879
     × 600

71. 111
     × 111

72. 123
     × 321

73. 532
     × 200

74. 277
     × 900

75. 856
     × 232

76. 455
     × 248

77. 976
     × 628

78. 432
     × 555

79. 2,468
     × 135

80. 2,725
     × 324

81. 24,563
     ×   735

82. 56,728
     ×   852

83. 44,777
     × 5,888

84. 33,999
     × 2,555

Complete the following tables.

85.

First Number a	Second Number b	Their Product ab
11	11	
11	22	
22	22	
22	44	

86.

First Number a	Second Number b	Their Product ab
25	15	
25	30	
50	15	
50	30	

87.

First Number a	Second Number b	Their Product $a \cdot b$
25	10	
25	100	
25	1,000	
25	10,000	

88.

First Number a	Second Number b	Their Product $a \cdot b$
11	111	
11	222	
22	111	
22	222	

89.

First Number a	Second Number b	Their Product $(a)(b)$
12	20	
36	20	
12	40	
36	40	

90.

First Number a	Second Number b	Their Product $(a)(b)$
10	12	
100	12	
1,000	12	
10,000	12	

D Find the area enclosed by each figure. (Note that some of the units on the figures come from the metric system. The abbreviations are as follows: Meter is abbreviated m, centimeter is cm, and millimeter is abbreviated mm. A meter is about 3 inches longer than a yard.)

91.

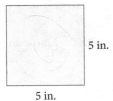

5 in.

5 in.

92.

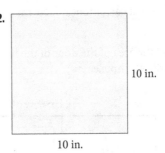

10 in.

10 in.

93.

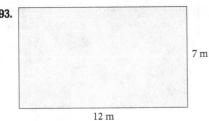

7 m

12 m

94.

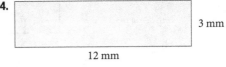

3 mm

12 mm

95.

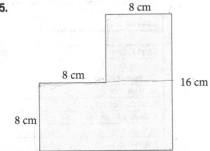

8 cm

8 cm

16 cm

8 cm

96.

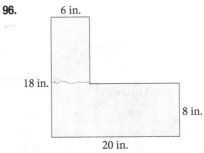

6 in.

18 in.

8 in.

20 in.

E Find a solution for each equation.

97. $4 \cdot n = 12$

98. $3 \cdot n = 12$

99. $9 \cdot n = 81$

100. $6 \cdot n = 36$

101. $0 = n \cdot 5$

102. $6 = 1 \cdot n$

103. $48 = 4 \cdot n$

104. $50 = 5 \cdot n$

105. $n \cdot 6 = 66$

106. $n \cdot 5 = 45$

107. $81 = 9 \cdot n$

108. $49 = 7 \cdot n$

109. Planning a Trip A family decides to drive their compact car on their vacation. They figure it will require a total of about 130 gallons of gas for the vacation. If each gallon of gas will take them 22 miles, how long is the trip they are planning?

110. Rent A student pays $475 rent each month. How much money does she spend on rent in 2 years?

111. Reading House Plans Find the area of the floor of the house shown here if the garage is not included with the house, and if the garage is included with the house.

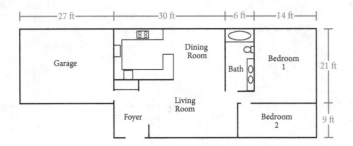

Exercise and Calories The table below is an extension of the table we used in Example 13 of this section. It gives the amount of energy expended during 1 hour of various activities for people of different weights. The accompanying figure is a nutrition label from a bag of cheddar crackers. Use the information from the table and the nutrition label to answer the following problems.

Calories Burned Through Exercise

| | Calories Per Hour | | |
Activity	120 Pounds	150 Pounds	180 Pounds
Bicycling	299	374	449
Bowling	212	265	318
Handball	544	680	816
Jazzercise	272	340	408
Jogging	544	680	816
Skiing	435	544	653

Nutrition Facts

Serving Size 55 pieces
Servings Per Container About 4

Amount Per Serving

Calories 140   Calories from fat 45

                                    % Daily Value*

Total Fat 5g	**8%**
Saturated Fat 1g	5%
Cholesterol 5mg	2%
Sodium 250mg	10%
Total Carbohydrate 20g	7%
Dietary Fiber 1g	4%
Sugars 1g	
Protein 4g	

Vitamin A 0%	●	Vitamin C 0%
Calcium 4%	●	Iron 2%

*Percent Daily Values are based on a 2,000 calorie diet

112. Suppose you weigh 180 pounds. How many calories would you burn if you play handball for 2 hours and then ride your bicycle for 1 hour?

113. How many calories are burned by a 120-lb person who jogs for 1 hour and then goes bike riding for 2 hours?

114. How many calories would you consume if you ate the entire bag of crackers?

115. Approximately how many crackers are in the bag?

116. If you weigh 180 pounds, will you burn off the calories consumed by eating 3 servings of crackers if you ride your bike 1 hour?

117. If you weigh 120 pounds, will you burn off the calories consumed by eating 3 servings of crackers if you ride your bike for 1 hour?

Estimating

Mentally estimate the answer to each of the following problems by rounding each number to the indicated place and then multiplying.

118.   750   hundred
      × 12   ten

119.   591   hundred
      × 323   hundred

120.   3,472   thousand
      × 511   hundred

121.   399   hundred
      × 298   hundred

122.   2,399   thousand
      × 698   hundred

123.   9,999   thousand
      × 666   hundred

One Step Further: Number Sequences

A geometric sequence is a sequence of numbers in which each number is obtained from the previous number by multiplying by the same number each time. For example, the sequence 3, 6, 12, 24, . . . is a geometric sequence, starting with 3, in which each number comes from multiplying the previous number by 2. Find the next number in each of the following geometric sequences.

124. 5, 10, 20, . . .

125. 10, 50, 250, . . .

126. 2, 6, 18, . . .

127. 12, 24, 48, . . .

FIND THE MISTAKE ·

Each sentence below contains a mistake. Circle the mistake and write the correct word(s) or number(s) on the line provided.

1. Factors are numbers that when multiplied together give a sum. _____

2. The distributive property is used to show that $16(5 + 9) = 16(5) + 9$. _____

3. The first step when multiplying 73 and 4 is to multiply 4 and 3 by writing down the 1 and carrying the 2.
   _____

4. The area of a rectangle with a length of 35 inches and a width of 8 inches is 43 square inches.
   _____

1.6

DIVISION WITH WHOLE NUMBERS

OBJECTIVES

A Describe the relationship between multiplication and division.

B Find quotients of whole numbers with no remainder.

C Find quotients of whole numbers with nonzero remainders.

KEY WORDS

quotient

dividend

divisor

long division

remainder

VIDEO EXAMPLES

SECTION 1.6

Over a billion people travel across China each year via high-speed rail. Each day, over 2,300 pairs of high-speed trains travel 22,000 kilometers (13,600 miles) of rail, connecting cities across the nation. These bullet locomotives, as they are sometimes called, offer passengers fast, punctual, and convenient travel at reasonable costs.

The route from Beijing to Shanghai, two large cities in China, is approximately 1,200 kilometers. If it takes four hours to travel between these cities via train, what is the speed of the locomotive in kilometers per hour? To answer this question, we need to divide 1,200 by 4. In this section, we will work with division problems like this one.

Division is the inverse operation of multiplication. For example, because two times three is 6, six divided by two is 3.

A Notation

As was the case with multiplication, there are many ways to indicate division. All the following statements are equivalent. They all mean 10 divided by 5.

$$10 \div 5, \quad \frac{10}{5}, \quad 10/5, \quad 5\overline{)10}$$

The kind of notation we use to write division problems will depend on the situation. We will use the notation $5\overline{)10}$ mostly with the long division problems found in this chapter. The notation $\frac{10}{5}$ will be used in the chapter on fractions and in other chapters. The horizontal line used with the notation $\frac{10}{5}$ is called the fraction bar.

Vocabulary

The word **quotient** is used to indicate division. If we say, "The quotient of 10 and 5 is 2," then we mean

$$10 \div 5 = 2 \quad \text{or} \quad \frac{10}{5} = 2$$

The 10 is called the **dividend,** and the 5 is called the **divisor.** All the expressions, $10 \div 5$, $\frac{10}{5}$, and 2, are called the quotient of 10 and 5.

Table 1 gives some word statements involving division and their mathematical equivalents written in symbols.

Table 1

In English	In Symbols
The quotient of 15 and 3	$15 \div 3$, or $\frac{15}{3}$, or 15/3
The quotient of 8 and n	$8 \div n$, or $\frac{8}{n}$, or 8/n
x divided by 2	$x \div 2$, or $\frac{x}{2}$, or x/2
The quotient of 21 and 3 is 7.	$21 \div 3 = 7$, or $\frac{21}{3} = 7$

The Meaning of Division

One way to arrive at an answer to a division problem is by thinking in terms of multiplication. For example, if we want to find the quotient of 32 and 8, we may ask, "What do we multiply 8 by to get 32?"

$$32 \div 8 = ? \qquad \text{means} \qquad 8 \cdot ? = 32$$

Because we know from our work with multiplication that $8 \cdot 4 = 32$, it must be true that

$$32 \div 8 = 4$$

Table 2 lists some additional examples.

Table 2

Division		Multiplication
$18 \div 6 = 3$	because	$6 \cdot 3 = 18$
$32 \div 8 = 4$	because	$8 \cdot 4 = 32$
$10 \div 5 = 2$	because	$5 \cdot 2 = 10$
$72 \div 9 = 8$	because	$9 \cdot 8 = 72$

B Division by One-Digit Numbers

Consider the following division problem:

$$465 \div 5$$

We can think of this problem as asking the question, "How many fives can we subtract from 465?" To answer the question, we begin subtracting multiples of 5. Using estimation, we can guess that there are at least 90 fives in 465. We find $90(5) = 450$ and subtract this from 465:

$$
\begin{array}{r}
465 \\
- 450 \\
\hline
15
\end{array}
$$

What we have done so far is subtract 90 fives from 465, and 15 remains. Because $3 \cdot 5 = 15$, there are 3 fives in 15. Therefore, the total number of fives we have subtracted from 465 is

$$90 + 3 = 93$$

We now summarize the results of our work.

$$465 \div 5 = 93$$

which we check with multiplication

$$
\begin{array}{r}
\overset{1}{9}3 \\
\times 5 \\
\hline
465
\end{array}
$$

Note This is what we consider an intuitive approach to division. In the upcoming example we will show a shortened method of division. This discussion shows us why that method works.

Notation

The division problem just shown can be shortened by eliminating some of the information.

The shorthand form for this problem

$$
\begin{array}{r}
3 \\
90 \\
5\overline{)465} \\
-450 \\
\hline
15 \\
-15 \\
\hline
0
\end{array}
$$

looks like this.

$$
\begin{array}{r}
93 \\
5\overline{)465} \\
-45\downarrow \\
\hline
15 \\
-15 \\
\hline
0
\end{array}
$$

The arrow indicates that we bring down the 5 after we subtract.

The problem shown above on the right is the shortcut form of what is called **long division.** Here is an example showing this shortcut form of long division from start to finish.

Practice Problems

1. Divide: $1{,}272 \div 8$

Example 1   Divide: $595 \div 7$

Solution   Because $7(8) = 56$, our first estimate of the number of sevens that can be subtracted from 595 is 80.

$$
\begin{array}{r}
8 \\
7\overline{)595} \\
-56\downarrow \\
\hline
35
\end{array}
$$

← The 8 is placed above the tens column, so we know our first estimate is 80.
← $8(7) = 56$
← $59 - 56 = 3$; then bring down the 5.

Since $7(5) = 35$, we have

$$
\begin{array}{r}
85 \\
7\overline{)595} \\
-56\downarrow \\
\hline
35 \\
-35 \\
\hline
0
\end{array}
$$

← There are 5 sevens in 35.

← $5(7) = 35$
← $35 - 35 = 0$

Our result is $595 \div 7 = 85$, which we can check with multiplication.

$$
\begin{array}{r}
\overset{3}{85} \\
\times 7 \\
\hline
595
\end{array}
$$

Division by Two-Digit Numbers

2. Divide: $13{,}152 \div 24$

Example 2   Divide: $9{,}380 \div 35$

Solution   In this case our divisor, 35, is a two-digit number. The process of division is the same. We still want to find the number of thirty-fives we can subtract from 9,380.

$$
\begin{array}{r}
2 \\
35\overline{)9380} \\
-70\downarrow \\
\hline
238
\end{array}
$$

← The 2 is placed above the hundreds column, because 2 thirty-fives is the most that can go into 93.
← $2(35) = 70$
← $93 - 70 = 23$; then bring down the 8.

We can make a few preliminary calculations to help estimate how many thirty-fives are in 238.

$$5 \times 35 = 175 \qquad 6 \times 35 = 210 \qquad 7 \times 35 = 245$$

Answers

1. 159
2. 548

Because 210 is the closest to 238 without being larger than 238, we use 6 as our next estimate. We now repeat the process of multiplying, subtracting, and bringing down the next digit.

```
        26    ←— 6 in the tens column means this estimate is 60.
   35)9380
    − 70↓|
      238
    − 210↓  ←— 6(35) = 210
      280    ←— 238 − 210 = 28; bring down the 0.
```

Because 35(8) = 280, we have

```
       268
  35)9380
   − 70↓|
     238
   − 210↓
     280
   − 280   ←— 8(35) = 280
       0   ←— 280 − 280 = 0
```

We can check our result with multiplication.

```
      268
   ×   35
    1,340
  + 8,040
    9,380
```

Example 3   Divide: 1,872 by 18

3. Divide: 5,200 ÷ 16

Solution   Here is the first step:

```
       1    ←——— 1 is placed above hundreds column.
  18)1872
   − 18    ←——— Multiply 1(18) to get 18.
      0    ←——— Subtract to get 0.
```

The next step is to bring down the 7, repeating the cycle.

```
      10    ←——— 0 is placed above tens column. 0 is the largest
  18)1872          number we can multiply by 18 and not go over 7.
   − 18↓
      07
    − 0    ←——— Multiply 0(18) to get 0.
      7    ←——— Subtract to get 7.
```

Here is the complete problem:

```
      104
  18)1872
   − 18↓|
      07|
    − 0↓
      72
    − 72
       0
```

To show our answer is correct, we multiply.

$$18(104) = 1,872$$

4. An individual has an annual income of $34,320. How much is her average monthly income?

$\mathcal{Note}$ To estimate the answer to Example 4 quickly, we can replace 35,880 with 36,000 and mentally calculate

$$36,000 \div 12$$

which gives an estimate of 3,000. Our actual answer, 2,990, is close enough to our estimate to convince us that we have not made a major error in our calculation.

Example 4   An individual has an annual income of $35,880. How much is his average monthly income?

Solution   Because there are 12 months in a year and the yearly (annual) income is $35,880, we want to know what $35,880 divided into 12 equal parts is. Therefore, we have

$$
\begin{array}{r}
2990 \\
12\overline{)35880} \\
-24\downarrow \\
\hline
118 \\
-108\downarrow \\
\hline
108 \\
-108\downarrow \\
\hline
00
\end{array}
$$

Because 35,880 ÷ 12 = 2,990, his monthly income is $2,990.

C Division with Remainders

Suppose Darlene is making bread using a five-pound (80 oz.) bag of flour. Her bread recipe calls for 30 ounces of flour for each loaf. To see how many ounces she could get from a 80-ounce bag, she would divide 80 by 30. If she did so, she would find that she could make two loaves, but she would have 20 ounces of flour left over. In mathematics, we call the "left over" a **remainder.** A diagram of this problem is shown in Figure 1.

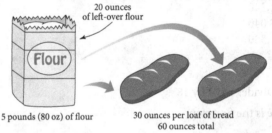

20 ounces of left-over flour

Flour

5 pounds (80 oz) of flour   30 ounces per loaf of bread
                                    60 ounces total

FIGURE 1

Writing the results in the diagram as a division problem looks like this:

$$
\begin{array}{r}
2 \quad\leftarrow \text{Quotient} \\
\text{Divisor} \longrightarrow 30\overline{)80} \quad\leftarrow \text{Dividend} \\
-60 \\
\hline
20 \quad\leftarrow \text{Remainder}
\end{array}
$$

Example 5   Divide: 1,690 ÷ 67

Solution   Dividing as we have previously, we get

$$
\begin{array}{r}
25 \\
67\overline{)1690} \\
-134\downarrow \\
\hline
350 \\
-335 \\
\hline
15 \quad\leftarrow \text{15 is the remainder.}
\end{array}
$$

We have 15 left, and because 15 is less than 67, no more sixty-sevens can be subtracted. In a situation like this, we call 15 the remainder and write

These indicate that the remainder is 15.

$$
\begin{array}{r}
25 \text{ R } 15 \\
67\overline{)1690} \\
-134\downarrow \\
\hline
350 \\
-335 \\
\hline
15
\end{array}
\qquad \text{or} \qquad
\begin{array}{r}
25\tfrac{15}{67} \\
67\overline{)1690} \\
-134\downarrow \\
\hline
350 \\
-335 \\
\hline
15
\end{array}
$$

5. Divide: 1,572 ÷ 23

Both forms of notation shown indicate that 15 is the remainder. The notation R 15 is the notation we will use in this chapter. The notation $\frac{15}{67}$ will be useful in the chapter on fractions. This notation indicates that, if we continued to divide, we would divide 15 by 67.

To check a problem like this, we multiply the divisor and the quotient as usual, and then add the remainder to this result.

$$
\begin{array}{r}
67 \\
\times\ 25 \\
\hline
335 \\
+\ 1{,}340 \\
\hline
1{,}675
\end{array}
\quad \longleftarrow \text{ Product of divisor and quotient}
$$

$$1{,}675 + 15 = 1{,}690$$

$$\text{Remainder} \qquad \text{Dividend}$$

Division by Zero

We cannot divide by 0. That is, we cannot use 0 as a divisor in any division problem. Here's why. Suppose there was an answer to the problem

$$\frac{8}{0} = ?$$

That would mean that $0 \cdot ? = 8$. But we already know that multiplication by 0 always produces 0. There is no number we can use for the ? to make a true statement out of $0 \cdot ? = 8$. Because this was equivalent to the original division problem

$$\frac{8}{0} = ?$$

we have no number to associate with the expression $\frac{8}{0}$. We say it is undefined.

PROPERTY **Division by Zero**

Division by 0 is undefined. Any expression with a divisor of 0 is undefined. We cannot divide by 0.

 KEY CONCEPT REVIEW

After reading through the preceding section, respond in your own words and in complete sentences.

A. Which sentence below describes the problem shown in Example 1?

    a. The quotient of 7 and 595 is 85.

    b. Seven divided by 595 is 85.

    c. The quotient of 595 and 7 is 85.

B. To find a solution to a division problem, how would you think in terms of multiplication?

C. Example 5 shows that $1{,}690 \div 67$ gives a quotient of 25 with a remainder of 15. If we were to divide 1,692 by 67, what would the remainder be?

D. Explain why division by 0 is undefined in mathematics.

EXERCISE SET 1.6 ·

Problems

A Write each of the following in symbols.

1. The quotient of 6 and 3

2. The quotient of 3 and 6

3. The quotient of 45 and 9

4. The quotient of 12 and 4

5. The quotient of r and s

6. The quotient of s and r

7. The quotient of 20 and 4 is 5.

8. The quotient of 20 and 5 is 4.

Write a multiplication statement that is equivalent to each of the following division statements.

9. $6 \div 2 = 3$

10. $6 \div 3 = 2$

11. $\dfrac{36}{9} = 4$

12. $\dfrac{36}{4} = 9$

13. $\dfrac{48}{6} = 8$

14. $\dfrac{35}{7} = 5$

15. $28 \div 7 = 4$

16. $81 \div 9 = 9$

B Find each of the following quotients. (Divide.)

17. $25 \div 5$

18. $72 \div 8$

19. $40 \div 5$

20. $12 \div 2$

21. $9 \div 0$

22. $7 \div 1$

23. $360 \div 0$

24. $285 \div 0$

25. $\dfrac{138}{6}$

26. $\dfrac{267}{3}$

27. $5\overline{)7,650}$

28. $5\overline{)5,670}$

29. $5\overline{)6,750}$ **30.** $5\overline{)6,570}$ **31.** $3\overline{)54,000}$ **32.** $3\overline{)50,400}$

33. $3\overline{)50,040}$ **34.** $3\overline{)50,004}$ **35.** $4\overline{)96,000}$ **36.** $5\overline{)25,450}$

Divide. Verify your answer is correct using multiplication.

37. $1,440 \div 32$ **38.** $1,206 \div 67$ **39.** $\dfrac{2,401}{49}$ **40.** $\dfrac{4,606}{49}$

41. $28\overline{)12,096}$ **42.** $28\overline{)96,012}$ **43.** $63\overline{)90,594}$ **44.** $45\overline{)17,595}$

45. $87\overline{)61,335}$ **46.** $79\overline{)48,032}$ **47.** $45\overline{)135,900}$ **48.** $56\overline{)227,920}$

C Divide. The following division problems all have remainders.

49. $6\overline{)370}$ **50.** $8\overline{)390}$ **51.** $3\overline{)271}$ **52.** $3\overline{)172}$

53. $26\overline{)345}$ **54.** $26\overline{)543}$ **55.** $71\overline{)16,620}$ **56.** $71\overline{)33,240}$

57. $23\overline{)9,250}$ **58.** $23\overline{)20,800}$ **59.** $169\overline{)5,950}$ **60.** $391\overline{)34,450}$

Complete the following tables.

61.

First Number	Second Number	The Quotient of a and b
a	b	$\dfrac{a}{b}$
100	25	
100	26	
100	27	
100	28	

62.

First Number	Second Number	The Quotient of a and b
a	b	$\dfrac{a}{b}$
100	25	
101	25	
102	25	
103	25	

Estimating

Work these problems mentally, without using a calculator.

63. The quotient 845 ÷ 93 is closest to which of the following numbers?

　　a. 10　　**b.** 100　　**c.** 1,000　　**d.** 10,000

64. The quotient 762 ÷ 43 is closest to which of the following numbers?

　　a. 2　　**b.** 20　　**c.** 200　　**d.** 2,000

65. The quotient 15,208 ÷ 771 is closest to which of the following numbers?

　　a. 2　　**b.** 20　　**c.** 200　　**d.** 2,000

66. The quotient 24,471 ÷ 523 is closest to which of the following numbers?

　　a. 5　　**b.** 50　　**c.** 500　　**d.** 5,000

Without a calculator give a one-digit estimate for each of the following quotients. That is, for each quotient, mentally estimate the answer using one of the digits 1, 2, 3, 4, 5, 6, 7, 8, or 9.

67. 316 ÷ 289　　　　**68.** 662 ÷ 289　　　　**69.** 728 ÷ 355　　　　**70.** 728 ÷ 177

71. 921 ÷ 243　　　　**72.** 921 ÷ 442　　　　**73.** 673 ÷ 109　　　　**74.** 673 ÷ 218

Applying the Concepts

The application problems that follow may involve more than division. Some may require addition, subtraction, or multiplication, whereas others may use a combination of two or more operations.

75. Monthly Income A family has an annual income of $22,200. How much is their monthly income?

76. Hourly Wages If a man works an 8-hour shift and is paid $96, how much does he make for 1 hour?

77. Price per Pound If 6 pounds of a certain kind of fruit cost 96¢ at a wholesale price, how much does 1 pound cost?

78. Cost of a Dress A dress shop orders 45 dresses for a total of $675. If they paid the same amount for each dress, how much was each dress?

79. Fitness Walking The guidelines for fitness indicate that a person who walks 10,000 steps daily is physically fit. According to experts, it takes just over 2,000 steps to walk one mile. If that is the case, how many miles do you need to walk in order to take 10,000 steps?

80. Filling Glasses How many 8-ounce glasses can be filled from three 32-ounce bottles of soda?

81. Filling Glasses How many 5-ounce glasses can be filled from a 32-ounce bottle of milk? How many ounces of milk will be left in the bottle when all the glasses are full?

82. Filling Glasses How many 3-ounce glasses can be filled from a 28-ounce bottle of milk? How many ounces of milk will be left in the bottle when all the glasses are filled?

83. Filling Glasses How many 32-ounce bottles of Coke™ will be needed to fill sixteen 6-ounce glasses?

84. Filling Glasses How many 28-ounce bottles of 7-Up™ will be needed to fill fourteen 6-ounce glasses?

85. Miles per Gallon A truck driver kept track of her mileage for a week. She found that she traveled 2,356 miles and used 124 gallons of gas. How many miles did she travel on each gallon of gas?

86. Miles per Gallon A traveling salesman kept track of his mileage for 1 month. He found that he traveled 1,104 miles and used 48 gallons of gas. How many miles did he travel on each gallon of gas?

87. Milligrams of Calcium Suppose one egg contains 25 milligrams of calcium, a piece of toast contains 40 milligrams of calcium, and a glass of milk contains 215 milligrams of calcium. How many milligrams of calcium are contained in a breakfast that consists of three eggs, two glasses of milk, and four pieces of toast?

88. Milligrams of Iron Suppose a glass of juice contains 3 milligrams of iron and a piece of toast contains 2 milligrams of iron. If Diane drinks two glasses of juice and has three pieces of toast for breakfast, how much iron is contained in the meal?

Calculator Problems

Find each of the following quotients using a calculator.

89. $305,026 \div 698$

90. $771,537 \div 949$

91. 18,436,466 divided by 5,678

92. 2,492,735 divided by 2,345

93. The quotient of 603,955 and 695

94. The quotient of 875,124 and 876

95. $4,903 \overline{)27,868,652}$

96. $3,090 \overline{)2,308,230}$

97. Gallons per Minute If a 79,768-gallon tank can be filled in 472 minutes, how many gallons enter the tank each minute?

98. Weight per Case A truckload of 632 crates of motorcycle parts weighs 30,968 pounds. How much does each of the crates weigh, if they each weigh the same amount?

 **FIND THE MISTAKE** •

Each sentence below contains a mistake. Circle the mistake and write the correct word(s) or number(s) on the line provided.

1. The division notation $\frac{10}{5}$ is equivalent to $10 \overline{)5}$. _____

2. The quotient of 198 and 11 is 11. _____

3. To divide 1,640 by 12, first subtract 12 from 40. _____

4. Dividing 2,380 by 13 gives a remainder of 13. _____

1.7

EXPONENTS AND ORDER OF OPERATIONS

· · · **OBJECTIVES** · · ·

A Evaluate exponential expressions with whole numbers.

B Evaluate expressions using order of operations.

· · · **KEY WORDS** · · ·

base

exponent

squared

cubed

order of operations

VIDEO EXAMPLES

SECTION 1.7

In 1856, the steamboat *Arabia* got stuck in sunken woody debris in the Missouri River. One of the dead trees ripped a hole in the ship's hull, which subsequently filled with water and sank the ship. Over the years, the course of the river has shifted a half mile away, leaving the ship buried far below a Kansas City cornfield for more than a century.

In 1987, the local Hawley family set out to uncover the ship. After three weeks of digging using heavy equipment, the Hawleys finally reached the hull of the ship. The nutrient-rich mud had preserved much of the hull's cargo in pristine condition. The family uncovered artifacts such as elegant china, fancy clothes made of silk and beaver furs, medicines, perfumes, tools, weapons, eyeglasses, even jars of preserved food that are still edible nearly 150 years later!

The hole dug to find the Arabia was as large as a football field and was 45 feet deep. To calculate the volume of dirt excavated in order to unearth the Arabia, we need to multiply the square footage of a football field by the depth of the hole. A football field is 57,600 square feet (ft²), therefore the hole's volume is 2,592,000 cubic feet (ft³)! The notation for square feet and cubic feet uses exponents, which we will discuss further now.

A Exponents

Exponents are a shorthand way of writing repeated multiplication. In the expression 2^3, 2 is called the **base** and 3 is called the **exponent.** The expression 2^3 is read "2 to the third power" or "2 cubed." The exponent 3 tells us to use the base 2 as a multiplication factor three times.

$$2^3 = 2 \cdot 2 \cdot 2 \qquad \text{2 is used as a factor three times.}$$

We can simplify the expression by multiplication.

$$2^3 = 2 \cdot 2 \cdot 2$$
$$= 4 \cdot 2$$
$$= 8$$

The expression 2^3 is equal to the number 8. We can summarize this discussion with the following definition:

DEFINITION exponent

An **exponent** is a whole number that indicates how many times the base is to be used as a factor. Exponents indicate repeated multiplication.

For example, in the expression 5^2, 5 is the base and 2 is the exponent. The meaning of the expression is

$$5^2 = 5 \cdot 5 \qquad \text{5 is used as a factor two times.}$$

$$= 25$$

The expression 5^2 is read "5 to the second power" or "5 squared."

Example 1 Name the base and the exponent.

a. 3^2 **b.** 5^3 **c.** 2^4

Solution

a. The base is 3, and the exponent is 2. The expression is read "3 to the second power" or "3 squared."

b. The base is 5, and the exponent is 3. The expression is read "5 to the third power" or "5 cubed."

c. The base is 2, and the exponent is 4. The expression is read "2 to the fourth power."

As you can see from this example, a base raised to the second power is also said to be **squared,** and a base raised to the third power is also said to be **cubed.** These are the only two exponents (^{2} and ^{3}) that have special names. All other exponents are referred to only as "fourth powers," "fifth powers," "sixth powers," and so on.

The next example shows how we can simplify expressions involving exponents by using repeated multiplication.

Example 2 Expand and multiply.

a. 3^2 **b.** 4^2 **c.** 3^3 **d.** 2^4

Solution

a. $3^2 = 3 \cdot 3 = 9$ **b.** $4^2 = 4 \cdot 4 = 16$

c. $3^3 = 3 \cdot 3 \cdot 3 = 9 \cdot 3 = 27$ **d.** $2^4 = 2 \cdot 2 \cdot 2 \cdot 2 = 4 \cdot 4 = 16$

We should also consider what happens when the numbers 0 and 1 are used as exponents.

RULE Exponent One

Any number raised to the first power is itself. That is, if we let the letter a represent any number, then

$$a^1 = a$$

RULE Exponent Zero

Any number other than 0 raised to the 0 power is 1. That is, if a represents any nonzero number, then it is always true that

$$a^0 = 1$$

Later, we will revisit this property and explore why $a^0 = 1$.

Practice Problems

1. Name the base and exponent.
   a. 3^4
   b. 5^{10}
   c. x^5

2. Expand and multiply.
   a. 5^2
   b. 4^3
   c. 3^4

Answers

1. **a.** Base = 3, exponent = 4
   b. Base = 5, exponent = 10
   c. Base = x, exponent = 5
2. **a.** 25 **b.** 64 **c.** 81

Example 3   Simplify.

a. 5^1 **b.** 9^1 **c.** 4^0 **d.** 8^0

Solution

a. $5^1 = 5$ **b.** $9^1 = 9$ **c.** $4^0 = 1$ **d.** $8^0 = 1$

3. Simplify.
  a. 8^1
  b. 10^0
  c. 16^1
  d. x^0

B Order of Operations

The symbols we use to specify operations, $+$, $-$, $\cdot$, $\div$, along with the symbols we use for grouping, ( ) and [ ], serve the same purpose in mathematics as punctuation marks in English. They may be called the punctuation marks of mathematics.

Consider the following sentence:

Bob said John is tall.

It can have two different meanings, depending on how we punctuate it:

1. "Bob," said John, "is tall."
2. Bob said, "John is tall."

Without the punctuation marks we don't know which meaning the sentence has.

Now, consider the following mathematical expression:

$$4 + 5 \cdot 2$$

What should we do? Should we add 4 and 5 first, or should we multiply 5 and 2 first? There seem to be two different answers. In mathematics, we want to avoid situations in which two different results are possible. Therefore, we follow the rule for **order of operations.**

Note   There are several ways to remember the order of operations. We recommend using an internet search to find one that will help you remember the order.

RULE   **Order of Operations**

When evaluating mathematical expressions, we will perform the operations in the following order:

1. If the expression contains grouping symbols, such as parentheses ( ), brackets [ ], or a fraction bar, then we perform the operations inside the grouping symbols, or above and below the fraction bar, first.

2. Then we evaluate, or simplify, any numbers with exponents.

3. Then we do all multiplications and divisions in order, starting at the left and moving right.

4. Finally, we do all additions and subtractions, from left to right.

According to our rule, the expression $4 + 5 \cdot 2$ would have to be evaluated by multiplying 5 and 2 first, and then adding 4. The correct answer—and the only answer—to this problem is 14.

$$4 + 5 \cdot 2 = 4 + 10 \qquad \textit{Multiply first, then add.}$$

$$= 14$$

Here are some more examples that illustrate how we apply the rule for order of operations to simplify (or evaluate) expressions.

4. Simplify: $5 \cdot 12 - 3 \cdot 7$

Example 4   Simplify: $4 \cdot 8 - 2 \cdot 6$

Solution   We multiply first and then subtract.

$$4 \cdot 8 - 2 \cdot 6 = 32 - 12 \qquad \textit{Multiply first, then subtract.}$$

$$= 20$$

Answers

3. a. 8   **b.** 1   **c.** 16   **d.** 1
4. 39

Example 5 Simplify: $5 + 2(7 - 1)$

Solution According to the rule for the order of operations, we must do the operations inside the parentheses first.

$$5 + 2(7 - 1) = 5 + 2(6) \quad \text{Work inside parentheses first.}$$
$$= 5 + 12 \quad \text{Then multiply.}$$
$$= 17 \quad \text{Then add.}$$

5. Simplify: $3 + 7(8 - 3)$

Example 6 Simplify: $9 \cdot 2^3 + 36 \div 3^2 - 8$

Solution

$$9 \cdot 2^3 + 36 \div 3^2 - 8 = 9 \cdot 8 + 36 \div 9 - 8 \quad \text{Evaluate exponents first.}$$
$$= 72 + 4 - 8 \quad \text{Then multiply and divide, left to right.}$$
$$= 76 - 8 \quad \text{Add and subtract left to right.}$$
$$= 68$$

6. Simplify: $4 \cdot 3^2 + 24 \div 2^3 - 6$

Example 7 Simplify: $3 + 2[10 - 3(5 - 2)]$

Solution The brackets, [ ], are used in the same way as parentheses. In a case like this, we move to the innermost grouping symbols first and begin simplifying.

$$3 + 2[10 - 3(5 - 2)] = 3 + 2[10 - 3(3)] \quad \text{Perform multiplication in grouping symbols.}$$
$$= 3 + 2[10 - 9] \quad \text{Subtract within brackets.}$$
$$= 3 + 2[1] \quad \text{Multiply.}$$
$$= 3 + 2 \quad \text{Add.}$$
$$= 5$$

7. Simplify: $4 + 2[12 - 2(6 - 3)]$

Table 1 lists some English expressions and their corresponding mathematical expressions written in symbols.

Table 1

In English	Mathematical Equivalent
5 times the sum of 3 and 8	$5(3 + 8)$
Twice the difference of 4 and 3	$2(4 - 3)$
6 added to 7 times the sum of 5 and 6	$6 + 7(5 + 6)$
The sum of 4 times 5 and 8 times 9	$4 \cdot 5 + 8 \cdot 9$
3 subtracted from the quotient of 10 and 2	$10 \div 2 - 3$

 KEY CONCEPT REVIEW

After reading through the preceding section, respond in your own words and in complete sentences.

A. What is an exponent?

B. Give a written description of how you would use the order of operations to simplify this expression: $3 + 4(5 + 6)$

C. What happens when 0 is used as an exponent?

D. Name the four steps in the order of operations.

Answers
5. 38
6. 33
7. 16

EXERCISE SET 1.7 ....

....

Choose the correct words to fill in the blanks below.

zero	right	factor	left	grouping symbols
squared	multiplication	exponent	base	cubed

1. Exponents are a way of writing repeated _____.

2. An exponent is a whole number that indicates how many times the base is to be used as a _____.

3. In the expression 4^3, the 3 is called the _____ and the 4 is called the _____.

4. Any number other than zero raised to the _____ power is 1.

5. For the order of operations, we perform all operations inside the _____ before any other operations.

6. When performing addition and subtraction, we always start at the _____ and move to the _____. The same is true of multiplication and division.

7. When a base is raised to the power of two, we say it is _____. When the power is three, we say the base is _____.

Problems

A For each of the following expressions, name the base and the exponent.

1. 4^5 **2.** 5^4 **3.** 3^6 **4.** 6^3 **5.** 8^2

6. 2^8 **7.** 9^1 **8.** 1^9 **9.** 4^0 **10.** 0^4

Use the definition of exponents as indicating repeated multiplication to simplify each of the following expressions.

11. 6^2 **12.** 7^2 **13.** 2^3 **14.** 2^4 **15.** 1^4

16. 5^1 **17.** 9^0 **18.** 27^0 **19.** 9^2 **20.** 8^2

21. 10^1 **22.** 8^1 **23.** 12^1 **24.** 16^0 **25.** 45^0

26. 3^4

B Use the rule for the order of operations to simplify each expression. (Hint: Remember to perform multiplication and division left to right. The same is true for addition and subtraction.)

27. $16 - 8 + 4$

28. $16 - 4 + 8$

29. $20 \div 2 \cdot 10$

30. $40 \div 4 \cdot 5$

31. $20 - 4 \cdot 4$

32. $30 - 10 \cdot 2$

33. $3 + 5 \cdot 8$

34. $7 + 4 \cdot 9$

35. $3 \cdot 6 - 2$

36. $5 \cdot 1 + 6$

37. $6 \cdot 2 + 9 \cdot 8$

38. $4 \cdot 5 + 9 \cdot 7$

39. $4 \cdot 5 - 3 \cdot 2$

40. $5 \cdot 6 - 4 \cdot 3$

41. $5^2 + 7^2$

42. $4^2 + 9^2$

43. $480 + 12(32)^2$

44. $360 + 14(27)^2$

45. $3 \cdot 2^3 + 5 \cdot 4^2$

46. $4 \cdot 3^2 + 5 \cdot 2^3$

47. $8 \cdot 10^2 - 6 \cdot 4^3$

48. $5 \cdot 11^2 - 3 \cdot 2^3$

49. $\dfrac{6 + 4}{2 - 2}$

50. $\dfrac{2 - 2}{6 + 4}$

51. $19 + 50 \div 5^2$

52. $9 + 8 \div 2^2$

53. $9 - 2(4 - 3)$

54. $15 - 6(9 - 7)$

55. $4 \cdot 3 + 2(5 - 3)$

56. $6 \cdot 8 + 3(4 - 1)$

57. $4[2(3) + 3(5)]$

58. $3[2(5) + 3(4)]$

59. $(7 - 3)(8 + 2)$

60. $(9 - 5)(9 + 5)$

61. $3(9 - 2) + 4(7 - 2)$

62. $7(4 - 2) - 2(5 - 3)$

63. $18 + 12 \div 4 - 3$

64. $20 + 16 \div 2 - 5$

65. $4(10^2) + 20 \div 4$

66. $3(4^2) + 10 \div 5$

67. $8 \cdot 2^4 + 25 \div 5 - 3^2$

68. $5 \cdot 3^4 + 16 \div 8 - 2^2$

69. $5 + 2[9 - 2(4 - 1)]$

70. $6 + 3[8 - 3(1 + 1)]$

71. $3 + 4[6 + 8(2 - 0)]$

72. $2 + 5[9 + 3(4 - 1)]$

73. $\dfrac{15 + 5(4)}{17 - 12}$

74. $\dfrac{20 + 6(2)}{11 - 7}$

Translate each English expression into an equivalent mathematical expression written in symbols. Then simplify.

75. 8 times the sum of 4 and 2

76. 3 times the difference of 6 and 1

77. Twice the sum of 10 and 3

78. 5 times the difference of 12 and 6

79. 4 added to 3 times the sum of 3 and 4

80. 25 added to 4 times the difference of 7 and 5

81. 9 subtracted from the quotient of 20 and 2

82. 7 added to the quotient of 6 and 2

83. The sum of 8 times 5 and 5 times 4

84. The difference of 10 times 5 and 6 times 2

Applying the Concepts

Nutrition Labels Use the three nutrition labels below to work Problems 85–88.

Pizza Dough (Crust)	Tomato Sauce	Shredded Mozzarella Cheese

Nutrition Facts
Serving Size 1/6 of package (65g)
Servings Per Container: 6
 	
Amount Per Serving
Calories 160 — Calories from fat 18
 	
% Daily Value*
Total Fat 2g — 3%
  Saturated Fat 0.5g — 3%
  Poly unsaturated Fat 0g
  Monounsaturated Fat 0g
Cholesterol 0mg — 0%
Sodium 470mg — 20%
Total Carbohydrate 31g — 10%
  Dietary Fiber 1g — 4%
  Sugars 4g
Protein 5g
 	
Vitamin A 0% • Vitamin C 0%
Calcium 0% • Iron 10%
*Percent Daily Values are based on a 2,000 calorie diet
	Nutrition Facts
	Serving Size 1/4 cup (62g)
	Servings Per Container: 5
	
	Amount Per Serving
	Calories 15 — Calories from fat 0
	
	% Daily Value*
	Total Fat 0g — 0%
	  Saturated Fat 0g — 0%
	Cholesterol 0mg — 0%
	Sodium 360mg — 15%
	Potassium 0mg — 0%
	Total Carbohydrate 3g — 1%
	  Dietary Fiber 1g — 4%
	  Sugars 2g
	Protein 1g
	
	Vitamin A 4% • Vitamin C 8%
	Calcium 0% • Iron 0%
	*Percent Daily Values are based on a 2,000 calorie diet. Your daily values may be higher or lower depending on your calorie needs.
		Nutrition Facts
		Serving Size 1 oz (28.3g)
		Servings Per Container: 12
		
		Amount Per Serving
		Calories 72 — Calories from fat 41
		
		% Daily Value*
		Total Fat 4.5g — 7%
		  Saturated Fat 2.9g — 14%
		Cholesterol 18mg — 6%
		Sodium 175mg — 7%
		Total Carbohydrate 0.8g — 0%
		  Fiber 0g — 0%
		  Sugars 0.3g
		Protein 6.9g
		
		Vitamin A 3% • Vitamin C 0%
		Calcium 22% • Iron 0%
		*Percent Daily Values (DV) are based on a 2,000 calorie diet

Find the total number of calories in each of the following meals.

85. Pizza Crust — 1 serving
Tomato Sauce — 1 serving
Cheese — 1 serving

86. Pizza Crust — 1 serving
Tomato Sauce — 2 servings
Cheese — 1 serving

87. Pizza Crust — 2 servings
Tomato Sauce — 1 serving
Cheese — 1 serving

88. Pizza Crust — 2 servings
Tomato Sauce — 1 serving
Cheese — 2 servings

The following table lists the number of calories consumed by eating some popular fast foods. Use the table to work Problems 89 and 90.

Calories in Food	
Food	**Calories**
McDonald's hamburger	270
Burger King hamburger	260
Jack in the Box hamburger	280
McDonald's Big Mac	510
Burger King Whopper	630
Jack in the Box Colossus burger	940

89. Compare the total number of calories in the meal in Problem 85 with the number of calories in a McDonald's Big Mac.

90. Compare the total number of calories in the meal in Problem 88 with the number of calories in a Burger King hamburger.

One Step Further: Number Sequences

There is a relationship between the two sequences below. The first sequence is the *sequence of odd numbers*. The second sequence is called the *sequence of squares*.

$$1, 3, 5, 7, \ldots \qquad \text{The sequence of odd numbers}$$
$$1, 4, 9, 16, \ldots \qquad \text{The sequence of squares}$$

91. Add the first two numbers in the sequence of odd numbers.

92. Add the first three numbers in the sequence of odd numbers.

93. Add the first four numbers in the sequence of odd numbers.

94. Add the first five numbers in the sequence of odd numbers.

95. Compare the answers to Problems 91–94 with the numbers in the sequence of squares. In your own words, explain how the sequence of odd numbers can be used to obtain the sequence of squares.

96. Draw a diagram that shows how the sequence of odd numbers can be used to produce the sequence of squares. The diagram can contain numbers, addition symbols, equal signs, and arrows, but it should not contain any words. Your goal is to draw the diagram so that anyone who knows how to add whole numbers can look at it and see the relationship between the numbers in the two sequences.

FIND THE MISTAKE •

Each sentence below contains a mistake. Circle the mistake and write the correct word(s) or number(s) on the line provided.

1. The expression 8^4 means that the exponent 4 is used as a factor 8 times. _____

2. The number 7 raised to the third power equals $3^7 = 2,187$. _____

3. Following the order of operations, work all additions and subtractions before evaluating any exponents. _____

4. Simplifying $(4 + 1)^3 - (9 + 1)^2$ gives 189. _____

SUPPLIES NEEDED

piece of graph paper

a pen or pencil

a ruler

Trail Guide Project

Fibonacci Sequence

Fibonacci was an Italian mathematician in the 12th and 13th centuries. He enjoyed investigating sequences of numbers and is credited with discovering the sequence of numbers written below.

$$1, 1, 2, 3, 5, 8, 13, 21, 34, 55...$$

1. If you were to describe the Fibonacci sequence in words, you would start this way: "The first two numbers are 1's. After that, each number is found by..." Finish the sentence so that someone reading it will know how to find members of the Fibonacci sequence.

2. On a sheet of graph paper, draw a 1 x 1 square and write the number 1 in the center. To the right of your first square, draw a second 1 x 1 square that shares a side with your first square. Write the number 1 in this second square as well. On top of the two 1 x 1 squares, draw a 2 x 2 square that shares the side length of the first two squares. Write the number 2 in this new square. To the left of the first three squares, draw a square with a side length of 3 that shares a side with the 2 x 2 square and the first 1 x 1 square. The fifth square you draw should be below the others, have a side length of 5, and share a side with the 3 x 3 square and both 1 x 1 squares (see illustration).

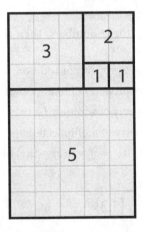

Continue drawing new squares in a spiral until you have drawn eight squares. Write the length of each new square's side in its center. Keep an ongoing list of each square's side length. Recognize the pattern?

If you draw a spiral curve that follows a diagonal in each square, beginning your curve at the upper left corner of the first 1 x 1 square, you will end up with what is known as the golden spiral. This spiral can be observed in nature, such as in the arrangement of artichoke leaves or pinecone scales.

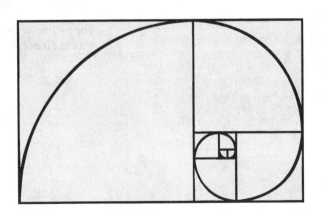

The numbers in brackets indicate the sections in which the topics were discussed.

Place Values for Whole Numbers [1.1]

The place values for the digits of any base 10 number are as follows:

The margins of the chapter summaries will be used for examples of the topics being reviewed, whenever it is convenient.

1. The number 42,103,045 written in words is "forty-two million, one hundred three thousand, forty-five." The number 5,745 written in expanded form is $5,000 + 700 + 40 + 5$.

Table 1

Trillions			Billions			Millions			Thousands			Ones		
Hundred	Ten	One	Hundred	Ten	One	Hundred	Ten	One	Hundred	Ten	One	Hundred	Ten	One

Vocabulary Associated with Addition, Subtraction, Multiplication, and Division [1.2, 1.3, 1.5, 1.6]

2. The sum of 5 and 2 is $5 + 2$. The difference of 5 and 2 is $5 - 2$. The product of 5 and 2 is $5 \cdot 2$. The quotient of 10 and 2 is $10 \div 2$.

The word sum indicates addition.

The word difference indicates subtraction.

The word product indicates multiplication.

The word quotient indicates division.

Properties of Addition and Multiplication [1.2, 1.5]

3. a. $3 + 2 = 2 + 3$
b. $3 \cdot 2 = 2 \cdot 3$
c. $(x + 3) + 5 = x + (3 + 5)$
d. $(4 \cdot 5) \cdot 6 = 4 \cdot (5 \cdot 6)$
e. $3(4 + 7) = 3(4) + 3(7)$

If a, b, and c represent any three numbers, then the properties of addition and multiplication used most often are

Commutative property of addition: $a + b = b + a$

Commutative property of multiplication: $a \cdot b = b \cdot a$

Associative property of addition: $(a + b) + c = a + (b + c)$

Associative property of multiplication: $(a \cdot b) \cdot c = a \cdot (b \cdot c)$

Distributive property: $a(b + c) = a(b) + a(c)$ or $a(b - c) = a(b) - a(c)$

Perimeter of a Polygon [1.2]

4. The perimeter of the rectangle below is
$P = 37 + 37 + 24 + 24$
$ = 122$ feet

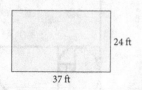

24 ft

37 ft

The perimeter of any polygon is the sum of the lengths of the sides, and it is denoted with the letter P.

Steps for Rounding Whole Numbers [1.4]

1. Find the place you are going to round to and locate the digit to the right of it.
2. If that digit is less than 5, replace it and all digits to its right with zeros.
3. If that digit is 5 or more, add 1 to the digit to the left and replace all digits to the right with zeros.

5. 5,482 to the nearest ten is 5,480.
5,482 to the nearest hundred is 5,500.
5,482 to the nearest thousand is 5,000.

Formulas for Area [1.5]

Below are two common geometric figures, along with the formulas for their areas.

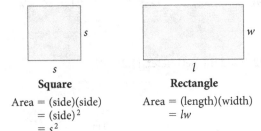

Square
Area = (side)(side)
= (side)^2
= s^2

Rectangle
Area = (length)(width)
= lw

6. The area of the rectangle below is
$A = 37(24)$
$= 888 \text{ ft}^2$

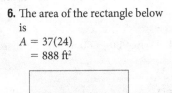

24 ft

37 ft

Division by Zero [1.6]

Division by 0 is undefined. We cannot use 0 as a divisor in any division problem.

7. Each of the expressions below are undefined.
$5 \div 0 \quad \dfrac{7}{0} \quad 4/0$

Order of Operations [1.7]

To simplify a mathematical expression:

1. We simplify the expression inside the grouping symbols first. Grouping symbols are parentheses ( ), brackets [ ], or a fraction bar.
2. Then we evaluate any numbers with exponents.
3. We then perform all multiplications and divisions in order, starting at the left and moving right.
4. Finally, we do all the additions and subtractions, from left to right.

8. $4 + 6(8 - 2)$
$= 4 + 6(6)$ Work inside parentheses first.
$= 4 + 36$ Then multiply.
$= 40$ Then add.

Exponents [1.7]

In the expression 2^3, 2 is the base and 3 is the exponent. An exponent is a shorthand notation for repeated multiplication. The exponent 0 is a special exponent. Any nonzero number to the 0 power is 1.

9. $2^3 = 2 \cdot 2 \cdot 2 = 8$
$5^0 = 1$
$3^1 = 3$

At the end of each chapter, we will provide a review of problems similar to those you have seen in the chapter's previous sections. These problems are meant to supplement, not replace, a thorough review of the concepts, examples, and exercise sets presented in the chapter.

Give the place value of each digit in the following numbers. [1.1]

1. 789

2. 6,481

3. Write the number 50,631 in words. [1.1]

4. Write $900 + 60 + 5$ in standard form. [1.1]

5. Write the number twelve million, seventy-two thousand, nine with digits instead of words. [1.1]

Write the following numbers in expanded form. [1.1]

6. 50,905

7. 123,321

Identify each of the statements in Problems 8-11 as an example of one of the following properties. [1.2, 1.5]

  a. Addition property of 0

  b. Multiplication property of 0

  c. Identity property of multiplication

  d. Commutative property of addition

  e. Commutative property of multiplication

  f. Associative property of addition

  g. Associative property of multiplication

8. $9 \cdot 1 = 9$

9. $4 + (7 + 2) = (4 + 7) + 2$

10. $9 \cdot 2 = 2 \cdot 9$

11. $5 + 0 = 5$

Find each of the following sums. (Add.) [1.2]

12. $5 + 6 + 7 + 8 + 9$

13. $7 + 3 + 6 + 4$

14.   128
   + 541

15.   2,749
   +1,250

16.   521
   340
  +135

17.   21
   43
   65
  +87

18.   646
   464
   525
  +252

19.   5,213
    927
  + 10,182

Find a solution for each equation by inspection. [1.2]

20. $5 + n = 7$

21. $24 = 16 + n$

22. Find the perimeter. [1.2]

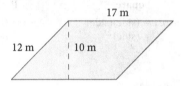

Write each of the following expressions in symbols. [1.3]

23. The difference of x and 2

24. a subtracted from b

25. Subtract 71 from 89.

26. Find the difference of 37 and 27.

Find each of the following differences. (Subtract.) [1.3]

27.   952
  − 141

28.   9,014
  − 6,528

29. $86,492 − 78,506$

Find the solution to each equation by inspection.

30. $15 − n = 10$

31. $25 − n = 24$

Round each of the numbers to the nearest hundred. [1.4]

32. 604

33. 56,990

34. Round the number 625,963 to the nearest ten thousand. [1.4]

Estimate the answer to the following problems by rounding each number to the indicated place value and then subtracting. [1.4]

35. Thousand
    $18,955 - 12,049$

36. Thousand
    $49,899 - 29,846$

Use the distributive property to rewrite each expression, then simplify. [1.5]

37. $4(5 + 8)$

38. $5(x - 8)$

Find each of the following products. (Multiply.) [1.5]

39. $8(137)$

40. $71(238)$

41. $\begin{array}{r} 432 \\ \times\ 555 \\ \hline \end{array}$

42. $\begin{array}{r} 56,728 \\ \times\ \ \ \ 852 \\ \hline \end{array}$

Find the area enclosed by the figure. [1.5]

43.

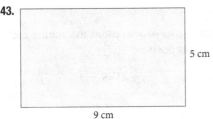

5 cm

9 cm

Find a solution for each equation. [1.5]

44. $50 = 5 \cdot n$

45. $n \cdot 5 = 45$

Find each of the following quotients. (Divide.) [1.6]

46. $1,235 \div 19$

47. $499\overline{)13,473}$

48. $\dfrac{4,606}{49}$

49. $79\overline{)48,032}$

50. $71\overline{)33,240}$

51. $391\overline{)34,450}$

Write the following in numbers, then simplify as much as possible.

52. Three times the sum of 11 and 4. [1.2, 1.3, 1.5, 1.6]

53. The quotient of 30 and 5 decreased by 2. [1.2, 1.3, 1.5, 1.6]

Translate each English expression into an equivalent mathematical expression written in symbols. Then simplify. [1.7]

54. 7 added to the quotient of 6 and 2

55. The difference of 10 times 5 and 6 times 2

Use the definition of exponents as indicating repeated multiplication to simplify each of the following expressions. [1.7]

56. 8^1

57. 16^0

Use the rule for the order of operations to simplify each expression as much as possible. [1.7]

58. $360 + 14(27)^2$

59. $\dfrac{9 - 5}{3 - 3}$

60. $4(6)^2 - 5(3)^3$

61. $6 - 2(5 - 4)$

62. $5 + 4(57 - 7)$

63. $7(x - 2)$

64. $6 + 3[8 - 3(1 + 1)]$

65. $\dfrac{20 - 10(2)}{11 - 7}$

The chart shows some of the most expensive cars in the world. Use the information to answer the following questions.

MOST EXPENSIVE CARS
source: statista.com

Lamborghini Veneno $4,500,000
Lykan Hypersport $3,400,000
Bugatti Veyron $2,400,000
Aston Martin One-77 $1,850,000
Pagani Zonda Cinque $1,850,000

66. How much more does a Lamborghini Veneno cost than an Aston Martin? Write your answer in digits and words.

67. How much less does a Bugatti Veyron cost than a Lykan Hypersport? Write your answer in digits and words.

68. Home Prices Mr. Hicks paid $137,500 for his home. He sold it for $260,600. What is the difference between what he sold it for and what he bought it for? [1.3]

69. Rent A student pays $475 rent each month. How much money does she spend on rent in 2 years? [1.5]

70. Miles per Gallon A traveling salesman kept track of his mileage for 1 month. He found that he traveled 1,104 miles and used 48 gallons of gas. How many miles did he travel on each gallon of gas? [1.6]

TEST CHAPTER 1 . . . .

At the end of each chapter, we will provide a test that you should use as a helpful study tool for a chapter exam. Remember, it is still important to study every aspect of the material presented in the chapter, and not rely solely on the Chapter Test to study for an exam.

1. Write the number 30,652 in words. [1.1]

2. Write the number six million, seven thousand, twenty-nine with digits instead of words. [1.1]

3. Write the number 285,634 in expanded form. [1.1]

Identify each of the statements in Problems 4–7 as an example of one of the following properties. [1.2, 1.5]

   a. Addition property of 0
   b. Multiplication property of 0
   c. Identity property of multiplication
   d. Commutative property of addition
   e. Commutative property of multiplication
   f. Associative property of addition
   g. Associative property of multiplication

4. $8 + 9 = 9 + 8$ 5. $(5 \cdot 7) \cdot 8 = 5 \cdot (7 \cdot 8)$

6. $4 \cdot 1 = 4$ 7. $8 \cdot 0 = 0$

Find each of the following sums. (Add.) [1.2]

8.   237
    + 461

9.   3,821
     467
   + 20,315

10. Find the perimeter. [1.2]

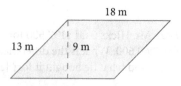

Find each of the following differences. (Subtract.) [1.3]

11.   846
   − 325

12.   8,502
  − 3,715

13. Round the number 238,543 to the nearest ten thousand. [1.4]

Find each of the following products. (Multiply.) [1.5]

14. 5(162)   15. 74(267)

Find each of the following quotients. (Divide.) [1.6]

16. $1,224 \div 17$ 17. $512\overline{)11,776}$

Write the following in numbers, then simplify as much as possible.

18. Twice the sum of 13 and 4. [1.2, 1.3, 1.5, 1.6]

19. The quotient of 18 and 6 increased by 12. [1.2, 1.3, 1.5, 1.6]

Use the rule for the order of operations to simplify each expression as much as possible. [1.7]

20. $5(4)^2 - 5(2)^3$ 21. $9 - 3(7 - 5)$

22. $5 + 3(29 - 4)$ 23. $5(x - 4)$

24. $\dfrac{10 - 5}{2 - 2}$ 25. $\dfrac{2 - 2}{10 - 5}$

The chart shows how many Twitter followers each person has. Use the information to answer the following questions.

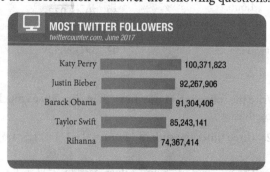

26. How many more fans does Barack Obama have than Taylor Swift? Write your answer in digits and words.

27. How many fewer fans does Rihanna have than Katy Perry? Write your answer in digits and words.

OPERATIONS WITH INTEGERS

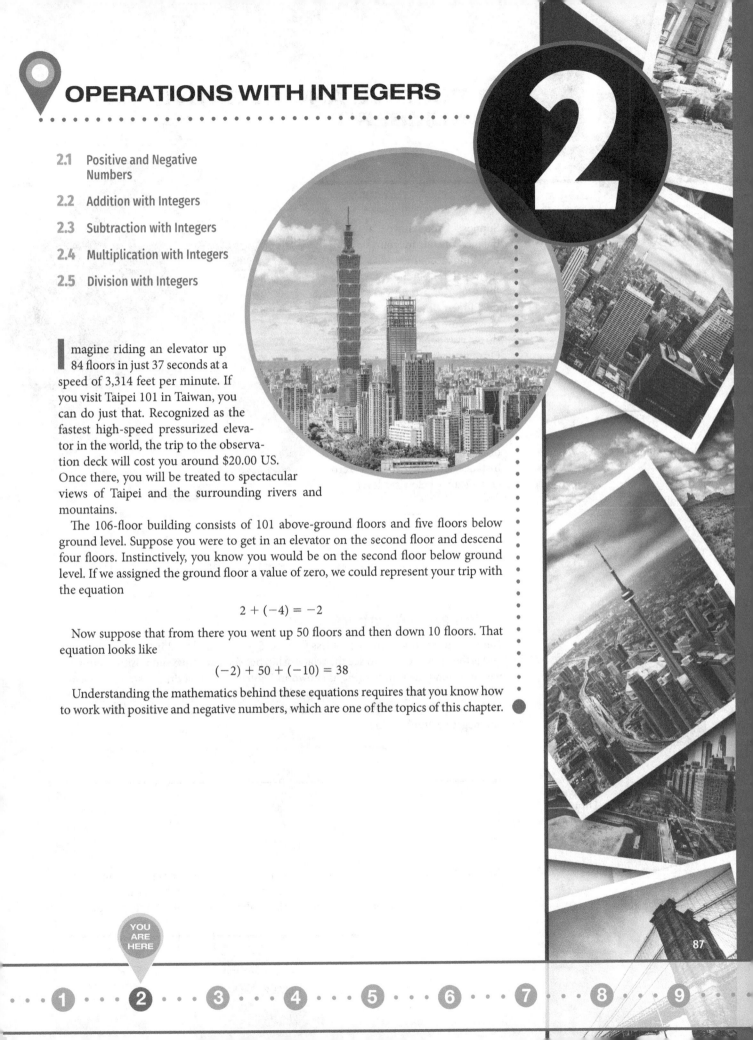

Imagine riding an elevator up 84 floors in just 37 seconds at a speed of 3,314 feet per minute. If you visit Taipei 101 in Taiwan, you can do just that. Recognized as the fastest high-speed pressurized elevator in the world, the trip to the observation deck will cost you around $20.00 US. Once there, you will be treated to spectacular views of Taipei and the surrounding rivers and mountains.

The 106-floor building consists of 101 above-ground floors and five floors below ground level. Suppose you were to get in an elevator on the second floor and descend four floors. Instinctively, you know you would be on the second floor below ground level. If we assigned the ground floor a value of zero, we could represent your trip with the equation

$$2 + (-4) = -2$$

Now suppose that from there you went up 50 floors and then down 10 floors. That equation looks like

$$(-2) + 50 + (-10) = 38$$

Understanding the mathematics behind these equations requires that you know how to work with positive and negative numbers, which are one of the topics of this chapter.

YOU
ARE
HERE

POSITIVE AND NEGATIVE NUMBERS

OBJECTIVES

A Compare positive and negative numbers.

B Find the absolute value and opposite of a number.

KEY WORDS

negative numbers

origin

inequality

absolute value

opposites

integers

VIDEO EXAMPLES

SECTION 2.1

Note It is assumed that when there is no sign in front of a number, it is positive. That is, $5 = +5$.

Suppose you have a balance of $20 in your checking account and then make a purchase for $30. You are now overdrawn by $10. How will you write this new balance? One way is with a negative number by writing the balance as $-\$10$.

Negative numbers can be used to describe other situations as well—for instance, temperature below zero and distance below sea level.

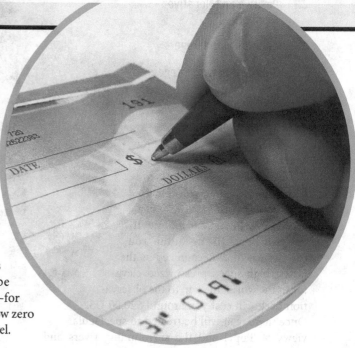

DATE	TRANSACTION	TYPE	AMOUNT	BALANCE
Feb 4	REMOTE DEPOSIT	DEPOSIT	$30.00	$20.00
Mar 6	CVS PHARMACY	DEBIT CARD	-$30.00	-$10.00

A Negative Numbers

Negative numbers are numbers less than zero. For example, -2 is two less than zero and is the opposite of 2. To see the relationship between negative and positive numbers, we can extend the number line as shown in Figure 1. We first draw a straight line and label a convenient point with 0. This is called the **origin,** and it is usually in the middle of the line. We then label positive numbers to the right (as we have done previously), and negative numbers to the left.

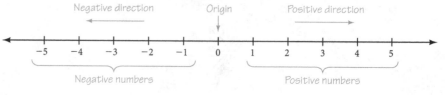

FIGURE 1

The numbers increase going from left to right. If we move to the right, we are moving in the positive direction. If we move to the left, we are moving in the negative direction. Any number to the left of another number is smaller than the number to its right.

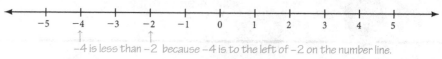

-4 is less than -2 because -4 is to the left of -2 on the number line.

FIGURE 2

We see from the line that every negative number is less than every positive number. In mathematics, we can use inequality symbols when comparing numbers.

> **NOTATION** inequalities
>
> If a and b are any two numbers on the number line, then
>
> $a < b$ is read "a is less than b."
>
> $a > b$ is read "a is greater than b."

As you can see, the inequality symbols always point to the smaller of the two numbers being compared. Here are some examples that illustrate how we use the inequality symbols.

Example 1 Write each inequality in words and state whether it is true or false.

a. $3 < 5$ **b.** $0 > 100$ **c.** $-3 < 5$ **d.** $-5 < -2$

Solution

a. $3 < 5$ is read "3 is less than 5." This is a true statement.

b. $0 > 100$ is read "0 is greater than 100." This is a false statement.

c. $-3 < 5$ is read "−3 is less than 5." This is a true statement, because -3 is to the left of 5 on the number line.

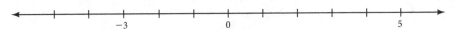

d. $-5 < -2$ is read "−5 is less than −2." This is a true statement, because -5 is to the left of -2 on the number line.

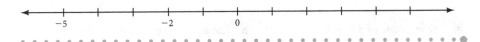

B Absolute Value and Opposites

It is sometimes convenient to talk about the magnitude or distance a number is from zero. That is, only talk about the numerical part of a number and disregard the sign in front of it. The following definition gives us a way of doing this.

> **DEFINITION** absolute value
>
> The **absolute value** of a number is its distance from 0 on the number line. We denote the absolute value of a number with vertical lines. For example, the absolute value of -3 is written $|-3|$.

The absolute value of a number is never negative because it is a distance, and a nonzero distance is always measured in positive units.

2. Simplify each expression.

   a. $|7|$

   b. $|-9|$

   c. $|-12|$

Example 2 Simplify each expression.

   a. $|5|$ **b.** $|-3|$ **c.** $|-7|$

Solution

   a. $|5| = 5$ The number 5 is 5 units from 0.

   b. $|-3| = 3$ The number -3 is 3 units from 0.

   c. $|-7| = 7$ The number -7 is 7 units from 0.

Note The only number whose opposite is itself is zero. That is, $-0 = 0$. Zero is also not considered to be positive or negative.

DEFINITION opposites

Two numbers that are the same distance from 0 but in opposite directions from 0 are called **opposites**. The notation for the opposite of a is $-a$.

From this definition, we can see that the opposite of a positive number is a negative number and likewise the opposite of a negative number is a positive number. That means the opposite of -10 is 10. In symbols, $-(-10) = 10$. We can extend this example to the following property:

PROPERTY Opposite of a Negative Number

If a represents any positive number, then it is always true that
$$-(-a) = a$$

3. Give the opposite of each of the following numbers:

   a. 3

   b. -4

   c. 8

   d. 1

   e. -6

Example 3 Give the opposite of each of the following numbers:

   a. 5   **b.** 7   **c.** 1   **d.** -5 **e.** -8

Solution

   a. The opposite of 5 is -5.   **b.** The opposite of 7 is -7.

   c. The opposite of 1 is -1.   **d.** The opposite of -5 is $-(-5)$, or 5.

   e. The opposite of -8 is $-(-8)$, or 8.

Hopefully you've noticed that the symbols $+$ and $-$ can be used to indicate several different ideas in mathematics. In the past, we have used them to indicate addition and subtraction. They can also be used to indicate the direction a number is from 0 on the number line. For instance, the number $+3$ (read "positive 3") is the number that is 3 units from zero in the positive direction. On the other hand, the number -3 (read "negative 3") is the number that is 3 units from 0 in the negative direction. The symbol $-$ can also be used to indicate the opposite of a number, as in $-(-2) = 2$. The interpretation of the symbols $+$ and $-$ depends on the context in which they are used. They can also be used to denote the operations addition and subtraction. For example,

         $3 + 5$ The $+$ sign indicates addition.

         $7 - 2$ The $-$ sign indicates subtraction.

         -7 The $-$ sign is read "negative 7."

         $-(-5)$ The first $-$ sign is read "the opposite of."
                    The second $-$ sign is read "negative 5."

Answers

2. a. 7   **b.** 9   **c.** 12

3. a. -3 **b.** 4   **c.** -8 **d.** -1 **e.** 6

This may seem confusing at first, but as you work through the problems in this chapter, hopefully you will get accustomed to the different interpretations of the symbols + and −.

DEFINITION integers

The set of positive whole numbers, their opposites, and 0 form the set called **integers**. That is,

integers = {. . ., −3, −2, −1, 0, 1, 2, 3, . . .}

We will now look at two problems that involve absolute value and opposites. To simplify, we will find the absolute value first and then find the opposite.

Example 4   Simplify each of the following:
a. −|8| **b.** −|−10|

Solution

a.   We start by taking the absolute value of each number:

$$-|8|$$
$$-8 \qquad |8| = 8$$

Consequently −|8| = −8

b.   Again, we take the absolute value:

$$-|-10|$$
$$-10 \qquad |-10| = 10$$

Therefore −|−10| = −10

4. Simplify each of the following:
   a. −|12|
   b. − |−15|

  KEY CONCEPT REVIEW · · · · · · · · · · · · · ·

After reading through the preceding section, respond in your own words and in complete sentences.

A. Write the statement "3 is less than 5" in symbols.

B. What is the absolute value of a number?

C. Describe what we mean by numbers that are "opposites" of each other.

D. If you locate two different numbers on the real number line, which one will be the smaller number?

EXERCISE SET 2.1 ·

VOCABULARY REVIEW ·

Choose the correct words to fill in the blanks below.

less than	absolute value	origin	integers
opposites	greater than	positive	negative

1. The _____ on a real number line that includes negative numbers is found at zero.

2. A number, other than zero, with no sign in front of it is assumed to be _____.

3. The inequality symbol < means _____, whereas the symbol > means _____.

4. The _____ of a number is its distance from 0 on the number line.

5. Two numbers that are the same distance from 0 but in opposite directions from 0 are called _____.

6. The opposite of a _____ number is a positive number.

7. The set of whole numbers along with their opposites forms the set of _____.

Problems

A Write each of the following in words.

1. $4 < 7$

2. $0 < 10$

3. $5 > -2$

4. $8 > -8$

5. $-10 < -3.$

6. $-20 < -5$

7. $0 > -4$

8. $0 > -100$

Write each of the following in symbols.

9. 30 is greater than -30.

10. -30 is less than 30.

11. -10 is less than 0.

12. 0 is greater than -10.

13. -3 is greater than -15.

14. -15 is less than -3.

Place either $<$ or $>$ between each of the following pairs of numbers so that the resulting statement is true.

15. 3   7

16. 17   0

17. 7 -5

18. 2 -13

19. -6 0

20. -14 0

21. -12 -2

22. -20 -1

23. -9 $|9|$

24. $|12|$ -7

25. -3 $|6|$

26. $|8|$ -2

27. 15 $|-4|$

28. 20 $|-6|$

29. $|-2|$ $|-7|$

30. $|-3|$ $|-1|$

B Find the absolute value of each integer.

31. $|2|$

32. $|7|$

33. $|100|$

34. $|10,000|$

35. $|-8|$

36. $|-9|$

37. $|-231|$

38. $|-457|$

39. $|-42|$

40. $|-9,500|$

41. $|-200|$

42. $|-350|$

43. $|8|$

44. $|9|$

45. $|231|$

46. $|457|$

Give the opposite of each of the following integers.

47. 3

48. -5

49. -2

50. 15

51. 75

52. -32

53. 0

54. 1

Simplify each of the following.

55. $-(-2)$ **56.** $-(-5)$ **57.** $-(-8)$ **58.** $-(-3)$

59. $-|-2|$ **60.** $-|-5|$ **61.** $-|-8|$ **62.** $-|-3|$

Check your understanding by answering each of the following.

63. What number is its own opposite?

64. Is $|a| = a$ always a true statement?

65. If n is a negative number, is $-n$ positive or negative?

66. If n is a positive number, is $-n$ positive or negative?

Estimating

Work the next problems mentally, without pencil and paper or a calculator.

67. Is -60 closer to 0 or -100?

68. Is -20 closer to 0 or -30?

69. Is -10 closer to -20 or 20?

70. Is -20 closer to -40 or 10?

71. Is -362 closer to -360 or -370?

72. Is -368 closer to -360 or -370?

Applying the Concepts

73. Temperature and Altitude Yamina is flying from Phoenix to San Francisco on a Boeing 737 jet. When the plane reaches an altitude of 33,000 feet, the temperature outside the plane is 61 degrees below zero Fahrenheit. Using the symbol for degrees Fahrenheit, °F, represent this temperature with an integer.

74. Temperature Change At 11:00 in the morning in Superior, Wisconsin, Jim notices the temperature is 15 degrees below zero Fahrenheit. Write this temperature as an integer.

75. Temperature Change At 10:00 in the morning in White Bear Lake, Wisconsin, Zach notices the temperature is 5 degrees below zero Fahrenheit. Write this temperature as a negative number.

76. Snorkeling Steve is snorkeling in the ocean near his home in Maui. At one point he is 6 feet below the surface. Represent this situation with a negative number.

Table 2 lists various wind chill temperatures. The top row gives air temperature, while the first column gives wind speed, in miles per hour. The numbers within the table indicate how cold the weather will feel. For example, if the thermometer reads 30 degrees Fahrenheit and the wind is blowing at 15 miles per hour, the wind chill temperature is 9 degrees Fahrenheit.

Table 2

Wind chill temperatures

Wind Speed	Air Temperatures (°F)							
	30°	25°	20°	15°	10°	5°	0°	−5°
10 mph	16°	10°	3°	−3°	−9°	−15°	−22°	−27°
15 mph	9°	2°	−5°	−11°	−18°	−25°	−31°	−38°
20 mph	4°	−3°	−10°	−17°	−24°	−31°	−39°	−46°
25 mph	1°	−7°	−15°	−22°	−29°	−36°	−44°	−51°
30 mph	−2°	−10°	−18°	−25°	−33°	−41°	−49°	−56°

77. Wind Chill Find the wind chill temperature if the thermometer reads 25 degrees Fahrenheit and the wind is blowing at 20 miles per hour (mph).

78. Wind Chill Find the wind chill temperature if the thermometer reads 10 degrees Fahrenheit and the wind is blowing at 25 miles per hour (mph).

79. Wind Chill Which will feel colder: a day with an air temperature of 10 degrees Fahrenheit and a 25-mph wind, or a day with an air temperature of 5 degrees below zero Fahrenheit and a 10-mph wind?

80. Wind Chill Which will feel colder: a day with an air temperature of 15 degrees Fahrenheit and a 20-mph wind, or a day with an air temperature of 5 degrees Fahrenheit and a 10-mph wind?

Getting Ready for the Next Section

Add or subtract.

81. $10 + 15$ **82.** $12 + 15$ **83.** $15 - 10$ **84.** $15 - 12$

85. $10 - 5 - 3 + 4$ **86.** $12 - 3 - 7 + 5$ **87.** $[3 + 10] + [8 - 2]$ **88.** $[2 + 12] + [7 - 5]$

FIND THE MISTAKE •

Each problem below contains a mistake. Circle the mistake and write the correct number(s) or word(s) on the line provided.

1. The expression $-4 < 1$ is read "-4 is more than 1." _____

2. The number -3 appears to the left of the number -24 on the number line. _____

3. The opposite of -18 is 9. _____

4. The absolute value of -36 is -3. _____

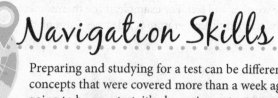

Preparing and studying for a test can be different from completing homework. Often it requires reviewing concepts that were covered more than a week ago in class. Despite what material or how much material is going to be on a test, it's always important to practice problems. Practice questions you struggled with in the homework or problems that you've never done. One fundamental difference between homework and studying for a test is that multiple concepts are combined on a test. Reviewing and studying can be helpful in preparing for this. At the end of each chapter in this book there is a review, or maybe your instructor has provided you with one of his or her own. In either scenario, these are helpful resources to help you begin to prepare for your test. Also, at the end of each chapter, we've included a practice test that you can use. One technique is to put away your notes and course materials and take the test as if you were in class. If you're ever in a class that doesn't have a review or a practice test, you can always make your own. Use practice problems and homework problems to make your own. The most important thing is that you try questions that are representative of the problems you may see on your test.

ADDITION WITH INTEGERS

Suppose you are in Las Vegas playing blackjack and you lose $3 on the first hand and then you lose $5 on the next hand. If you represent winning with positive numbers and losing with negative numbers, how will you represent the results from your first two hands? Since you lost $3 and $5 for a total loss of $8, one way to represent the situation is with addition of negative numbers.

$$(-\$3) + (-\$5) = -\$8$$

OBJECTIVES

A Add any two numbers, including negative numbers.

B Evaluate algebraic expressions.

KEY WORDS

expression

evaluate

VIDEO EXAMPLES

SECTION 2.2

From this example we see that the sum of two negative numbers is a negative number. To generalize addition of positive and negative numbers, we can use the number line.

We can think of each number on the number line as having two characteristics: (1) a *distance* from 0 (absolute value) and (2) a *direction* from 0 (to the left or right). The distance from 0 is represented by the numerical part of the number (like the 5 in the number −5), and its direction is represented by the + or − sign in front of the number.

A Addition of Numbers on the Number Line

We can visualize addition of numbers on the number line by thinking in terms of distance and direction from 0. Let's begin with a problem we know the answer to. We interpret the sum 3 + 5 on the number line as follows:

1. The first number is 3, which tells us to start at 3.

2. The + sign is read "and then move."

3. The 5 means "5 units in the positive direction."

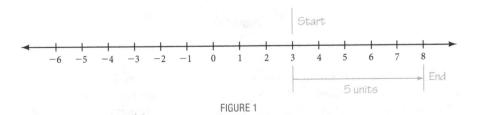

FIGURE 1

Note This method of adding numbers may seem a little complicated at first, but it will allow us to add numbers we couldn't otherwise add.

Figure 1 shows these steps. To summarize, 3 + 5 means to start at 3, and then move 5 units in the *positive* direction. We end up at 8, which is the sum we are looking for: 3 + 5 = 8.

Practice Problems

1. Add $-4 + (-6)$ using the number line.

In the introduction to this section we discussed a scenario in which $3 and $5 were lost playing blackjack. Let's find the total loss.

Example 1   Add $-3 + (-5)$ using the number line.

Solution   We start at -3 and then move 5 more units in the negative direction. This is shown on the number line in Figure 2. As you can see, the last arrow ends at -8. We must conclude that the sum of -3 and -5 is -8. That is,

$$-3 + (-5) = -8$$

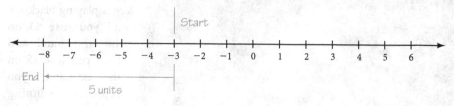

FIGURE 2

2. Add $4 + (-6)$ using the number line.

Example 2   Add $3 + (-5)$ using the number line.

Solution   We start at 3 on the number line, then move 5 units in the negative direction, as shown in Figure 3. The last arrow ends at -2, which must be the sum of 3 and -5. That is,

$$3 + (-5) = -2$$

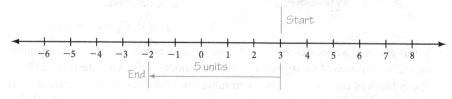

FIGURE 3

3. Add $-5 + 7$ using the number line.

Example 3   Add $-3 + 5$ using the number line.

Solution   We start at -3 on the number line, and then move 5 units in the positive direction, as shown in Figure 4. We end up at 2, which is the sum of -3 and 5. That is,

$$-3 + 5 = 2$$

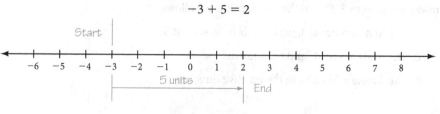

FIGURE 4

Adding numbers on the number line as we have done in these first three examples gives us a way of visualizing addition of integers. We want to be able to write a rule for addition of integers that doesn't involve the number line. The number line is a way of justifying the rule we will write. Here is a summary of the results we have so far:

$$3 + 5 = 8 \qquad\qquad -3 + 5 = 2$$
$$3 + (-5) = -2 \qquad\qquad -3 + (-5) = -8$$

Answers
1. -10
2. -2
3. 2

Looking over these results, we write the following rule for adding any two numbers:

SUMMARY Adding Any Two Numbers

1. To add two numbers with the same sign: Add their absolute values, and use the common sign. If both numbers are positive, the answer is positive. If both numbers are negative, the answer is negative.

2. To add two numbers with different signs: Subtract the smaller absolute value from the larger absolute value. The answer will have the sign of the number with the larger absolute value..

Note This rule covers all possible addition problems involving positive and negative numbers. Being proficient at these skills is extremely helpful. After you have worked some problems, the process will seem almost automatic.

The following examples show how the rule is used. You will find that the rule for addition is consistent with all the results obtained using the number line.

Example 4   Add all combinations of positive and negative 10 and 15.

Solution

$$10 + 15 = 25$$
$$10 + (-15) = -5$$
$$-10 + 15 = 5$$
$$-10 + (-15) = -25$$

4. Add all combinations of positive and negative 8 and 4.

Notice that when we add two numbers with the same sign, the answer also has that sign. When the signs are not the same, the answer has the sign of the number with the larger absolute value.

Once you have become familiar with the rule for adding positive and negative numbers, you can apply it to more complicated sums.

Example 5   Simplify: $10 + (-5) + (-3) + 4$

Solution   Adding left to right, we have

$$10 + (-5) + (-3) + 4 = 5 + (-3) + 4 \qquad 10 + (-5) = 5$$
$$= 2 + 4 \qquad 5 + (-3) = 2$$
$$= 6$$

5. Simplify: $12 + (-4) + (-5) + 6$

Example 6   Simplify: $[-3 + (-10)] + [8 + (-2)]$

Solution   We begin by adding the numbers inside the brackets.

$$[-3 + (-10)] + [8 + (-2)] = [-13] + [6] = -7$$

6. Simplify:
$[-5 + (-8)] + [7 + (-5)]$

B Evaluating Algebraic Expressions

Often we talk about a number without knowing the exact quantity. For example, we found a number x, such that

$$x + 3 = 5$$

This is the essence of algebra! We also stated properties in terms of variables. For instance, we stated the commutative property of addition as $a + b = b + a$. In this case, both a and b are variables.

We can also combine numbers, variables, and operations to make **expressions.** Each of the following are expressions:

$$5a \qquad\qquad 2(x + y) \qquad\qquad b + 8 \qquad\qquad 7r + 10s$$

Answers

4. $8 + 4 = 12, 8 + (-4) = 4$
$-8 + 4 = -4, -8 + (-4) = -12$
5. 9
6. -11

An expression such as $b + 8$ will take on different values depending on what value b has. For example, when $b = 5$, the expression is

$$5 + 8$$

$$13$$

Likewise, when $b = -10$, the expression becomes

$$-10 + 8$$

$$-2$$

The process of substituting a value for the variable in an expression and then simplifying the result is called evaluating an expression.

7. Evaluate $-7 + x$
for $x = 9$ and $x = -11$.

Example 7   Evaluate the expression $-10 + x$ for $x = 4$ and $x = -7$.

Solution   We will substitute 4 for x and simplify, giving us

$$-10 + 4$$

$$-6$$

Therefore, when $x = 4$, the expression becomes -6.

Now we will substitute -7 for x and simplify, giving us

$$-10 + (-7)$$

$$-17$$

Therefore, when $x = -7$, the expression becomes -17.

 KEY CONCEPT REVIEW

After reading through the preceding section, respond in your own words and in complete sentences.

A. Explain how you would use the number line to add 3 and 5.

B. If two numbers are negative, such as -3 and -5, what sign will their sum have?

C. If you add two numbers with different signs, how do you determine the sign of the answer?

D. With respect to addition with positive and negative numbers, does the phrase "two negatives make a positive" make any sense?

Answers

7. $2, -18$

EXERCISE SET 2.2

VOCABULARY REVIEW

Choose the correct words to fill in the blanks in the paragraph below.

different   smaller   absolute values
sign   same   larger

To add two numbers with the _____ sign, add their _____, and use the common sign. If both numbers are positive, the answer is positive. If both numbers are negative, the answer is negative. To add two numbers with _____ signs, subtract the _____ absolute value from the _____ absolute value. The answer will have the _____ of the number with the larger absolute value.

Problems

A Draw a number line and use it to add the following numbers.

1. $2 + 3$

2. $2 + (-3)$

3. $-2 + 3$

4. $-2 + (-3)$

5. $5 + (-7)$

6. $-5 + 7$

7. $-4 + (-2)$

8. $-8 + (-2)$

9. $10 + (-6)$

10. $-9 + 3$

11. $7 + (-3)$

12. $-7 + 3$

13. $-4 + (-5)$

14. $-2 + (-7)$

Add. (Your goal is to be fast and accurate at addition, with the latter being more important.)

15. $7 + 8$

16. $9 + 12$

17. $5 + (-8)$

18. $4 + (-11)$

19. $-6 + (-5)$

20. $-7 + (-2)$

21. $-10 + 3$

22. $-14 + 7$

23. $-1 + (-2)$

24. $-5 + (-4)$

25. $-11 + (-5)$

26. $-16 + (-10)$

27. $4 + (-12)$

28. $9 + (-1)$

29. $-85 + (-42)$

30. $-96 + (-31)$

31. $-121 + 170$

32. $-130 + 158$

33. $-375 + 409$

34. $-765 + 213$

Complete the following tables.

35.

a	b	a + b
5	−3	
5	−4	
5	−5	
5	−6	
5	−7	

36.

a	b	a + b
−5	3	
−5	4	
−5	5	
−5	6	
−5	7	

37.

x	y	x + y
−5	−3	
−5	−4	
−5	−5	
−5	−6	
−5	−7	

38.

x	y	x + y
30	−20	
−30	20	
−30	−20	
30	20	
−30	0	

Add the following numbers left to right.

39. $10 + (−18) + 4$

40. $−2 + 4 + (−6)$

41. $24 + (−6) + (−8)$

42. $35 + (−5) + (−30)$

43. $−201 + (−143) + (−101)$

44. $−27 + (−56) + (−89)$

45. $−321 + 752 + (−324)$

46. $−571 + 437 + (−502)$

47. $−8 + 3 + (−5) + 9$

48. $−9 + 2 + (−10) + 3$

49. $−2 + (−5) + (−6) + (−7)$

50. $−8 + (−3) + (−4) + (−7)$

51. $15 + (−30) + 18 + (−20)$

52. $20 + (−15) + 30 + (−18)$

53. $−78 + (−42) + 57 + 13$

54. $−89 + (−51) + 65 + 17$

Use order of operations to simplify each of the following.

55. $(-8 + 5) + (-6 + 2)$

56. $(-3 + 1) + (-9 + 4)$

57. $(-10 + 4) + (-3 + 12)$

58. $(-11 + 5) + (-3 + 2)$

59. $20 + (-30 + 50) + 10$

60. $30 + (-40 + 20) + 50$

61. $108 + (-456 + 275)$

62. $106 + (-512 + 318)$

63. $[5 + (-8)] + [3 + (-11)]$

64. $[8 + (-2)] + [5 + (-7)]$

65. $[57 + (-35)] + [19 + (-24)]$

66. $[63 + (-27)] + [18 + (-24)]$

Evaluate each expression for $a = -8$

67. $-10 + a$

68. $-12 + a$

69. $0 + a$

70. $14 + a$

71. $19 + a$

72. $2 + a$

73. $5 + a$

Find each of the following. Translate to symbols first to help you find the solution.

74. Find the sum of -8, -10, and -3.

75. Find the sum of -4, 17, and -6.

76. What number do you add to 8 to get 3?

77. What number do you add to 10 to get 4?

78. What number do you add to -3 to get -7?

79. What number do you add to -5 to get -8?

80. What number do you add to -4 to get 3?

81. What number do you add to -7 to get 2?

82. If the sum of -3 and 5 is increased by 8, what number results?

83. If the sum of -9 and -2 is increased by 10, what number results?

Estimating

Work the following problems mentally, without pencil and paper or a calculator.

84. The answer to $251 + 249$ is closest to which of the following numbers?

   a. 500   **b.** 0   **c.** -500

85. The answer to $251 + (-249)$ is closest to which of the following numbers?

   a. 500   **b.** 0   **c.** -500

86. The answer to $-251 + 249$ is closest to which of the following numbers?

   a. 500   **b.** 0   **c.** -500

87. The answer to $-251 + (-249)$ is closest to which of the following numbers?

   a. 500   **b.** 0   **c.** -500

88. The sum of 77 and 22 is closest to which of the following numbers?

   a. -100 **b.** -60 **c.** 60   **d.** 100

89. The sum of -77 and 22 is closest to which of the following numbers?

   a. -100 **b.** -60 **c.** 60   **d.** 100

90. The sum of 77 and -22 is closest to which of the following numbers?

   a. -100 **b.** -60 **c.** 60   **d.** 100

91. The sum of -77 and -22 is closest to which of the following numbers?

   a. -100 **b.** -60 **c.** 60   **d.** 100

Applying the Concepts

92. Account Balance Ethan has a balance of –$40 in his checking account. If he deposits $100 and then buys something for $50, what is the new balance in his account?

93. Account Balance Justin has a balance of –$20 in his checking account. If he deposits $70 and then buys something for $50, what is the new balance in his account?

94. Gambling While gambling in Las Vegas, a person wins $74 playing blackjack and then loses $141 on roulette. Use positive and negative numbers to write this situation in symbols. Then give the person's net loss or gain.

95. Gambling While playing blackjack, a person loses $17 on his first hand, then wins $14, and then loses $21. Write this situation using positive and negative numbers and addition; then simplify.

96. Stock Gain/Loss Suppose a certain stock gains 3 points on the stock exchange on Monday and then loses 5 points on Tuesday. Express the situation using positive and negative numbers, and then give the net gain or loss of the stock for this 2-day period.

97. Stock Gain/Loss A stock gains 2 points on Wednesday, then loses 1 on Thursday, and gains 3 on Friday. Use positive and negative numbers and addition to write this situation in symbols, and then simplify.

98. Temperature Change At 11:00 in the morning in Superior, Wisconsin, Jim notices the temperature is 15 degrees below zero Fahrenheit. Write this temperature as an integer. At noon it has warmed up by 8 degrees. What is the temperature at noon?

99. Temperature Change At 10:00 in the morning in White Bear Lake, Wisconsin, Zach notices the temperature is 5 degrees below zero Fahrenheit. Write this temperature as an integer. By noon the temperature has dropped another 10 degrees. What is the temperature at noon?

Getting Ready for the Next Section

Give the opposite of each number.

100. 2   **101.** 3   **102.** -4 **103.** -5 **104.** -30 **105.** -15

106. Subtract 3 from 5.

107. Subtract 2 from 8.

108. Find the difference of 7 and 4.

109. Find the difference of 8 and 6.

FIND THE MISTAKE •

Each problem below contains a mistake. Circle the mistake and write the correct number(s) or word(s) on the line provided.

1. The problem $6 + (-10) = -4$ is interpreted as, "Start at 6 on the number line, and then move 10 units in the positive direction." _____

2. Adding two numbers with different signs will give an answer that has the same sign as the number with the smaller absolute value. _____

3. Adding -8 and -5 gives us 13. _____

4. The sum of -2, 4, -3, and -5 is -2. _____

SUBTRACTION WITH INTEGERS

VIDEO EXAMPLES

SECTION 2.3

Cave diving is an extreme form of scuba diving in which caves deep below the surface of the water can be explored. With specialized training and equipment, divers are able to discover areas of the ocean, viewing exotic animals and rare sea life. The sport is considered extreme because swimmers are unable to easily return to the water's surface and must be aware of the exit of the cave at all times.

Imagine a diver standing at the edge of a boat that is 5 feet above the surface of the ocean. The diver jumps into the water and descends to a depth of 15 feet. We can use a number line to show the diver's height. If we consider the diver's height on the boat as 5, then the ocean surface would be 0, and the diver's depth would be -15. What is the difference in the diver's height between the boat and her final depth? Intuitively, we may know the difference in the two heights is 20 feet. We have also learned that the word **difference** indicates subtraction. The difference between 5 and -15 is written

$$5 - (-15)$$

It must be true that $5 - (-15) = 20$. In this section, we will see how our definition for subtraction confirms that this last statement is in fact correct. Let's start with a formal definition for subtraction that uses the rules we have developed for addition to help us solve problems.

A Subtraction of Any Two Numbers

DEFINITION subtraction

If a and b represent any two numbers, subtracting a number is equivalent to adding its opposite.

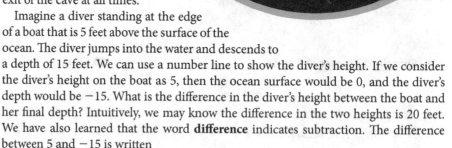

$$a - b = a + (-b)$$

To subtract b add its opposite, $-b$.

Let's see if this definition conflicts with what we already know to be true about subtraction.

Note This definition of subtraction may seem a little strange at first. In Example 1, you will notice that using the definition gives us the same results we are used to getting with subtraction. As we progress further into the section, we will use the definition to subtract numbers we haven't been able to subtract before.

From previous experience, we know that

$$5 - 2 = 3$$

We can get the same answer by using the definition we just gave for subtraction. Instead of subtracting 2, we can add its opposite, -2. Here is how it looks:

$5 - 2 = 5 + (-2)$ *Change subtraction to addition of the opposite.*

$\quad\quad = 3$ *Apply the rule for addition of positive and negative numbers.*

The result is the same whether we use our previous knowledge of subtraction or the new definition. The new definition is essential when the problems begin to get more complicated.

Note A real-life analogy to Example 1 would be: "If the temperature were 7 degrees below 0 and then it dropped another 2 degrees, what would the temperature be then?"

Example 1 Subtract: $-7 - 2$

Solution We have never subtracted a positive number from a negative number before. We must apply our definition of subtraction.

$-7 - 2 = -7 + (-2)$ *Instead of subtracting 2, we add its opposite, -2.*

$\quad\quad = -9$ *Apply the rule for addition.*

Practice Problems

1. Subtract: $-10 - 4$

Example 2 Subtract: $12 - (-6)$

Solution The first $-$ sign is read "subtract," and the second one is read "negative." The problem in words is "12 subtract negative 6." We can use the definition of subtraction to change this to the addition of positive 6.

$12 - (-6) = 12 + 6$ *Subtracting -6 is equivalent to adding 6.*

$\quad\quad = 18$ *Add.*

2. Subtract: $10 - (-5)$

We've seen in this example that subtracting a negative number is equivalent to adding the absolute value of that number. This is always true.

The following table shows the relationship between subtraction and addition:

Subtraction	Addition of the opposite	Answer
$7 - 9$	$7 + (-9)$	-2
$-7 - 9$	$-7 + (-9)$	-16
$7 - (-9)$	$7 + 9$	16
$-7 - (-9)$	$-7 + 9$	2
$15 - 10$	$15 + (-10)$	5
$-15 - 10$	$-15 + (-10)$	-25
$15 - (-10)$	$15 + 10$	25
$-15 - (-10)$	$-15 + 10$	-5

The previous examples illustrate all the possible combinations of subtraction with positive and negative numbers. There are no new rules for subtraction. We apply the definition to change each subtraction problem into an equivalent addition problem. The rule for addition can then be used to obtain the correct answer.

Answers

1. -14
2. 15

3. Combine: $-5 + 8 - 3$

Example 3   Combine: $-3 + 6 - 2$

Solution   The first step is to change subtraction to addition of the opposite. After that has been done, we add left to right.

$$-3 + 6 - 2 = -3 + 6 + (-2)$$ *Subtracting 2 is equivalent to adding -2.*

$$= 3 + (-2)$$ *Add left to right.*

$$= 1$$

4. Subtract 5 from -8.

Example 4   Subtract 3 from -5.

Solution   First we need to translate to symbols. Then we will use the fact that subtracting 3 is equivalent to adding -3.

$$-5 - 3 = -5 + (-3) = -8$$

Subtracting 3 from -5 gives us -8.

5. For the airplane described in Example 5, find the difference in temperature inside the plane if it was 70 degrees Fahrenheit at takeoff and drops to 5 degrees below zero Fahrenheit.

Example 5   Many of the planes used by the United States during World War II were not pressurized or sealed from outside air. As a result, the temperature inside these planes was the same as the surrounding air temperature outside. Suppose the temperature inside a B-17 Flying Fortress is 50 degrees Fahrenheit at takeoff and then drops to 30 degrees below zero Fahrenheit when the plane reaches its cruising altitude of 28,000 feet. Find the difference in temperature inside this plane at takeoff and at 28,000 feet.

Solution   The temperature at takeoff is 50 degrees Fahrenheit, whereas the temperature at 28,000 feet is 30 degrees below zero Fahrenheit. To find the difference we subtract, with the numbers in the same order as they are given in the problem.

$$50 - (-30) = 50 + 30 = 80$$

The difference in temperature is 80 degrees Fahrenheit, or in symbols, 80°F.

Subtraction and Taking Away

Some people may believe that the answer to $-5 - 9$ should be -4 or 4, not -14. If this is happening to you, you are probably thinking of subtraction in terms of taking one number away from another. Thinking of subtraction in this way works well with positive numbers if you always subtract the smaller number from the larger. In algebra, however, we encounter many situations other than this. The definition of subtraction, that $a - b = a + (-b)$ clearly indicates the correct way to use subtraction. That is, when working subtraction problems, you should think "addition of the opposite," not "taking one number away from another."

   KEY CONCEPT REVIEW

After reading through the preceding section, respond in your own words and in complete sentences.

A. Write the subtraction problem $5 - 3$ as an equivalent addition problem.

B. Explain the process you would use to subtract 2 from -7.

C. Write an addition problem that is equivalent to the subtraction problem $-20 - (-30)$.

D. Why is it important to think of subtraction as addition of the opposite?

Answers
3. 0
4. -13
5. 75

EXERCISE SET 2.3 ··

VOCABULARY REVIEW •

Choose the correct words to fill in the blanks below.

opposite   negative   addition   positive   subtract

1. To _____ b from a, add its opposite, $-b$.

2. Subtracting a number is equivalent to adding its _____.

3. Once you turn a subtraction problem into the addition of the opposite, apply the rule for _____ of positive and negative numbers.

4. When you subtract 10 from -15, you get a _____ answer.

5. When you subtract -10 from 15, you get a _____ answer.

Problems

A Subtract.

1. $7 - 5$ **2.** $5 - 7$ **3.** $8 - 6$ **4.** $6 - 8$

5. $-3 - 5$ **6.** $-5 - 3$ **7.** $-4 - 1$ **8.** $-1 - 4$

9. $5 - (-2)$ **10.** $2 - (-5)$ **11.** $3 - (-9)$ **12.** $9 - (-3)$

13. $-4 - (-7)$ **14.** $-7 - (-4)$ **15.** $-10 - (-3)$ **16.** $-3 - (-10)$

17. $15 - 18$ **18.** $20 - 32$ **19.** $100 - 113$ **20.** $121 - 21$

21. $-30 - 20$ **22.** $-50 - 60$ **23.** $-79 - 21$ **24.** $-86 - 31$

25. $156 - (-243)$ **26.** $292 - (-841)$ **27.** $-35 - (-14)$ **28.** $-29 - (-4)$

Complete the following tables.

29.

x	y	x − y
8	6	
8	7	
8	8	
8	9	
8	10	

30.

x	y	x − y
10	12	
10	11	
10	10	
10	9	
10	8	

31.

x	y	x − y
8	−6	
8	−7	
8	−8	
8	−9	
8	−10	

32.

x	y	x − y
−10	−12	
−10	−11	
−10	−10	
−10	−9	
−10	−8	

Simplify as much as possible by first changing all subtractions to addition of the opposite and then adding left to right.

33. $4 - 5 - 6$

34. $7 - 3 - 2$

35. $-8 + 3 - 4$

36. $-10 - 1 + 16$

37. $-8 - 4 - 2$

38. $-7 - 3 - 6$

39. $33 - (-22) - 66$

40. $44 - (-11) + 55$

41. $-900 + 400 - (-100)$

42. $-300 + 600 - (-200)$

Evaluate each expression for $w = 6$ and $w = 3$.

43. $10 - w$

44. $14 - w$

45. $w - 6$

46. $3 - w$

47. $w - 1$

48. $w - 2$

Find each of the following. Translate to symbols first to help you find the solution.

49. Subtract −6 from 5.

50. Subtract 8 from −2.

51. Find the difference of −5 and −1.

52. Find the difference of −7 and −3.

53. Subtract −4 from the sum of −8 and 12.

54. Subtract −7 from the sum of 7 and −12.

55. What number do you subtract from −3 to get −9?

56. What number do you subtract from 5 to get 8?

Estimating

Work the next problems mentally, without pencil and paper or a calculator.

57. The answer to the problem $52 - 49$ is closest to which of the following numbers?

    a. 100   **b.** 0   **c.** -100

58. The answer to the problem $-52 - 49$ is closest to which of the following numbers?

    a. 100   **b.** 0   **c.** -100

59. The answer to the problem $52 - (-49)$ is closest to which of the following numbers?

    a. 100   **b.** 0   **c.** -100

60. The answer to the problem $-52 - (-49)$ is closest to which of the following numbers?

    a. 100   **b.** 0   **c.** -100

61. Is the difference $-161 - (-62)$ closer to -200 or -100?

62. Is the difference $-553 - 50$ closer to -600 or -500?

63. The difference of 37 and 61 is closest to which of the following numbers?

    a. -100 **b.** -20 **c.** 20   **d.** 100

64. The difference of 37 and -61 is closest to which of the following numbers?

    a. -100 **b.** -20 **c.** 20   **d.** 100

65. The difference of -37 and 61 is closest to which of the following numbers?

    a. -100 **b.** -20 **c.** 20   **d.** 100

66. The difference of -37 and -61 is closest to which of the following numbers?

    a. -100 **b.** -20 **c.** 20   **d.** 100

Applying the Concepts

67. Temperature On Monday, the temperature reached a high of 28 degrees. That night it dropped to 16 degrees below 0. What is the difference between the high and the low temperatures for Monday?

68. Account Balance Susan has a balance of $572 in her checking account when she writes a check for $435 to pay the rent. Then she spends $172 on textbooks. Write a subtraction problem that gives the new balance in her checking account. What is the new balance in her checking account?

Repeated below is the table of wind chill temperatures that we used previously. Use it to answer the following problems.

Air Temperature (°F)								
Wind speed	30°	25°	20°	15°	10°	5°	0°	−5°
10 mph	16°	10°	3°	−3°	−9°	−15°	−22°	−27°
15 mph	9°	2°	−5°	−11°	−18°	−25°	−31°	−38°
20 mph	4°	−3°	−10°	−17°	−24°	−31°	−39°	−46°
25 mph	1°	−7°	−15°	−22°	−29°	−36°	−44°	−51°
30 mph	−2°	−10°	−18°	−25°	−33°	−41°	−49°	−56°

69. Wind Chill If the temperature outside is 15 degrees Fahrenheit, what is the difference in wind chill temperature between a 15-mile-per-hour wind and a 25-mile-per-hour wind?

70. Wind Chill If the temperature outside is 0 degrees Fahrenheit, what is the difference in wind chill temperature between a 15-mile-per-hour wind and a 25-mile-per-hour wind?

71. Wind Chill Find the difference in temperature between a day in which the air temperature is 20 degrees Fahrenheit and the wind is blowing at 10 miles per hour and a day in which the air temperature is 10 degrees Fahrenheit and the wind is blowing at 20 miles per hour.

72. Wind Chill Find the difference in temperature between a day in which the air temperature is 0 degrees Fahrenheit and the wind is blowing at 10 miles per hour and a day in which the air temperature is 5 degrees below zero Fahrenheit and the wind is blowing at 20 miles per hour.

Use the tables below to answer the following problems.

Table 1	
Record low temperatures for Lake Placid, New York	
Month	Temperature
January	−36°F
February	−30°F
March	−14°F
April	−2°F
May	19°F
June	22°F
July	35°F
August	30°F
September	19°F
October	15°F
November	−11°F
December	−26°F

Table 2	
Record high temperatures for Lake Placid, New York	
Month	Temperature
January	54°F
February	59°F
March	69°F
April	82°F
May	90°F
June	93°F
July	97°F
August	93°F
September	90°F
October	87°F
November	67°F
December	60°F

73. Temperature Difference Find the difference between the record high temperature and the record low temperature for the month of December.

74. Temperature Difference Find the difference between the record high temperature and the record low temperature for the month of March.

75. Temperature Difference Find the difference between the record low temperatures of March and December.

76. Temperature Difference Find the difference between the record high temperatures of March and December.

Getting Ready for the Next Section

Perform the indicated operations.

77. $3(2)(5)$

78. $5(2)(4)$

79. 6^2

80. 8^2

81. 4^3

82. 3^3

83. $6(3 + 5)$

84. $2(5 + 8)$

85. $3(9 - 2) + 4(7 - 2)$

86. $2(5 - 3) - 7(4 - 2)$

87. $(3 + 7)(6 - 2)$

88. $(6 + 1)(9 - 4)$

FIND THE MISTAKE •

Each problem below contains a mistake. Circle the mistake and write the correct number(s) or word(s) on the line provided.

1. Subtracting 5 from 4 is the same as adding 4 and 5. _____

2. To subtract -1 from 8, we must move 1 unit in the negative direction from 8 on the number line. _____

3. The problem $11 - (-7)$ is read, "11 negative subtract 7." _____

4. To find the difference of -5 and 6, change -5 to 5 and add 6. _____

LANDMARK REVIEW: CHECKING YOUR PROGRESS • • • • • • • • • • • • • • • •

This feature is intended as a review of key skills from the preceding sections in the chapter. Each review will give you the opportunity to utilize important concepts and check your progress as you practice problems of different types. Take note of any problems in this review that you find difficult. There is no better time than now to revisit and master those difficult concepts in preparation for any upcoming exams or subsequent chapters.

Find the absolute value and the opposite of each of the following numbers.

1. 2

2. -11

3. 25

4. -110

Simplify each of the following.

5. $-(-7)$

6. $-(5)$

7. $-|-3|$

8. $-|15|$

Add the following numbers.

9. $5 + 6$

10. $-7 + 4$

11. $7 + (-5)$

12. $-15 + (-5)$

Subtract the following numbers.

13. $10 - 6$

14. $6 - 12$

15. $-5 - 7$

16. $7 - (-8)$

17. $-12 - (-3)$

18. $-27 - (-38)$

2.4 MULTIPLICATION WITH INTEGERS

OBJECTIVES

A Multiply any numbers, including negative numbers.

B Simplify exponent expressions with positive and negative bases.

C Evaluate algebraic expressions.

VIDEO EXAMPLES

SECTION 2.4

Australia is the largest country by area in Oceania and the sixth largest in the world. The country, which was at one time a European colony, is approximately the size of the contiguous 48 states of the United States, yet has a significantly smaller population (it's about 10% of that of the US). On a visit to Australia, travelers can visit the famous Sydney Opera House and the Great Barrier reef. With tropical, desert and snow-covered mountain ranges, the landscape is very diverse.

The following bar chart contains record low temperature readings for various cities in Australia rounded to the nearest integer. Notice that some of these temperatures are represented by negative numbers.

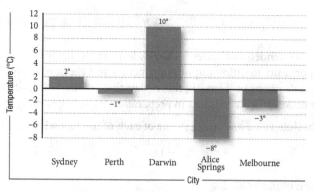

FIGURE 1

Suppose the record low temperature in Canberra is ten times lower than the record low in Perth. How would we calculate the temperature for Canberra? One approach is to multiply the lowest temperature in Perth by 10.

$$10(-1) = -10$$

From this we conclude that it is reasonable to say that the product of a positive number and a negative numbers is a negative number.

In this section, we will explore multiplication of integers. First, let's revisit how we defined multiplication as repeated addition. That is,

$$\underbrace{3 \cdot 2}_{\text{Multiplication}} = \underbrace{2 + 2 + 2}_{\text{Repeated addition}}$$

A Multiplication with Integers

The concept of multiplication as repeated addition is very helpful when it comes to developing the rule for multiplication problems that involve both positive and negative numbers. For the next example, we look at what happens when we multiply a negative number by a positive number.

Example 1   Multiply: $3(-5)$

Solution   Writing this product as repeated addition, we have

$$3(-5) = (-5) + (-5) + (-5) \qquad \textit{Write as repeated addition.}$$
$$= -10 + (-5) \qquad \textit{Add from left to right.}$$
$$= -15$$

The result, -15, is obtained by adding the three negative 5s.

Example 2   Multiply: $-3(5)$

Solution   In order to write this multiplication problem in terms of repeated addition, we will have to reverse the order of the two numbers. This can be done, because multiplication is a commutative operation.

$$-3(5) = 5(-3) \qquad \textit{Commutative property}$$
$$= (-3) + (-3) + (-3) + (-3) + (-3) \qquad \textit{Repeated addition}$$
$$= -15$$

The product of -3 and 5 is -15.

Example 3   Multiply: $-3(-5)$

Solution   It is impossible to write this product in terms of repeated addition. We will find the answer to $-3(-5)$ by solving a different problem. Look at the following problem:

$$-3[5 + (-5)] = -3[0] = 0$$

The result is 0, because multiplying by 0 always produces 0. Now we can work the same problem another way and in the process find the answer to $-3(-5)$. Applying the distributive property to the same expression, we have

$$-3[5 + (-5)] = -3(5) + (-3)(-5) \qquad \textit{Distributive property}$$
$$= -15 + (?) \qquad \qquad -3(5) = -15$$

The question mark must be 15, because we already know that the answer to the problem is 0, and 15 is the only number we can add to -15 to get 0. So our problem is solved.

$$-3(-5) = 15$$

Practice Problems

1. Multiply: $5(-2)$

2. Multiply: $-5(2)$

3. Multiply: $-5(-2)$

Note   We want to be able to justify everything we do in mathematics. This discussion tells *why* $-3(-5) = 15$.

Answers

1. -10
2. -10
3. 10

Table 1 gives a summary of what we have done so far with multiplication.

Table 1

Original numbers have	For example	The answer is
Same signs	$3(5) = 15$	Positive
Different signs	$-3(5) = -15$	Negative
Different signs	$3(-5) = -15$	Negative
Same signs	$-3(-5) = 15$	Positive

From the multiplication examples we have done so far and their summaries in Table 1, we can make the following conclusions about multiplication of positive and negative numbers:

SUMMARY **Multiplication of Any Two Numbers**

To multiply any two numbers, we multiply their absolute values.

1. The answer is positive if both the original numbers have the same sign. That is, the product of two numbers with the same sign is positive.

2. The answer is negative if the original two numbers have different signs. The product of two numbers with different signs is negative.

By the time you have finished reading this section and working the problems at the end of the section, you should be fast and accurate at multiplication with positive and negative numbers.

4. Find the following products:
 a. $7(8)$
 b. $-7(-8)$
 c. $7(-8)$
 d. $-7(8)$

Example 4   Find the following products:

a. $2(4)$ **b.** $-2(-4)$ **c.** $2(-4)$ **d.** $-2(4)$

Solution

a. $2(4) = 8$ Like signs; positive answer

b. $-2(-4) = 8$ Like signs; positive answer

c. $2(-4) = -8$ Unlike signs; negative answer

d. $-2(4) = -8$ Unlike signs; negative answer

5. Simplify: $-6(3)(-2)$.

Example 5   Simplify: $-3(2)(-5)$.

Solution   We will multiply from left to right.

$$-3(2)(-5) = -6(-5)   \text{Multiply } -3 \text{ and } 2 \text{ to get } -6.$$
$$= 30   \text{Multiply } -6 \text{ and } -5.$$

6. Simplify: $-6 + 2(-4 + 8)$.

Example 6   Simplify: $-4 + 5(-6 + 2)$.

Solution   By the order of operations we start by simplifying the parentheses first.

$$-4 + 5(-6 + 2) = -4 + 5(-4)   \text{Simplify inside parentheses.}$$
$$= -4 + (-20)   \text{Multiply.}$$
$$= -24   \text{Add.}$$

Answers
4. a. 56 **b.** 56 **c.** −56 **d.** −56
5. 36
6. 2

Example 7 Simplify: $-3(2 - 9) + 4(-7 - 2)$

Solution We begin by subtracting inside the parentheses.

$$-3(2 - 9) + 4(-7 - 2) = -3(-7) + 4(-9) \quad \text{Simplify inside parentheses.}$$
$$= 21 + (-36) \quad \text{Multiply.}$$
$$= -15 \quad \text{Add.}$$

7. Simplify: $-2(3 - 5) + 5(-6 - 1)$

B Evaluating Exponents

Example 8 Use the definition of exponents to expand each expression. Then simplify by multiplying.

a. $(-6)^2$ **b.** -6^2 **c.** $(-4)^3$ **d.** -4^3

Solution Notice parts a and c have a negative base, but parts b and d do not. We know this is true because of the use of parentheses.

a. $(-6)^2$ means -6 multiplied by itself:
$$(-6)(-6) = 36$$

b. -6^2 means the opposite of 6^2:
$$-(6)(6) = -36$$

c. $(-4)^3 = $ means -4 multiplied 3 times:
$$(-4)(-4)(-4) = -64$$

d. $-4^3 = $ means the opposite of 4^3:
$$-(4)(4)(4) = -64$$

8. Use the definition of exponents to expand each expression. Then simplify.
  a. $(-4)^2$
  b. -4^2
  c. $(-3)^2$
  d. -3^2

C Evaluating Expressions

As we've seen in the previous sections, algebraic expressions will take on different values depending on which value is selected for the variable. In this section we will evaluate expressions involving multiplication, addition, and subtraction.

Table 1 lists some other algebraic expressions, along with specific values for the variables and the corresponding value of the expression after the variable has been replaced with the given number.

Table 1		
Original Expression	Value of the Variable	Value of the Expression
$5x + 2$	$x = 4$	$5(4) + 2 = 20 + 2$
		$= 22$
$3x - 9$	$x = 2$	$3(2) - 9 = 6 - 9$
		$= -3$
$-2a + 7$	$a = 3$	$-2(3) + 7 = -6 + 7$
		$= 1$
$6p + 3$	$p = -2$	$6(-2) + 3 = -12 + 3$
		$= -9$
$-4y + 9$	$y = -1$	$-4(-1) + 9 = 4 + 9$
		$= 13$

Answers
7. -31
8. **a.** 16   **b.** -16 **c.** 9   **d.** -9

9. Evaluate $-4y + 2$ for $y = 5$.

Example 9   Evaluate $-2x + 3$ for $x = 4$.

Solution   We will substitute 4 for x and simplify.

$$-2(4) + 3$$

$$-8 + 3$$

$$-5$$

Thus, when $x = 4$, the value of $-2x + 3$ is -5.

 KEY CONCEPT REVIEW

After reading through the preceding section, respond in your own words and in complete sentences.

A. Write the multiplication problem $3(-5)$ as an addition problem.

B. How may we apply the distributive property to a multiplication problem?

C. If two numbers have the same sign, then their product will have what sign?

D. If two numbers have different signs, then their product will have what sign?

 $\mathcal{S}potlight\ on\ Success$

CYNTHIA, student instructor

Each time we face our fear, we gain strength, courage, and confidence in the doing.

~ Unknown

I must admit, when it comes to math, it takes me longer to learn the material compared to other students. Because of that, I was afraid to ask questions, especially when it seemed like everyone else understood what was going on. Because I wasn't getting my questions answered, my quiz and exam scores were only getting worse. I realized that I was already paying a lot to go to college and that I couldn't afford to keep doing poorly on my exams. I learned how to overcome my fear of asking questions by studying the material before class, and working on extra problem sets until I was confident enough that at least I understood the main concepts. By preparing myself beforehand, I would often end up answering the question myself. Even when that wasn't the case, the professor knew that I tried to answer the question on my own. If you want to be successful, but you are afraid to ask a question, try putting in a little extra time working on problems before you ask your instructor for help. I think you will find, like I did, that it's not as bad as you imagined it, and you will have overcome an obstacle that was in the way of your success.

Answer

9. -18

EXERCISE SET 2.4 ....

VOCABULARY REVIEW •

Choose the correct words to fill in the blanks below.

positive   zero   exponent   negative   base

1. In $(-5)^2$, -5 is the _____ and 2 is the_____

2. The product of two numbers with the same sign is _____.

3. The product of two numbers with different signs is _____.

4. Multiplication by _____ always produces 0.

Problems

A Find each of the following products. (Multiply.)

1. $7(-8)$

2. $-3(5)$

3. $-6(10)$

4. $4(-8)$

5. $-7(-8)$

6. $-4(-7)$

7. $-9(-9)$

8. $-6(-3)$

9. $3(-2)(4)$

10. $5(-1)(3)$

11. $-4(3)(-2)$

12. $-4(5)(-6)$

13. $-1(-2)(-3)$

14. $-2(-3)(-4)$

B Use the definition of exponents to expand each of the following expressions. Then multiply according to the rule for multiplication.

15. a. $(-4)^2$

16. a. $(-5)^2$

17. a. $(-5)^3$

 b. -4^2

 b. -5^2

 b. -5^3

18. a. $(-4)^3$

19. a. $(-2)^4$

20. a. $(-1)^4$

 b. -4^3

 b. -2^4

 b. -1^4

A, B Complete the following tables. Remember, if $x = -5$, then $x^2 = (-5)^2 = 25$.

21.

x	x^2
-3	
-2	
-1	
0	
1	
2	
3	

22.

x	x^3
-3	
-2	
-1	
0	
1	
2	
3	

23.

x	y	xy
6	2	
6	1	
6	0	
6	-1	
6	-2	

24.

x	y	xy
7	4	
7	2	
7	0	
7	-2	
7	-4	

25.

a	b	ab
-5	3	
-5	2	
-5	1	
-5	0	
-5	-1	
-5	-2	
-5	-3	

26.

a	b	ab
-9	6	
-9	4	
-9	2	
-9	0	
-9	-2	
-9	-4	
-9	-6	

Use order of operations along with the rules for addition, subtraction, and multiplication to simplify each of the following expressions.

27. $4(-3 + 2)$

28. $7(-6 + 3)$

29. $-10(-2 - 3)$

30. $-5(-6 - 2)$

31. $-3 + 2(5 - 3)$

32. $-7 + 3(6 - 2)$

33. $-7 + 2[-5 - 9]$

34. $-8 + 3[-4 - 1]$

35. $2(-5) + 3(-4)$

36. $6(-1) + 2(-7)$

37. $3(-2)4 + 3(-2)$

38. $2(-1)(-3) + 4(-6)$

39. $(8 - 3)(2 - 7)$ **40.** $(9 - 3)(2 - 6)$ **41.** $(2 - 5)(3 - 6)$ **42.** $(3 - 7)(2 - 8)$

43. $3(5 - 8) + 4(6 - 7)$ **44.** $-2(8 - 10) + 3(4 - 9)$ **45.** $-3(4 - 7) - 2(-3 - 2)$ **46.** $-5(-2 - 8) - 4(6 - 10)$

47. $3(-2)(6 - 7)$ **48.** $4(-3)(2 - 5)$

C Evaluate each expression for $p = -9$.

49. $2p - 7$ **50.** $3p - 6$

51. $-4p - 10$ **52.** $-7p - 20$

53. $5(p + 1)$ **54.** $6(p + 2)$

55. $-8(p - 3) + 1$ **56.** $-6(p - 4) + 2$

Find each of the following. Translate to symbols first to help you find the solution.

57. Find the product of -3, -2, and -1.   **58.** Find the product of -7, -1, and 0.

59. What number do you multiply by -3 to get 12?   **60.** What number do you multiply by -7 to get -21?

61. Subtract -3 from the product of -5 and 4.   **62.** Subtract 5 from the product of -8 and 1.

Applying the Concepts

63. Temperature Change A hot-air balloon is rising to its cruising altitude. Suppose the air temperature around the balloon drops 4 degrees each time the balloon rises 1,000 feet. What is the net change in air temperature around the balloon as it rises from 2,000 feet to 6,000 feet?

64. Temperature Change A small airplane is rising to its cruising altitude. Suppose the air temperature around the plane drops 4 degrees each time the plane increases its altitude by 1,000 feet. What is the net change in air temperature around the plane as it rises from 5,000 feet to 12,000 feet?

65. Day Trading   Larry is buying and selling stock. He owns 100 shares of Company A and 50 shares of Company B. Suppose that in one day, those stocks had the gain and loss shown in the table below. What was Larry's net gain or loss for the day on those two stocks?

Stock	Number Of Shares	Gain/Loss
Company A	100	−2
Company B	50	+8

66. Stock Gain/Loss   Amy owns stock that she keeps in her retirement account. She owns 200 shares of Nike and 100 shares of Lululemon. Suppose that in one month those stocks had the gain and loss shown in the table below. What was Amy's net gain or loss for the month on those two stocks?

Stock	Number Of Shares	Gain/Loss
Nike	200	+14
Lululemon	100	−5

Baseball   Major league baseball has various player awards at the end of the year. One award that was granted from 1976 to 2012 was the Rolaids Relief Man of the Year. To compute the Relief Man standings, points were awarded or taken away based on the number of wins, losses, saves, and blown saves a relief pitcher has at the end of the year. The pitcher with the most Rolaids Points was the Rolaids Relief Man of the Year. The formula $P = 3s + 2w + t − 2l − 2b$ gives the number of Rolaids points a pitcher earns, where s = saves, w = wins, t = tough saves, l = losses, and b = blown saves. Use this formula to complete the following tables for several of the more recent winners.

67.

Pitcher, Team, Year	W	L	Saves	Tough Saves	Blown Saves	Rolaids Points
John Smoltz, Atlanta Braves, 2002	3	2	55	5	4	
Trevor Hoffman, San Diego Padres, 2006	0	2	46	0	5	
Rafael Soriano, Tampa Bay Rays, 2010	3	2	45	0	3	
Jim Johnson, Baltimore Orioles, 2012	2	1	51	0	3	
Craig Kimbrel, Atlanta Braves, 2012	3	1	42	1	3	

68.

Pitcher, Team, Year	W	L	Saves	Tough Saves	Blown Saves	Rolaids Points
Mariano Rivera, New York Yankees, 2001	4	6	50	3	7	
Eric Gagne, Los Angeles Dodgers, 2003	2	3	55	2	0	
Francisco Rodriguez, Los Angeles Angels, 2006	2	3	47	3	4	
Heath Bell, San Diego Padres, 2009	6	4	42	3	6	
John Axford, Milwaukee Brewers, 2011	2	2	46	0	2	

Golf One way to give scores in golf is in relation to par, the number of strokes considered necessary to complete a hole or course at the expert level. Scoring this way, if you complete a hole in one stroke less than par, your score is −1, which is called a *birdie*. If you shoot 2 under par, your score is −2, which is called an *eagle*. Shooting 1 over par is a score of +1, which is a *bogie*. A *double bogie* is 2 over par, and results in a score of +2.

69. Sergio Garcia's Scorecard The table below shows the scores Sergio Garcia had on the first round of a PGA tournament. Fill in the last column by multiplying each value by the number of times it occurs. Then add the numbers in the last column to find the total. If par for the course was 72, what was Sergio Garcia's score?

	Value	Number	Product
Eagle	−2	0	
Birdie	−1	7	
Par	0	7	
Bogie	+1	3	
Double Bogie	+2	1	
			Total:

70. Karrie Webb's Scorecard The table below shows the scores Karrie Webb had on the final round of an LPGA Standard Register Ping Tournament. Fill in the last column by multiplying each value by the number of times it occurs. Then add the numbers in the last column to find the total. If par for the course was 72, what was Karrie Webb's score?

	Value	Number	Product
Eagle	−2	1	
Birdie	−1	5	
Par	0	8	
Bogie	+1	3	
Double Bogie	+2	1	
			Total:

Estimating

Work the next problems mentally, without pencil and paper or a calculator.

71. The product −32(−522) is closest to which of the following numbers?

   a. 15,000   **b.** −500   **c.** −1,500   **d.** −15,000

72. The product 32(−522) is closest to which of the following numbers?

   a. 15,000   **b.** −500   **c.** −1,500   **d.** −15,000

73. The product −222(−987) is closest to which of the following numbers?

   a. 200,000   **b.** 800   **c.** −800   **d.** −1,200

74. The sum −222 + (−987) is closest to which of the following numbers?

   a. 200,000   **b.** 800   **c.** −800   **d.** −1,200

75. The difference −222 − (−987) is closest to which of the following numbers?

   a. 200,000   **b.** 800   **c.** −800   **d.** −1,200

76. The difference −222 − 987 is closest to which of the following numbers?

   a. 200,000   **b.** 800   **c.** −800   **d.** −1,200

Getting Ready for the Next Section

Perform the indicated operations.

77. $35 \div 5$ | **78.** $32 \div 4$ | **79.** $\dfrac{20}{4}$ | **80.** $\dfrac{30}{5}$

81. $12 - 17$ | **82.** $7 - 11$ | **83.** $\dfrac{6(3)}{2}$ | **84.** $\dfrac{8(5)}{4}$

85. $80 \div 10 \div 2$ | **86.** $80 \div 2 \div 10$ | **87.** $\dfrac{15 + 5(4)}{17 - 12}$ | **88.** $\dfrac{20 + 6(2)}{11 - 7}$

89. $4(10^2) + 20 \div 4$ | **90.** $3(4^2) + 10 \div 5$ | **91.** $\dfrac{15 - 2(4)}{3(-2) + 6}$ | **92.** $\dfrac{18 - 3(2)}{2(-4) + 8}$

FIND THE MISTAKE •

Each problem below contains a mistake. Circle the mistake and write the correct number(s) or word(s) on the line provided.

1. Writing the problem $6(-4)$ as repeated addition gives us $(-4)(-4)(-4)(-4)(-4)(-4)$.
   _____

2. Multiplying a negative by a positive and then by another negative will give us a negative answer. _____

3. The problem $(-5)^3$ can also be written as $-3(5)(5)(5)$. _____

4. Work for the problem $-5(3 - 6) - 2(3 + 1)$ looks like the following:

   $$-5(3 - 6) - 2(3 + 1) = -5(-3) - 2(4) \quad \text{_____}$$
   $$= 15 + 8 \quad \text{_____}$$
   $$= 23 \quad \text{_____}$$

DIVISION WITH INTEGERS

2.5

Suppose four friends invest equal amounts of money in a moving truck to start a small business. After two years the truck has dropped $10,000 in value. If we represent this change with the number $-\$10,000$, then the loss to each of the four partners can be found with division.

$$(-\$10,000) \div 4 = -\$2,500$$

From this example, it seems reasonable to assume that a negative number divided by a positive number will give a negative answer. In this section, we will work division problems involving negative numbers.

OBJECTIVES

A Divide integers.

B Perform order of operations with integers.

VIDEO EXAMPLES

SECTION 2.5

A Division with Any Number

To cover all the possible situations we can encounter with division of negative numbers, we use the relationship between multiplication and division. If we let n be the answer to the problem $12 \div (-2)$, then we know that

$$12 \div (-2) = n \quad \text{and} \quad -2(n) = 12$$

From our work with multiplication, we know that n must be -6 in the multiplication problem above, because -6 is the only number we can multiply -2 by to get 12. Because of the relationship between the two problems above, it must be true that

$$12 \div (-2) = -6$$

The following pairs of problems show more quotients of positive and negative numbers. In each case, the multiplication problem on the right justifies the answer to the division problem on the left.

$$6 \div 3 = 2 \quad \text{because} \quad 3(2) = 6$$
$$6 \div (-3) = -2 \quad \text{because} \quad -3(-2) = 6$$
$$-6 \div 3 = -2 \quad \text{because} \quad 3(-2) = -6$$
$$-6 \div (-3) = 2 \quad \text{because} \quad -3(2) = -6$$

These results for division with negative numbers can be summarized as follows.

SUMMARY   Division with Negative Numbers

To divide two numbers, we divide their absolute values.

1. The answer is positive if both the original numbers have the same sign. That is, the quotient of two numbers with the same signs is positive.

2. The answer is negative if the original two numbers have different signs. That is, the quotient of two numbers with different signs is negative.

Practice Problems

1. Divide.
   a. $10 \div 5$
   b. $-10 \div 5$
   c. $10 \div (-5)$
   d. $-10 \div (-5)$

Example 1   Divide.

a. $12 \div 4$ **b.** $-12 \div 4$ **c.** $12 \div (-4)$ **d.** $-12 \div (-4)$

Solution

a. $12 \div 4 = 3$ Like signs; positive answer
b. $-12 \div 4 = -3$ Unlike signs; negative answer
c. $12 \div (-4) = -3$ Unlike signs; negative answer
d. $-12 \div (-4) = 3$ Like signs; positive answer

2. Simplify.
   a. $\frac{12}{4}$
   b. $\frac{-12}{4}$
   c. $\frac{12}{-4}$
   d. $\frac{-12}{-4}$

Example 2   Simplify.

a. $\frac{20}{5}$ **b.** $\frac{-20}{5}$ **c.** $\frac{20}{-5}$ **d.** $\frac{-20}{-5}$

Solution   Recall, the fraction bar indicates division.

a. $\frac{20}{5} = 4$ **b.** $\frac{-20}{5} = -4$ **c.** $\frac{20}{-5} = -4$ **d.** $\frac{-20}{-5} = 4$

From the examples we have done so far, we can make the following generalization about quotients that contain negative signs:

> If a and b are numbers and b is not equal to 0, then
>
> $$\frac{-a}{b} = \frac{a}{-b} = -\frac{a}{b} \quad \text{and} \quad \frac{-a}{-b} = \frac{a}{b}$$

B Order of Operations

The last examples in this section involve more than one operation. We use the concepts developed previously in this chapter and the order of operations to simplify each.

3. Simplify: $\dfrac{-12 + 2\,(-3)}{10 - 16}$

Example 3   Simplify: $\dfrac{-15 + 5(-4)}{12 - 17}$

Solution   Simplifying the numerator and denominator, we have

$$\frac{-15 + 5(-4)}{12 - 17} = \frac{-15 + (-20)}{-5} = \frac{-35}{-5} = 7$$

Answers

1. a. 2   **b.** -2 **c.** -2 **d.** 2
2. a. 3   **b.** -3 **c.** -3 **d.** 3
3. 3

Example 4 Simplify: $-4(10^2) + 20 \div (-4)$

Solution Applying the order of operations, we have

$$-4(10^2) + 20 \div (-4) = -4(100) + 20 \div (-4) \quad \text{Simplify exponents first.}$$
$$= -400 + (-5) \quad \text{Multiply and divide.}$$
$$= -405 \quad \text{Add.}$$

4. Simplify: $-3(5^2) + 16 \div (-2)$

Example 5 Simplify: $10 - 2^3 \, | -3 - 1 \, |$

Solution Applying the order of operations, we have

$$10 - 2^3 \, | -3 - 1 \, | = 10 - 2^3 \, | -4 \, |$$
$$= 10 - 2^3(4) \quad \text{Simplify inside grouping symbols.}$$
$$= 10 - 8(4) \quad \text{Simplify exponents.}$$
$$= 10 - 32 \quad \text{Multiply.}$$
$$= -22 \quad \text{Subtract.}$$

5. Simplify: $12 - 4^2 \, | -2 - 1 \, |$

Example 6 Evaluate $\dfrac{a^4 - 7}{3}$ for $a = -2$.

Solution We substitute -2 for a and simplify.

$$\frac{(-2) - 7}{3} = \frac{16 - 7}{3} \quad \text{Simplify exponents.}$$
$$= \frac{9}{3} \quad \text{Subtract.}$$
$$= 3 \quad \text{Divide.}$$

6. Evaluate $\dfrac{a^2 - 5}{2}$ for $a = -3$.

DESCRIPTIVE STATISTICS

Displaying Negative Numbers

Below is a table of temperatures in which the temperatures below zero are represented by negative numbers. We will use the information in Table 1 to draw a scatter diagram and a line graph.

Table 1   Record low temperatures for Denver, Colorado

Month	Temperature	Month	Temperature
January	−21°F	July	40°F
February	−23°F	August	37°F
March	−8°F	September	14°F
April	4°F	October	2°F
May	21°F	November	−5°F
June	33°F	December	−24°F

(continued)

Answers
4. −83
5. −36
6. 2

DESCRIPTIVE STATISTICS

Displaying Negative Numbers *(continued)*

Notice that the vertical axis in Figure 1 looks like the number line we have been using. To produce the scatter diagram, we place a dot above each month, across from the temperature for that month. For example, the dot above July will be across from 40°. Doing the same for each of the months, we have the scatter diagram shown in Figure 1. To produce the line graph in Figure 2, we simply connect the dots in Figure 1 with line segments.

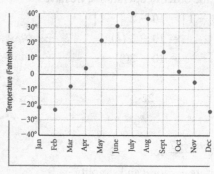

FIGURE 1

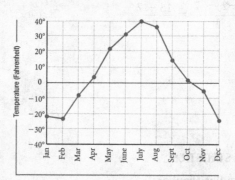

FIGURE 2

KEY CONCEPT REVIEW

After reading through the preceding section, respond in your own words and in complete sentences.

A. Write a multiplication problem that is equivalent to the division problem $-12 \div 4 = -3$.

B. Write a multiplication problem that is equivalent to the division problem $-12 \div (-4) = 3$.

C. If two numbers have the same sign, then their quotient will have what sign?

VOCABULARY REVIEW •

Choose the correct words to fill in the blanks below.

  same   different

1. The quotient of two numbers with the _____ sign is positive.

2. The quotient of two numbers with _____ signs is negative.

Problems

A Find each of the following quotients.

1. $-15 \div 5$ **2.** $15 \div (-3)$ **3.** $20 \div (-4)$ **4.** $-20 \div 4$

5. $-30 \div (-10)$ **6.** $-50 \div (-25)$ **7.** $\dfrac{-14}{-7}$ **8.** $\dfrac{-18}{-6}$

9. $\dfrac{12}{-3}$ **10.** $\dfrac{12}{-4}$ **11.** $-22 \div 11$ **12.** $-35 \div 7$

13. $\dfrac{0}{-3}$ **14.** $\dfrac{0}{-5}$ **15.** $125 \div (-25)$ **16.** $-144 \div (-9)$

Complete the following tables.

17.

a	b	$a \div b$
100	-5	
100	-10	
100	-25	
100	-50	

18.

a	b	$a \div b$
24	-4	
24	-3	
24	-2	
24	-1	

19.

a	b	$\dfrac{a}{b}$
-100	-5	
-100	5	
100	-5	
100	5	

20.

a	b	$\dfrac{a}{b}$
-24	-2	
-24	-4	
-24	-6	
-24	-8	

Use any of the rules developed in this chapter and the order of operations to simplify each of the following expressions.

21. $\dfrac{4(-7)}{-28}$

22. $\dfrac{6(-3)}{-18}$

23. $\dfrac{-3(-10)}{-5}$

24. $\dfrac{-4(-12)}{-6}$

25. $\dfrac{2(-3)}{6-3}$

26. $\dfrac{2(-3)}{3-6}$

27. $\dfrac{4-8}{8-4}$

28. $\dfrac{9-5}{5-9}$

29. $\dfrac{8-8}{8+8}$

30. $\dfrac{9-9}{-9-9}$

31. $\dfrac{5(-5)}{-5+5}$

32. $\dfrac{-7(7)}{7-7}$

33. $\dfrac{2(-3)+10}{-4}$

34. $\dfrac{7(-2)-6}{-10}$

35. $\dfrac{2+3(-6)}{4-12}$

36. $\dfrac{3+9(-1)}{5-7}$

37. $\dfrac{6(-7)+3(-2)}{20-4}$

38. $\dfrac{9(-8)+5(-1)}{12-1}$

39. $\dfrac{-5(4)-10}{3(8)-24}$

40. $\dfrac{7(-3)-10}{4(9)-36}$

41. $100 \div (-5)^2$

42. $400 \div (-4)^2$

43. $-100 \div 10 \div 2$

44. $-500 \div 50 \div 10$

45. $\dfrac{|-2(1)+10(5)|}{12-6}$

46. $\dfrac{|-10(4)+6(2)|}{10-3}$

47. $(-3)^2 - [15 - 9]$

48. $(-2)^4 - [7 - 14]$

49. $7 - 1(16 - 4^3)$

50. $12 - 5(3 - 2^3)$

51. $(-2)^5 - 6\,|\,4 - 10\,|$

52. $(-3)^3 - 7\,|\,9 - 12\,|$

53. $-5^2 + 2\,|\,14 - 3\,|$

54. $-4^2 + 3\,|\,13 - 9\,|$

55. $(12 - 5)^2 + 2(7 - 6)^4$

56. $(13 - 10)^3 + 3(10 - 8)^3$

Evaluate each expression for $a = 3$.

57. $\dfrac{2a - 1}{a - 2}$ **58.** $\dfrac{3a - 2}{a - 2}$ **59.** $\dfrac{a^2 + 6}{3}$ **60.** $\dfrac{a^2 + 3}{4}$

Evaluate each expression for $a = -4$.

61. $2(a^2 - 1)$ **62.** $2(a^3 + 2)$ **63.** $\dfrac{a^2 - 6}{10}$ **64.** $\dfrac{a^2 - 2}{7}$

Find each of the following. Translate to symbols first to help you find the solution.

65. Find the quotient of -25 and 5.

66. Find the quotient of -38 and -19.

67. What number do you divide by -5 to get -7?

68. What number do you divide by 6 to get -7?

69. Subtract -3 from the quotient of 27 and 9.

70. Subtract -7 from the quotient of -72 and -9.

Estimating

Work the following problems mentally, without pencil and paper or a calculator.

71. Is $397 \div (-401)$ closer to 1 or -1?

72. Is $-751 \div (-749)$ closer to 1 or -1?

73. The quotient $-121 \div 27$ is closest to which of the following numbers?

    a. -150 **b.** -100 **c.** -4 **d.** 6

74. The quotient $1{,}000 \div (-337)$ is closest to which of the following numbers?

    a. 663 **b.** -3 **c.** -30 **d.** -663

75. Which number is closest to the sum $-151 + (-49)$?

    a. -200 **b.** -100 **c.** 3   **d.** 7,500

76. Which number is closest to the difference $-151 - (-49)$?

    a. -200 **b.** -100 **c.** 3   **d.** 7,500

77. Which number is closest to the product $-151(-49)$?

    a. -200 **b.** -100 **c.** 3   **d.** 7,500

78. Which number is closest to the quotient $-151 \div (-49)$?

    a. -200 **b.** -100 **c.** 3   **d.** 7,500

Applying the Concepts

79. Temperature Line Graph The table below gives the low temperature for each day of one week in White Bear Lake, Minnesota. Draw a line graph of the information in the table.

Low temperatures in White Bear Lake, Minnesota	
Day	Temperature
Monday	10°F
Tuesday	8°F
Wednesday	−5°F
Thursday	−3°F
Friday	−8°F
Saturday	5°F
Sunday	7°F

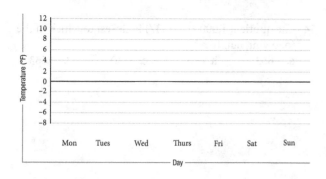

80. Temperature Line Graph The table below gives the low temperature for each day of one week in Fairbanks, Alaska. Draw a line graph of the information in the table.

Low temperatures in Fairbanks, Alaska	
Day	Temperature
Monday	−26°F
Tuesday	−5°F
Wednesday	9°F
Thursday	12°F
Friday	3°F
Saturday	−15°F
Sunday	−20°F

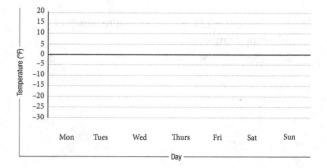

Getting Ready for the Next Section

Apply the distributive property to each expression.

81. $5(3 + 7)$

82. $8(4 + 2)$

Simplify.

83. 6^2

84. 12^2

85. $100(75)$

86. $100(53)$

87. $2(100) + 2(75)$

88. $2(100) + 2(53)$

89. a. $4 + 3$

    b. $-5 + 7$

    c. $8 - 1$

    d. $-4 - 2$

    e. $3 - 7$

90. a. $5 + 2$

    b. $-6 + 7$

    c. $9 - 1$

    d. $-5 - 3$

    e. $2 - 5$

FIND THE MISTAKE

Write true or false for each of the following sentences. If false, circle the mistake and write the correct word on the line provided.

1. True or False: Dividing a negative number by a positive number will give a positive number for an answer.

_____

2. True or False: Dividing two numbers with like signs will give a positive answer. _____

The work for the problems below contains mistakes. Circle where the mistake first occurs and write the correct work on the lines provided.

3. Simplify $\dfrac{-6(-6 - 2)}{-11 - 1}$.

$$\dfrac{-6(-6 - 2)}{-11 - 1} = \dfrac{-6(-4)}{-10} = \dfrac{24}{-10} = \dfrac{-12}{5}$$

_____

4. Simplify $[(-5)(5) - 20] \div -3^2$.

$$[(-5)(5) - 20] \div -3^2 = -45 \div 9$$

$$= -5$$

_____

_____

Trail Guide Project

Exponential Decay

In 2011, Japan was the victim of a devastating earthquake and tsunami. The earthquake caused a multitude of nuclear meltdowns, most notably at the Fukushima I Nuclear Power Plant. Cesium-137 is a radioactive isotope created by nuclear fission. The fallout from the Fukushima I Power Plant contained dangerously high levels of Cesium-137, which caused widespread evacuations of the surrounding areas. This isotope has a half life of approximately 30.17 years. As Cesium-137 undergoes exponential decay, the area surrounding the nuclear disaster will slowly become less radioactive, therefore, less dangerous for humans. Research the nuclear disaster in Japan, as well as the importance of exponents in the half-life of Cesium-137. When will it be safe for residents to return to their homes near the power plant?

Absolute Value [2.1]

The absolute value of a number is its distance from 0 on the number line. The absolute value of a number is never negative.

1. $|3| = 3$ and $|-3| = 3$

Opposites [2.1]

Two numbers are called opposites if they are the same distance from 0 on the number line but in opposite directions from 0. The opposite of a positive number is a negative number, and the opposite of a negative number is a positive number.

2. $-(5) = -5$ and $-(-5) = 5$

Addition of Positive and Negative Numbers [2.2]

1. To add two numbers with *the same sign*: Add absolute values and use the common sign. If both numbers are positive, the answer is positive. If both numbers are negative, the answer is negative.
2. To add two numbers with *different signs*: Subtract the smaller absolute value from the larger absolute value. The answer has the same sign as the number with the larger absolute value.

3. $3 + 5 = 8$
$-3 + (-5) = -8$

Subtraction [2.3]

Subtracting a number is equivalent to adding its opposite. If a and b represent numbers, then subtraction is defined in terms of addition as follows:

$$a - b = a + (-b)$$

4. $3 - 5 = 3 + (-5) = -2$
$-3 - 5 = -3 + (-5) = -8$
$3 - (-5) = 3 + 5 = 8$
$-3 - (-5) = -3 + 5 = 2$

Multiplication with Positive and Negative Numbers [2.4]

To multiply two numbers, multiply their absolute values.

1. The answer is *positive* if both numbers have the same sign.
2. The answer is *negative* if the numbers have different signs.

5. $3(5) = 15$
$3(-5) = -15$
$-3(5) = -15$
$-3(-5) = 15$

Division with Positive and Negative Numbers [2.5]

The rule for assigning the correct sign to the answer in a division problem is the same as the rule for multiplication. That is, like signs give a positive answer, and unlike signs give a negative answer.

6. $12 \div 4 = 3$
$-12 \div 4 = -3$
$12 \div -4 = -3$
$-12 \div -4 = 3$

Evaluating Expressions [2.2, 2.3, 2.4, 2.5]

An algebraic expression is a mathematical phrase that contains numbers, variables, and operations. Expressions will take on different values depending on the value of the variable.

7. When $x = -10$
the expression $3x - 7$ becomes

$3(-10) - 7 = -30 - 7 = -37$

1. Write $-25 < -7$ in words. [2.1]

2. Write -17 is less than -2 in symbols. [2.1]

Give the opposite and absolute value of each number. [2.1]

3. -24

4. 16

Place an inequality symbol ($<$ or $>$) between each pair of numbers so that the resulting statement is true. [2.1]

5. $-8 \quad -1$

6. $-9 \quad 7$

7. $20 \quad |-6|$

8. $|-3| \quad |-1|$

Find each of the following absolute values. [2.1]

9. $|-8,500|$

10. $|4|$

Simplify each expression. [2.1]

11. $-(-6)$

12. $-|-3|$

Perform the indicated operations. [2.2-2.5]

13. $6 + (-14)$

14. $-7 + (-4)$

15. $-130 + 159$

16. $-76 - (-19)$

17. $-86 - 31$

18. $-7 - 3 - 6$

19. $(-12)(-7)$

20. $-2(-3)(-4)$

21. $-42 \div 3$

22. $-144 \div (-9)$

Simplify the following expressions as much as possible. [2.2-2.5]

23. $-572 + 437 + (-502)$

24. $20 + (-15) + 30 + (-19)$

25. $(-5)^2$

26. $(-4)^3$

27. -5^2

28. -4^3

29. $(-6)(5) - (3)(-7)$

30. $(9 - 2)(2 - 17)$

31. $-2(8 - 10) + 3(4 - 9)$

32. $4(-3)(2 - 5)$

33. $\dfrac{24 - 3(-5)}{-9 + 9}$

34. $\dfrac{|-3(8) + 5(6)|}{3 - 5}$

35. $(-2)^4 - [12 + (-5)]$

36. $(-3)(8) - (9)(4)$

37. $9 - 4(9 - 3^3)$

38. $3(15) + 9(-2)$

39. $\dfrac{-9 - 5(3)}{20 - 4(5)}$

40. $5|6 - 10| + 8^2$

41. $(-4)^3 - 5|2 - 7|$

42. $-6^2 - 5(8 - 4)$

43. $\dfrac{-3(-2) - 6}{-10}$

44. $\dfrac{8(5) + 5(6 - 11)}{3 + 2}$

Evaluate each expression for $x = -8$. [2.2-2.5]

45. $x + 10$

46. $x + 6$

47. $5 - x$

48. $x - 7$

49. $2x - 4$

50. $3x + 30$

51. $\dfrac{5x + 4}{9}$

52. $\dfrac{x^2 - 1}{7}$

Find the indicated number. [2.2–2.5]

53. What number do you add to 10 to get 3?

54. Give the sum of −16 and −57.

55. Subtract −9 and −27.

56. Subtract −7 from the sum of 7 and −12.

57. What is the product of −11 and 7?

58. What number do you multiply by −7 to get −28?

59. Give the quotient of 96 and −8.

60. What number do you divide by 6 to get −8?

61. What is five times the sum of −9 and 13?

62. Three times the difference of 7 and 19 is increased by 9.

63. Distance The distance between two numbers is 8. If one of the numbers is −4, what are the two possibilities for the other number?

64. Gambling A gambler loses $107 Saturday night and wins $357 on Sunday. Give the gambler's net loss or gain as a negative or positive number.

65. Temperature On Friday, the temperature reaches a high of 47 degrees and a low of 3 degrees below 0. What is the difference between the high and low temperatures for Friday?

66. Temperature The record high temperature for one city is 83 degrees Fahrenheit and the record low temperature is 4 degrees below 0. What is the difference between the high and low temperatures?

67. Gambling Brian loses $323 at the casino on Friday night. The next week he makes $148 at the casino. Give Brian's net loss or gain as a negative or positive number.

The snapshot shows the number of text messages sent and voice minutes used by different age groups in one month. Use the information to answer the following questions.

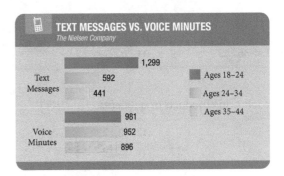

68. Write an expression to describe the difference between the number of text messages sent by 35-44 year-olds and 18-24 year-olds. Solve the expression.

69. Write an expression to describe the difference between the number of voice minutes used by 35-44 year-olds and 24-34 year-olds. Solve the expression.

1. Write $4000 + 300 + 7$ in condensed form.

2. What is the place value for each digit in 684?

3. Round 5,698 to the nearest hundred.

Find the following sums or differences.

4. $7 + 5 + 8$

5. $9 - 1 - 5$

6. $\begin{array}{r} 125 \\ 16 \\ + 233 \\ \hline \end{array}$

7. $\begin{array}{r} 2{,}984 \\ - 567 \\ \hline \end{array}$

Find a solution for each equation.

8. $a + 8 = 11$

9. $9 - n = 2$

10. $4 \cdot t = 36$

11. $n \cdot 5 = 25$

Find the following products or quotients.

12. $5(354)$

13. $\begin{array}{r} 2{,}123 \\ \times 462 \\ \hline \end{array}$

14. $255 \div 17$

15. $24\overline{)3288}$

Rewrite the following in a mathematical expression, then simplify.

16. 6 times the sum of 10 and 4.

17. The sum of 9 times 3 and 7 times 4.

Use the definition of exponents to simplify the following expressions.

18. 14^1

19. 23^0

20. -5^2

21. $(-7)^2$

Use the order of operations to simplify each expression as much as possible.

22. $845 - 2(15)^2$

23. $6 + 5|43 - 3|$

24. $\dfrac{25 + 3(7)}{11 + 12}$

25. $(5 - 3)^3 + 4(6 - 1)^2$

26. What number is the opposite of 10?

27. Find $|-144|$.

28. Simplify $-(-8)$.

Perform the indicated operations and simplify.

29. $-11 - 6$

30. $12 + (-8)$

31. $-63 - (-12)$

32. $5(-9)$

33. $(-11)(-6)$

34. $125 \div 5$

35. $-2(3) - 5(-7)$

36. $(-3)^4$

37. $7(-1)(-9)$

38. $2^3 - |8 - 11|$

39. $\dfrac{4[8 - (-4)]}{8(-2)}$

40. $\dfrac{7(8) + 10}{6 - (-5)}$

41. $\dfrac{-8(2) + 3(9)}{2(6) - 12}$

42. $\dfrac{6(10) + 5(-12)}{8(7)}$

Evaluate each expression for $b = -5$

43. $b + 3$

44. $b - 7$

45. $3b + 20$

46. What number do you add to 16 to get -1?

47. What is the product of -10 and -5?

48. What number do you divide by 9 to get 27?

49. What is 6 times the sum of -5 and -4?

50. What is the perimeter of a square with a side of length 6 cm? What is the area?

51. If the area of a square is 144 in.^{2}, what is the length of each side?

52. The distance between two numbers is 12. If one of the numbers is -5, what are the two possibilities for the other number?

53. Ellie is twice her sister's age. If Ellie is 8, how old is her younger sister?

Give the opposite and absolute value of each number. [2.1]

1. 27

2. −18

Place an inequality symbol ($<$ or $>$) between each pair of numbers so that the resulting statement is true. [2.1]

3. −4   3

4. $|4|$ $|-6|$

Simplify each expression. [1.1]

5. $-(-4)$

6. $-|-14|$

Perform the indicated operations. [2.2, 2.3]

7. $9 + (-12)$

8. $-84 - (-48)$

9. $(-8)(-9)$

10. $63 \div (-3)$

Simplify the following expressions as much as possible. [2.2–2.5]

11. $(-3)^3$

12. $(-2)^2$

13. $(-5)(2) - (-6)(4)$

14. $(7 - 4)(9 - 15)$

15. $\dfrac{-6 + 2(-4)}{5 - 5}$

16. $\dfrac{|-4(5) + 4(7)|}{5 - 7}$

17. $-3^3 - (9 + 7)$

18. $5 - 3(7 - 2^3)$

19. $2(-8) + 6(-3)$

20. $\dfrac{-8 + 4(2)}{15 - 9(3)}$

21. $4|2 - 5| + 5^2$

22. $-3^2 - 4(7 - 4)$

23. $\dfrac{7(-3) - 4(8 - 5)}{3(9 + 2)}$

24. Evaluate $3x + 2$ for $x = -7$.

25. Evaluate $x^2 - 10$ for $x = 2$.

26. Give the sum of −9 and −32.

27. Subtract −7 and −24.

28. What is the product of −9 and −4?

29. Give the quotient of 56 and −7.

30. What is three times the sum of 12 and −17.

31. Two times the difference of 6 and 11 is increased by 4.

32. Gambling A gambler loses $215 Saturday night and wins $156 on Sunday. Give the gambler's net loss or gain as a negative or positive number.

33. Temperature On Friday, the temperature reaches a high of 14 degrees and a low of 3 degrees below 0. What is the difference between the high and low temperatures for Friday?

The illustration shows the number of animals housed at some of the large zoos in the United States. Use the information to answer the following questions.

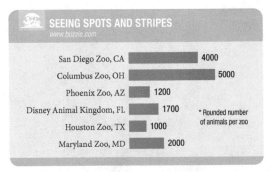

SEEING SPOTS AND STRIPES
www.buzzle.com

San Diego Zoo, CA	4000
Columbus Zoo, OH	5000
Phoenix Zoo, AZ	1200
Disney Animal Kingdom, FL	1700
Houston Zoo, TX	1000
Maryland Zoo, MD	2000

* Rounded number of animals per zoo

34. Write an expression to describe the difference between the number of animals at the Maryland Zoo and the Columbus Zoo. Solve the expression.

35. Write an expression to describe the difference between the number of animals at the Houston Zoo and the San Diego Zoo. Solve the expression.

SOLVING EQUATIONS

One of Canada's most celebrated structures is the CN Tower, which defines the Toronto, Ontario skyline. While the impressive height of 1,815 feet has drawn tourists from all over the world, the origins of the tower came out of practicality. In the 1960s, construction in Toronto was booming. The skyline was changing from one dominated by low-lying buildings to one defined by skyscrapers. This created serious problems in the city's communication transmissions; existing towers were not high enough to broadcast over the new taller buildings. To alleviate this problem, the CN Tower opened in June 1976, after a 40-month project that employed 1,537 workers for 24 hours a day, five days a week. Today the tower serves as a telecommunications hub for 16 Canadian television and FM stations.

Suppose you wanted to visit the CN Tower on your next vacation. The following table shows the ticket prices in Canadian dollars for admission under several packages.

	SkyPod Experience	General Admission	Timed Admission
Adult	$48	$36	$39
Senior	$43	$31	$34
Children	$38	$26	$29

Imagine that the capacity of the facility is 500 visitors at a time, and the SkyPod Experience is sold out. If you know that there will be 250 adults and 125 seniors on the tour, solving the following equation will tell you how many children will also be there.

$$x + 250 + 125 = 500$$

Using the information above, how much money will the CN Tower bring in for that tour? Answering these questions involves knowledge of the addition property of equality, which is a topic covered in this chapter. You will also encounter these specific problems later in the chapter.

YOU ARE HERE

3.1

THE DISTRIBUTIVE PROPERTY AND ALGEBRAIC EXPRESSIONS

OBJECTIVES

A Simplify algebraic expressions using the associative property.

B Apply the distributive property to algebraic expressions.

C Simplify algebraic expressions with like terms.

D Evaluate algebraic expressions.

E Solve problems involving supplementary and complementary angles.

KEY WORDS

terms

distributive property

like terms

angles

complementary

supplementary

VIDEO EXAMPLES

SECTION 3.1

The Olympic Aquatics Stadium, in Rio de Janeiro, Brazil, hosted the swimming events of the 2016 Summer Olympics. Assume the pool is 50 meters long by 25 meters wide. Suppose the base of one side of bleachers that stretches the length of the pool is x meters wide. Look at Figure 1A and 1B below.

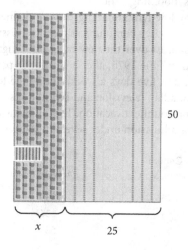

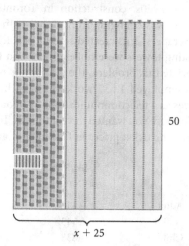

FIGURE 1A

$$\text{Area} = 50(x) + 50(25)$$
$$= 50x + 1250$$

FIGURE 1B

$$\text{Area} = 50(x + 25)$$
$$= 50x + 1250$$

Here we have used a variable to represent an unknown length and the distributive property to write an expression for the area, concepts we will cover in this section.

In the expression $5x + 1250$, $5x$ and 1250 are called **terms.** Terms can be a number or a number and a variable multiplied together. Later, we will even see a number multiplied by more than one variable, such as $3ab$. This is still a term.

A Expressions with Variables

To begin, let's review how we use the associative properties for addition and multiplication to simplify expressions.

Consider the expression $4(5x)$. We can apply the associative property of multiplication to this expression to change the grouping so that the 4 and the 5 are grouped together, instead of the 5 and the x. Here's how it looks:

$$4(5x) = (4 \cdot 5)x \qquad \text{Associative property}$$

$$= 20x \qquad \text{Multiply: } 4 \cdot 5 = 20$$

We have simplified the expression to $20x$, which in most cases in algebra will be easier to work with than the original expression.

Here are some examples:

Practice Problems

Example 1   Simplify: $-2(5x)$

1. Simplify: $-3(4x)$

Solution

$$-2(5x) = (-2 \cdot 5)x \qquad \text{Associative property}$$

$$= -10x \qquad \text{Multiply.}$$

We can also use the associative property of addition to simplify expressions.

Example 2   Simplify: $(2x + 5) + 10$

2. Simplify: $(3x + 4) + 12$

Solution

$$(2x + 5) + 10 = 2x + (5 + 10) \qquad \text{Associative property}$$

$$= 2x + 15 \qquad \text{Add.}$$

B The Distributive Property

Previously, we introduced the **distributive property.** In symbols, it looks like this:

$$a(b + c) = ab + ac$$

Because subtraction is defined as addition of the opposite, the distributive property holds for subtraction as well as addition. That is,

$$a(b - c) = ab - ac$$

We say that multiplication distributes over addition and subtraction. Here are some examples that review how the distributive property is applied to expressions that contain variables.

Example 3   Simplify: $2(a - 3)$

3. Simplify: $3(n - 4)$

Solution

$$2(a - 3) = 2(a) - 2(3) \qquad \text{Distributive property}$$

$$= 2a - 6 \qquad \text{Multiply.}$$

The distributive property can be applied to expressions involving negative numbers.

Answers
1. $-12x$
2. $3x + 16$
3. $3n - 12$

4. Multiply: $-2(5n + 2)$

Example 4   Multiply: $-4(3x + 5)$

Solution   Multiplying both the $3x$ and the 5 by -4, we have

$$-4(3x + 5) = -4(3x) + (-4)5 \qquad \text{Distributive property}$$
$$= -12x + (-20) \qquad \text{Multiply.}$$
$$= -12x - 20 \qquad \text{Definition of subtraction}$$

Notice, first of all, that when we apply the distributive property here, we multiply through by -4. It is important to include the sign with the number when we use the distributive property. Second, when we multiply -4 and $3x$, the result is $-12x$ because

$$-4(3x) = (-4 \cdot 3)x \qquad \text{Associative property}$$
$$= -12x \qquad \text{Multiply.}$$

We can also use the distributive property to simplify expressions like $4x + 3x$. Recall that multiplication is a commutative operation, so we can rewrite the distributive property like this:

$$ba + ca = (b + c)a$$

Applying the distributive property in this form to the expression $4x + 3x$, we have

$$4x + 3x = (4 + 3)x \qquad \text{Distributive Property}$$
$$= 7x \qquad \text{Add.}$$

C Like Terms

Expressions like $4x$ and $3x$ are called **like terms** because the variable parts are the same. Some other examples of like terms are $5y$ and $-6y$ and the terms $7a$ and $-13a$. To simplify an algebraic expression (an expression that involves both numbers and variables), we combine like terms by applying the distributive property. Table 1 shows several pairs of like terms and how they can be combined using the distributive property.

Note $4x$ and $10x^2$ are not like terms. This is because their variable part is not the same.

Table 1

Original Expression		Apply Distributive Property		Simplified Expression
$4x + 3x$	$=$	$(4 + 3)x$	$=$	$7x$
$7a + a$	$=$	$(7 + 1)a$	$=$	$8a$
$-5x + 7x$	$=$	$(-5 + 7)x$	$=$	$2x$
$8y - y$	$=$	$(8 - 1)y$	$=$	$7y$
$-4a - 2a$	$=$	$(-4 - 2)a$	$=$	$-6a$
$3x - 7x$	$=$	$(3 - 7)x$	$=$	$-4x$

As you can see from the table, the distributive property can be applied to any combination of positive and negative terms so long as they are like terms.

5. Simplify: $14y + 2y$

Example 5   Simplify: $12x + 3x$

Solution

$$12x + 3x = (12 + 3)x \qquad \text{Distributive property}$$
$$= 15x \qquad \text{Add.}$$

Answers

4. $-10n - 4$
5. $16y$

Example 6   Simplify: $5x - 2 + 3x + 7$

Solution   We begin by changing subtraction to addition of the opposite and applying the commutative property to rearrange the order of the terms. We want like terms to be written next to each other.

$$5x - 2 + 3x + 7 = 5x + 3x + (-2) + 7 \qquad \text{Commutative property}$$
$$= (5 + 3)x + (-2) + 7 \qquad \text{Distributive property}$$
$$= 8x + 5 \qquad \text{Add.}$$

Notice that we take the negative sign in front of the 2 with the 2 when we rearrange terms. We can justify this step because subtracting a number is the same as adding its opposite.

6. Simplify: $4y - 1 + 2y + 5$

Example 7   Simplify: $2(3y + 4) + 5$

Solution   We begin by distributing the 2 across the sum of $3y$ and 4. Then we combine like terms.

$$2(3y + 4) + 5 = 6y + 8 + 5 \qquad \text{Distributive property}$$
$$= 6y + 13 \qquad \text{Add 8 and 5.}$$

7. Simplify: $5(2x + 1) + 3$

8. Simplify: $4(2y - 2) + 3(3y - 2)$

Example 8   Simplify: $2(3x + 1) + 4(2x - 5)$

Solution   Again, we apply the distributive property first; then we combine like terms. Here is the solution showing the essential steps:

$$2(3x + 1) + 4(2x - 5) = 6x + 2 + 8x - 20 \qquad \text{Distributive property}$$
$$= 14x - 18 \qquad \text{Combine like terms.}$$

Notice we have not used the commutative property to rearrange terms; it is understood that this property was used.

D The Value of an Algebraic Expression

Like we saw in Chapter 2, an expression such as $3x + 5$ will take on different values depending on what x is. If we were to let x equal 2, the expression $3x + 5$ would become 11. On the other hand, if x is 10, the same expression has a value of 35, as we have shown below:

$x = 2$	$x = 10$
$3x + 5$	$3x + 5$
$3(2) + 5$	$3(10) + 5$
$6 + 5$	$30 + 5$
11	35

Example 9   Evaluate $5a - 12$ when $a = 2$.

Solution   We will substitute 2 for a and simplify.

$$5(2) - 12$$
$$10 - 12$$
$$-2$$

9. Evaluate $6b - 16$ when $b = 3$.

10. Evaluate $b(b - 4)$
when $b = -7$.

Example 10 Evaluate $a(3 - a)$ when $a = -5$.

Solution   We will substitute -5 for a and simplify using the order of operations.

$-5(3 - (-5))$ Substitute -5 for a.

$-5(3 + 5)$ Simplify within grouping symbols.

$-5(8)$

-40 Multiply.

E Angles

FACTS FROM GEOMETRY

Angles

An angle is formed by two rays with the same endpoint. The common endpoint is called the *vertex* of the angle, and the rays are called the *sides* of the angle.

In Figure 2, angle θ (theta) is formed by the two rays OA and OB. The vertex of θ is O. Angle θ is also denoted as angle AOB, where the letter associated with the vertex is always the middle letter in the three letters used to denote the angle.

Degree Measure The angle formed by rotating a ray through one complete revolution about its endpoint (Figure 3) has a measure of 360 degrees, which we write as 360°.

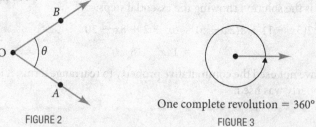

FIGURE 2

One complete revolution = 360°

FIGURE 3

One degree of angle measure is written 1°. It takes 360 1° to rotate a ray completely around its endpoint; there are 360° in one full rotation. (The number 360 was decided upon by early civilizations because it was believed that Earth was at the center of the universe and the sun would rotate once around Earth every 360 days.) Similarly, 180° is half of a complete rotation, and 90° is a quarter of a full rotation. Angles that measure 90° are called *right angles*, and angles that measure 180° are called *straight angles*. If an angle measures between 0° and 90° it is called an *acute angle*, and an angle that measures between 90° and 180° is an *obtuse angle*. Figure 4 illustrates further.

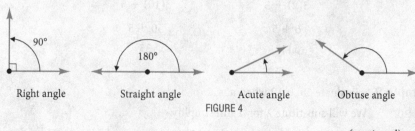

Right angle   Straight angle   Acute angle   Obtuse angle

FIGURE 4

(continued)

FACTS FROM GEOMETRY *(continued)* • • • • • • • • • • • • • • • •

Complementary Angles and Supplementary Angles If two angles add up to 90°, we call them *complementary angles*, and each is called the *complement* of the other. If two angles have a sum of 180°, we call them *supplementary angles*, and each is called the *supplement* of the other. Figure 5 illustrates the relationship between angles that are complementary and angles that are supplementary.

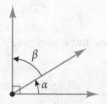

Complementary angles: $\alpha + \beta = 90°$ Supplementary angles: $\alpha + \beta = 180°$

FIGURE 5

Example 11 Find x in each of the following diagrams.

a.

b.

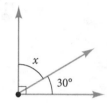

Complementary angles

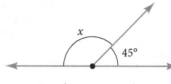

Supplementary angles

11. Find y in each of the following diagrams.

a.

b.

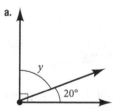

Solution We use subtraction to find each angle.

a. Because the two angles are complementary, we can find x by subtracting 30° from 90°.

$$x = 90° - 30° = 60°$$

We say 30° and 60° are complementary angles. The complement of 30° is 60°.

b. The two angles in the diagram are supplementary. To find x, we subtract 45° from 180°.

$$x = 180° - 45° = 135°$$

We say 45° and 135° are supplementary angles. The supplement of 45° is 135°.

• •

KEY CONCEPT REVIEW •

After reading through the preceding section, respond in your own words and in complete sentences.

A. What property allows $5(x + 3)$ to be rewritten as $5x + 5(3)$?

B. Why is simplifying an algebraic expression using like terms important?

C. What does it mean to find the value of an algebraic expression?

D. How do complementary angles differ from supplementary angles?

Answers

11. a. 70° **b.** 60°

VOCABULARY REVIEW •

Choose the correct words to fill in the blanks below.

| straight | acute | equal | variable | protractor |
| obtuse | complementary | right | supplementary | |

1. The distributive property of multiplication states that $a(b + c)$ is _____ to $ab + ac$.

2. An algebraic expression will take on different values depending on the value of the _____.

3. Angles that measure 90 degrees are called _____ angles, and angles that measure 180 degrees are called _____ angles.

4. Angles between 0 degrees and 90 degrees are called _____ angles, whereas angles between 90 degrees and 180 degrees are called _____ angles.

5. Two angles that add up to 90 degrees are called _____ angles.

6. Two angles that add up to 180 degrees are called _____ angles.

7. A _____ can be used to draw and measure angles.

Problems

A Apply the associative property to each expression, and then simplify the result.

1. $5(4a)$ **2.** $8(9a)$ **3.** $-6(3x)$ **4.** $-2(7x)$

5. $5(-2y)$ **6.** $3(-8y)$ **7.** $-6(-10y)$ **8.** $-5(-5y)$

9. $2 + (3 + x)$ **10.** $9 + (6 + x)$ **11.** $5 + (8 + x)$ **12.** $3 + (9 + x)$

13. $(12a + 2) + 19$ **14.** $(6a + 3) + 14$ **15.** $(7x + 8) + 20$ **16.** $(14x + 3) + 15$

B Apply the distributive property to each expression, and then simplify.

17. $7(x + 5)$ **18.** $8(x + 3)$ **19.** $6(a - 7)$ **20.** $4(a - 9)$

21. $4(5 + x)$ **22.** $8(3 + x)$ **23.** $3(2x + 5)$ **24.** $8(5x + 4)$

25. $-2(6x - 3y)$ **26.** $-7(5x - y)$ **27.** $5(7 - 4y)$ **28.** $8(6 - 3y)$

C Combine each of the following pairs of like terms.

29. $2x + 8x$ **30.** $3x + 7x$ **31.** $6a - 2a$ **32.** $9a - 3a$

33. $-4y + 5y$ **34.** $-3y + 10y$ **35.** $-6x - 2x$ **36.** $-9x - 4x$

37. $4a - a$ **38.** $9a - a$ **39.** $x - 6x$ **40.** $x - 9x$

Simplify the following expressions by combining like terms. It may be helpful to first rearrange terms using the commutative property.

41. $4x + 2x + 3 + 8$ **42.** $7x + 5x + 2 + 9$ **43.** $7x - 5x + 6 - 4$ **44.** $10x - 7x + 9 - 6$

45. $-2a + a + 7 + 5$ **46.** $-8a + 3a + 12 + 1$ **47.** $6y - 2y - 5 + 1$ **48.** $4y - 3y - 7 + 2$

49. $4x + 2x - 8x + 4$ **50.** $6x + 5x - 12x + 6$ **51.** $9x - x - 5 - 1$ **52.** $2x - x - 3 - 8$

53. $3x + 2 - 4x + 1$ **54.** $7x + 5 - 2x + 6$ **55.** $4a - 3 - 5a + 2a$ **56.** $6a - 4 - 2a + 6a$

Simplify.

57. $2(3x + 4) + 8$

58. $2(5x + 1) + 10$

59. $5(2x - 3) + 4$

60. $6(4x - 2) + 7$

61. $8(2y + 4) + 3y$

62. $2(5y + 1) + 2y$

63. $-6(4y - 3) + 6y$

64. $-5(2y - 6) + 4y$

65. $2(x + 3) + 4(x + 2)$

66. $3(x + 1) + 2(x + 5)$

67. $3(2a + 4) - 7(3a - 1)$

68. $7(2a + 2) - 4(5a - 1)$

D Find the value of each of the following expressions when $x = 5$.

69. $2x + 4$

70. $3x + 2$

71. $7x - 8$

72. $8x - 9$

73. $-4x + 1$

74. $-3x + 7$

75. $-8 - 3x$

76. $-7 - 2x$

77. $3(x - 1)$

78. $9(x + 2)$

79. $x(x - 10)$

80. $x(x - 2)$

Evaluate each expression when $a = -2$.

81. $2a + 5$

82. $3a + 4$

83. $-7a + 4$

84. $-9a + 3$

85. $-a + 10$

86. $-a + 8$

87. $-4 - 3a$

88. $-6 - 5a$

89. $7(4 - a)$

90. $2(5 + a)$

91. $a(a - 7)$

92. $a(a - 4)$

Find the value of each of the following expressions when $x = 3$. You may substitute 3 for x in each expression the way it is written, or you may simplify each expression first and then substitute 3 for x.

93. $3x + 5x + 4$

94. $6x + 8x + 7$

95. $9x + x + 3 + 7$

96. $5x + 3x + 2 + 4$

97. $4x + 3 + 2x + 5$

98. $7x + 6 + 2x + 9$

99. $3x - 8 + 2x - 3$

100. $7x - 2 + 4x - 1$

E Find x in each of the following diagrams.

101.

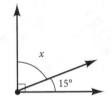

Complementary angles

102.

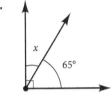

Complementary angles

103.

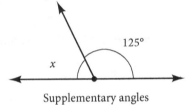

Supplementary angles

104.

Supplementary angles

Applying the Concepts

Use the distributive property to write two equivalent expressions for the area of each figure.

105.

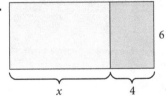

106.

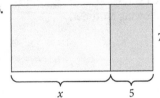

Write an expression for the perimeter of each figure.

107. Square

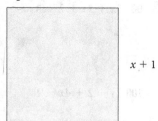

$x + 1$

108. Rectangle

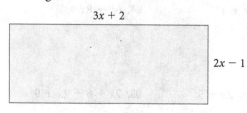

$3x + 2$

$2x - 1$

109.

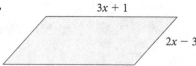

$3x + 1$

$2x - 3$

110.

$4x + 1$ $4x + 1$

$5x + 4$

111. Geometry Find the complement and supplement of 25°. Is 25° an acute angle or an obtuse angle?

112. Geometry Find the supplement of 125°. Is 125° an acute angle or an obtuse angle?

113. Temperature and Altitude On a certain day, the temperature on the ground is 72 degrees Fahrenheit, and the temperature at an altitude of A feet above the ground is found from the expression $72 - \frac{A}{300}$. Find the temperature at the following altitudes.

a. 12,000 feet

b. 15,000 feet

c. 27,000 feet

114. Perimeter of a Rectangle As you know, the expression $2l + 2w$ gives the perimeter of a rectangle with length l and width w. A garden has a width of 3 feet and a length of 8 feet. What is the length of the fence that surrounds the garden?

115. Cost of Bottled Water A water bottling company charges $7 per month for their water dispenser and $2 for each gallon of water delivered. If you have g gallons of water delivered in a month, then the expression $7 + 2g$ gives the amount of your bill for that month. Find the monthly bill for each of the following deliveries:

a. 10 gallons

b. 20 gallons

116. Purchasing Stocks An investment company charges clients a $6 transaction fee for each stock transaction. If you purchase s shares of stock at $10 per share, then the expression $6+10s$ gives the total amount owed for the stock purchase. Find the amount for each of the following transactions:

a. 25 shares

b. 47 shares

Getting Ready for the Next Section

Perform the indicated operation.

117. $4 - 4$

118. $2 - 2$

119. $-2 - 4$

120. $-2 - 5$

121. $-5 + 2$

122. $-3 + 12$

123. $-8 + 3$

124. $-14 + 5$

Simplify.

125. $x + 0$

126. $y + 0$

127. $y + 4 - 6$

128. $y + 6 - 2$

FIND THE MISTAKE •

Each problem below contains a mistake. Circle the mistake and write the correct number(s) or word(s) on the line provided.

1. Multiplying $-3(4x - 2)$ using the distributive property gives us $4x + 6$. _____

2. The first step when simplifying $2(5y + 1) + 4(5y - 1)$ is to add the terms inside the parentheses to get $2(6y) + 4(4y) = 12y + 16y = 28y$. _____

3. To find the value of $-3y + 2y$ when $y = 6$, we must simplify the problem $6(-3y + 2y)$. _____

4. Suppose x and y are complementary angles. If $x = 25°$, then y must equal 155°. _____

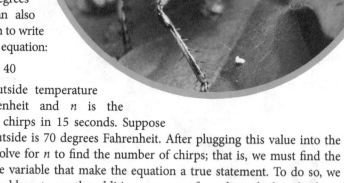

OBJECTIVES

OBJECTIVES

A Determine if a number is a solution to an equation.

B Find the solution to an equation using the addition property of equality.

C Find the solution to an equation using the subtraction property of equality.

KEY WORDS

solution

addition property of equality

subtraction property of equality

VIDEO EXAMPLES

SECTION 3.2

Note In this section, we will begin solving equations. It's important to consider the difference between expressions and equations. For example, $4x - 7$ is an expression, whereas $x + 3 = 7$ is an equation.

Did you know you can calculate the outside temperature by counting the number of times a cricket chirps? Focus on one cricket and count the number of chirps in 15 seconds. Then add 40 to that number and you'll get the approximate outside temperature in degrees Fahrenheit. We can also use this information to write the following linear equation:

$$t = n + 40$$

where t is the outside temperature in degrees Fahrenheit and n is the number of cricket chirps in 15 seconds. Suppose the temperature outside is 70 degrees Fahrenheit. After plugging this value into the equation, we can solve for n to find the number of chirps; that is, we must find the replacement for the variable that make the equation a true statement. To do so, we must first understand how to use the addition property of equality, which is the focus of this section.

A Solutions to Equations

The replacements for a variable in an equation that give a true statement are called solutions.

DEFINITION solution

A **solution** for an equation is a number that when used in place of the variable makes the equation a true statement.

For example, the equation $x + 3 = 7$ has as its solution the number 4, because replacing x with 4 in the equation gives a true statement.

$$x = 4$$
$$x + 3 = 7$$
$$4 + 3 = 7$$
$$7 = 7 \qquad \text{A true statement}$$

Example 1   Is $a = -2$ the solution to the equation $7a + 4 = 3a - 2$?

Solution   We substitute -2 for a and simplify.

$$7a + 4 = 3a - 2$$
$$7(-2) + 4 = 3(-2) - 2$$
$$-14 + 4 = -6 - 2$$
$$-10 = -8 \qquad \text{A false statement}$$

Because the result is a false statement, we must conclude that $a = -2$ is not a solution to the equation $7a + 4 = 3a - 2$.

Practice Problems

1. Is $n = -4$ a solution to the equation $2x + 5 = 5x - 4$?

B   Addition Property of Equality

We want to develop a process for solving equations with one variable. One important property needed for solving the equations in this section is called the **addition property of equality.** The formal definition looks like this:

PROPERTY   **Addition Property of Equality**

Let A, B, and C represent algebraic expressions.

$$\text{If} \qquad A = B$$
$$\text{then} \quad A + C = B + C$$

In words: Adding the same quantity to both sides of an equation never changes the solution to the equation.

This property is extremely useful in solving equations. Our goal in solving equations is to isolate the variable on one side of the equation. We want to end up with an expression of the form

$$x = \text{a number}$$

To do so, we use the addition property of equality.

Example 2   Solve the equation $x - 5 = 12$ for x.

Solution   Because we want x alone on the left side, we choose to add 5 to both sides.

$$x - 5 + 5 = 12 + 5 \qquad \text{Addition property of equality}$$
$$x + 0 = 17$$
$$x = 17 \qquad \text{Addition property of zero}$$

To check our solution, we substitute 17 for x in the original equation:

$$\text{When} \rightarrow \qquad x = 17$$
$$\text{the equation} \rightarrow \quad x - 5 = 12$$
$$\text{becomes} \rightarrow \qquad 17 - 5 \overset{?}{=} 12$$
$$12 = 12 \qquad \text{A true statement}$$

As you can see, our solution checks. The purpose for checking a solution to an equation is to catch any mistakes we may have made in the process of solving the equation.

2. Solve $x - 3 = 10$ for x.

Note   With some of the equations in this section, you will be able to see the solution just by looking at the equation. But it is important that you show all the steps used to solve the equations anyway. The equations you come across in the future will not be as easy to solve, so you should learn the steps involved very well.

Answers

1. No
2. 13

3. Solve for n: $2n - 1 - 4n = 3 - 6$

Example 3   Solve for x: $3x - 2 - 2x = 4 - 9$

Solution   Simplifying each side as much as possible, we have

$$3x - 2 - 2x = 4 - 9$$
$$x - 2 = -5 \qquad \text{─} 3x - 2x = x$$
$$x - 2 + 2 = -5 + 2 \qquad \text{Add 2 to both sides.}$$
$$x + 0 = -3 \qquad \text{Add.}$$
$$x = -3 \qquad \text{Simplify.}$$

4. Solve: $3(4n - 2) - 11n = 3 - 6$

Example 4   Solve: $4(2a - 3) - 7a = 2 - 5$

Solution   We must begin by applying the distributive property to separate terms on the left side of the equation. Following that, we combine like terms and then apply the addition property of equality.

$$4(2a - 3) - 7a = 2 - 5 \qquad \text{Original equation}$$
$$8a - 12 - 7a = 2 - 5 \qquad \text{Distributive property}$$
$$a - 12 = -3 \qquad \text{Simplify each side.}$$
$$a - 12 + 12 = -3 + 12 \qquad \text{Add 12 to each side.}$$
$$a = 9$$

C Subtraction Property of Equality

PROPERTY Subtraction Property of Equality

For any three algebraic expressions A, B, and C,

$$\text{If} \qquad A = B$$
$$\text{then} \qquad A - C = B - C$$

In words: Subtracting the same quantity from both sides of an equation will not change the solution set.

5. Solve $y + 3 = 1$ for y.

Example 5   Solve $x + 4 = -2$ for x.

Solution   We want to isolate x on one side of the equation. If we subtract 4 from both sides, the left side will be $x + 4 - 4$, which is $x + 0$ or just x.

$$x + 4 = -2$$
$$x + 4 - 4 = -2 - 4 \qquad \text{Subtract 4 from both sides.}$$
$$x + 0 = -6 \qquad \text{Simplify.}$$
$$x = -6$$

The solution is -6. We can check it if we want to by replacing x with -6 in the original equation.

$$x = -6$$
$$x + 4 = -2$$
$$-6 + 4 = -2$$
$$-2 = -2 \qquad \text{A true statement}$$

Answers
3. $n = 1$
4. $n = 3$
5. $y = -2$

Sometimes it is necessary to simplify each side of an equation before using the addition and subtraction properties of equality. The reason we simplify both sides first is that we want as few terms as possible on each side of the equation before we use these properties. The following examples illustrate this procedure.

Example 6   Solve for x: $-x + 2 + 2x = 7 + 5$

Solution   We begin by combining like terms on each side of the equation. Then we use the subtraction property to solve the simplified equation.

$-x + 2 + 2x = 7 + 5$	Original equation
$x + 2 = 12$	Simplify both sides first.
$x + 2 - 2 = 12 - 2$	Subtraction property of equality
$x = 10$	The solution is 10.

Checking our answer: $-10 + 2 + 2(10) = -8 + 20 = 7 + 5 = 12$.

6. Solve for x:
$$-2x + 3 + 3x = 6 + 8$$

Example 7   Solve: $10 = -3y + 2(5 + 2y)$

Solution   We begin by applying the distributive property to separate terms on the right side of the equation. Following that, we combine like terms and then apply the subtraction property of equality to isolate y on the right side.

$10 = -3y + 2(5 + 2y)$	Original equation
$10 = -3y + 10 + 4y$	Distributive property
$10 = y + 10$	Simplify right side.
$10 - 10 = y + 10 - 10$	Subtract 10 on both sides.
$0 = y$	The solution is 0.

Checking our answer: $10 = -3(0) + 2(5 + 2(0)) = 2 \cdot 5 = 10$.

7. Solve: $8 = -2x + 4(2 + x)$

  KEY CONCEPT REVIEW

After reading through the preceding section, respond in your own words and in complete sentences.

A. What is a solution to an equation?

B. True or false? According to the addition property of equality, adding the same value to both sides of an equation will never change the solution to the equation.

C. Show that $x = 5$ is a solution to the equation $3x + 2 = 17$ without solving the equation.

D. True or false? The equations below have the same solution.

Equation 1: $7x + 5 = 19$

Equation 2: $7x + 5 - 3 = 19 - 3$

EXERCISE SET 3.2 ·

VOCABULARY REVIEW ·

Choose the correct words to fill in the blanks below.

addition　　　isolate　　　　　solution　　　　　variable　　　　　subtraction

1. A solution for an equation is a number that when used in place of the _____ makes the equation a true statement.

2. The _____ property of equality states that $A + C = B + C$ if A equals B.

3. Adding the same quantity to both sides of an equation never changes the _____ to the equation.

4. The goal when solving an equation is to _____ the variable on one side of the equation.

5. The _____ property of equality states that $A - C = B - C$ if A equals B.

Problems

A Check to see if the number to the right of each of the following equations is the solution to the equation.

1. $2x + 1 = 5; 2$　　　　**2.** $4x + 3 = 7; 1$　　　　**3.** $3x + 4 = 19; 5$　　　　**4.** $3x + 8 = 14; 2$

5. $2x - 4 = 2; 4$　　　　**6.** $5x - 6 = 9; 3$　　　　**7.** $2x + 1 = 3x + 3; -2$　　　　**8.** $4x + 5 = 2x - 1; -6$

9. $x - 4 = 2x + 1; -4$　　　**10.** $x - 8 = 3x + 2; -5$　　　**11.** $-x = 4x + 7; -2$　　　**12.** $-x = 5x - 3; -8$

B, C Solve each equation. You can check your solution by replacing the variable in the original equation.

13. $x + 2 = 8$　　　　**14.** $x + 3 = 5$　　　　**15.** $x - 4 = 7$　　　　**16.** $x - 6 = 2$

17. $a + 9 = -6$　　　　**18.** $a + 3 = -1$　　　　**19.** $x - 5 = -4$　　　　**20.** $x - 8 = -3$

21. $y - 3 = -6$　　　　**22.** $y - 5 = -1$　　　　**23.** $b + 3 = -10$　　　　**24.** $b + 7 = -20$

158

Solve each equation by simplifying each side of the following equations before applying the addition or subtraction property.

25. $x + 4 - 7 = 3 - 10$ **26.** $x + 6 - 2 = 5 - 12$ **27.** $x - 6 + 4 = -3 - 2$ **28.** $x - 8 + 2 = -7 - 1$

29. $3 - 5 = a - 4$ **30.** $2 - 6 = a - 1$ **31.** $3a + 7 - 2a = 1$ **32.** $5a + 6 - 4a = 4$

33. $6a - 2 - 5a = -9 + 1$ **34.** $7a - 6 - 6a = -3 + 1$ **35.** $8 - 5 = 3x - 2x + 4$ **36.** $10 - 6 = 8x - 7x + 6$

The following equations contain parentheses. Solve each equation by first applying the distributive property to remove the parentheses, then simplify each side before using the addition property of equality or subtraction property of equality.

37. $2(x + 3) - x = 4$ **38.** $5(x + 1) - 4x = 2$ **39.** $-3(x - 4) + 4x = 3 - 7$

40. $-2(x - 5) + 3x = 4 - 9$ **41.** $5(2a + 1) - 9a = 8 - 6$ **42.** $4(2a - 1) - 7a = 9 - 5$

43. $-(x + 3) + 2x - 1 = 6$ **44.** $-(x - 7) + 2x - 8 = 4$ **45.** $-(4x - 4) + 5x - 2 = 10$

Applying the Concepts

Find the value of x for each of the figures, given the perimeter.

46. $P = 36$

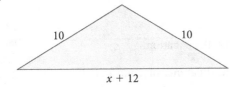

47. $P = 30$

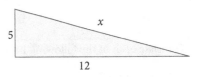

48. $P = 16$

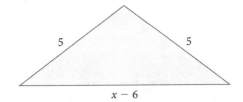

49. $P = 60$

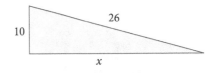

50. Geometry Two angles are complementary angles. If one of the angles is 23°, then solving the equation $x + 23° = 90°$ will give you the other angle. Solve the equation.

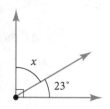

Complementary angles

51. Geometry Two angles are supplementary angles. If one of the angles is 23°, then solving the equation $x + 23° = 180°$ will give you the other angle. Solve the equation.

52. CN Tower Suppose the capacity of the CN Tower mentioned in the chapter opener is 500 people. The prices for several of the visitor packages are shown below.

	SkyPod Experience	General Admission	Timed Admission
Adult	$48	$36	$39
Senior	$43	$31	$34
Children	$38	$26	$29

If the SkyPod Experience is sold out and there will be 250 adults and 125 seniors, the number of children on the tour can be given by the equation

$$x + 250 + 125 = 500.$$

a. Solve the equation for x.

b. How much money will the CN Tower bring in for this tour?

53. Geometry The sum of the angles in the triangle on the swing set is 180°. Use this fact to write an equation containing x. Then solve the equation.

Translating Translate each of the following into an equation, and then solve the equation.

54. The sum of x and 12 is 30.

55. The difference of x and 12 is 30.

56. The difference of 8 and 5 is equal to the sum of x and 7.

57. The sum of 8 and 5 is equal to the difference of x and 7.

Improving Your Quantitative Literacy

58. Facebook Users The chart shows the number of active Facebook users over several years. Use the information to answer the following questions.

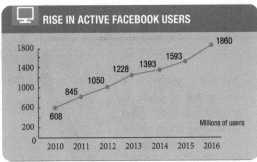

RISE IN ACTIVE FACEBOOK USERS

Millions of users

a. How many more users were there in 2016 than in 2010?

b. Between which years was the increase the most?

c. Using this data set, how many users will there be in 2017 if the trend from 2015 to 2016 continues?

Getting Ready for the Next Section

Simplify.

59. $7 - 2$

60. $-5 - 7$

61. $\dfrac{-20}{4}$

62. $\dfrac{-12}{-3}$

63. $1 \cdot x$

64. $1 \cdot a$

65. $4x - 11 + 3x$

66. $2x - 11 + 3x$

67. $2\left(\dfrac{1}{2}\right)$

68. $3 \cdot \dfrac{1}{3}$

69. $\dfrac{4}{4}$

70. $\dfrac{-3}{3}$

FIND THE MISTAKE •

Each sentence below contains a mistake. Circle the mistake and write the correct word(s) or numbers(s) on the line provided.

1. The solution for an equation is a number that when used in place of the variable makes the equation a false statement. _____

2. Adding the same quantity to both sides of an equation will change the solution to the equation.

_____

3. To solve the problem $x - 2 = 3$, subtract 2 from each side of the equation. _____

4. Solving $-3x - 6 + 4x = 9$ gives us $x = 3$. _____

OBJECTIVES

A Solve equations using the multiplication property of equality.

B Solve equations using the division property of equality.

KEY WORDS

multiplication property of equality

division property of equality

VIDEO EXAMPLES

SECTION 3.3

Assume you've been saving for a while for a trip abroad. After picking up extra shifts at work and diligently budgeting, you've been able to save $1,650. Airfare will cost approximately $900, leaving you $750 for accommodations and spending money. If you expect to spend $150 a day on accommodations, food, and other purchases, how many days can you afford to be on your vacation? To answer this question, we must use the given information to set up the following equation:

$$750 = 150x$$

To solve the equation, we need to use the division property of equality, which we will learn about in this section.

A Multiplication Property of Equality

Here is the formal explanation of the multiplication property of equality:

PROPERTY Multiplication Property of Equality

Let A, B, and C represent real numbers, with C not equal to 0.

If $\qquad A = B$

then $\qquad AC = BC$

In words: Multiplying both sides of an equation by the same nonzero quantity never changes the solution to the equation.

Example 1 Solve $\frac{x}{2} = 3$ for x.

Solution Our goal here is the same as it was in the previous section. We want to isolate x (that is, $1x$) on one side of the equation. We have x divided by 2 on the left side. If we multiply both sides by 2, we will have $1x$ on the left side.

$$\frac{x}{2} = 3$$

$$2\left(\frac{x}{2}\right) = 2(3) \qquad \text{Multiply both sides by 2.}$$

$$x = 6 \qquad \text{Simplify.}$$

Practice Problems

1. Solve $\frac{y}{4} = 2$ for y.

Answer

1. $y = 8$

Example 2 Solve $\frac{a}{3} + 2 = 7$ for a.

Solution 　　We begin by subtracting 2 from both sides to get $\frac{a}{3}$ by itself. We then multiply by 3 to solve for a.

$$\frac{a}{3} + 2 = 7$$

$$\frac{a}{3} + 2 - 2 = 7 - 2 \qquad \text{Subtract 2 from both sides.}$$

$$\frac{a}{3} = 5$$

$$3 \cdot \frac{a}{3} = 3 \cdot 5 \qquad \text{Multiply both sides by 3.}$$

$$a = 15 \qquad \text{Simplify.}$$

We can check our solution to see that it is correct.

$$\frac{a}{3} + 2 = 7$$

$$\frac{15}{3} + 2 = 7$$

$$5 + 2 = 7$$

$$7 = 7 \qquad \text{A true statement}$$

2. Solve $\frac{n}{5} + 3 = 6$ for n.

B Division Property of Equality

A similar property also holds for division, allowing us to divide each side of an equation by the same nonzero quantity.

PROPERTY Division Property of Equality

Let A, B, and C represent real numbers, with C not equal to 0.

$$\text{If} \qquad A = B$$

$$\text{then} \qquad \frac{A}{C} = \frac{B}{C}$$

In words: Dividing both sides of an equation by the same nonzero quantity never changes the solution to the equation.

Example 3 Solve $4x = -20$ for x.

Solution 　　If we divide both sides by 4, the left side will be just x, which is what we want. It is okay to divide both sides by 4 by the division property of equality.

$$4x = -20$$

$$\frac{4x}{4} = \frac{-20}{4} \qquad \text{Divide both sides by 4.}$$

$$x = -5 \qquad \text{Simplify.}$$

3. Solve $3y = -15$ for y.

Answers
2. $n = 15$
3. $y = -5$

4. Solve $-2y + 5 = -3$ for y.

Example 4   Solve $-3x + 7 = -5$ for x.

Solution   We begin by subtracting 7 from both sides to reduce the left side to $-3x$.

$$-3x + 7 = -5$$

$$-3x + 7 - 7 = -5 - 7 \qquad \text{Subtract 7 from both sides.}$$

$$-3x = -12 \qquad \text{Simplify.}$$

$$\frac{-3x}{-3} = \frac{-12}{-3} \qquad \text{Divide both sides by } -3.$$

$$x = 4$$

With more complicated equations we simplify each side separately before applying the addition or multiplication properties of equality. The example below illustrates.

5. Solve $4y - 6y + 4 = 3 - 5$ for y.

Example 5   Solve $5x - 8x + 3 = 4 - 10$ for x.

Solution   We combine like terms to simplify each side and then solve as usual.

$$5x - 8x + 3 = 4 - 10$$

$$-3x + 3 = -6 \qquad \text{Simplify each side.}$$

$$-3x + 3 - 3 = -6 - 3 \qquad \text{Subtract 3 from both sides.}$$

$$-3x = -9 \qquad \text{Simplify.}$$

$$\frac{-3x}{-3} = \frac{-9}{-3} \qquad \text{Divide both sides by } -3.$$

$$x = 3$$

  COMMON MISTAKE

Before we end this section, we should mention a very common mistake. It involves trying to subtract away the number in front of the variable, like this:

$$7x = 21$$

$$7x - 7 = 21 - 7 \qquad \text{Subtract 7 from both sides.}$$

$$x = 14$$

The mistake is not in trying to subtract 7 from both sides of the equation. The mistake occurs when we say $7x - 7 = x$. It just isn't true. We can add and subtract only like terms. The numbers $7x$ and 7 are not like, because one contains x and the other doesn't. Another common mistake is:

$$\frac{7x}{-7} = \frac{21}{-7} \qquad \text{Divide both sides by } -7.$$

$$x = 3.$$

The mistake is dividing by -7 and not 7. If we divide by -7 we would get $-x$ on the left side. Thus, we'd need to divide by -1 to isolate x.

The correct way to do the problem is like this:

$$7x = 21$$

$$\frac{7x}{7} = \frac{21}{7} \qquad \text{Divide both sides by 7.}$$

$$x = 3$$

Answers

4. $y = 4$

5. $y = 3$

KEY CONCEPT REVIEW

After reading through the preceding section, respond in your own words and in complete sentences.

A. Use symbols to explain the multiplication property of equality.

B. True or false? Multiplying both sides of an equation by the same nonzero quantity will never change the solution to the equation.

C. If we were to divide the right side of an equation by 2, then the left side should be divided by _____.

Spotlight on Success

A Message from the Author

Dear Students,

Many of you who are enrolled in this course are just beginning your college career. Some of you are arriving at college after just having graduated high school while others are returning to college after years in the workforce or taking time away from school to raise a family. Some of you are planning to complete only a couple of classes while others are here to earn a degree. Whatever your background and goals may be, I would like to share some advice with you that I hope you find helpful in this course and others.

Know your resources. In this text, there are several resources to help you learn and understand the material. This includes links to videos, worked-out examples and strategically placed Landmark Reviews. It's also important to know the resources provided by your instructor and your institution. Although these may not seem relevant at the moment, being aware of these support structures may be extremely helpful later in the semester.

Invest time in your education. Setting aside time each week to focus solely on your coursework allows for quality and efficient studying. Also, reviewing your course notes and examples for a couple of minutes each day, especially before class, can be helpful in committing the information to memory. Making small investments of time in your education will make a significant difference in the long run.

Ask for assistance. One of the major differences between high school and college is that students are more responsible for seeking out assistance in college. Don't be afraid to ask your peers, faculty, and others for help. This doesn't have to be limited to how to solve the problems in this text. You can also ask your friends for techniques for studying for a math test, for example. Also, don't hesitate to ask friends and family for help. Balancing the demands of college with work and other responsibilities is a challenge. When you're struggling, lean on your support system to get through those difficult times.

I wish you all the best in your future academic and professional career.

Megan Cavanah

EXERCISE SET 3.3 ·

Problems

A Use the multiplication property of equality to solve each of the following equations. In each case, show all steps.

1. $\dfrac{x}{4} = 2$ **2.** $\dfrac{x}{3} = 7$ **3.** $\dfrac{x}{2} = -3$ **4.** $\dfrac{x}{5} = -6$

5. $\dfrac{x}{-3} = 2$ **6.** $\dfrac{x}{-3} = 5$ **7.** $\dfrac{x}{-6} = 1$ **8.** $\dfrac{x}{-2} = -4$

9. $\dfrac{y}{4} = 12$ **10.** $\dfrac{y}{3} = 18$ **11.** $\dfrac{y}{7} = -4$ **12.** $\dfrac{y}{8} = -9$

B Use the division property of equality to solve each of the following equations. In each case, show all steps.

13. $3a = 48$ **14.** $2a = 28$ **15.** $5x = -35$ **16.** $7x = -35$

17. $-8y = 64$ **18.** $-9y = 27$ **19.** $-7x = -42$ **20.** $-6x = -42$

21. $-8x = 56$ **22.** $-9x = 54$ **23.** $15y = -60$ **24.** $12y = -72$

Using the addition or subtraction property of equality first, solve each of the following equations.

25. $3x - 1 = 5$ **26.** $2x + 4 = 6$ **27.** $-4a + 3 = -9$ **28.** $-5a + 10 = 50$

29. $6x - 5 = 19$ **30.** $7x - 5 = 30$ **31.** $\frac{a}{3} + 3 = -5$ **32.** $\frac{a}{2} + 2 = -7$

33. $\frac{a}{-4} + 5 = 2$ **34.** $\frac{a}{-5} + 3 = 7$ **35.** $2x - 4 = -20$ **36.** $3x - 5 = -26$

37. $\frac{2x}{3} - 4 = 6$ **38.** $\frac{3x}{4} - 2 = 7$ **39.** $-11a + 4 = -29$ **40.** $-12a + 1 = -47$

41. $-3y - 2 = 1$ **42.** $-2y - 8 = 2$ **43.** $-2x - 5 = -7$ **44.** $-3x - 6 = -36$

Simplify each side of the following equations first, then solve.

45. $2x + 3x - 5 = 7 + 3$ **46.** $4x + 5x - 8 = 6 + 4$ **47.** $4x - 7 + 2x = 9 - 10$ **48.** $5x - 6 + 3x = -6 - 8$

49. $3a + 2a + a = 7 - 13$ **50.** $8a - 6a + a = 8 - 14$ **51.** $5x - 4x + 3x = 4 - 8$ **52.** $4x + 8x - 2x = 30 - 10$

53. $5 - 18 = 3y - 2y + 1$ **54.** $7 - 16 = 4y - 3y + 2$

Applying the Concepts

Find the value of x for each of the figures, given the perimeter. The first two figures are squares.

55. A square with a perimeter of 72 units

2x

56. A square with a perimeter of 96 units

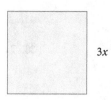

3x

57. A rectangle with a perimeter of 80 units

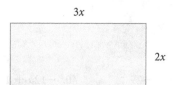

3x

2x

58. A rectangle with a perimeter of 64 units

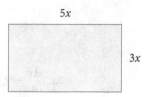

5x

3x

59. Basketball Kendra plays basketball for her high school. In one game she scored 21 points total, with a combination of free throws, field goals, and three-pointers. Each free throw is worth 1 point, each field goal is 2 points, and each three-pointer is worth 3 points. If she made 1 free throw and 4 field goals, then solving the equation

$$1 + 2(4) + 3x = 21$$

will give us the number of three-pointers she made. Solve the equation to find the number of three-point shots Kendra made.

60. Break-Even Point The El Portal Center for the Arts is showing a movie to raise money for a local charity. The cost to put on the event is $1,840, which includes rent on the Center and movie, insurance, and wages for the paid attendants. If tickets cost $8 each, then solving the equation $8x = 1,840$ gives the number of tickets they must sell in order to cover their costs. This number is called the break-even point. Solve the equation for x to find the break-even point.

Translate each sentence below into an equation, then solve the equation.

61. The sum of $2x$ and 5 is 19.

62. The sum of 8 and $3x$ is 2.

63. The difference of $5x$ and 6 is 9.

64. The difference of 9 and $6x$ is 21.

65. The product of 6 and x is -24.

66. The product of 12 and x is -36.

Getting Ready for the Next Section

Apply the distributive property to each of the following expressions.

67. $2(3a - 8)$ **68.** $4(2a - 5)$ **69.** $-3(5x - 1)$ **70.** $-2(7x - 3)$

Simplify each of the following expressions as much as possible.

71. $3(y - 5) + 6$ **72.** $5(y + 3) + 7$ **73.** $6(2x - 1) + 4x$ **74.** $8(3x - 2) + 4x$

FIND THE MISTAKE •

Each sentence below contains a mistake. Circle the mistake and write the correct word(s) or numbers(s) on the line provided.

1. The multiplication property of equality says that adding the same nonzero quantity to both sides of an equation never changes the solution. _____

2. To isolate x on the left side of the equation $\frac{x}{3} = -9$, we must multiply each side by -9. _____

3. The first step to finding a solution for the equation $-6 = 12 - 6y$ is to multiply both sides by 12. _____

4. The first step to solving $-9x = 45$ is to subtract 9 from both sides of the equation to get $x = 4$. _____

Navigation Skills

Expect to encounter problems you find difficult when taking this course. Also expect to make mistakes. Mistakes highlight possible difficulties you are having and help you learn how to overcome them. We suggest making a list of problems you find difficult. As the course progresses, add new problems to the list, rework the problems on your list, and use the list to study for exams. Be aware of the mistakes you make and what you need to do to ensure you will not make that same mistake twice.

LINEAR EQUATIONS IN ONE VARIABLE

A Solve linear equations in one variable.

KEY WORDS

linear equation in one variable

variable term

constant term

VIDEO EXAMPLES

SECTION 3.4

A group of data scientists have recently developed an algorithm for computing what they consider to be the optimal road trip around the United States. To visit the 48 contiguous states and 50 landmarks, this road trip by car would require 224 hours of driving time and likely take two or three months to complete.

The route includes a stop at the Hoover Dam in Nevada, followed by a visit to the Grand Canyon in Arizona and then Bryce Canyon National Park in Utah. The distance from the Grand Canyon to Bryce Canyon is approximately 100 miles less than the distance from the Hoover Dam to the Grand Canyon. If the total distance from the Hoover Dam to Bryce Canyon is 384 miles, what is the distance from the Hoover Dam to the Grand Canyon? In this section, we will learn how to solve problems like this.

A Linear Equations in One Variable

In this chapter, we have been solving what are called **linear equations in one variable.** They are equations that contain only one variable, and that variable is always raised to the first power and never appears in a denominator. Here are some examples of linear equations in one variable:

$$3x + 2 = 17, \quad 7a + 4 = 3a - 2, \quad 2(3y - 5) = 6$$

Because of the work we have done in the first three sections of this chapter, we are now able to solve any linear equation in one variable. The steps outlined in the How To box can be used as a guide to solving these equations.

HOW TO   Steps to Solve a Linear Equation in One Variable

Step 1:   Simplify each side of the equation as much as possible. This step is done using the commutative, associative, and distributive properties.

Step 2:   Use the addition or subtraction property of equality to get all variable terms on one side of the equation and all constant terms on the other, then combine like terms. A variable term is any term that contains the variable. A constant term is any term that contains only a number.

Step 3:   Use the multiplication or division property of equality to get the variable by itself on one side of the equation.

Step 4:   Check your solution in the original equation if you think it is necessary.

Practice Problems

1. Solve: $2(y + 4) = -2$

Example 1   Solve: $3(x + 2) = -9$

Solution   We begin by applying the distributive property to the left side.

$$3(x + 2) = -9$$
$$3x + 6 = -9 \qquad \textit{Distributive property}$$
$$3x + 6 - 6 = -9 - 6 \qquad \textit{Subtract 6 from both sides.}$$
$$3x = -15$$
$$\frac{3x}{3} = \frac{-15}{3} \qquad \textit{Divide both sides by 3.}$$
$$x = -5$$

We check our solution by substituting -5 for x in the original equation.

$$3(-5 + 2) = -9$$
$$3(-3) = -9$$
$$-9 = -9$$

Because the result was a true statement, our solution checks.

This general method of solving linear equations involves using the two properties we have already developed. We can add or subtract any number to or from both sides of an equation, or multiply or divide both sides by the same nonzero number and always be sure we have not changed the solution to the equation. The equations may change in form, but the solution to the equation stays the same. Looking back to Example 1, we can see that each equation looks a little different from the preceding one. What is interesting, and useful, is that each of the equations says the same thing about x. They all say that x is -5. The last equation, of course, is the easiest to read. That is why our goal is to end up with x isolated on one side of the equation.

Answer

1. $y = -5$

2. Solve: $5n + 3 = 3n - 1$

Example 2   Solve: $4a + 5 = 2a - 7$

Solution   Neither side can be simplified any further. What we have to do is get the variable terms ($4a$ and $2a$) on the same side of the equation. We can eliminate the variable term from the right side by subtracting $2a$ from both sides. We will then move the constants to the right side of the equation by subtracting five from both sides.

$$4a + 5 = 2a - 7$$

$$4a - 2a + 5 = 2a - 2a - 7 \qquad \text{Subtract } 2a \text{ from both sides.}$$

$$2a + 5 = -7$$

$$2a + 5 - 5 = -7 - 5 \qquad \text{Subtract 5 from both sides.}$$

$$2a = -12$$

$$\frac{2a}{2} = \frac{-12}{2} \qquad \text{Divide by 2.}$$

$$a = -6$$

We could also check our solution by substituting -6 into the original equation.

3. Solve: $3(y - 2) + 7 = -8$

Example 3   Solve: $2(x - 4) + 5 = -11$

Solution   We begin by applying the distributive property.

$$2(x - 4) + 5 = -11$$

$$2x - 8 + 5 = -11 \qquad \text{Distributive property}$$

$$2x - 3 = -11 \qquad \text{Add.}$$

$$2x - 3 + 3 = -11 + 3 \qquad \text{Add 3 to both sides.}$$

$$2x = -8$$

$$\frac{2x}{2} = \frac{-8}{2} \qquad \text{Divide by 2.}$$

$$x = -4$$

4. Solve: $4(3y - 2) + 5 = 5y + 11$

Example 4   Solve: $5(2x - 4) + 3 = 4x - 5$

Solution   We apply the distributive property. We then combine like terms and solve.

$$5(2x - 4) + 3 = 4x - 5$$

$$10x - 20 + 3 = 4x - 5 \qquad \text{Distributive property}$$

$$10x - 17 = 4x - 5 \qquad \text{Simplify the left side.}$$

$$10x - 4x - 17 = 4x - 4x - 5 \qquad \text{Subtract } 4x \text{ from both sides.}$$

$$6x - 17 = -5 \qquad \text{Simplify.}$$

$$6x - 17 + 17 = -5 + 17 \qquad \text{Add 17 to both sides.}$$

$$6x = 12$$

$$\frac{6x}{6} = \frac{12}{6} \qquad \text{Divide by 6.}$$

$$x = 2$$

Answers

2. $n = -2$

3. $y = -3$

4. $y = 2$

KEY CONCEPT REVIEW

After reading through the preceding section, respond in your own words and in complete sentences.

A. What is the first step to solve a linear equation in one variable?

B. Why should you get all the variable terms on one side of the equation and all the constant terms on the other side?

C. Write the equation that results when $4a$ is subtracted from both sides of the equation below.

$$6a + 9 = 4a - 3$$

Spotlight on Success

OCTABIO, student instructor

The best thing about the future is that it comes one day at a time.

~ Abraham Lincoln

For my family, education was always the way to go. Education would move us ahead, but the path through education was not always clear. My parents had immigrated to this country and had not had the opportunity to continue in education. Luckily, with the help of school counselors and the A.V.I.D. (Advancement Via Individual Determination) program in our school district, my older sister and brother were able to get into some of their top colleges. Later, with A.V.I.D. and the guidance of my siblings, I was able to take the right courses and was lucky enough to be accepted at my dream university.

Math has been my favorite subject ever since I can remember. When I got to higher level math classes, however, I struggled more than I had with previous levels of math. This struggle initially stopped me from enjoying the class, but as my understanding grew, I became more and more interested in seeing how things connected. I have found these connections at all levels of mathematics, including prealgebra. These connections continue to be a source of satisfaction for me.

VOCABULARY REVIEW ·

Choose the correct words to fill in the blanks below.

solution	linear	fractions	variable
simplify	constant	multiplication	division

1. A _____ equation in one variable contains only one variable that is always raised to the first power and never appears in a denominator.

2. The first step to solving a linear equation in one variable is to _____ each side of the equation as much as possible.

3. A _____ term is any term in an equation that contains the variable.

4. A _____ term is any term in an equation that contains only a number.

5. When solving a linear equation in one variable, use the _____ or _____ property of equality to get the variable by itself on one side of the equation.

6. The last step to solving a linear equation in one variable is to check your _____ in the original equation.

Problems

A Solve each equation using the methods shown in this section.

1. $5(x + 1) = 20$

2. $4(x + 2) = 24$

3. $6(x - 3) = -6$

4. $7(x - 2) = -7$

5. $2x + 4 = 3x + 7$

6. $5x + 3 = 2x - 3$

7. $7y - 3 = 4y - 15$

8. $15x + 1 = -4x + 20$

9. $6x - 8 = -x - 8$

10. $7x - 5 = -x - 5$

11. $7(a - 1) + 4 = 11$

12. $3(a - 2) + 1 = 4$

13. $8(x + 5) - 6 = 18$

14. $7(x + 8) - 4 = 10$

15. $2(3x - 6) + 1 = 7$

16. $5(2x - 4) + 8 = 38$

17. $10(y + 1) + 4 = 3y + 7$

18. $12(y + 2) + 5 = 2y - 1$

19. $4(x - 6) + 1 = 2x - 9$

20. $7(x - 4) + 3 = 5x - 9$

21. $2(3x + 1) = 4(x - 1)$

22. $7(x - 8) = 2(x - 13)$

23. $3a + 4 = 2(a - 5) + 15$

24. $10a + 3 = 4(a - 1) + 1$

25. $9x - 6 = -3(x + 2) - 24$

26. $8x - 10 = -4(x + 3) + 2$

27. $3x - 5 = 11 + 2(x - 6)$

28. $5x - 7 = -7 + 2(x + 3)$

29. $4(x + 7) - 5 = 3(4x - 3) - 8$

30. $5(x + 2) - 4 = 7(2x - 5) - 13$

Applying the Concepts

Find the value of x for each of the figures, given the perimeter.

31. $P = 36$

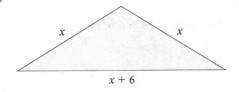

32. $P = 30$

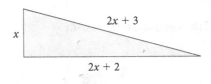

33. $P = 16$

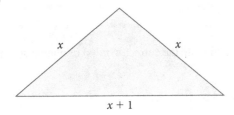

34. $P = 60$

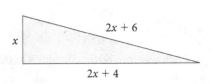

35. The distance from the Grand Canyon to Bryce Canyon is approximately 100 miles less than the distance from the Hoover Dam to the Grand Canyon. If one route from the Hoover Dam to Bryce Canyon is 384 miles, what is the distance from the Hoover Dam to the Grand Canyon?

Hoover Dam to Grand Canyon	Grand Canyon to Bryce Canyon	Total Distance
x	$x - 100$	384

36. The distance from Pikes Peak to Carlsbad Caverns is approximately 30 miles less than the distance from Yellowstone to Pikes Peak. If one route from Yellowstone to Carlsbad Caverns is 1,170 miles, what is the distance from Pikes Peak to Carlsbad Caverns?

Yellowstone to Pikes Peak	Pikes Peak to Carlsbad Caverns	Total Distance
x	$x - 30$	1,170

37. The distance from Pensacola to Cape Canaveral is approximately 301 miles more than the distance from New Orleans to Pensacola. If the total distance from New Orleans to Cape Canaveral is 703 miles, what is the distance from Pensacola to Cape Canaveral?

38. The distance from Denver to Des Moines is approximately 380 miles more than the distance from Des Moines to Madison. If the total distance from Denver to Madison is 960 miles, what is the distance from Des Moines to Madison?

Getting Ready for the Next Section

Simplify.

39. $\dfrac{5(95 - 32)}{9}$

40. $\dfrac{5(77 - 32)}{9}$

41. Find the value of $90 - x$ when $x = 25$.

42. Find the value of $180 - x$ when $x = 25$.

43. Find the value of $2x + 6$ when $x = -2$.

44. Find the value of $2x + 6$ when $x = 0$.

Solve.

45. $40 = 2l + 12$

46. $80 = 2l + 12$

47. $6 + 3y = 0$

48. $-8 + 3y = 4$

FIND THE MISTAKE ·

Each sentence below contains a mistake. Circle the mistake and write the correct word(s) or numbers(s) on the line provided.

1. The solution to the linear equation $6a + 1 = -3a - 8$ is a positive number. _____

2. The last step to finding the solution to the linear equation $2(3x - 2) = -x + 10$ uses the addition property of equality to isolate the variable on one side of the equation. _____

3. To solve $4x = 28$, we divide each side by -4. _____

LANDMARK REVIEW: CHECKING YOUR PROGRESS

Simplify each of the following.

1. $4(3x + 7) - 4$ **2.** $6(2y - 3) + 1$ **3.** $5(2x + 1) + 2(4x + 3)$ **4.** $3(4x - 3) - 2(3x - 1)$

Find the value of each of the following expressions for the given value of the variable.

5. $x - 3, x = 1$ **6.** $x - 3, x = 5$ **7.** $2y - 3, y = 2$ **8.** $-4y - 7, y = 4$

Solve each equation.

9. $x + 3 = 9$ **10.** $y - 4 = 15$ **11.** $z + 7 = 14$ **12.** $a - 5 = -15$

13. $y + 3 - 7 = 1 - 5$ **14.** $4x - 5 - 3x = 7 + 3$ **15.** $6(x - 4) - 5(x + 3) = 2 + 5$ **16.** $3(2a - 2) - 5a = 3 + 4$

17. $\dfrac{x}{3} = 5$ **18.** $\dfrac{-x}{5} = 2$ **19.** $\dfrac{y}{6} = -10$ **20.** $\dfrac{x}{-4} = 9$

21. $-2x + 3 = 5$ **22.** $3x + 5 = -10$ **23.** $-2y - 4 = -24$ **24.** $5a - 3 = -38$

In the previous chapter, we presented the bar chart in Figure 1 with the record low temperatures for various cities in Australia, rounded to the nearest integer.

These temperatures are recorded in Celsius, a temperature scale used in many parts of the world. In Celsius, water freezes at 0 degrees and boils at 100 degrees, while room temperature is approximately 20 degrees Celsius. To convert from Celsius to Fahrenheit, the temperature scale used in the United States, we use the following formula:

$$F = \frac{9C}{5} + 32$$

In this section, we will solve application problems with different formulas. For example, we will use the formula above, the perimeter formula $P = 2l + 2w$, and the distance formula $d = rt$, which uses the given quantities of rate and time.

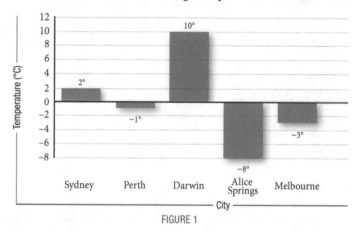

FIGURE 1

A Formulas

 **DEFINITION** formula

In mathematics, a **formula** is an equation with more than one variable.

   Although there are many kinds of problems we can work using formulas, we will limit ourselves to those that require only substitutions and solving for an unknown quantity. The examples that follow illustrate these types of problems.

Algebraic Equations Representing Area and Perimeter

Below are a square with a side of length s and a rectangle with a length of l and a width of w. The table that follows the figures gives the formulas for the area and perimeter of each.

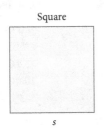

Square

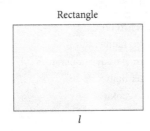

Rectangle

s l

	Square	Rectangle
Area A	s^2	lw
Perimeter P	$4s$	$2l + 2w$

Example 1   Find the area and perimeter of a square with a side 6 inches long.

Solution   Substituting 6 for s in the formulas for area and perimeter of a square, we have

$$\text{Area} = A = s^2 = 6^2 = 36 \text{ square inches}$$

$$\text{Perimeter} = P = 4s = 4(6) = 24 \text{ inches}$$

Example 2   If a rectangle has a width of 18 feet and a perimeter of 82 feet, find the length of the rectangle.

Solution   Using the formula for perimeter of a rectangle, $P = 2l + 2w$, we substitute 18 for w and 82 for P and solve for l.

$$P = 2l + 2w$$
$$82 = 2l + 2(18) \qquad \text{Substitute.}$$
$$82 = 2l + 36 \qquad \text{Multiply.}$$
$$82 - 36 = 2l + 36 - 36 \qquad \text{Subtract 36 from both sides.}$$
$$\frac{46}{2} = \frac{2l}{2} \qquad \text{Simplify.}$$
$$23 = l \qquad \text{Divide both sides by 2.}$$

Thus, the length of the rectangle is 23 feet.

Practice Problems

1. Find the area and perimeter of a square with a side of 8 inches.

2. A rectangle has a width of 9 feet and a perimeter of 40 feet. Find the length of the rectangle.

Answers

1. Area = 64 in.^{2}, Perimeter = 32 in.
2. 11 feet

In the section introduction, we mentioned the two temperature scales, Fahrenheit and Celsius. Table 1 is intended to give you a sense of the relationship between the two temperature scales.

Table 1

Comparing Two Temperature Scales

Situation	Temperature Fahrenheit	Temperature Celsius
Water freezes	32°F	0°C
Room temperature	68°F	20°C
Normal body temperature	98.6°F	37°C
Water boils	212°F	100°C
Bake cookies	365°F	185°C

Table 2 gives the formulas, in both symbols and words, that are used to convert between the two scales.

Table 2

Formulas for Converting Between Temperature Scales

To convert from	Formula in symbols
Fahrenheit to Celsius	$C = \dfrac{5(F - 32)}{9}$
Celsius to Fahrenheit	$F = \dfrac{9C}{5} + 32$

We will now convert between two temperature scales using the given formulas. When using these formulas, we will follow the order of operations.

3. Using the formula from Example 3, find C when F is 77 degrees.

Example 3   Use the formula $C = \dfrac{5(F - 32)}{9}$ to find C when F is 95 degrees.

Solution   Substituting 95 for F in the formula gives us the following:

$$C = \frac{5(F - 32)}{9}$$

$$= \frac{5(95 - 32)}{9} \qquad \text{Substitute.}$$

$$= \frac{5(63)}{9} \qquad \text{Subtract.}$$

$$= \frac{315}{9} \qquad \text{Multiply.}$$

$$= 35 \qquad \text{Simplify.}$$

A temperature of 95 degrees Fahrenheit is the same as a temperature of 35 degrees Celsius.

• •

Answer

3. 25°

We can also solve problems involving equations for x and y.

Example 4 Use the formula $y = 2x + 6$ to find y when x is -2.

Solution Proceeding as we have in the previous examples, we will substitute -2 for x and simplify.

$$y = 2x + 6$$
$$y = 2(-2) + 6 \qquad \text{Substitute.}$$
$$= -4 + 6 \qquad \text{Multiply.}$$
$$= 2 \qquad \text{Add.}$$

In some cases, evaluating a formula also involves solving an equation, as the next example illustrates.

Example 5 Find y when x is 8 in the formula $2x + 3y = 4$.

Solution First, we substitute 8 for x; then we solve the resulting equation for y.

$$2x + 3y = 4$$
$$2(8) + 3y = 4 \qquad \text{Substitute.}$$
$$16 + 3y = 4$$
$$16 + 3y - 16 = 4 - 16 \qquad \text{Subtract 16 from both sides.}$$
$$3y = -12$$
$$y = -4 \qquad \text{Divide each side by 3.}$$

Rate Equation

Now we will look at some problems that use what is called the **rate equation**. You use this equation on an intuitive level when you are estimating how long it will take you to drive long distances. For example, if you drive at 50 miles per hour for 2 hours, you will travel 100 miles. Here is the rate equation:

$$\text{Distance} = \text{rate} \cdot \text{time, or } d = rt$$

Example 6 At 1 p.m. Jordan leaves her house and drives at an average speed of 50 miles per hour to her sister's house. She arrives at 4 p.m.

a. How many hours was the drive to her sister's house?

b. How many miles from her sister does Jordan live?

Solution

a. If she left at 1:00 p.m. and arrived at 4:00 p.m., the elapsed time is 3 hours.

b. We are asked to find a distance in miles given a rate of 50 miles per hour and a time of 3 hours. We will use the rate equation, $d = rt$, to solve this. We have

$$d = 50 \text{ miles per hour} \cdot 3 \text{ hours}$$

$$d = 50(3)$$

$$d = 150 \text{ miles}$$

4. Use the formula from Example 4 to find y when $x = 2$.

5. Use the formula in Example 5 to find y when x is 17.

6. Rework Example 6 if Jordan left at 10 a.m., drove an average speed of 60 miles per hour, and arrived at 3 p.m.

Answers
4. $y = 10$
5. $y = -10$
6. a. 5 hours **b.** 300 miles

Notice that we were asked to find a distance in miles, so our answer has a unit of miles. When we are asked to find a time, our answer will include a unit of time, like days, hours, minutes, or seconds. When we are asked to find a rate, our answer will include units of rate, like miles per hour, feet per second, problems per minute, and so on.

 FACTS FROM GEOMETRY • • • • • • • • • • • • • • • • •

Earlier we defined complementary angles as angles that add to 90°. That is, if x and y are complementary angles, then

$$x + y = 90°$$

Also, supplementary angles are angles that add to 180°. If x and y are supplementary angles, then

$$x + y = 180°$$

7. Find the complement and supplement of 50°.

Example 7   Find the complement and the supplement of 25°.

Solution   We can use the formulas above with $x = 25°$.

To find the complement, we substitute $x = 25$ into the formula $x + y = 90$.

$$25 + y = 90$$
$$25 + y - 25 = 90 - 25 \qquad \textit{Subtract 25 from both sides.}$$
$$y = 65 \qquad \textit{Simplify.}$$

To find the supplement, we substitute $x = 25$ into the formula $x + y = 180$.

$$25 + y = 180$$
$$25 + y - 25 = 180 - 25 \qquad \textit{Subtract 25 from both sides.}$$
$$y = 155 \qquad \textit{Simplify.}$$

 KEY CONCEPT REVIEW •

After reading through the preceding section, respond in your own words and in complete sentences.

A. What is a formula?

B. How do you solve a formula for one of its variables?

C. What is the rate equation?

D. What is the formula that converts temperature on the Celsius scale to temperature on the Fahrenheit scale?

Answers

7. Complement = 40°,
   Supplement = 130°

EXERCISE SET 3.5 ·············

VOCABULARY REVIEW ·

Choose the correct words to fill in the blanks below.

    rate   formula   variable   time

1. The equation $y = 6x + 8$ is an example of a _____, but $4x + 2 = 14$ is not.

2. A formula is an equation with more than one _____.

3. In the rate equation $d = rt$, the d represents distance, the r represents _____, and the t represents _____.

Problems

A Use the formulas that were presented in this section to find the perimeter and area of a rectangle with the given dimensions.

1. $l = 32$ feet and $w = 22$ feet.

2. $l = 22$ feet and $w = 12$ feet.

3. If a rectangle has a width of 4 inches and a perimeter of 32 inches, find the length of the rectangle.

4. If a rectangle has a width of 24 meters and a perimeter of 108 meters, find the length of the rectangle.

5. If a rectangle has a length of 30 yards and a perimeter of 106 yards, find the width of the rectangle.

6. If a rectangle has a length of 18 feet and a perimeter of 68 feet, find the width of the rectangle.

7. The perimeter of a square is 32 centimeters. What is the length of one side?

8. The perimeter of a square is 60 inches. What is the length of one side?

The formula $G = H \cdot R$ tells us how much gross pay G a person receives for working H hours at an hourly rate of pay R. In Problems 9–10, find G.

9. $H = 40$ hours and $R = \$6$

10. $H = 36$ hours and $R = \$8$

Because there are 3 feet in every yard, the formula $F = 3 \cdot Y$ will convert Y yards into F feet. In Problems 11–12, find F.

11. $Y = 4$ yards

12. $Y = 8$ yards

13. Let $F = 212°$ in the formula $C = \frac{5\,(F-32)}{9}$, and solve for C. Does the value of C agree with the information in Table 1?

14. Let $F = 68°$ in the formula $C = \frac{5(F-32)}{9}$, and solve for C. Does the value of C agree with the information in Table 1?

15. Let $C = 0°$ in the formula $F = \frac{9C}{5} + 32$, and solve for F. Does the value of F agree with the information in Table 1?

16. Let $C = 100°$ in the formula $F = \frac{9C}{5} + 32$, and solve for F. Does the value of F agree with the information in Table 1?

17. Find C when F is $86°$.

18. Find C when F is $-4°$.

19. Find F when C is $-15°$.

20. Find F when C is $25°$.

Use the rate equation $d = rt$ to solve Problems 21–24.

21. At 2:30 p.m. Kimberly leaves her house and drives at an average speed of 55 miles per hour to her sister's house. She arrives at 6:30 p.m.

   a. How many hours was the drive to her sister's house?

   b. How many miles from her sister does Kimberly live?

22. At 1:30 p.m. Cory leaves his house and drives at an average speed of 65 miles per hour to his brother's house. He arrives at 5:30 p.m.

   a. How many hours was the drive to his brother's house?

   b. How many miles from his brother's house does Cory live?

23. At 2:30 p.m. Alyse leaves her house and drives 260 miles to her sister's house. She arrives at 6:30 p.m.

   a. How many hours was the drive to her sister's house?

   b. What was Alyse's average speed?

24. At 8:30 a.m. Cole leaves his house and drives 220 miles to his brother's house. He arrives at 12:30 p.m.

   a. How many hours was the drive to his brother's house?

   b. What was Cole's average speed?

The volume V enclosed by a rectangular solid with length l, width w, and height h is $V = lwh$. In Problems 25–26, find V if

25. $l = 6$ inches, $w = 12$ inches, and $h = 5$ inches

26. $l = 16$ inches, $w = 22$ inches, and $h = 15$ inches

Suppose $y = 3x - 2$. In Problems 27–30, find y if

27. $x = -3$ **28.** $x = -5$ **29.** $x = 0$ **30.** $x = 5$

Suppose $x + y = 5$. In Problems 31–34, find x if

31. $y = 2$ **32.** $y = 5$ **33.** $y = -2$ **34.** $y = -3$

Suppose $x + y = 3$. In Problems 35–38, find y if

35. $x = 2$ **36.** $x = -2$ **37.** $x = 0$ **38.** $x = 3$

Suppose $4x + 3y = 12$. In Problems 39–42, find y if

39. $x = 3$ **40.** $x = 0$ **41.** $x = -3$ **42.** $x = -6$

Suppose $4x + 3y = 12$. In Problems 43–46, find x if

43. $y = 4$ **44.** $y = 0$ **45.** $y = -4$ **46.** $y = -12$

Find the complement and supplement of each angle.

47. 45°   **48.** 75°   **49.** 31°   **50.** 59°

Applying the Concepts

Maximum Heart Rate In exercise physiology, a person's maximum heart rate, in beats per minute, is found by subtracting his age in years from 220. So, if A represents your age in years, then your maximum heart rate is

$$M = 220 - A$$

Use this formula to complete the following tables.

51.

Age (years)	Maximum Heart Rate (beats per minute)
18	
19	
20	
21	
22	
23	

52.

Age (years)	Maximum Heart Rate (beats per minute)
15	
20	
25	
30	
35	
40	

53. Trapezoid A common polygon, a trapezoid, is shown at the right. The area of a trapezoid can be found using the formula

$$Area = \frac{Base_1 + Base_2}{2} \cdot Height$$

  a. Find the area if $Base_1 = 6$ inches, $Base_2 = 10$ inches and $Height = 6$ inches

  b. Find $Base_1$ if $Area = 80mm^2$, $Base_2 = 6mm$ and $Height = 8mm$

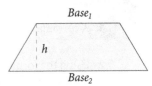

Estimating Vehicle Weight If you can measure the area that the tires on your car contact the ground, and you know the air pressure in the tires, then you can estimate the weight of your car, in pounds, with the following formula:

$$W = APN$$

where W is the vehicle's weight in pounds, A is the average tire contact area with a hard surface in square inches, P is the air pressure in the tires in pounds per square inch (psi, or lb/in²), and N is the number of tires.

54. What is the approximate weight of a car if the average tire contact area is a rectangle 6 inches by 5 inches and if the air pressure in the tires is 30 psi?

55. What is the approximate weight of a car if the average tire contact area is a rectangle 5 inches by 4 inches, and the tire pressure is 30 psi?

Getting Ready for the Next Section

Write the mathematical expressions that are equivalent to each of the following English phrases.

56. The sum of a number and 2

57. The sum of a number and 5

58. Twice a number

59. Three times a number

60. Twice the sum of a number and 6

61. Three times the sum of a number and 8

62. The difference of x and 4

63. The difference of 4 and x

64. 5 less than twice a number

65. 4 less than three times a number

FIND THE MISTAKE •

Each sentence below contains a mistake. Circle the mistake and write the correct word(s) or numbers(s) on the line provided.

1. A formula is an equation with only one variable. _____

2. Using the formula $C = \frac{5(F-32)}{9}$ to find C when $F = 75°$, we have $75 = \frac{5(F-32)}{9}$. _____

3. To find y when $x = 6$ in the equation $5x + 8y = 24$, we must solve $5x + 8(6) = 24$. _____

4. Two angles, x and y, are complementary if $x + y = 180°$. _____

APPLICATIONS

Central Park, in the middle of New York City, is the most visited urban park with 35-40 million visitors annually. Covering 843 acres of land, over 600 football fields could fit into Central Park. In addition to walking and biking paths, the park also includes two ice-skating rinks, the Central Park Zoo, and a conservatory garden. The park also hosts many events and festivals.

Suppose you wanted to run around the edge of Central Park. You know that the total distance will be 6 miles, and a New York City resident tells you that the length of the park is approximately five times the width. How would you find the length and the width? In this section, we will use our knowledge of linear equations to solve similar application problems.

OBJECTIVES

A Solve application problems.

VIDEO EXAMPLES

SECTION 3.6

A Blueprint for Problem Solving

To begin this section, we list the steps used in solving application problems. We call this strategy the Blueprint for Problem Solving. It is an outline that will overlay the solution process we use on all application problems.

BLUEPRINT FOR PROBLEM SOLVING

Step 1: *Read* the problem, and then mentally *list* the items that are known and the items that are unknown.

Step 2: *Assign a variable to* one of the unknown items. (In most cases, this will amount to letting *x* equal the item that is asked for in the problem.) Then *translate the other information* in the problem to expressions involving the variables. *Draw a picture if it's helpful.*

Step 3: *Reread* the problem, and then *write an equation,* using the items and the variable listed in Steps 1 and 2, that describes the situation.

Step 4: *Solve the equation* found in Step 3.

Step 5: *Write* your *answer* using a complete sentence.

Step 6: *Reread* the problem, and *check* your solution with the original words in the problem. *Verify* that your answer makes sense in the context of the problem.

1. The sum of a number and 3 is 12. Find the number.

Note Although many problems in this section may seem contrived, they provide excellent practice for our problem solving strategy. This practice will prove useful when we encounter more difficult application problems.

Number Problems

Example 1   The sum of a number and 2 is 8. Find the number.

Solution   Using our blueprint for problem solving as an outline, we solve the problem as follows:

Step 1: *Read and list.*

>   *Known items:* The numbers 2 and 8

>   *Unknown item:* The number in question

Step 2: *Assign a variable and translate the information.*

>   Let x = the number asked for in the problem.

>   Then "The sum of a number and 2" translates to $x + 2$.

Step 3: *Reread and write an equation.*

>   With all word problems, the word "is" translates to $=$.
>   The sum of x and 2 is 8.

$$x + 2 \quad = 8$$

Step 4: *Solve the equation.*

$$x + 2 = 8$$
$$x + 2 - 2 = 8 - 2 \qquad \text{Subtract 2 from each side.}$$
$$x = 6$$

Step 5: *Write your answer.*

>   The number is 6.

Step 6: *Reread and check.*

>   The sum of 6 and 2 is 8.   A true statement

To help with other problems of the type shown in Example 1, here are some common English words and phrases and their mathematical translations.

English	Algebra
The sum of a and b	$a + b$
The difference of a and b	$a - b$
The product of a and b	$a \cdot b$
The quotient of a and b	$\dfrac{a}{b}$
Of (multiply)	$\cdot$
Is (equals)	$=$
A number	x
4 more than x	$x + 4$
4 times x	$4x$
4 less than x	$x - 4$

You may find some examples and problems in this section and the problem set that follows that you can solve without using algebra or our blueprint. It is very important that you solve those problems using the methods we are showing here. The purpose behind these problems is to give you experience using the blueprint as a guide to solving problems written in words. Your answers are much less important than the work that you show in obtaining your answer.

Example 2   If 5 is added to the sum of twice a number and three times the number, the result is 25. Find the number.

Solution

Step 1: *Read and list.*

    Known items: The numbers 5 and 25, twice a number, and three times a number

    Unknown item: The number in question

Step 2: *Assign a variable and translate the information.*

    Let x = the number asked for in the problem.
    Then "The sum of twice a number and three times the number" translates to $2x + 3x$.

Step 3: *Reread and write an equation.*

5	added to	the sum of twice a number and three times the number	is 25
5	+	$2x + 3x$	= 25

Step 4: *Solve the equation.*

$$5 + 2x + 3x = 25$$

$$5x + 5 = 25 \qquad \text{Simplify the left side.}$$

$$5x + 5 - 5 = 25 - 5 \qquad \text{Subtract 5 from both sides.}$$

$$5x = 20$$

$$\frac{5x}{5} = \frac{20}{5} \qquad \text{Divide by 5.}$$

$$x = 4$$

Step 5: *Write your answer.*

    The number is 4.

Step 6: *Reread and check.*

    Twice 4 is 8, and three times 4 is 12. Their sum is $8 + 12 = 20$. Five added to this is 25. Therefore, 5 added to the sum of twice 4 and three times 4 is 25.

Geometry Problems

Example 3   The length of a rectangle is three times the width. The perimeter is 72 centimeters. Find the width and the length.

Solution

Step 1: *Read and list.*

    Known items: The length is three times the width.
    The perimeter is 72 centimeters.

    Unknown items: The length and the width

Step 2: *Assign a variable, and translate the information.*

    We let x = the width. Because the length is three times the width, the length must be $3x$. A picture will help.

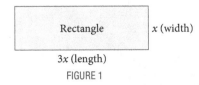

Rectangle x (width)

$3x$ (length)

FIGURE 1

2. If 6 is added to the sum of twice a number and three times the number the result is 16. Find the number.

3. The length of a rectangle is four times the width. The perimeter is 100 inches. Find the length and width.

Step 3: *Reread and write an equation.*

Because the perimeter is the sum of the sides, we will use the formula
$P = 2l + 2w$ and the given perimeter of 72 centimeters. Hence,

$$2(3x) + 2(x) = 72$$

Step 4: *Solve the equation.*

$$2(3x) + 2(x) = 72$$
$$6x + 2x = 72$$
$$8x = 72$$
$$x = 9$$

Step 5: *Write your answer.*

The width, x, is 9 centimeters. The length, $3x$, must be 27 centimeters.

Step 6: *Reread and check.*

From the diagram below, we see that these solutions check.

Perimeter is 72.   Length = 3 · Width

$$2(27) + 2(9) = 72$$ $$27 = 3 \cdot 9$$

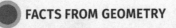

FIGURE 2

Next we review some facts about triangles that we introduced in a previous chapter.

● FACTS FROM GEOMETRY

Labeling Triangles and the Sum of Angles in a Triangle

One way to label the important parts of a triangle is to label the vertices with capital letters and the sides with lower case letters, as shown in Figure 4. In Figure 3, notice that side a is opposite vertex A, side b is opposite vertex B, and side c is opposite vertex C. Also, because each vertex is the vertex of one of the angles of the triangle, we refer to the three interior angles as A, B, and C.

In any triangle, the sum of the interior angles is 180°. For the triangle shown in Figure 3, the relationship is written

$$A + B + C = 180°$$

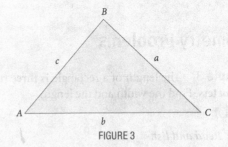

FIGURE 3

Example 4   The angles in a triangle are such that one angle is twice the smallest angle, while the third angle is three times as large as the smallest angle. Find the measure of all three angles.

Solution

Step 1:   *Read and list.*

     Known items: The sum of all three angles is 180°, one angle is twice the smallest angle, and the largest angle is three times the smallest angle.

     Unknown items: The measure of each angle

Step 2:   *Assign a variable and translate information.*

     Let x be the smallest angle, then $2x$ will be the measure of another angle, and $3x$ will be the measure of the largest angle.

     When working with geometric objects, drawing a diagram will sometimes help us visualize what it is that we are asked to find. In Figure 4, we draw a triangle with angles A, B, and C.

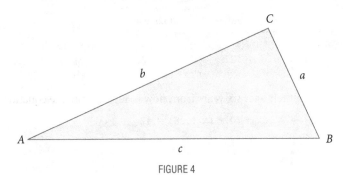

FIGURE 4

Step 3:   *Reread and write an equation.*

     We can let the measure of $A = x$, the measure of $B = 2x$, and the measure of $C = 3x$. We know that the sum of angles A, B, and C will be 180°, so our equation becomes

$$x + 2x + 3x = 180°$$

Step 4:   *Solve the equation.*

$$x + 2x + 3x = 180°$$
$$6x = 180°$$
$$x = 30°$$

Step 5:   *Write the answer.*

     The smallest angle A measures 30°

     Angle B measures $2x$, or $2(30°) = 60°$

     Angle C measures $3x$, or $3(30°) = 90°$

Step 6:   *Reread and check.*

     The angles must add to 180°.

$$A + B + C = 180°$$
$$30° + 60° + 90° = 180°$$
$$180° = 180° \qquad \textit{Our answers check.}$$

4. The angles in a triangle are such that one angle is five times the smallest angle, while the third is three times the smallest. Find the measure of all three angles.

5. Mark is 18 years older than his cousin Hayley. In five years, the sum of their ages will be 50. How old are they now?

Age Problem

Example 5   Jo Ann is 22 years older than her daughter Stacey. In six years, the sum of their ages will be 42. How old are they now?

Solution

Step 1: *Read and list.*

> *Known items:* Jo Ann is 22 years older than Stacey. Six years from now their ages will add to 42.
>
> *Unknown items:* Their ages now

Step 2: *Assign a variable and translate the information.*

> Let x = Stacey's age now. Because Jo Ann is 22 years older than Stacey, her age is $x + 22$.

Step 3: *Reread and write an equation.*

> As an aid in writing the equation, we use the following table:

	Now	In six years
Stacey	x	$x + 6$
Jo Ann	$x + 22$	$x + 28$

Their ages in six years will be their ages now plus 6.

Because the sum of their ages six years from now is 42, we write the equation as

$$(x + 6) + (x + 28) = 42$$

Stacey's age in 6 years   Jo Ann's age in 6 years

Step 4: *Solve the equation.*

$$x + 6 + x + 28 = 42$$
$$2x + 34 = 42$$
$$2x = 8$$
$$x = 4$$

Step 5: *Write your answer.*

> Stacey is now 4 years old, and Jo Ann is $4 + 22 = 26$ years old.

Step 6: *Reread and check.*

> To check, we see that in six years, Stacey will be 10, and Jo Ann will be 32. The sum of 10 and 32 is 42, which checks.

 KEY CONCEPT REVIEW

After reading through the preceding section, respond in your own words and in complete sentences.

A. What is the first step in solving a word problem?

B. Why is the last step of the Blueprint for Problem Solving so important?

C. Write a mathematical expression equivalent to the phrase "twice the sum of a number and ten."

D. Suppose the length of a rectangle is three times the width. If we let x represent the width of the rectangle, what expression do we use to represent the length?

Answers

5. Hayley is 11. Mark is 29.

EXERCISE SET 3.6 ....

VOCABULARY REVIEW . . . .

The following is a list of steps for the Blueprint for Problem Solving. Choose the correct words to fill in the blanks below.

variable	sentence	known
reread	unknown	equation

Step 1: Read the problem, and then mentally list the items that are _____ and unknown.

Step 2: Assign a variable to one of the _____ items, and then translate the other information in the problem to expressions involving the variable.

Step 3: Reread the problem, and then write an equation, using the _____ from Step 2.

Step 4: Solve the _____ found in Step 3.

Step 5: Write your answer using a complete _____ .

Step 6: _____ the problem and check your solution with the original words in the problem.

Problems

A Write each of the following phrases in symbols using the variable x.

1. The sum of x and 3

2. The difference of x and 2

3. The sum of twice x and 1

4. The sum of three times x and 4

5. Five x decreased by 6

6. Twice the sum of x and 5

7. Three times the sum of x and 1

8. Four times the sum of twice x and 1

9. Five times the sum of three x and 4

10. Three x added to the sum of twice x and 1

11. Seven less than four times x

12. Twelve less than twice x

Use the six steps in the Blueprint for Problem Solving to solve the following word problems. You may recognize the solution to some of them by just reading the problem. In all cases, be sure to assign a variable and write the equation used to describe the problem. Write your answer using a complete sentence.

Number Problems

13. The sum of a number and 3 is 5. Find the number.

14. If 2 is subtracted from a number, the result is 4. Find the number.

15. The sum of twice a number and 1 is -3. Find the number.

16. If three times a number is increased by 4, the result is -8. Find the number.

17. When 6 is subtracted from five times a number, the result is 9. Find the number.

18. Twice the sum of a number and 5 is 4. Find the number.

19. Three times the sum of a number and 1 is 18. Find the number.

20. Four times the sum of twice a number and 6 is −8. Find the number.

21. Five times the sum of three times a number and 4 is −10. Find the number.

22. If the sum of three times a number and two times the same number is increased by 1, the result is 16. Find the number.

Geometry Problems

23. The length of a rectangle is twice its width. The perimeter is 30 meters. Find the length and the width.

24. The length of a rectangle is three times its width. The perimeter is 48 inches. Find the length and the width.

25. The length of a rectangle is 4 feet longer than the width. The perimeter is 36 feet. What is the width?

26. The width of a rectangle is 3 feet less than its length. If the perimeter is 22 feet, what is the width?

27. One angle in a triangle measures twice the smallest angle, while the largest angle is six times the smallest angle. Find the measures of all three angles.

28. One angle in a triangle measures seven times the smallest angle, while the largest angle is ten times the smallest angle. Find the measures of all three angles.

29. One angle in a triangle measures three times the smallest angle, while the largest angle is six times the smallest angle. Find the measure of the largest angle.

30. One angle in a triangle measures five times the smallest angle, while the largest angle is thirty times the smallest angle. Find the measure of the largest angle.

31. Two angles in a triangle are equal, and their sum is equal to the third angle in the triangle. What are the measures of each of the three interior angles?

32. Two angles in a triangle are equal. The other angle is three times as large. What are the measures of each interior angle?

33. Two angles are supplementary. If one angle is eleven times the other angle, find the two angles.

34. Two angles are complementary. If one angle is eight times the other angle, find the two angles.

35. Two angles are complementary. If one angle is six degrees larger than twice the other angle, find the two angles.

36. Two angles are supplementary. If one angle is 36 degrees more than three times the other angle, find the two angles.

Age Problems

37. Pat is 20 years older than his son Patrick. In 2 years, the sum of their ages will be 90. How old are they now?

	Now	In 2 Years
Patrick	x	
Pat		

38. Diane is 23 years older than her daughter Amy. In 5 years, the sum of their ages will be 91. How old are they now?

	Now	In 5 Years
Amy	x	
Diane		

39. Dale is 4 years older than Sue. Five years ago the sum of their ages was 64. How old are they now?

40. Pat is 2 years younger than his wife, Wynn. Ten years ago the sum of their ages was 48. How old are they now?

Miscellaneous Problems

41. Magic Square The sum of the numbers in each row, each column, and each diagonal of the square shown here is 15. Use this fact, along with the information in the first column of the square, to write an equation containing the variable x, then solve the equation to find x. Next, write and solve equations that will give you y and z.

x	1	y
3	5	7
4	z	2

42. Magic Square The sum of the numbers in each row, each column, and each diagonal of the square shown here is 3. Use this fact, along with the information in the second row of the square, to write an equation containing the variable a, then solve the equation to find a. Next, write and solve an equation that will allow you to find the value of b. Next, write and solve equations that will give you c and d.

4	d	b
a	1	3
0	c	−2

43. Wages JoAnn works in the publicity office at the state university. She is paid $14 an hour for the first 35 hours she works each week and $21 an hour for every hour after that. If she makes $574 one week, how many hours did she work?

44. Ticket Sales Stacey is selling tickets to the school play. The tickets are $6 for adults and $4 for children. She sells twice as many adult tickets as children's tickets and brings in a total of $112. How many of each kind of ticket did she sell?

Yoga Lessons Ike and Nancy give yoga lessons on Sunday mornings. The lessons cost $6 for studio members and $10 for nonmembers. Half of the money collected for the lessons is paid to Ike and Nancy. The studio keeps the other half. One Sunday morning Ike counts 36 people in the lesson. Use this information to work Problems 45 through 48.

45. What is the least amount of money Ike and Nancy could make?

46. What is the largest amount of money Ike and Nancy could make?

47. At the end of the lesson, the studio gives Ike and Nancy a check for $160 to cover half of the receipts. Can this amount be correct?

48. Besides the number of people in the lesson, what additional information does Ike need to know in order to be sure he is being paid the correct amount?

Getting Ready for the Next Section

Simplify.

49. $\dfrac{10}{5}$

50. $\dfrac{-12}{4}$

51. $\dfrac{-20}{-5}$

52. $\dfrac{16}{-2}$

Find the missing value.

53. $4 \cdot \underline{\quad} = 20$

54. $6 \cdot \underline{\quad} = 30$

55. $4 \cdot \underline{\quad} = 12x$

56. $3 \cdot \underline{\quad} = 15x$

57. $12 \div \underline{\quad} = 6$

58. $25 \div \underline{\quad} = 5$

59. $48 \div \underline{\quad} = 6$

60. $32 \div \underline{\quad} = 8$

FIND THE MISTAKE •

Each sentence below contains a mistake. Circle the mistake and write the correct word(s) or numbers(s) on the line provided.

Each application problem below is followed by the equation needed to solve the problem. However, each equation contains a mistake. Circle the mistake and write the correct equation on the line provided.

1. The sum of a number and 7 times that number is 16. Find the number.

$$7x = 16$$

_____

2. The perimeter of an equilateral triangle is 18 in. What is the length of one side?

$$x + x = 18$$

_____

3. Lisa is 6 years older than her sister Nicole. In 10 years, the sum of their ages will be 56. How old is each now?

$$6x + 10 = 56$$

_____

4. A dance studio charges $8 per class for members and $12 per class for non-members. Suppose the studio made $180 from a class that has 3 times as many members as non-members. How many members are in the class?

$$96(3x) + 12x = 180$$

_____

Trail Guide Project

Math Puzzle

On a sheet of graph paper, compose a math-themed crossword puzzle using the key words in this book. Copy the puzzle, without the answers, and the clues to a separate piece of paper. Exchange puzzles with a partner. Complete your partner's puzzle. Use this project as a great way to study for the final exam.

Combining Like Terms [3.1]

1. $7x + 2x = (7 + 2)x$
     $= 9x$

Two terms are like terms if they have the same variable part. The expressions $7x$ and $2x$ are like because the variable part in each is the same. Like terms are combined by using the distributive property.

Finding the Value of an Algebraic Expression [3.1]

2. When $x = 5$, the expression $2x + 7$ becomes
$2(5) + 7 = 10 + 7 = 17$

An algebraic expression is a mathematical expression that contains numbers and variables. Expressions that contain a variable will take on different values depending on the value of the variable.

The Solution to an Equation [3.2]

3. Is $a = -3$ the solution to the equation $2a - 7 = -13$?
$2(-3) - 7 = -13$
$-6 - 7 = -13$
$-13 = -13$
                yes

A solution to an equation is a number that, when used in place of the variable, makes the equation a true statement.

The Addition Property of Equality [3.2]

4. We solve $x - 4 = 9$ by adding 4 to each side.
$x - 4 = 9$
$x - 4 + 4 = 9 + 4$
$x + 0 = 13$
$x = 13$

Let A, B, and C represent algebraic expressions.

$$\text{If} \qquad A = B$$
$$\text{then} \quad A + C = B + C$$

In words: Adding the same quantity to both sides of an equation will not change the solution.

The Subtraction Property of Equality [3.2]

5. We solve $x + 5 = 20$ by subtracting 5 from each side.
$x + 5 = 20$
$x + 5 - 5 = 20 - 5$
$x + 0 = 15$
$x = 15$

Let A, B, and C represent algebraic expressions.

$$\text{If} \qquad A = B$$
$$\text{then} \quad A - C = B - C$$

In words: Subtracting the same quantity to both sides of an equation will not change the solution.

The Multiplication Property of Equality [3.3]

6. We solve $\frac{x}{3} = 5$ by multiplying each side by 3.

$\frac{x}{3} = 5$

$3 \cdot \frac{x}{3} = 3 \cdot 5$

$x = 15$

Let A, B, and C represent algebraic expressions with C not equal to 0.

$$\text{If} \qquad A = B$$
$$\text{then} \qquad AC = BC$$

In words: Multiplying both sides of an equation by the same nonzero number will not change the solution to the equation.

The Division Property of Equality [3.3]

Let A, B, and C represent real numbers, with C not equal to 0.

$$\text{If} \qquad A = B$$
$$\text{then} \qquad \frac{A}{C} = \frac{B}{C}$$

In words: Dividing both sides of an equation by the same nonzero quantity never changes the solution to the equation.

7. We solve $3x = 18$ by dividing each side by 3.

$$3x = 18$$
$$\frac{3x}{3} = \frac{18}{3}$$
$$x = 6$$

Steps Used to Solve a Linear Equation in One Variable [3.4]

Step 1: Simplify each side of the equation as much as possible. This step is done using the commutative, associative, and distributive properties.

Step 2: Use the addition or subtraction property of equality to get all variable terms on one side of the equation and all constant terms on the other, then combine like terms. A variable term is any term that contains the variable. A constant term is any term that contains only a number.

Step 3: Use the multiplication or division property of equality to get the variable by itself on one side of the equation.

Step 4: Check your solution in the original equation if you think it is necessary.

Evaluating Formulas [3.5]

In mathematics, a formula is an equation that contains more than one variable. For example, the formula for the perimeter of a rectangle is $P = 2l + 2w$. We evaluate a formula by substituting values for all but one of the variables and then solving the resulting equation for that variable.

8. Use the formula $2x + 5y = 14$ to find y when $x = 2$.

$$2(2) + 5y = 14$$
$$4 + 5y = 14$$
$$4 + 5y - 4 = 14 - 4$$
$$5y = 10$$
$$y = 2$$

Blueprint for Problem Solving [3.6]

Step 1: *Read* the problem, and then mentally *list* the items that are known and the items that are unknown.

Step 2: *Assign a variable t*o one of the unknown items. (In most cases, this will amount to letting x equal the item that is asked for in the problem.) Then *translate the other information* in the problem to expressions involving the variables. *Draw a picture if it's helpful.*

Step 3: *Reread* the problem, and then *write an equation,* using the items and the variable listed in Steps 1 and 2, that describes the situation.

Step 4: *Solve the equation* found in Step 3.

Step 5: *Write* your *answer* using a complete sentence.

Step 6: *Reread* the problem, and *check* your solution with the original words in the problem. *Verify* that your answer makes sense in the context of the problem.

Simplify each expression by combining like terms. [3.1]

1. $10a - 2a$

2. $2x - 10x$

3. $12x - 4 + x + 12$

4. $7b - 4 - 9b - 6$

5. $-3(x - 5) + 7x$

6. $5(5x - 2) - 13x + 16$

7. $3(x + 1) + 2(x + 5)$

8. $7(2a + 2) + 4(5a - 1)$

Find the value of each expression when $x = -12$. [3.1]

9. $3x + 14$

10. $-x - 15$

Find the value of each expression when $x = 6$. [3.1]

11. $-3x + 7$

12. $-7 + 2x$

13. Is $x = -4$ a solution to $3x - 6 = 18$? [3.2]

14. Is $x = -3$ a solution to $7x + 4 = -15$? [3.2]

15. Is $x = -3$ a solution to $-2x + 9 = 15$? [3.2]

16. Use the equation $y = 7x - 4$ to find y when $x = -2$. [3.5]

17. Use the equation $4x + 2y = -2$ to find y when $x = 2$. [3.5]

18. Use the equation $y = 3x - 7$ to find x when $y = 8$. [3.6]

Solve each equation. [3.2, 3.3, 3.4]

19. $x - 5 = -12$

20. $x + 3 = 5$

21. $\frac{x}{8} = -15$

22. $6x - 13 = 5x + 3$

23. $5(2x - 9) = -15$

24. $x + 6 - 2 = 5 - 12$

25. $10 - 6 = 8x - 7x + 6$

26. $5(x + 1) - 4x = 2$

27. $-3(x - 7) + 2x - 8 = 4$

28. $4(3x - 11) = 16$

29. $7x = -35$

30. $7 - 16 = 4y - 3y + 2$

31. $3(a - 2) + 1 = 4$

32. $7(x + 8) - 4 = 10$

33. $8x - 10 = -4(x + 3) + 2$

34. $5x - 7 = -7 + 2(x + 3)$

35. **Perimeter of a Rectangle** If a rectangle has a length of 21 meters and a perimeter of 72 meters, find the width of the rectangle. [3.5]

36. **Temperature** Recall that the formula for converting Celsius temperature to Fahrenheit is $F = \frac{9C}{5} + 32$. What is the Fahrenheit temperature if the Celsius temperature is 40 degrees? [3.5]

37. **Temperature** Let $F = 50°$ in the formula $C = \frac{5(F - 32)}{9}$, and solve for C. [3.5]

38. **Rate** Recall that the rate equation is $d = rt$. Find the distance traveled by a car if travels at a constant rate of 65 miles per hour for three hours. [3.5]

39. **Rate** Find the average speed of an airplane that travels 1,422 miles in 3 hours. [3.5]

40. **Volume** The volume V enclosed by a rectangular solid with length l, width w, and height h is $V = lwh$. Find V if $l = 42$ yards, $w = 4$ yards, and $h = 3$ yards. [3.5]

Find the complement and supplement of each angle. [3.5]

41. 72°   **42.** 60°

43. Number Problem Five times the sum of a number and 9 is 25. Find the number. [3.6]

44. Number Problem If the sum of three times a number and two times the same number is increased by 1, the result is 21. Find the number. [3.6]

45. Age Problem Molly is 6 years older than Kevin. Five years ago, Molly was three times older than Kevin. How old are they now? [3.6]

46. Age Problem Sarah is three years younger than her husband Turner. Ten years ago the sum of their ages was 79. How old are they now? [3.6]

47. Geometry The largest angle in a triangle is five times larger than the smallest angle. The other angle is three times the smallest angle. Find the three angles. [3.6]

48. Geometry The width of a rectangle is 3 feet less than its length. If the perimeter is 22 feet, what is the width? [3.6]

49. Geometry Two angles are complementary. If one angle is 3 degrees bigger than twice the other angle, find the two angles. [3.6]

50. Geometry The length of a rectangle is 4 centimeters longer than its width. If the perimeter is 60 centimeters, find the length and the width. [3.6]

Simplify.

1. 6,824
    371
    +4,857

2. 7,849
    − 2,957

Round each of the numbers to the nearest thousand.

3. 9,054

4. 688,909

Simplify.

5. 45
    × 7

6. 56,728
    × 852

7. $\dfrac{267}{3}$

8. $26\overline{)543}$

Use the rule for the order of operations to simplify each expression.

9. $7 + 4 \cdot 9$

10. $4 \cdot 3^2 + 5 \cdot 2^3$

11. $3[2(5) + 3(4)]$

12. $5 \cdot 3^4 + 16 \div 8 - 2^2$

Place either $<$ or $>$ between each of the following pairs of numbers so that the resulting statement is true.

13. $|8| \quad -2$

14. $|-3| \quad |-1|$

Simplify each of the following.

15. $-(-7)$

16. $-|-4|$

17. $-14 + 7$

18. $-571 + 437 + (-502)$

19. $[8 + (-2)] + [5 + (-7)]$ 20. $-86 - 31$

21. $-29 - (-4)$

22. $(-3)^4$

23. -3^4

24. $-8 + 3[-4 - 1]$

25. $-5(-2 - 8) - 4(6 - 10)$ 26. $4(-3)(2 - 5)$

27. $-50 \div (-25)$

28. $\dfrac{0}{-5}$

29. $\dfrac{7(-2) - 6}{-10}$

30. $400 \div (-4)^2$

31. $(3y + 7) + 8$

32. $8(5x + 4)$

33. $-3x + 9x$

34. $5x - 11x$

Evaluate each expression for $x = -4$.

35. $7x - 4$

36. $x^2 - 3$

37. $\dfrac{9x + 2}{2}$

38. $\dfrac{x^3 - 1}{5}$

Solve.

39. $x - 11 = 15$

40. $-3x = 96$

41. $-6x + 1 = 49$

42. $4(2x - 3) = 2(x + 5) + 2$

43. $8(x - 3) - 5x = -30$ 44. $4x - 5 = -2(x + 3) + 1$

45. Use the equation $y = -8x + 1$ to find y when $x = 3$.

46. Use the equation $3x + y = 7$ to find y when $x = -1$.

47. **Number Problem** The sum of five times a number and 9 is -6. Find the number.

48. **Number Problem** Eight less than triple a number is 7. Find the number.

Simplify each expression by combining like terms. [3.1]

1. $7x - 9 + 3x + 4$

2. $3b + 9 - 5b - 6$

3. $4(x - 9) + 7x$

4. $3(4x + 3) - 7x + 4$

Find the value of each expression when $x = -4$. [3.1]

5. $4x + 9$

6. $-2x - 11$

7. Is $x = -2$ a solution to $2x - 10 = 12$? [3.2]

8. Is $x = 4$ a solution to $2x + 5 = 13$? [3.2]

9. Use the equation $y = 4x - 9$ to find x when $y = 3$. [3.5]

10. Use the equation $3x - 2y = -6$ to find y when $x = -4$. [3.5]

Solve each equation. [3.2, 3.3, 3.4]

11. $x - 9 = 4$

12. $\dfrac{x}{9} = -7$

13. $4x - 11 = 3x + 7$

14. $3(x + 7) = -3$

15. $3(2x - 3) - 2 = 2x - 7$

16. $3(x - 9) = 6$

17. Perimeter of a Rectangle If a rectangle has a length of 15 meters and a perimeter of 54 meters, find the width of the rectangle. [3.5]

18. Temperature Recall that the formula for converting Fahrenheit temperature to Celsius $C = \dfrac{5(F - 32)}{9}$. What is the Celsius temperature if the Fahrenheit temperature is 59 degrees? [3.5]

19. Rate Recall that the rate equation is $d = rt$. Find the distance traveled by a car if travels at a constant rate of 45 miles per hour for five hours. [3.5]

20. Rate Find the average speed of an airplane that travels 2,530 miles in 5 hours. [3.5]

21. Number Problem Three times the sum of a number and 7 is -6. Find the number. [3.6]

22. Age Problem Karen is 3 years younger than Susan. Five years ago, the sum of their ages was 41. How old are they now? [3.6]

23. Geometry The largest angle in a triangle is 7 times bigger than the smallest angle. The third angle is 2 times bigger than the smallest angle. Find the three angles. [3.6]

24. Geometry Two angles are complementary. If one angle is 4 times bigger than the other angle, find the two angles. [3.6]

25. Geometry The length of a rectangle is 6 centimeters longer than its width. If the perimeter is 40 centimeters, find the length and the width. [3.6]

FRACTIONS

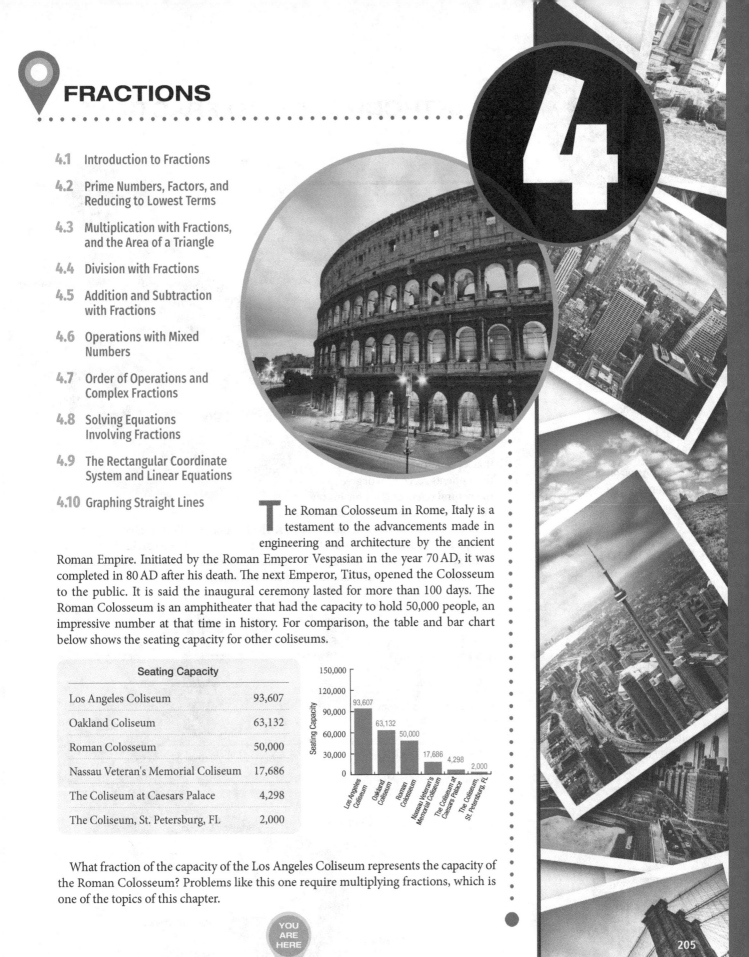

The Roman Colosseum in Rome, Italy is a testament to the advancements made in engineering and architecture by the ancient Roman Empire. Initiated by the Roman Emperor Vespasian in the year 70 AD, it was completed in 80 AD after his death. The next Emperor, Titus, opened the Colosseum to the public. It is said the inaugural ceremony lasted for more than 100 days. The Roman Colosseum is an amphitheater that had the capacity to hold 50,000 people, an impressive number at that time in history. For comparison, the table and bar chart below shows the seating capacity for other coliseums.

Seating Capacity	
Los Angeles Coliseum	93,607
Oakland Coliseum	63,132
Roman Colosseum	50,000
Nassau Veteran's Memorial Coliseum	17,686
The Coliseum at Caesars Palace	4,298
The Coliseum, St. Petersburg, FL	2,000

What fraction of the capacity of the Los Angeles Coliseum represents the capacity of the Roman Colosseum? Problems like this one require multiplying fractions, which is one of the topics of this chapter.

YOU ARE HERE

4.1 INTRODUCTION TO FRACTIONS

KEY WORDS

fraction

numerator

denominator

proper fraction

improper fraction

equivalent fractions

multiplication property for fractions

division property for fractions

mixed numbers

VIDEO EXAMPLES

SECTION 4.1

The information in the table below shows the degrees and certificates by division awarded by El Camino College for one fall semester. The pie chart was created from the table. Both the table and pie chart use fractions to describe the disciplines in which students at El Camino College receive degrees or certificates.

From the table, we see that $\frac{1}{20}$ (one-twentieth) of the students received a degree in the natural sciences. This means one out of every twenty students at El Camino College studies one of the natural sciences. The fraction $\frac{1}{20}$ tells us we have 1 part of 20 equal parts. That is, the students at El Camino College could be divided into 20 equal groups, so that one of the groups contained all the students receiving a degree in natural sciences and only students in natural sciences.

El Camino College Compton Center			
Discipline	Fraction of Students	Discipline	Fraction of Students
General Studies	$\frac{37}{100}$	Natural Sciences	$\frac{1}{20}$
Industry & Technology	$\frac{9}{50}$	Fine Arts	$\frac{1}{25}$
Business	$\frac{13}{100}$	Humanities	$\frac{1}{40}$
Behavioral & Social Sciences	$\frac{11}{100}$	Mathematical Sciences	$\frac{1}{40}$
Health Sciences & Athletics	$\frac{7}{100}$		

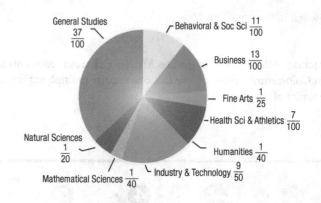

A Identifying Parts of a Fraction

Figure 1 shows a rectangle that has been divided into equal parts, four different ways. The shaded area for each rectangle is $\frac{1}{2}$ the total area.

Now that we have an intuitive idea of the meaning of fractions, here are the more formal definitions and vocabulary associated with fractions.

DEFINITION fraction

A **fraction** is any number that can be put in the form $\frac{a}{b}$ (sometimes written a/b), where a and b are numbers and b is not 0.

Some examples of fractions are

$$\frac{1}{2} \qquad \frac{3}{4} \qquad \frac{7}{8} \qquad \frac{9}{5}$$

One-half   Three-fourths   Seven-eighths   Nine-fifths

We can also visualize fractions as parts of a whole, like so:

 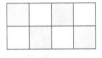

a. $\frac{1}{2}$ is shaded   **b.** $\frac{2}{4}$ are shaded   **c.** $\frac{3}{6}$ are shaded   **d.** $\frac{4}{8}$ are shaded

FIGURE 1

DEFINITION numerator and denominator

The fraction $\frac{a}{b}$ is made of two parts. We call a the **numerator,** and b the **denominator.** Both a and b are called terms of the fraction.

Example 1 Name the numerator and denominator for each fraction.

a. $\frac{3}{4}$ **b.** $\frac{a}{5}$ **c.** 7

Solution

a. The terms of the fraction $\frac{3}{4}$ are 3 and 4. The 3 is called the numerator, and the 4 is called the denominator.

b. The numerator of the fraction $\frac{a}{5}$ is a. The denominator is 5. Both a and 5 are called terms.

c. The number 7 may also be put in fraction form, because it can be written as $\frac{7}{1}$. Because $7 = 7 \div 1$, in this case, 7 is the numerator and 1 is the denominator. We can put any number over 1. Sometimes this is helpful when making computations.

Note As we mentioned earlier, when we use a letter to represent a number, or a group of numbers, that letter is called a variable. In the definition for a fraction, we are restricting the numbers that the variable b can represent to numbers other than 0. We want to avoid writing an expression that would imply division by the number 0.

Practice Problems

1. Name the numerator and denominator for each fraction.

   a. $\frac{5}{6}$ **b.** $\frac{x}{3}$ **c.** 10

Note We are using the word *terms* here differently than we have previously. Now we are using terms to refer to the numerator and denominator. Before, we used the word to describe numbers and/or variables that were separated by addition or subtraction.

Answers

1. **a.** Numerator: 5; denominator: 6
   b. Numerator: x; denominator: 3
   c. Numerator: 10; denominator: 1

DEFINITION proper and improper fraction

A **proper** fraction is a fraction in which the numerator is less than the denominator. If the numerator is greater than or equal to the denominator, the fraction is considered an **improper** fraction.

For example, the fractions $\frac{3}{4}$, $\frac{1}{8}$, and $\frac{9}{10}$ are all proper fractions, because in each case the numerator is less than the denominator.

On the other hand, numbers $\frac{9}{5}$, $\frac{10}{10}$, and 6 are all improper fractions, because in each case the numerator is greater than or equal to the denominator. As we have seen, 6 can be written as $\frac{6}{1}$, in which case 6 is the numerator and 1 is the denominator. The number 1 is also improper because the numerator equals the denominator.

B Fractions on the Number Line

We can give meaning to the fraction $\frac{2}{3}$ by using a number line. If we take that part of the number line from 0 to 1 and divide it into *three equal parts* (because the denominator is 3), we say that we have divided it into thirds (see Figure 2). Each of the three segments is $\frac{1}{3}$ (one third) of the whole segment from 0 to 1.

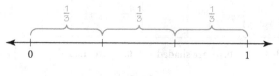

FIGURE 2

Two of these smaller segments together are $\frac{2}{3}$ (two thirds) of the whole segment. And three of them would be $\frac{3}{3}$ (three thirds), or the whole segment, as indicated in Figure 3.

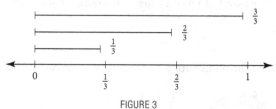

FIGURE 3

Let's do the same thing again with six and twelve equal divisions of the segment from 0 to 1, as seen in Figure 4.

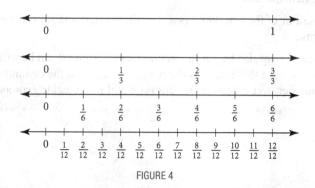

FIGURE 4

The same point that we labeled with $\frac{1}{3}$ in Figure 3 is now labeled with $\frac{2}{6}$ and with $\frac{4}{12}$. Although these three fractions look different, each names the same point on the number line, as shown in Figure 4. All three fractions have the same value, because they all represent the same number. Thus $\frac{4}{12} = \frac{2}{6} = \frac{1}{3}$.

Note There are many ways to give meaning to fractions like $\frac{2}{3}$ other than by using the number line. One popular way is to think of cutting a pie into three equal pieces, as shown below. If you take two of the pieces, you have taken $\frac{2}{3}$ of the pie. This is similar to what we did in Figure 1, but with a circle.

C Equivalent Fractions

DEFINITION   equivalent fractions

Fractions that represent the same number are said to be equivalent. **Equivalent fractions** may look different, but they must have the same value.

Figure 4 helped us find several equivalent fractions. One example is $\frac{4}{12}$, $\frac{2}{6}$, and $\frac{1}{3}$. From this discussion, we can conclude that every fraction has many different representations, each of which is equivalent to the original fraction. The next two properties give us a way of changing the terms of a fraction without changing its value.

PROPERTY   Multiplication Property for Fractions

If a, b, and c are numbers and b and c are not 0, then it is always true that

$$\frac{a}{b} = \frac{a \cdot c}{b \cdot c}$$

In words: If the numerator and the denominator of a fraction are multiplied by the same nonzero number, the resulting fraction is equivalent to the original fraction.

Example 2   Write $\frac{3}{4}$ as an equivalent fraction with a denominator of 20.

Solution   The denominator of the original fraction is 4. The fraction we are trying to find must have a denominator of 20. We know that if we multiply 4 by 5, we get 20. The multiplication property for fractions indicates that we can multiply the denominator by 5 so long as we do the same to the numerator.

$$\frac{3}{4} = \frac{3 \cdot 5}{4 \cdot 5} = \frac{15}{20}$$

The fraction $\frac{15}{20}$ is equivalent to the fraction $\frac{3}{4}$. This is a more efficient method of finding equivalent fractions than drawing a number line.

2. Write $\frac{5}{6}$ as an equivalent fraction with a denominator of 30.

Example 3   Write $\frac{3}{4}$ as an equivalent fraction with a denominator of $12x$.

Solution   If we multiply 4 by $3x$, we will have $12x$. Thus, we multiply the numerator and denominator by $3x$.

$$\frac{3}{4} = \frac{3 \cdot 3x}{4 \cdot 3x} = \frac{9x}{12x}$$

3. Write $\frac{2}{3}$ as an equivalent fraction with a denominator of $15x$.

A similar property holds for division as well.

PROPERTY   Division Property for Fractions

If a, b, and c are integers and b and c are not 0, then it is always true that

$$\frac{a}{b} = \frac{a \div c}{b \div c}$$

In words: If the numerator and the denominator of a fraction are divided by the same nonzero number, the resulting fraction is equivalent to the original fraction.

Answers

2. $\frac{25}{30}$

3. $\frac{10x}{15x}$

4. Write $\frac{20}{25}$ as an equivalent fraction with a denominator of 5.

Example 4   Write $\frac{10}{12}$ as an equivalent fraction with a denominator of 6.

Solution   If we divide the original denominator 12 by 2, we obtain 6. The division property for fractions indicates that if we divide both the numerator and the denominator by 2, the resulting fraction will be equal to the original fraction.

$$\frac{10}{12} = \frac{10 \div 2}{12 \div 2} = \frac{5}{6}$$

From the previous properties we could derive the following about fractions containing negative numbers:

If a and b are numbers and b is not equal to 0, then

$$\frac{-a}{b} = \frac{a}{-b} = -\frac{a}{b} \quad \text{and} \quad \frac{-a}{-b} = \frac{a}{b}$$

5. Write the following as equivalent fractions without a negative sign.
   a. $\frac{-6}{-7}$
   b. $\frac{-x}{-y}$
   c. $\frac{-a}{-4}$

Example 5   Write the following as equivalent fractions without a negative sign.

a. $\frac{-1}{-5}$ b. $\frac{-a}{-b}$ c. $\frac{-5}{-y}$

Solution   Applying the rules for negative numbers, we have

a. $\frac{-1}{-5} = \frac{1}{5}$ b. $\frac{-a}{-b} = \frac{a}{b}$ c. $\frac{-5}{-y} = \frac{5}{y}$

6. Write the following as equivalent fractions by moving the negative sign in front of the fraction bar.
   a. $\frac{-2}{9}$
   b. $\frac{x}{-y}$
   c. $\frac{-8}{b}$

Example 6   Write the following as equivalent fractions by moving the negative sign in front of the fraction bar.

a. $\frac{-1}{4}$ b. $\frac{-a}{b}$ c. $\frac{6}{-y}$

Solution   Applying our rules for negative numbers, we have

a. $\frac{-1}{4} = -\frac{1}{4}$ b. $\frac{-a}{b} = -\frac{a}{b}$ c. $\frac{6}{-y} = -\frac{6}{y}$

The Number 1 and Fractions

There are two situations involving fractions and the number 1 that occur frequently in mathematics. The first is when the denominator of a fraction is 1. In this case, if we let a represent any number, then

$$\frac{a}{1} = a$$

The second situation occurs when the numerator and the denominator of a fraction are the same nonzero number.

$$\frac{a}{a} = 1$$

Answers

4. $\frac{4}{5}$

5. a. $\frac{6}{7}$ b. $\frac{x}{y}$ c. $\frac{a}{4}$

6. a $-\frac{2}{9}$ b. $-\frac{x}{y}$ c. $-\frac{8}{b}$

Example 7 Simplify each fraction.

a. $\frac{24}{1}$　b. $\frac{24}{24}$　c. $-\frac{48}{24}$　d. $-\frac{72}{24}$

Solution In each case, we divide the numerator by the denominator.

a. $\frac{24}{1} = 24$　b. $\frac{24}{24} = 1$

c. $-\frac{48}{24} = -2$ because: $\frac{-48 \div 24}{24 \div 24} = \frac{-2}{1} = -2$

d. $-\frac{72}{24} = -3$ because: $\frac{-72 \div 24}{24 \div 24} = \frac{-3}{1} = -3$

7. Simplify each fraction.

a. $\frac{15}{1}$

b. $\frac{15}{15}$

c. $-\frac{45}{15}$

d. $-\frac{150}{15}$

D Comparing Fractions

We can compare fractions to see which is larger or smaller when they have the same denominator.

Example 8 Write each fraction as an equivalent fraction with denominator 24. Then write the original fractions in order from smallest to largest.

$$\frac{5}{8} \qquad \frac{5}{6} \qquad \frac{3}{4} \qquad \frac{2}{3}$$

Solution We begin by writing each fraction as an equivalent fraction with denominator 24.

$$\frac{5}{8} = \frac{15}{24} \qquad \frac{5}{6} = \frac{20}{24} \qquad \frac{3}{4} = \frac{18}{24} \qquad \frac{2}{3} = \frac{16}{24}$$

Now that they all have the same denominator, we can order them using the values in the numerators. Writing them in order from smallest to largest we have

$$\frac{15}{24} \quad < \quad \frac{16}{24} \quad < \quad \frac{18}{24} \quad < \quad \frac{20}{24}$$

or

$$\frac{5}{8} \quad < \quad \frac{2}{3} \quad < \quad \frac{3}{4} \quad < \quad \frac{5}{6}$$

8. Write each fraction as an equivalent fraction with denominator 36. Then write the original fractions in order from smallest to largest.

$$\frac{5}{9}, \frac{1}{3}, \frac{5}{6}, \frac{5}{12}$$

Example 9 Write each fraction as an equivalent fraction with denominator 24. Then order them from least to greatest.

$$-\frac{1}{4} \qquad -\frac{3}{8} \qquad -\frac{5}{6} \qquad -\frac{5}{8}$$

Solution We begin by writing each fraction as an equivalent fraction with denominator 24.

$$-\frac{1}{4} = -\frac{6}{24} \qquad -\frac{3}{8} = -\frac{9}{24} \qquad -\frac{5}{6} = -\frac{20}{24} \qquad -\frac{5}{8} = -\frac{15}{24}$$

Now we can write them in order from smallest to largest.

$$-\frac{20}{24} \quad < \quad -\frac{15}{24} \quad < \quad -\frac{9}{24} \quad < \quad -\frac{6}{24}$$

or

$$-\frac{5}{6} \quad < \quad -\frac{5}{8} \quad < \quad -\frac{3}{8} \quad < \quad -\frac{1}{4}$$

9. Write each fraction as an equivalent fraction with denominator 36. Then order them from least to greatest.

$$-\frac{1}{3}, -\frac{5}{9}, -\frac{7}{12}, -\frac{1}{6}$$

Answers

7. a. 15　**b.** 1　**c.** -3　**d.** -10

8. $\frac{1}{3} < \frac{5}{12} < \frac{5}{9} < \frac{5}{6}$

9. $-\frac{5}{6} < -\frac{5}{8} < -\frac{3}{8} < -\frac{1}{4}$

E Mixed Numbers

So far, we have defined proper fractions, improper fractions, and equivalent fractions. Another type of fraction is a mixed number. A **mixed number** is the sum of a whole number and a proper fraction. For example, if your friend says she is $5\frac{1}{2}$ feet tall, $5\frac{1}{2}$ is a mixed number.

Here are some further examples of mixed number notation:

$$2\frac{1}{8} = 2 + \frac{1}{8}, \quad 6\frac{5}{9} = 6 + \frac{5}{9}, \quad 11\frac{2}{3} = 11 + \frac{2}{3}$$

The notation used in writing mixed numbers (writing the whole number and the proper fraction next to each other) must always be interpreted as addition. It is a mistake to read $5\frac{3}{4}$ as meaning 5 times $\frac{3}{4}$. With fractions, if we want to indicate multiplication, we must use parentheses or a multiplication symbol. That is,

$$5\frac{3}{4} \text{ is } \textbf{not} \text{ the same as } 5\left(\frac{3}{4}\right).$$

This implies ↗   ↖ These imply
addition. ↘   ↗ multiplication.

$$5\frac{3}{4} \text{ is } \textbf{not} \text{ the same as } 5 \cdot \frac{3}{4}.$$

Later in this chapter, we will learn how to do computations with fractions. For now, we will convert between improper fractions and mixed numbers.

Changing Mixed Numbers to Improper Fractions

To change a mixed number to an improper fraction, we multiply the whole number by the denominator of the fraction, and add the result to the numerator of the fraction. The result is the numerator of the improper fraction we are looking for. The denominator is the same as the original denominator. Let's look at an example.

10. Change $5\frac{2}{7}$ to an improper fraction.

Example 10   Change $2\frac{3}{4}$ to an improper fraction.

Solution   We first multiply 2 and 4 to get 8. Next, we add 8 to 3 to get 11. This is the numerator of our improper fraction. Using the original denominator, we have $\frac{11}{4}$.

The mixed number $2\frac{3}{4}$ is equal to the improper fraction $\frac{11}{4}$. The diagram that follows further illustrates the equivalence of $2\frac{3}{4}$ and $\frac{11}{4}$.

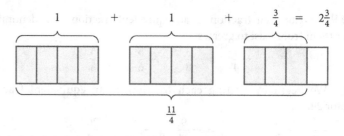

$$1 \qquad + \qquad 1 \qquad + \qquad \frac{3}{4} \quad = \quad 2\frac{3}{4}$$

$$\frac{11}{4}$$

Example 11   Change $5\frac{3}{4}$ to an improper fraction.

Solution   We multiply 5 by 4 and add 3 to get 23. This is the numerator. The denominator is the same as the original. Therefore, the improper fraction equal to $5\frac{3}{4}$ is $\frac{23}{4}$.

Here is a diagram showing what we have done:

Step 1 Multiply $4 \cdot 5 = 20$.

Step 2 Add $20 + 3 = 23$.

Step 2: +

$5\frac{3}{4}$

Step 1: ×

Mathematically, our shortcut is written like this:

$$5\frac{3}{4} = \frac{(4 \cdot 5) + 3}{4} = \frac{20 + 3}{4} = \frac{23}{4}$$

The result will always have the same denominator as the original mixed number

Example 12   Change $-3\frac{7}{8}$ to an improper fraction.

Solution   We will convert $3\frac{7}{8}$ to an improper fraction like we did in the previous example, and then make the result negative.

$$3\frac{7}{8} = \frac{(8 \cdot 3) + 7}{8} = \frac{31}{8}$$

Thus, $-3\frac{7}{8} = -\frac{31}{8}$

Changing Improper Fractions to Mixed Numbers

To change an improper fraction to a mixed number, we divide the numerator by the denominator. The result is used to write the mixed number.

Example 13   Change $\frac{11}{4}$ to a mixed number.

Solution   Dividing 11 by 4 gives us

$$\begin{array}{r} 2 \\ 4\overline{)11} \\ -8 \\ \hline 3 \end{array}$$

We see that 4 goes into 11 two times with 3 for a remainder. We write this result as

$$\frac{11}{4} = 2 + \frac{3}{4} = 2\frac{3}{4}$$

The improper fraction $\frac{11}{4}$ is equivalent to the mixed number $2\frac{3}{4}$.

One way to visualize the results in Example 13 is to imagine running 11 laps on a $\frac{1}{4}$ mile track. Your 11 laps are equivalent to $\frac{11}{4}$ miles. In miles, your laps are equal to 2 miles plus 3 quarter-miles, or $2\frac{3}{4}$ miles.

11. Change $5\frac{7}{8}$ to an improper fraction.

12. Change $-2\frac{4}{9}$ to an improper fraction.

13. Change $\frac{13}{3}$ to a mixed number.

Note   This division process shows us how many ones are in $\frac{11}{4}$ and, when the ones are taken out, how many fourths are left.

Answers

11. $\frac{47}{8}$

12. $-\frac{22}{9}$

13. $4\frac{1}{3}$

14. Write as a mixed number.

a. $\frac{27}{4}$

b. $\frac{76}{8}$

Example 14   Write $\frac{10}{3}$ as a mixed number.

Solution   We will divide by 3 and use the remainder to write the improper fraction as a mixed number.

$$3\overline{)10} \atop \underline{-9} \atop 1} \quad \text{so } \frac{10}{3} = 3 + \frac{1}{3} = 3\frac{1}{3}$$

KEY CONCEPT REVIEW

After reading through the preceding section, respond in your own words and in complete sentences.

A. Which term in the fraction $\frac{7}{8}$ is the numerator?

B. Is the fraction $\frac{3}{9}$ a proper fraction?

C. What word do we use to describe fractions such as $\frac{1}{5}$ and $\frac{4}{20}$, which look different, but have the same value?

D. Why is $\frac{13}{5}$ an improper fraction, but $\frac{3}{5}$ is not an improper fraction?

Answers

14. a. $6\frac{3}{4}$ **b.** $9\frac{1}{2}$

VOCABULARY REVIEW ·

Choose the correct words to fill in the blanks below.

    numerator   equivalent   proper   fraction
    denominator   improper   mixed

1. A _____ is any number that can be put in the form $\frac{a}{b}$, where a and b are numbers and b is not zero.

2. For the fraction $\frac{a}{b}$ (b is not zero), the term a is called the _____, and the term b is called the _____.

3. A(n) _____ fraction is a fraction in which the numerator is less than the denominator. A fraction is considered to be a(n) _____ fraction if the numerator is greater than or equal to the denominator.

4. _____ fractions are fractions that may look different but represent the same number.

5. To change an improper fraction to a _____ number, divide the numerator by the denominator.

Problems

A Name the numerator and denominator of each fraction.

1. $\dfrac{1}{3}$
    2. $\dfrac{3}{5}$
    3. $\dfrac{-2}{3}$
    4. $\dfrac{2}{-4}$
    5. $\dfrac{6}{1}$
    6. $\dfrac{2}{1}$
    7. $\dfrac{a}{-b}$
    8. $\dfrac{-x}{y}$

Complete the following tables.

9.

Numerator a	Denominator b	Fraction $\frac{a}{b}$
3	5	
-1		$-\frac{1}{7}$
	$-y$	$\frac{x}{y}$
$x+1$	x	

10.

Numerator a	Denominator b	Fraction $\frac{a}{b}$
2	9	
	-3	$-\frac{4}{3}$
-1		$\frac{1}{x}$
x		$\frac{x}{x+1}$

11. For the set of numbers $\left\{ \frac{3}{4}, \frac{6}{5}, \frac{12}{3}, \frac{1}{2}, \frac{9}{10}, \frac{20}{10} \right\}$, list all the proper fractions.

12. For the set of numbers $\left\{ \frac{1}{8}, \frac{7}{9}, \frac{6}{3}, \frac{18}{6}, \frac{3}{5}, \frac{9}{8} \right\}$, list all the improper fractions.

B Locate each of the following numbers on this number line.

13. $-\dfrac{3}{4}$ **14.** $-\dfrac{7}{8}$ **15.** $-\dfrac{15}{16}$ **16.** $-\dfrac{3}{8}$ **17.** $-\dfrac{1}{4}$

18. $-\dfrac{1}{16}$ **19.** $\dfrac{1}{2}$ **20.** $\dfrac{1}{4}$ **21.** $\dfrac{15}{16}$ **22.** $\dfrac{7}{8}$

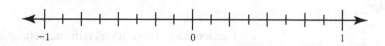

C Write each of the following fractions as an equivalent fraction with a denominator of 6.

23. $\dfrac{2}{3}$ **24.** $\dfrac{1}{2}$ **25.** $-\dfrac{55}{66}$ **26.** $-\dfrac{65}{78}$

Write each of the following fractions as an equivalent fraction with a denominator of 12.

27. $\dfrac{2}{3}$ **28.** $\dfrac{5}{6}$ **29.** $-\dfrac{56}{84}$ **30.** $-\dfrac{143}{156}$

Write each fraction as an equivalent fraction with a denominator of 12x.

31. $\dfrac{1}{6}$ **32.** $\dfrac{3}{4}$ **33.** $\dfrac{1}{2}$ **34.** $\dfrac{2}{3}$

Write each number as an equivalent fraction with a denominator of 8x.

35. 2   **36.** 1   **37.** -5 **38.** -8

Simplify by dividing the numerator by the denominator.

39. $\dfrac{3}{1}$ **40.** $\dfrac{3}{3}$ **41.** $-\dfrac{6}{3}$ **42.** $-\dfrac{12}{3}$ **43.** $\dfrac{-37}{-1}$ **44.** $\dfrac{-37}{-37}$

Divide the numerator and the denominator of each of the following fractions by 2.

45. $\dfrac{6}{8}$

46. $\dfrac{10}{12}$

47. $-\dfrac{86}{94}$

48. $-\dfrac{106}{142}$

Divide the numerator and the denominator of each of the following fractions by 3.

49. $\dfrac{12}{9}$

50. $\dfrac{33}{27}$

51. $\dfrac{-39}{51}$

52. $\dfrac{57}{-69}$

D Write each fraction with the given denominator. Then order the original fractions from least to greatest.

53. Denominator: 100

$\dfrac{3}{10} \quad \dfrac{1}{20} \quad \dfrac{4}{25} \quad \dfrac{2}{5}$

54. Denominator: 30

$\dfrac{1}{15} \quad \dfrac{5}{6} \quad \dfrac{7}{10} \quad \dfrac{1}{2}$

55. Denominator: 20

$\dfrac{7}{10} \quad \dfrac{3}{4} \quad \dfrac{-1}{5} \quad \dfrac{-9}{10}$

56. Denominator: 24

$\dfrac{1}{3} \quad \dfrac{-5}{6} \quad \dfrac{3}{4} \quad \dfrac{-7}{12}$

Change each mixed number to an improper fraction.

57. $4\dfrac{2}{3}$

58. $3\dfrac{5}{8}$

59. $-5\dfrac{1}{4}$

60. $-7\dfrac{1}{2}$

61. $1\dfrac{5}{8}$

62. $1\dfrac{6}{7}$

63. $-15\dfrac{2}{3}$

64. $-17\dfrac{3}{4}$

65. $4\dfrac{20}{21}$

66. $5\dfrac{18}{19}$

67. $12\dfrac{31}{33}$

68. $14\dfrac{29}{31}$

Change each improper fraction to a mixed number.

69. $\dfrac{9}{8}$

70. $\dfrac{10}{9}$

71. $\dfrac{-19}{4}$

72. $\dfrac{-23}{5}$

73. $\dfrac{29}{6}$

74. $\dfrac{7}{2}$

75. $\dfrac{13}{4}$

76. $\dfrac{41}{15}$

77. $\dfrac{-109}{27}$

78. $\dfrac{-319}{23}$

79. $-\dfrac{428}{15}$

80. $\dfrac{769}{27}$

Applying the Concepts

81. One fourth of the first circle below is shaded. Use the other three circles to show three other ways to shade one fourth of the circle.

82. The six-sided figures below are hexagons. One third of the first hexagon is shaded. Shade the other three hexagons to show three other ways to represent one third.

83. For each square below, what fraction of the area is given by the shaded region?

a.

b.

c.

d.

84. For each square below, what fraction of the area is given by the shaded region?

a.

b.

c.

d.

85. Number of Children If there are 3 girls in a family with 5 children, then we say that $\frac{3}{5}$ of the children are girls. If there are 4 girls in a family with 5 children, what fraction of the children are girls?

86. Medical School If 3 out of every 7 people who apply to medical school actually get accepted, what fraction of the people who apply get accepted?

87. Number of Students Of the 43 people who started a math class meeting at 10:00 each morning, only 29 finished the class. What fraction of the people finished the class?

88. Number of Students In a class of 51 students, 23 are freshmen and 28 are juniors. What fraction of the students are freshmen?

89. Height If a man is 71 inches tall, then in feet his height is $5\frac{11}{12}$ feet. Change $5\frac{11}{12}$ to an improper fraction.

90. Height If a woman is 65 inches tall, then her height in feet is $\frac{65}{12}$. Write $\frac{65}{12}$ as a mixed number.

91. Gasoline Prices The price of unleaded gasoline is $305\frac{1}{5}$¢ per gallon. Write this number as an improper fraction.

92. Gasoline Prices Suppose the price of gasoline is $308\frac{1}{5}$¢ if purchased with a credit card, but 5¢ less if purchased with cash. What is the cash price of the gasoline?

Use the chart on the right to answer the following questions.

93. Write the number of iPhones in Europe as an equivalent fraction with denominator 50.

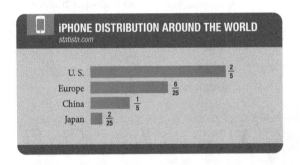

94. Write the number of iPhones in Japan as an equivalent fraction with denominator 75.

Estimating

95. Which of the following fractions is closest to the number 0?

a. $\frac{1}{2}$ b. $\frac{1}{3}$ c. $\frac{1}{4}$ d. $\frac{1}{5}$

96. Which of the following fractions is closest to the number 1?

a. $\frac{1}{2}$ b. $\frac{1}{3}$ c. $\frac{1}{4}$ d. $\frac{1}{5}$

97. Which of the following fractions is closest to the number 0?

a. $\frac{1}{8}$ b. $\frac{3}{8}$ c. $\frac{5}{8}$ d. $\frac{7}{8}$

98. Which of the following fractions is closest to the number 1?

a. $\frac{1}{8}$ b. $\frac{3}{8}$ c. $\frac{5}{8}$ d. $\frac{7}{8}$

Getting Ready for the Next Section

Multiply.

99. $2 \cdot 2 \cdot 3 \cdot 3 \cdot 3$ **100.** $2^2 \cdot 3^3$ **101.** $2^2 \cdot 3 \cdot 5$ **102.** $2 \cdot 3^2 \cdot 5$

Divide.

103. $12 \div 3$ **104.** $15 \div 3$ **105.** $20 \div 4$ **106.** $24 \div 4$

107. $42 \div 6$ **108.** $72 \div 8$ **109.** $102 \div 2$ **110.** $105 \div 7$

FIND THE MISTAKE

Each sentence below contains a mistake. Circle the mistake and write the correct word(s) or numbers(s) on the line provided.

1. For the fraction $\frac{21}{7}$, the numerator is 7. _____

2. The fraction $\frac{90}{15}$ is considered a proper fraction. _____

3. Changing $6\frac{4}{5}$ to an improper fraction gives us $\frac{29}{5}$. _____

4. If we divide the numerator and denominator of the fraction $\frac{8}{12}$ by 4, then we get the equivalent fraction $\frac{4}{3}$. _____

Your instructor is a vital resource for your success in this class. Make note of your instructor's office hours and utilize them regularly. Compile a resource list that you keep with your class materials. This list should contain your instructor's office hours and contact information (e.g., office phone number or email), as well as classmates' contact information that you can utilize outside of class. Communicate often with your classmates about how the course is going for you and any questions you may have. Odds are that someone else has the same question and you may be able to work together to find the answer.

PRIME NUMBERS, FACTORS, AND REDUCING TO LOWEST TERMS

In 2016, Alexander Schulz completed one of the highest and longest slackline walks at a height of 247 meters across Torre Reforma and Torre Bancomer, two of the tallest buildings in Mexico City. A slackline is made of flat nylon webbing and anchored between two points, similar to a tightrope. But in contrast to a taut tightrope, the slackline is strung to allow it to stretch and bounce under the walker's feet.

Suppose the length of a walker's slackline is 30 feet. If the walker walks 15 feet to the middle of the rope, we can say the the walker has walked $\frac{15}{30}$ of the rope's length. We know that he is also standing in the middle of the rope, therefore, he has walked $\frac{1}{2}$ of the rope's length. The fraction $\frac{15}{30}$ is equivalent to the fraction $\frac{1}{2}$; that is, they both have the same value. The mathematical process we use to rewrite $\frac{15}{30}$ as $\frac{1}{2}$ is called reducing to lowest terms. Before we look at that process, we need to define some new terms.

OBJECTIVES

A Identify prime factors of a composite number.

B Reduce fractions to lowest terms.

KEY WORDS

prime number

divisor

composite number

lowest terms

VIDEO EXAMPLES

SECTION 4.2

A Prime and Composite Numbers

DEFINITION prime number

A **prime number** is any whole number greater than 1 that has exactly two **divisors**—itself and 1. Recall, a number is a divisor of another number if it divides it without a remainder.

Prime numbers = {2, 3, 5, 7, 11, 13, 17, 19, 23, 29, 31, 37, . . . }

DEFINITION composite number

Any whole number greater than 1 that is not a prime number is called a **composite number**. A composite number always has at least one divisor other than itself and 1.

$\mathcal{N}ote$ The word *divisor* as we are using it here means the same as the word *factor*. A divisor and a factor of a number are the same thing. A number can't be a divisor of another number without also being a factor of it.

The number 1 is neither prime nor composite.

1. Identify each number as either prime or composite. For those that are composite, give two divisors other than the number itself or 1.
   a. 61
   b. 33

> *Note* This process works by writing the original composite number as the product of any two of its factors and then writing any factor that is not prime as the product of any two of its factors. The process is continued until all factors are prime numbers.

2. Factor 80 into a product of prime factors.

> *Note* There are some techniques for finding the divisors of a number. For instance, if a number ends in 0 or 5, then it is divisible by 5. If a number ends in an even number (0, 2, 4, 6, or 8), then it is divisible by 2. A number is divisible by 3 if the sum of its digits is divisible by 3. For example, 921 is divisible by 3 because the sum of its digits is $9 + 2 + 1 = 12$, which is divisible by 3. These are called divisibility rules.

Example 1   Identify each of the numbers below as either a prime number or a composite number. For those that are composite, give two divisors other than the number itself or 1.

a. 43   **b.** 12

Solution

a. 43 is a prime number, because the only numbers that divide it without a remainder are 43 and 1.

b. 12 is a composite number, because it can be written as $12 = 4 \cdot 3$, which means that 4 and 3 are divisors of 12. Two other divisors (other than 12 and 1) are 2 and 6, because $12 = 2 \cdot 6$.

Every composite number can be written as the product of prime factors. Let's look at the composite number 108. We know we can write 108 as $2 \cdot 54$. The number 2 is a prime number, but 54 is not prime. Because 54 can be written as $2 \cdot 27$, we have

$$108 = 2 \cdot 54$$
$$= 2 \cdot 2 \cdot 27$$

Now the number 27 can be written as $3 \cdot 9$ or $3 \cdot 3 \cdot 3$ (because $9 = 3 \cdot 3$), so

$$108 = 2 \cdot 54$$
$$108 = 2 \cdot 2 \cdot 27$$
$$108 = 2 \cdot 2 \cdot 3 \cdot 9$$
$$108 = 2 \cdot 2 \cdot 3 \cdot 3 \cdot 3$$

This last line is the number 108 written as the product of prime factors. We can use exponents to rewrite the last line.

$$108 = 2^2 \cdot 3^3$$

Example 2   Factor 60 into a product of prime factors.

Solution   We can begin by writing 60 as $6 \cdot 10$ and continue factoring until all factors are prime numbers.

$$60 = 6 \cdot 10$$
$$= 2 \cdot 3 \cdot 2 \cdot 5$$
$$= 2^2 \cdot 3 \cdot 5$$

Notice that if we had started by writing 60 as $3 \cdot 20$, we would have arrived at the same result:

$$60 = 3 \cdot 20$$
$$= 3 \cdot 2 \cdot 10$$
$$= 3 \cdot 2 \cdot 2 \cdot 5$$
$$= 2^2 \cdot 3 \cdot 5$$

Answers

1. a. Prime   **b.** Composite; 3, 11
2. $2^4 \cdot 5$

B Reducing Fractions

We can use the method of factoring numbers into prime factors to help reduce fractions to lowest terms. Here is the definition for lowest terms:

> **DEFINITION** **lowest terms**
>
> A fraction is said to be in **lowest terms** if the numerator and the denominator have no factors in common other than the number 1.

For example, the fractions $\frac{1}{2}, \frac{1}{3}, \frac{2}{3}, \frac{1}{4}, \frac{3}{4}, \frac{1}{5}, \frac{2}{5}, \frac{3}{5}$, and $\frac{4}{5}$ are all in lowest terms, because in each case the numerator and the denominator have no factors other than 1 in common. That is, in each fraction, no number other than 1 divides both the numerator and the denominator exactly (without a remainder).

Now consider the fraction $\frac{6}{8}$. It is not written in lowest terms, because the numerator and the denominator are both divisible by 2. To write $\frac{6}{8}$ in lowest terms, we apply the division property for fractions and divide both the numerator and the denominator by 2.

$$\frac{6}{8} = \frac{6 \div 2}{8 \div 2} = \frac{3}{4}$$

The fraction $\frac{3}{4}$ is in lowest terms, because 3 and 4 have no factors in common except the number 1.

Reducing a fraction to lowest terms is a matter of dividing the numerator and the denominator by all the factors they have in common. We know from the division property for fractions that this will produce an equivalent fraction.

Example 3 Reduce the fraction $\frac{12}{15}$ to lowest terms by first factoring the numerator and the denominator into prime factors, and then dividing both the numerator and the denominator by the factor they have in common.

3. Reduce the fraction $\frac{30}{45}$ to lowest terms by using prime factors.

Solution The numerator and the denominator factor as follows:

$$12 = 2 \cdot 2 \cdot 3 \quad \text{and} \quad 15 = 3 \cdot 5$$

The factor they have in common is 3. The division property for fractions tells us that we can divide both terms of a fraction by 3 to produce an equivalent fraction.

$$\frac{12}{15} = \frac{2 \cdot 2 \cdot 3}{3 \cdot 5} \qquad \text{Factor the numerator and the denominator completely.}$$

$$= \frac{2 \cdot 2 \cdot 3 \div 3}{3 \cdot 5 \div 3} \qquad \text{Divide by 3.}$$

$$= \frac{2 \cdot 2}{5} = \frac{4}{5}$$

The fraction $\frac{4}{5}$ is equivalent to $\frac{12}{15}$ and is in lowest terms, because the numerator and the denominator have no factors other than 1 in common.

We can shorten the work involved in reducing fractions to lowest terms by using a slash to indicate division. For example, we can write the above problem this way:

$$\frac{12}{15} = \frac{2 \cdot 2 \cdot \cancel{3}}{\cancel{3} \cdot 5} = \frac{4}{5}$$

So long as we understand that the slashes through the 3s indicate that we have divided both the numerator and the denominator by 3, we can use this notation.

Answer

3. $\frac{2}{3}$

4. Laura is baking cupcakes for her party. She bakes two dozen cupcakes, and six are eaten. What fraction of the cupcakes are left?

Example 4   Laura is having a party. She puts 4 six-packs of diet soda in a cooler for her guests. At the end of the party, she finds that only 4 sodas have been consumed. What fraction of the sodas are left? Write your answer in lowest terms.

Solution   She had 4 six-packs of soda, which is $4(6) = 24$ sodas. Only 4 were consumed at the party, so 20 are left. The fraction of sodas left is

$$\frac{20}{24}$$

Factoring 20 and 24 completely and then dividing out both the factors they have in common gives us

$$\frac{20}{24} = \frac{2 \cdot 2 \cdot 5}{2 \cdot 2 \cdot 2 \cdot 3} = \frac{5}{6}$$

Note   You may have noticed in Example 4 that we did not need to write the numerator and denominator using prime factors. Rather, we could have used

$$\frac{20}{24} = \frac{4 \cdot 5}{4 \cdot 6} = \frac{5}{6}$$

There is another method for reducing fractions; rather than writing the numerator and denominator as products of prime factors, we will divide the numerator and denominator by any common factor. Let's look at an example using this method.

5. Reduce $\frac{10}{35}$ to lowest terms.

Example 5   Reduce $\frac{6}{42}$ to lowest terms.

Solution   We need to find a common factor of 6 and 42. Because 6 and 42 are even, we can divide their numerator and denominator by 2:

$$\frac{6 \div 2}{42 \div 2} = \frac{3}{21}$$

We will now find a common divisor for 3 and 21. This common divisor is 3:

$$\frac{3 \div 3}{21 \div 3} = \frac{1}{7}$$

Therefore

$$\frac{6}{42} = \frac{1}{7}$$

Perhaps you saw that both 6 and 42 were divisible by 6, giving us:

$$\frac{6 \div 6}{42 \div 6} = \frac{1}{7}$$

By selecting a larger common divisor, we arrived at the simplified fraction faster. This will always happen.

6. Reduce $\frac{6}{30}$ to lowest terms.

Example 6   Reduce $\frac{4}{40}$ to lowest terms.

Solution   We need to find a common divisor for 4 and 40. Because 4 goes into both 4 and 40, we will divide the numerator and denominator by 4:

$$\frac{4 \div 4}{40 \div 4} = \frac{1}{10}$$

We could have arrived at the same answer by dividing the numerator and denominator by 2, twice.

Answers

4. $\frac{3}{4}$

5. $\frac{2}{7}$

6. $\frac{1}{5}$

Example 7 Reduce $\frac{-105}{30}$ to lowest terms.

Solution We need to find a number that goes into both -105 and 30. Because these numbers end in a 5 and a 0, respectively, they are both divisible by 5:

$$\frac{-105 \div 5}{30 \div 5} = \frac{-21}{6}$$

Because 3 is a divisor of -21 and 6, we will now divide the numerator and denominator by 3:

$$\frac{-21 \div 3}{6 \div 3} = \frac{-7}{2}$$

Therefore $\frac{-105}{30}$ is $\frac{-7}{2}$ in lowest terms. We could also have divided by 3 and then 5, or simply by 15.

7. Reduce $-\frac{140}{30}$ to lowest terms.

KEY CONCEPT REVIEW

After reading through the preceding section, respond in your own words and in complete sentences.

A. What is a prime number?

B. Why is the number 22 a composite number?

C. Factor 120 into a product of prime factors.

D. How would you reduce a fraction to lowest terms?

EXERCISE SET 4.2 ·

VOCABULARY REVIEW ·

Choose the correct words to fill in the blanks below.

| prime | composite | divisor | lowest terms |

1. A _____ number is any whole number greater than 1 that has exactly two divisors: 1 and the number itself.

2. A number is a _____ of another number if it divides it without a remainder.

3. Any whole number greater than 1 that is not a prime number is called a _____ number.

4. A fraction is said to be in _____ if the numerator and the denominator have no factors in common other than the number 1.

Problems

A Identify each of the numbers below as either a prime number or a composite number. For those that are composite, give at least one divisor (factor) other than the number itself or the number 1.

1. 11   **2.** 23   **3.** 105   **4.** 41

5. 81   **6.** 50   **7.** 13   **8.** 219

Factor each of the following into a product of prime factors.

9. 12   **10.** 8   **11.** 81   **12.** 210

13. 215   **14.** 75   **15.** 15   **16.** 42

B Reduce each fraction to lowest terms.

17. $\frac{5}{10}$ **18.** $\frac{3}{6}$ **19.** $\frac{4}{6}$ **20.** $\frac{4}{10}$ **21.** $\frac{8}{10}$ **22.** $\frac{6}{10}$

23. $-\frac{36}{20}$ **24.** $-\frac{32}{12}$ **25.** $\frac{42}{66}$ **26.** $\frac{36}{60}$ **27.** $-\frac{24}{40}$ **28.** $-\frac{50}{75}$

29. $-\frac{14}{98}$ **30.** $-\frac{12}{84}$ **31.** $\frac{70}{90}$ **32.** $\frac{80}{90}$ **33.** $\frac{42}{30}$ **34.** $\frac{18}{90}$

35. $-\frac{45}{75}$ **36.** $-\frac{180}{108}$ **37.** $\frac{60}{36}$ **38.** $\frac{66}{84}$ **39.** $\frac{126}{165}$ **40.** $\frac{210}{462}$

41. Reduce each fraction to lowest terms.

  a. $\dfrac{6}{51}$ b. $\dfrac{6}{52}$ c. $\dfrac{6}{54}$ d. $\dfrac{6}{56}$ e. $\dfrac{6}{57}$

42. Reduce each fraction to lowest terms.

  a. $\dfrac{6}{42}$ b. $\dfrac{6}{44}$ c. $\dfrac{6}{45}$ d. $\dfrac{6}{46}$ e. $\dfrac{6}{48}$

43. Reduce each fraction to lowest terms.

  a. $\dfrac{2}{90}$ b. $\dfrac{3}{90}$ c. $\dfrac{5}{90}$ d. $\dfrac{6}{90}$ e. $\dfrac{9}{90}$

44. Reduce each fraction to lowest terms.

  a. $\dfrac{3}{105}$ b. $\dfrac{5}{105}$ c. $\dfrac{7}{105}$ d. $\dfrac{15}{105}$ e. $\dfrac{21}{105}$

45. The approach to each problem below is wrong. Give the correct answer.

  a. $\dfrac{5}{15} = \dfrac{\cancel{5}}{3 \cdot \cancel{5}} = \dfrac{0}{3}$

  b. $\dfrac{5}{6} = \dfrac{3 + \cancel{2}}{4 + \cancel{2}} = \dfrac{3}{4}$

  c. $\dfrac{6}{30} = \dfrac{\cancel{2} \cdot \cancel{3}}{\cancel{2} \cdot \cancel{3} \cdot 5} = 5$

46. The approach to each problem below is wrong. Give the correct answer.

  a. $\dfrac{10}{20} = \dfrac{7 + \cancel{3}}{17 + \cancel{3}} = \dfrac{7}{17}$

  b. $\dfrac{9}{36} = \dfrac{\cancel{3} \cdot \cancel{3}}{2 \cdot 2 \cdot \cancel{3} \cdot \cancel{3}} = \dfrac{0}{4}$

  c. $\dfrac{4}{12} = \dfrac{\cancel{2} \cdot \cancel{2}}{\cancel{2} \cdot \cancel{2} \cdot 3} = 3$

47. Which of the fractions $\frac{6}{8}, \frac{15}{20}, \frac{9}{16},$ and $\frac{21}{28}$ does not reduce to $\frac{3}{4}$?

48. Which of the fractions $\frac{4}{9}, \frac{10}{15}, \frac{8}{12},$ and $\frac{6}{12}$ do not reduce to $\frac{2}{3}$?

Applying the Concepts

The number line below extends from 0 to 2, with the segment from 0 to 1 and the segment from 1 to 2 each divided into 8 equal parts. Locate each of the following numbers on this number line.

49.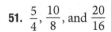

50.

51. $\dfrac{5}{4}, \dfrac{10}{8},$ and $\dfrac{20}{16}$

52. $\dfrac{1}{4}, \dfrac{2}{8},$ and $\dfrac{4}{16}$

53. Determine which of the following is the largest.

  $\dfrac{3}{2}, \ 2, \ \dfrac{5}{4}$

54. Determine which of the following is the smallest.

  $5, \ \dfrac{11}{2}, \ \dfrac{19}{4}$

55. Income A family's monthly income is $2,400, and they spend $600 each month on food. Write the amount they spend on food as a fraction of their monthly income in lowest terms.

56. Hours and Minutes There are 60 minutes in 1 hour. What fraction of an hour is 20 minutes? Write your answer in lowest terms.

57. Final Exam Suppose 33 people took the final exam in a math class. If 11 people got an A on the final exam, what fraction of the students did not get an A on the exam? Write your answer in lowest terms.

58. Income Tax A person making $21,000 a year pays $3,000 in income tax. What fraction of the person's income is paid as income tax? Write your answer in lowest terms.

Nutrition The nutrition labels below are from two different snack crackers. Use them to work the following problems.

Cheez-It™ Crackers

Nutrition Facts
Serving Size 30 g. (About 27 crackers)
Servings Per Container: 9

Amount Per Serving

Calories 150   Calories from fat 70

% Daily Value*

Total Fat 8g	12%
Saturated Fat 2g	10%
Trans Fat 0g	
Polysaturated Fat 4g	
Monounsaturated Fat 2g	
Cholesterol 0mg	0%
Sodium 230mg	10%
Total Carbohydrate 17g	6%
Dietary Fiber less than 1g	3%
Sugars 0g	
Protein 3g	

Vitamin A 2%	●	Vitamin C 0%
Calcium 4%	●	Iron 6%

*Percent Daily Values are based on a 2,000 calorie diet

Goldfish™ Crackers

Nutrition Facts
Serving Size 55 pieces
Servings Per Container About 4

Amount Per Serving

Calories 140   Calories from fat 45

% Daily Value*

Total Fat 5g	8%
Saturated Fat 1g	5%
Cholesterol 5mg	2%
Sodium 250mg	10%
Total Carbohydrate 20g	7%
Dietary Fiber 1g	4%
Sugars 1g	
Protein 4g	

Vitamin A 0%	●	Vitamin C 0%
Calcium 4%	●	Iron 2%

*Percent Daily Values are based on a 2,000 calorie diet

59. What fraction of the calories in Cheez-It™ crackers comes from fat?

60. What fraction of the calories in Goldfish™ crackers comes from fat?

61. For Cheez-It™ crackers, what fraction of the total fat is from saturated fat?

62. What fraction of the total carbohydrates in Goldfish™ crackers is from sugar?

Getting Ready for the Next Section

Multiply.

63. $1 \cdot 3 \cdot 1$

64. $2 \cdot 4 \cdot 5$

65. $3 \cdot 5 \cdot 3$

66. $5 \cdot 5 \cdot 1$

Factor into prime factors.

67. 60

68. 72

69. $15 \cdot 4$

70. $8 \cdot 9$

Expand and multiply.

71. 3^2

72. 4^2

73. 5^2

74. 6^2

Find the area.

75. square

7 in.

76. rectangle

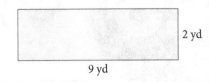

2 yd

9 yd

Improving Your Quantitative Literacy

77. Wimbledon The graphic shown here gives the most Wimbledon Men's Champions by country. Which of the following is the closest to the fraction of champions from France as compared to Australia?

a. $\frac{1}{10}$ **b.** $\frac{1}{3}$ **c.** $\frac{3}{4}$ **d.** $\frac{1}{2}$

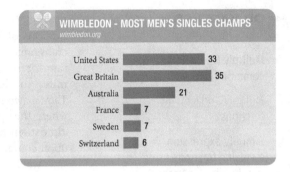

| WIMBLEDON - MOST MEN'S SINGLES CHAMPS |
| wimbledon.org |
United States	33
Great Britain	35
Australia	21
France	7
Sweden	7
Switzerland	6

FIND THE MISTAKE • • • • • • • • • • • • • • •

Each sentence below contains a mistake. Circle the mistake and write the correct word(s) or numbers(s) on the line provided.

1. The number 30 is a prime number because it has 10 as a divisor. _____

2. The number 70 factored into a product of primes is $7 \cdot 10$. _____

3. When reducing the fraction $\frac{32}{48}$ to lowest terms, we divide out the common factors 2 and 3 to get $\frac{2}{3}$.
_____

4. Reducing the fraction $\frac{112}{14}$ to lowest terms gives us $\frac{7}{2}$. _____

LANDMARK REVIEW: CHECKING YOUR PROGRESS • • • • • • • • • • • • • • • •

Name the numerator and denominator for each fraction.

1. $\frac{3}{5}$ **2.** $\frac{1}{3}$ **3.** $\frac{7}{15}$ **4.** $\frac{4}{x}$

Write each of the following fractions as an equivalent fraction with a denominator of $8x$.

5. $\frac{1}{2}$ **6.** $\frac{3}{4}$ **7.** $\frac{1}{8}$ **8.** $\frac{5}{2}$

Reduce each fraction to lowest terms.

9. $\frac{17}{34}$ **10.** $\frac{15}{25}$ **11.** $\frac{48}{80}$ **12.** $\frac{135}{216}$ **13.** $\frac{68}{72}$ **14.** $\frac{93}{126}$

4.3

MULTIPLICATION WITH FRACTIONS, AND THE AREA OF A TRIANGLE

• • • OBJECTIVES • • •

A Multiply fractions with no common factors.

B Multiply and simplify fractions.

C Simplify expressions involving fractions using the distributive property.

D Determine the area of a triangle.

• • • KEY WORDS • • •

product

area of a triangle

VIDEO EXAMPLES

SECTION 4.3

Once a year on Christmas Island, in Australia, millions of bright red crabs migrate from the rain forest for several miles to the beach. They spawn in the sea, where the eggs hatch almost immediately upon contact with the salt water. For days, the crabs swarm train tracks, highways, and other busy thoroughfares on the island. They even take over golf courses, and according to a special rule, a golfer must play a ball where it lies even if a crab knocks it to another spot.

Let's suppose a group of crabs are crawling around a putting green when they hear a golf cart coming. Assume $\frac{3}{4}$ of the crabs scurry into the bushes on either side of the green, $\frac{1}{2}$ of the $\frac{3}{4}$ going to the right and $\frac{1}{2}$ to the left. What fraction of the original group of crabs crawls to the right of the green? This question can be answered by multiplying $\frac{1}{2}$ and $\frac{3}{4}$. Here is the problem written in symbols:

$$\frac{1}{2} \cdot \frac{3}{4} = \frac{3}{8}$$

If you analyze this example, you will discover that to multiply two fractions, we multiply the numerators and then multiply the denominators. We begin this section with the rule for multiplication of fractions.

A Multiplication of Fractions

RULE Product of Two Fractions

The product of two fractions is a fraction whose numerator is the product of the two numerators, and whose denominator is the product of the two denominators. We can write this rule in symbols as follows:

If *a*, *b*, *c*, and *d* represent any numbers and *b* and *d* are not zero, then

$$\frac{a}{b} \cdot \frac{c}{d} = \frac{a \cdot c}{b \cdot d}$$

Recall, the term *product* indicates multiplication.

Example 1   Multiply: $\dfrac{3}{5} \cdot \dfrac{2}{7}$

Solution   Using our rule for the product of two fractions, we multiply the numerators and multiply the denominators.

$$\frac{3}{5} \cdot \frac{2}{7} = \frac{3 \cdot 2}{5 \cdot 7} = \frac{6}{35}$$

The product of $\frac{3}{5}$ and $\frac{2}{7}$ is the fraction $\frac{6}{35}$. The numerator 6 is the product of 3 and 2, and the denominator 35 is the product of 5 and 7.

Practice Problems

1. Multiply: $\dfrac{5}{6} \cdot \dfrac{7}{8}$

Example 2   Multiply: $\dfrac{3}{8} \cdot 5$

Solution   The number 5 can be written as $\frac{5}{1}$. That is, 5 can be considered a fraction with numerator 5 and denominator 1. Writing 5 this way enables us to apply the rule for multiplying fractions.

$$\begin{aligned} \frac{3}{8} \cdot 5 &= \frac{3}{8} \cdot \frac{5}{1} \\[2mm] &= \frac{3 \cdot 5}{8 \cdot 1} \\[2mm] &= \frac{15}{8} \end{aligned}$$

2. Multiply: $\dfrac{7}{12} \cdot 5$

Example 3   Multiply: $\dfrac{1}{2} \left(\dfrac{3}{4} \cdot \dfrac{1}{5} \right)$

Solution   By the order of operations, we find the product inside the parentheses first and then multiply the result by $\frac{1}{2}$.

$$\begin{aligned} \frac{1}{2} \left(\frac{3}{4} \cdot \frac{1}{5} \right) &= \frac{1}{2} \left(\frac{3}{20} \right) \\[2mm] &= \frac{1 \cdot 3}{2 \cdot 20} \\[2mm] &= \frac{3}{40} \end{aligned}$$

3. Multiply: $\dfrac{2}{3} \left(\dfrac{1}{3} \cdot \dfrac{5}{9} \right)$

The properties of multiplication apply to fractions as well. That is, if a, b, and c are fractions, then

$$a \cdot b = b \cdot a \qquad \text{Multiplication with fractions is commutative.}$$

$$a \cdot (b \cdot c) = (a \cdot b) \cdot c \qquad \text{Multiplication with fractions is associative.}$$

Let's solve Example 3 again by utilizing the associative property.

$$\begin{aligned} \frac{1}{2} \left(\frac{3}{4} \cdot \frac{1}{5} \right) &= \left(\frac{1}{2} \cdot \frac{3}{4} \right) \cdot \frac{1}{5} \qquad \text{Associative property} \\[2mm] &= \left(\frac{1 \cdot 3}{2 \cdot 4} \right) \cdot \frac{1}{5} \\[2mm] &= \left(\frac{3}{8} \right) \cdot \frac{1}{5} \\[2mm] &= \frac{3 \cdot 1}{8 \cdot 5} \\[2mm] &= \frac{3}{40} \end{aligned}$$

The result is identical to that of Example 3.

Answers

1. $\dfrac{35}{48}$

2. $\dfrac{35}{12}$

3. $\dfrac{10}{81}$

B Multiplying and Simplifying Fractions

The answers to all the examples so far in this section have been in lowest terms. Let's see what happens when we multiply two fractions to get a product that is not in lowest terms.

4. Multiply: $\frac{9}{16} \cdot \frac{4}{3}$

Example 4   Multiply: $\frac{15}{8} \cdot \frac{4}{9}$

Solution   Multiplying the numerators and multiplying the denominators, we have

$$\frac{15}{8} \cdot \frac{4}{9} = \frac{15 \cdot 4}{8 \cdot 9}$$

$$= \frac{60}{72}$$

> **Note**   Always check to see if your answer can be reduced to lowest terms.

The product is $\frac{60}{72}$, which can be reduced to lowest terms by factoring 60 and 72 and then dividing out any factors they have in common.

$$\frac{60}{72} = \frac{2 \cdot 2 \cdot 3 \cdot 5}{2 \cdot 2 \cdot 2 \cdot 3 \cdot 3}$$

$$= \frac{5}{6}$$

We can actually save ourselves some time by factoring before we multiply. Here's how it is done:

$$\frac{15}{8} \cdot \frac{4}{9} = \frac{15 \cdot 4}{8 \cdot 9}$$

$$= \frac{(3 \cdot 5) \cdot (2 \cdot 2)}{(2 \cdot 2 \cdot 2) \cdot (3 \cdot 3)}$$

$$= \frac{3 \cdot 5 \cdot 2 \cdot 2}{2 \cdot 2 \cdot 2 \cdot 3 \cdot 3}$$

$$= \frac{5}{6}$$

The result is the same in both cases. Reducing to lowest terms before we actually multiply takes less time. Here are some additional examples.

5. Multiply: $-\frac{9}{5} \cdot \frac{10}{21}$

Example 5   Multiply : $-\frac{9}{2} \cdot \frac{8}{18}$

Solution   We will factor, divide out common factors, and then multiply.

$$-\frac{9}{2} \cdot \frac{8}{18} = -\frac{9 \cdot 8}{2 \cdot 18}$$

$$= -\frac{(3 \cdot 3) \cdot (2 \cdot 2 \cdot 2)}{2 \cdot (2 \cdot 3 \cdot 3)}$$

$$= -\frac{3 \cdot 3 \cdot 2 \cdot 2 \cdot 2}{2 \cdot 2 \cdot 3 \cdot 3}$$

$$= -\frac{2}{1}$$

$$= -2$$

> **Note**   Although $-\frac{2}{1}$ is in lowest terms, it is still simpler to write the answer as just -2. We will always do this when the denominator is the number 1.

Answers

4. $\frac{3}{4}$

5. $-\frac{6}{7}$

Example 6 Multiply: $\dfrac{2}{3} \cdot \dfrac{6}{5} \cdot \dfrac{5}{8}$

Solution We can use the same technique, even with three fractions.

$$\dfrac{2}{3} \cdot \dfrac{6}{5} \cdot \dfrac{5}{8} = \dfrac{2 \cdot 6 \cdot 5}{3 \cdot 5 \cdot 8}$$

$$= \dfrac{2 \cdot (2 \cdot 3) \cdot 5}{3 \cdot 5 \cdot (2 \cdot 2 \cdot 2)}$$

$$= \dfrac{\cancel{2} \cdot 2 \cdot \cancel{3} \cdot \cancel{5}}{\cancel{3} \cdot \cancel{5} \cdot 2 \cdot 2 \cdot \cancel{2}}$$

$$= \dfrac{1}{2}$$

6. Multiply: $\dfrac{3}{4} \cdot \dfrac{4}{9} \cdot \dfrac{6}{7}$

In Chapter 1, we did some work with exponents. We can extend our work with exponents to include fractions, as the following examples indicate.

Example 7 Simplify: $\left(-\dfrac{3}{4}\right)^2$

Solution We will multiply $-\dfrac{3}{4}$ and $-\dfrac{3}{4}$.

$$\left(-\dfrac{3}{4}\right)^2 = -\dfrac{3}{4}\left(-\dfrac{3}{4}\right)$$

$$= \dfrac{3 \cdot 3}{4 \cdot 4} \qquad \text{\textit{The product of two negative numbers}}$$
$$\text{\textit{is a positive number.}}$$

$$= \dfrac{9}{16}$$

7. Simplify: $\left(-\dfrac{5}{6}\right)^2$

Example 8 Simplify: $\left(\dfrac{5}{6}\right)^2 \cdot \dfrac{1}{2}$

Solution We will follow the order of operations.

$$\left(\dfrac{5}{6}\right)^2 \cdot \dfrac{1}{2} = \left(\dfrac{5}{6} \cdot \dfrac{5}{6}\right) \cdot \dfrac{1}{2}$$

$$= \dfrac{25}{36} \cdot \dfrac{1}{2}$$

$$= \dfrac{25}{72}$$

8. Simplify: $\left(\dfrac{4}{5}\right)^2 \cdot \dfrac{5}{6}$

The word *of* used in mathematics often indicates multiplication. If we want to find $\dfrac{1}{2}$ of $\dfrac{2}{3}$, then we want to multiply $\dfrac{1}{2}$ and $\dfrac{2}{3}$.

Example 9 Find $\dfrac{1}{2}$ of $\dfrac{2}{3}$.

Solution Knowing the word *of*, as used here, indicates multiplication, we have

$$\dfrac{1}{2} \text{ of } \dfrac{2}{3} = \dfrac{1}{2} \cdot \dfrac{2}{3}$$

$$= \dfrac{1 \cdot 2}{2 \cdot 3} = \dfrac{1}{3}$$

Figure 1 shows how $\dfrac{1}{2}$ of $\dfrac{2}{3}$ is $\dfrac{1}{3}$.

> **Note** As you become familiar with multiplying fractions, you may notice shortcuts that reduce the number of steps in the problem. It's okay to use these shortcuts if you understand why they work and are consistently getting correct answers. If you are using shortcuts and not consistently getting correct answers, then your shortcut may not be accurate. It would be best to go back to showing all your work.

9. Find $\dfrac{3}{4}$ of $\dfrac{5}{6}$.

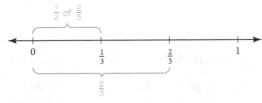

FIGURE 1

C The Distributive Property

The distributive property can also be applied to fractions. Recall that

$$a(b + c) = a \cdot b + a \cdot c \quad \text{or} \quad a(b - c) = a \cdot b - a \cdot c$$

The next example illustrates using the distributive property with fractions.

Example 10   Apply the distributive property, then simplify.

a. $6\left(2 + \frac{1}{3}\right)$ **b.** $12\left(\frac{3}{4} - \frac{1}{2}\right)$ **c.** $-5\left(4 - \frac{2}{5}\right)$

Solution   Apply the distributive property to each expression.

a. $6\left(2 + \frac{1}{3}\right) = 6 \cdot 2 + 6 \cdot \frac{1}{3} = 12 + \frac{6}{3} = 12 + 2 = 14$

b. $12\left(\frac{3}{4} - \frac{1}{2}\right) = 12 \cdot \frac{3}{4} - 12 \cdot \frac{1}{2} = \frac{12}{1} \cdot \frac{3}{4} - \frac{12}{1} \cdot \frac{1}{2} = 9 - 6 = 3$

c. $-5\left(4 - \frac{2}{5}\right) = -5 \cdot 4 - (-5)\frac{2}{5} = -20 + \frac{10}{5} = -20 + 2 = -18$

10. Apply the distributive property, then simplify.

a. $5\left(4 + \frac{3}{5}\right)$

b. $8\left(\frac{3}{4} - \frac{1}{2}\right)$

c. $-3\left(2 - \frac{1}{3}\right)$

FACTS FROM GEOMETRY

The Area of a Triangle
The formula for the area of a triangle is one application of multiplication with fractions. Figure 2 shows a triangle with base b and height h. Below the triangle is the formula for its area. As you can see, it is a product containing the fraction $\frac{1}{2}$.

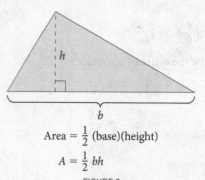

Area = $\frac{1}{2}$ (base)(height)

$A = \frac{1}{2} bh$

FIGURE 2

Note   Sometimes the commutative property is very helpful when finding the area of triangles. Consider a triangle with base 9 inches and height 8 inches. Then

$A = \frac{1}{2} \cdot 9 \cdot 8$
$= \frac{1}{2} \cdot 8 \cdot 9$
$= 4 \cdot 9$
$= 36 \text{ in.}^2$

Example 11   Find the area of the triangle in Figure 3.

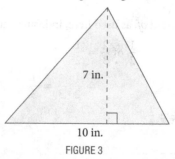

7 in.

10 in.

FIGURE 3

11. Find the area of a triangle with base 8 in. and height 11 in.

Solution   Applying the formula for the area of a triangle, we have

$$A = \frac{1}{2} bh = \frac{1}{2} \cdot 10 \cdot 7 = 5 \cdot 7 = 35 \text{ in}^2$$

Answers
10. a. 23   **b.** 2   **c.** −5
11. 44 in.²

KEY CONCEPT REVIEW · · · · · · · · · · · · · · · · · ·

After reading through the preceding section, respond in your own words and in complete sentences.

A. Explain how to multiply fractions.

B. Find $\frac{1}{3}$ of $\frac{6}{7}$.

C. Give an example of a problem involving fractions in which it would be helpful to use the commutative or associative property of multiplication.

D. Find the area of a triangle with a base of 9 inches and a height of 12 inches.

Choose the correct words to fill in the blanks below.

triangle   of   fractions   product

1. The _____ of two fractions is a fraction whose numerator is the product of the two numerators, and whose denominator is the product of the two denominators.

2. In symbols, the multiplication of _____ is written as $\frac{a}{b} \cdot \frac{c}{d} = \frac{a \cdot c}{b \cdot d}$.

3. The word _____ used in connection with fractions indicates multiplication.

4. The formula for the area of a _____ is $A = \frac{1}{2}bh$.

Problems

A Find each of the following products. (Multiply.)

1. $\frac{2}{3} \cdot \frac{4}{5}$

2. $\frac{5}{6} \cdot \frac{7}{4}$

3. $\frac{1}{2} \cdot \frac{7}{4}$

4. $\frac{3}{5}\left(-\frac{4}{7}\right)$

5. $\frac{5}{3} \cdot \frac{3}{5}$

6. $\frac{6}{7}\left(\frac{7}{6}\right)$

7. $\frac{3}{4} \cdot 9$

8. $\frac{2}{3}(-5)$

9. $\frac{1}{2} \cdot \frac{1}{3} \cdot \frac{1}{4}$

10. $\frac{2}{3} \cdot \frac{4}{5} \cdot \frac{1}{3}$

11. $\frac{2}{5} \cdot \frac{3}{5} \cdot \frac{4}{5}$

12. $\frac{3}{2} \cdot \frac{5}{2} \cdot \frac{7}{2}$

13. $\frac{1}{4}\left(-\frac{3}{4}\right)\frac{3}{4}$

14. $\frac{4}{3}\left(-\frac{5}{3}\right)\frac{7}{3}$

Complete the following tables.

15.

First Number x	Second Number y	Their Product xy
$\frac{1}{2}$	$\frac{2}{3}$	
$\frac{2}{3}$	$\frac{3}{4}$	
$\frac{3}{4}$	$\frac{4}{5}$	
$\frac{5}{a}$	$-\frac{a}{6}$	

16.

First Number x	Second Number y	Their Product xy
12	$\frac{1}{2}$	
12	$\frac{1}{3}$	
12	$\frac{1}{4}$	
12	$\frac{1}{6}$	

17.

First Number	Second Number	Their Product
x	y	xy
$\frac{1}{2}$	30	
$\frac{1}{5}$	30	
$\frac{1}{6}$	30	
$\frac{1}{15}$	30	

18.

First Number	Second Number	Their Product
x	y	xy
$\frac{1}{3}$	$\frac{3}{5}$	
$\frac{3}{5}$	$\frac{5}{7}$	
$\frac{5}{7}$	$\frac{7}{9}$	
$-\frac{7}{b}$	$\frac{b}{11}$	

B Multiply each of the following. Be sure all answers are written in lowest terms.

19. $\frac{4}{7}\left(-\frac{7}{4}\right)$

20. $-\frac{2}{9}\left(\frac{9}{2}\right)$

21. $\frac{9}{20} \cdot \frac{4}{3}$

22. $\frac{35}{16}\left(\frac{-2}{45}\right)$

23. $\frac{3}{4} \cdot 12$

24. $\frac{3}{4} \cdot 20$

25. $\frac{1}{3}(3)$

26. $\frac{1}{5}(5)$

27. $\frac{2}{5}(-20)$

28. $\frac{3}{5} \cdot 15$

29. $\frac{72}{35}\left(\frac{-5}{12}\right)\left(\frac{1}{10}\right)$

30. $\left(\frac{8}{3}\right)\left(\frac{8}{49}\right)\left(\frac{1}{10}\right)$

Expand and simplify each of the following.

31. $\left(\frac{2}{3}\right)^2$

32. $\left(\frac{3}{5}\right)^2$

33. $\left(\frac{3}{4}\right)^2$

34. $\left(\frac{2}{7}\right)^2$

35. $\left(\frac{1}{2}\right)^2$

36. $\left(-\frac{1}{3}\right)^2$

37. $\left(\frac{2}{3}\right)^3$

38. $\left(-\frac{3}{5}\right)^3$

39. $\left(\frac{3}{4}\right)^2 \cdot \frac{8}{9}$

40. $\left(\frac{5}{6}\right)^2 \cdot \frac{12}{15}$

41. $\left(\frac{1}{2}\right)^2 \left(\frac{3}{5}\right)^2$

42. $\left(\frac{3}{8}\right)^2 \left(-\frac{4}{3}\right)^2$

43. $\left(\frac{1}{2}\right)^2 \cdot 8 + \left(\frac{1}{3}\right)^2 \cdot 9$

44. $\left(\frac{2}{3}\right)^2 \cdot 9 + \left(\frac{1}{2}\right)^2 \cdot 4$

45. Find $\frac{3}{8}$ of 64.

46. Find $\frac{2}{3}$ of 18.

47. What is $\frac{1}{3}$ of the sum of 8 and 4?

48. What is $\frac{3}{5}$ of the sum of 8 and 7?

49. Find $\frac{1}{2}$ of $\frac{3}{4}$ of 24.

50. Find $\frac{3}{5}$ of $\frac{1}{3}$ of 15.

Find the mistakes in the following problems. Correct the right-hand side of each one.

51. $\frac{1}{2} \cdot \frac{3}{5} = \frac{4}{10}$

52. $\frac{2}{7} \cdot \frac{3}{5} = \frac{5}{35}$

53. $-\frac{3}{4}\left(-\frac{1}{3}\right) = -\frac{1}{4}$

54. $-\frac{2}{5}\left(-\frac{2}{3}\right) = -\frac{4}{15}$

C Apply the distributive property, then simplify.

55. $4\left(3 + \frac{1}{2}\right)$

56. $4\left(2 - \frac{3}{4}\right)$

57. $-12\left(\frac{1}{2} + \frac{2}{3}\right)$

58. $-12\left(\frac{3}{4} - \frac{1}{6}\right)$

59. $9\left(\frac{2}{3} - \frac{1}{9}\right)$

60. $12\left(\frac{1}{2} - \frac{1}{3}\right)$

61. $-16\left(\frac{5}{8} - \frac{1}{4}\right)$

62. $-24\left(\frac{2}{3} - \frac{1}{6}\right)$

D Find the area of each figure.

63.

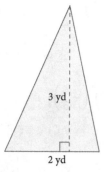

3 yd

2 yd

64.

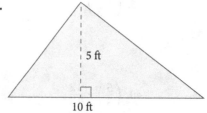

5 ft

10 ft

65. Find the area of the triangle with base 19 inches and height 14 inches.

66. Find the area of the triangle with base 13 inches and height 8 inches.

67. The base of a triangle is $\frac{4}{3}$ feet and the height is $\frac{2}{3}$ feet. Find the area.

68. The base of a triangle is $\frac{8}{7}$ feet and the height is $\frac{14}{5}$ feet. Find the area.

Applying the Concepts

Use the information in the pie chart to answer the following questions. Round to the nearest student.

69. Reading a Pie Chart If there are approximately 16,200 students attending State College, approximately how many of them are studying agriculture?

70. Reading a Pie Chart If there are approximately 16,200 students attending State College, how many of them are studying engineering?

State College Enrollment

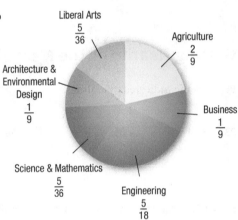

71. Hot Air Balloon Aerostar International makes a hot air balloon called the Rally 105 that has a volume of 105,400 cubic feet. Another balloon, the Rally 126, was designed with a volume that is approximately $\frac{6}{5}$ the volume of the Rally 105. Find the volume of the Rally 126 to the nearest hundred cubic feet.

72. Health Care According to the Department of Veteran's Affairs, approximately $\frac{4}{25}$ of military veterans have diabetes. If there approximately are 3 million veterans, how many have diabetes?

73. Bicycle Safety The National Safe Kids Campaign and Bell Sports sponsored a study that surveyed approximately 8,200 children ages 5 to 14 who were riding bicycles. Approximately $\frac{2}{5}$ of the children were wearing helmets, and of those, only $\frac{13}{20}$ were wearing the helmets correctly. About how many of the children were wearing helmets correctly?

74. Bicycle Safety From the information in the previous problem, how many of the children surveyed do not wear helmets?

Geometric Sequences A geometric sequence is a sequence in which each term comes from the previous term by multiplying by the same number each time. For example, the sequence $1, \frac{1}{2}, \frac{1}{4}, \frac{1}{8}, \ldots$ is a geometric sequence in which each term is found by multiplying the previous term by $\frac{1}{2}$. By observing this fact, we know that the next term in the sequence will be $\frac{1}{8} \cdot \frac{1}{2} = \frac{1}{16}$.

Find the next number in each of the geometric sequences below.

75. $1, \frac{1}{3}, \frac{1}{9}, \ldots$

76. $1, \frac{1}{4}, \frac{1}{16}, \ldots$

77. $\frac{3}{2}, 1, \frac{2}{3}, \frac{4}{9}, \ldots$

78. $\frac{2}{3}, 1, \frac{3}{2}, \frac{9}{4}, \ldots$

Estimating For each problem below, mentally estimate if the answer will be closest to 0, 1, 2 or 3. Make your estimate without using pencil and paper or a calculator.

79. $\frac{11}{5} \cdot \frac{19}{20}$

80. $\frac{3}{5} \cdot \frac{1}{20}$

81. $\frac{16}{5} \cdot \frac{23}{24}$

82. $\frac{9}{8} \cdot \frac{31}{32}$

Getting Ready for the Next Section

Perform the indicated operations.

83. $8 \div 4$

84. $8 \cdot \frac{1}{4}$

85. $15 \div 3$

86. $15 \cdot \frac{1}{3}$

87. $18 \div 6$

88. $18 \cdot \frac{1}{6}$

For each number below, find a number to multiply it by to obtain 1.

89. $\frac{3}{4}$

90. $\frac{9}{5}$

91. $\frac{1}{3}$

92. $\frac{1}{4}$

93. 7

94. 2

FIND THE MISTAKE •

Each sentence below contains a mistake. Circle the mistake and write the correct word(s) or numbers(s) on the line provided.

1. To find the product of two fractions, multiply the numerators and put them over the largest denominator. _____

2. To multiply $\frac{6}{7}$ by $\frac{12}{9}$, find the product of the numerators and divide it by the sum of the denominators to get $\frac{72}{63}$. _____

3. Simplifying $\left(\frac{5}{6}\right)^2 \cdot \frac{8}{9}$ gives $\frac{80}{54} = \frac{40}{27}$. _____

4. The area of a triangle with a height of 14 inches and a base of 32 inches is 448 square inches. _____

DIVISION WITH FRACTIONS

In 2010, a Peruvian inventor won the $200,000 grand prize for a competition that requested its entrants to suggest a new and ingenious way to save Earth. To battle global warming, the inventor proposed covering 173 acres of dry rocky land in the Andes Mountains with a mixture made from egg whites, lime, and water. The mixture creates a whitewash that when spread over the rocks would reflect sunlight and ideally reduce temperatures, thus slowing the melting of the area's glaciers.

Suppose a truck transports the whitewash in a 32-gallon tank up to the mountaintop. Let's say the inventor used a bucket that only held $\frac{3}{4}$ of a gallon to pour the whitewash onto the rocks. How many times would the inventor need to fill up his bucket to empty the tank? In order to answer this question, we need to learn more about how to divide with fractions. But before we define division with fractions, we must first introduce the idea of reciprocals. Look at the following multiplication problems:

$$\frac{3}{4} \cdot \frac{4}{3} = \frac{12}{12} = 1 \qquad \frac{7}{8} \cdot \frac{8}{7} = \frac{56}{56} = 1$$

In each case the product is 1. Whenever the product of two numbers is 1, we say the two numbers are reciprocals.

OBJECTIVES

A Divide fractions and simplify.

B Simplify expressions using order of operations with division of fractions.

KEY WORDS

reciprocal

divisor

quotient

VIDEO EXAMPLES

SECTION 4.4

A Dividing Fractions

DEFINITION reciprocals

Two numbers whose product is 1 are said to be **reciprocals.** In symbols, the reciprocal of $\frac{a}{b}$ is $\frac{b}{a}$, because

$$\frac{a}{b} \cdot \frac{b}{a} = \frac{a \cdot b}{b \cdot a} = \frac{a \cdot b}{a \cdot b} = 1 \qquad (a \neq 0, b \neq 0)$$

241

Every number has a reciprocal except 0. The reason 0 does not have a reciprocal is because the product of *any* number with 0 is 0. It can never be 1. Reciprocals of whole numbers are fractions with 1 as the numerator. For example, the reciprocal of 5 is $\frac{1}{5}$, because

$$5 \cdot \frac{1}{5} = \frac{5}{1} \cdot \frac{1}{5} = \frac{5}{5} = 1$$

Table 1 lists some numbers and their reciprocals.

Table 1

Number	Reciprocal	Reason
$\frac{3}{4}$	$\frac{4}{3}$	Because $\frac{3}{4} \cdot \frac{4}{3} = \frac{12}{12} = 1$
$\frac{9}{5}$	$\frac{5}{9}$	Because $\frac{9}{5} \cdot \frac{5}{9} = \frac{45}{45} = 1$
$\frac{1}{3}$	3	Because $\frac{1}{3} \cdot 3 = \frac{1}{3} \cdot \frac{3}{1} = \frac{3}{3} = 1$
7	$\frac{1}{7}$	Because $7 \cdot \frac{1}{7} = \frac{7}{1} \cdot \frac{1}{7} = \frac{7}{7} = 1$

Division with fractions is accomplished by using reciprocals. More specifically, we can define division by a fraction to be the same as multiplication by its reciprocal. Here is the precise definition:

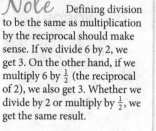

DEFINITION division by a fraction

If a, b, c, and d are numbers and b, c, and d are all not equal to 0, then

$$\frac{a}{b} \div \frac{c}{d} = \frac{a}{b} \cdot \frac{d}{c}$$

In words: We replace the divisor with its reciprocal and multiply.

> **Note** Defining division to be the same as multiplication by the reciprocal should make sense. If we divide 6 by 2, we get 3. On the other hand, if we multiply 6 by $\frac{1}{2}$ (the reciprocal of 2), we also get 3. Whether we divide by 2 or multiply by $\frac{1}{2}$, we get the same result.

Practice Problems

1. Divide: $\frac{3}{4} \div \frac{1}{6}$

Example 1   Divide: $\frac{1}{2} \div \frac{1}{4}$

Solution   The divisor is $\frac{1}{4}$, and its reciprocal is $\frac{4}{1}$. Applying the definition of division for fractions, we have

$$\frac{1}{2} \div \frac{1}{4} = \frac{1}{2} \cdot \frac{4}{1}$$

$$= \frac{1 \cdot 4}{2 \cdot 1}$$

$$= \frac{1 \cdot 2 \cdot 2}{2 \cdot 1}$$

$$= \frac{2}{1}$$

$$= 2$$

The quotient of $\frac{1}{2}$ and $\frac{1}{4}$ is 2. Or, $\frac{1}{4}$ "goes into" $\frac{1}{2}$ two times. Our definition for division of fractions gives us answers that are consistent with what we know about fractions from previous experience. Because 2 times $\frac{1}{4}$ is $\frac{2}{4}$ or $\frac{1}{2}$, it follows that $\frac{1}{2}$ divided by $\frac{1}{4}$ should be 2.

Answer

1. $\frac{9}{2}$

Example 2 Divide: $-\dfrac{3}{8} \div \dfrac{9}{4}$

Solution Dividing by $\dfrac{9}{4}$ is the same as multiplying by its reciprocal, which is $\dfrac{4}{9}$.

$$-\frac{3}{8} \div \frac{9}{4} = -\frac{3}{8} \cdot \frac{4}{9}$$

$$= -\frac{3 \cdot 2 \cdot 2}{2 \cdot 2 \cdot 2 \cdot 3 \cdot 3}$$

$$= -\frac{1}{6}$$

The quotient of $-\dfrac{3}{8}$ and $\dfrac{9}{4}$ is $-\dfrac{1}{6}$.

2. Divide: $-\dfrac{8}{15} \div \dfrac{4}{5}$

Example 3 Divide: $\dfrac{2}{3} \div 2$

Solution The reciprocal of 2 is $\dfrac{1}{2}$. Applying the definition for division of fractions, we have

$$\frac{2}{3} \div 2 = \frac{2}{3} \cdot \frac{1}{2}$$

$$= \frac{2 \cdot 1}{3 \cdot 2}$$

$$= \frac{1}{3}$$

3. Divide: $\dfrac{5}{6} \div 3$

Example 4 Divide: $2 \div \left(-\dfrac{1}{3}\right)$

Solution We replace $-\dfrac{1}{3}$ by its reciprocal, which is -3, and multiply.

$$2 \div \left(-\frac{1}{3}\right) = 2(-3)$$

$$= -6$$

4. Divide: $4 \div \left(-\dfrac{2}{3}\right)$

Here are some further examples of division with fractions. Notice we are simplifying using common factors and not all prime factors. We showed that this technique is valid earlier in the chapter.

Example 5 Divide: $-\dfrac{4}{27} \div \dfrac{16}{9}$

Solution We replace $\dfrac{16}{9}$ by its reciprocal and multiply.

$$-\frac{4}{27} \div \frac{16}{9} = -\frac{4}{27} \cdot \frac{9}{16}$$

$$= -\frac{4 \cdot 9}{3 \cdot 9 \cdot 4 \cdot 4}$$

$$= -\frac{1}{12}$$

5. Divide: $-\dfrac{9}{16} \div \dfrac{9}{4}$

Answers

2. $-\dfrac{2}{3}$

3. $\dfrac{5}{18}$

4. -6

5. $-\dfrac{1}{4}$

6. Divide.

   a. $\frac{15}{26} \div 5$

   b. $18 \div \frac{9}{10}$

Example 6   Divide.

  a. $\frac{16}{35} \div 8$ **b.** $27 \div \frac{3}{2}$

Solution

a. $\frac{16}{35} \div 8 = \frac{16}{35} \cdot \frac{1}{8}$ **b.** $27 \div \frac{3}{2} = 27 \cdot \frac{2}{3}$

$$= \frac{2 \cdot 8 \cdot 1}{35 \cdot 8} \qquad\qquad\qquad = \frac{3 \cdot 9 \cdot 2}{3}$$

$$= \frac{2}{35} \qquad\qquad\qquad\qquad = 18$$

B Order of Operations

The next two examples combine what we have learned about division of fractions with the order of operations.

7. Simplify: $25 \div \left(\frac{5}{6}\right)^2 + 32 \div \left(\frac{4}{5}\right)^2$

Example 7   Simplify $32 \div \left(\frac{4}{3}\right)^2 + 75 \div \left(\frac{5}{2}\right)^2$

Solution   According to the rule for order of operations, we must first evaluate the numbers with exponents, then we divide, and finally we add.

$$32 \div \left(\frac{4}{3}\right)^2 + 75 \div \left(\frac{5}{2}\right)^2 = 32 \div \frac{16}{9} + 75 \div \frac{25}{4}$$

$$= 32 \cdot \frac{9}{16} + 75 \cdot \frac{4}{25}$$

$$= 18 + 12$$

$$= 30$$

8. The quotient of $\frac{2}{3}$ and $\frac{1}{6}$ is decreased by 2. What number results?

Example 8   The quotient of $\frac{8}{3}$ and $\frac{1}{6}$ is increased by 5. What number results?

Solution   Translating to symbols, we have

$$\frac{8}{3} \div \frac{1}{6} + 5 = \frac{8}{3} \cdot \frac{6}{1} + 5$$

$$= 16 + 5$$

$$= 21$$

9. Repeat Example 9 if they have 16 yards of material, and each blanket requires $\frac{2}{3}$ yard of material.

Example 9   A 4-H Club is making blankets to keep their lambs clean at the county fair. If each blanket requires $\frac{3}{4}$ yard of material, how many blankets can they make from 9 yards of material?

Solution   To answer this question we must divide 9 by $\frac{3}{4}$ because we are dividing the 9 yards into pieces that measure $\frac{3}{4}$ yard.

$$9 \div \frac{3}{4} = 9 \cdot \frac{4}{3}$$

$$= 3 \cdot 4$$

$$= 12$$

They can make 12 blankets from the 9 yards of material.

Answers

6. a. $\frac{3}{26}$ **b.** 20

7. 86

8. 2

9. 24 blankets

KEY CONCEPT REVIEW

After reading through the preceding section, respond in your own words and in complete sentences.

A. What do we call two numbers whose product is 1?

B. True or false? The quotient of $\frac{3}{5}$ and $\frac{3}{8}$ is the same as the product of $\frac{3}{5}$ and $\frac{8}{3}$.

C. How are multiplication and division of fractions related?

D. Dividing by $\frac{19}{9}$ is the same as multiplying by what number?

 Spotlight on Success

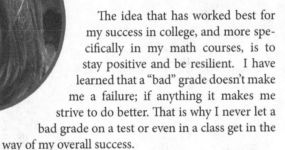

STEFANIE, student instructor

Never confuse a single defeat with a final defeat. ~ *F. Scott Fitzgerald*

The idea that has worked best for my success in college, and more specifically in my math courses, is to stay positive and be resilient. I have learned that a "bad" grade doesn't make me a failure; if anything it makes me strive to do better. That is why I never let a bad grade on a test or even in a class get in the way of my overall success.

By sticking with this positive attitude, I have been able to achieve my goals. My grades have never represented how well I know the material. This is because I have struggled with test anxiety and it has consistently lowered my test scores in a number of courses. However, I have not let it defeat me. When I applied to graduate school, I did not meet the grade requirements for my top two schools, but that did not stop me from applying.

One school asked that I convince them that my knowledge of mathematics was more than my grades indicated. If I had let my grades stand in the way of my goals, I wouldn't have been accepted to both of my top two schools, and will be attending one of them in the Fall, on my way to becoming a math teacher.

EXERCISE SET 4.4

Problems

A Find the quotient in each case by replacing the divisor by its reciprocal and multiplying.

1. $\frac{3}{4} \div \frac{1}{5}$ **2.** $\frac{1}{3} \div \frac{1}{2}$ **3.** $\frac{2}{3} \div \frac{1}{2}$ **4.** $\frac{5}{8} \div \frac{1}{4}$

5. $6 \div \frac{2}{3}$ **6.** $8 \div \left(-\frac{3}{4}\right)$ **7.** $20 \div \frac{1}{10}$ **8.** $16 \div \frac{1}{8}$

9. $\frac{3}{4} \div 2$ **10.** $\frac{3}{5} \div 2$ **11.** $\frac{7}{8} \div \left(-\frac{7}{8}\right)$ **12.** $\frac{4}{3} \div \frac{4}{3}$

13. $-\frac{7}{8} \div \frac{8}{7}$ **14.** $-\frac{4}{3} \div \frac{3}{4}$ **15.** $\frac{9}{16} \div \frac{3}{4}$ **16.** $\frac{25}{36} \div \frac{5}{6}$

17. $\frac{25}{46} \div \frac{40}{69}$ **18.** $-\frac{25}{24} \div \frac{15}{36}$ **19.** $\frac{28}{125} \div \frac{5}{2}$ **20.** $\frac{16}{135} \div \frac{2}{45}$

21. $\frac{25}{18} \div 5$ **22.** $-\frac{30}{27} \div 6$ **23.** $-6 \div \frac{4}{3}$ **24.** $-12 \div \frac{4}{3}$

25. $\frac{4}{3} \div (-6)$ **26.** $\frac{4}{3} \div (-12)$ **27.** $\frac{3}{4} \div \frac{1}{2} \cdot 6$ **28.** $12 \div \frac{6}{7} \cdot 7$

29. $\frac{2}{3} \cdot \frac{3}{4} \div \frac{5}{8}$ **30.** $4\left(-\frac{7}{6}\right) \div 7$ **31.** $\frac{35}{10} \cdot \frac{80}{63} \div \left(-\frac{16}{27}\right)$ **32.** $\frac{20}{72} \cdot \frac{42}{18} \div \frac{20}{16}$

B Simplify each expression using the order of operations.

33. $10 \div \left(\frac{1}{2}\right)^2$

34. $12 \div \left(\frac{1}{4}\right)^2$

35. $\frac{18}{35} \div \left(\frac{6}{7}\right)^2$

36. $\frac{48}{55} \div \left(-\frac{8}{11}\right)^2$

37. $\frac{4}{5} \div \frac{1}{10} + 5$

38. $\frac{3}{8} \div \frac{1}{16} + 4$

39. $10 + \frac{11}{12} \div \frac{11}{24}$

40. $15 + \frac{13}{14} \div \frac{13}{42}$

41. $24 \div \left(\frac{2}{5}\right)^2 + 25 \div \left(\frac{5}{6}\right)^2$

42. $18 \div \left(\frac{3}{4}\right)^2 + 49 \div \left(\frac{7}{9}\right)^2$

43. $100 \div \left(\frac{5}{7}\right)^2 + 200 \div \left(\frac{2}{3}\right)^2$

44. $64 \div \left(\frac{8}{11}\right)^2 + 81 \div \left(\frac{9}{11}\right)^2$

45. $\frac{21}{16} \div \frac{1}{2} \cdot \frac{20}{3}$

46. $\frac{28}{81} \div \frac{1}{3} \cdot \frac{45}{4}$

47. What is the quotient of $\frac{3}{8}$ and $\frac{5}{8}$?

48. Find the quotient of $\frac{4}{5}$ and $\frac{16}{25}$.

49. If the quotient of 18 and $\frac{3}{5}$ is increased by 10, what number results?

50. If the quotient of 50 and $\frac{5}{3}$ is increased by 8, what number results?

51. Show that multiplying 3 by 5 is the same as dividing 3 by $\frac{1}{5}$.

52. Show that multiplying 8 by $\frac{1}{2}$ is the same as dividing 8 by 2.

Applying the Concepts

Although many of the application problems that follow involve division with fractions, some do not. Be sure to read the problems carefully.

53. Sewing If $\frac{6}{7}$ yard of material is needed to make a blanket, how many blankets can be made from 12 yards of material?

54. Manufacturing A clothing manufacturer is making scarves that require $\frac{3}{8}$ yard of material each. How many can be made from 27 yards of material?

55. Capacity Suppose a bag of candy holds exactly $\frac{1}{4}$ pound of candy. How many of these bags can be filled from 12 pounds of candy?

56. Capacity A certain size bottle holds exactly $\frac{4}{5}$ pint of liquid. How many of these bottles can be filled from a 20-pint container?

57. Cooking Audra is making cookies from a recipe that calls for $\frac{3}{4}$ teaspoon of oil. If the only measuring spoon she can find is a $\frac{1}{8}$ teaspoon, how many of these will she have to fill with oil in order to have a total of $\frac{3}{4}$ teaspoon of oil?

58. Cooking A cake recipe calls for $\frac{1}{2}$ cup of sugar. If the only measuring cup available is a $\frac{1}{8}$ cup, how many of these will have to be filled with sugar to make a total of $\frac{1}{2}$ cup of sugar?

59. Student Population If 14 of every 32 students attending Cuesta College are female, what fraction of the students is female? (Simplify your answer.)

60. Population If 27 of every 48 residents of a small town are male, what fraction of the population is male? (Simplify your answer.)

61. Student Population If 14 of every 32 students attending Cuesta College are female, and the total number of students at the school is 4,064, how many of the students are female?

62. Population If 27 of every 48 residents of a small town are male, and the total population of the town is 17,808, how many of the residents are male?

63. Cartons of Milk If a small carton of milk holds exactly $\frac{1}{2}$ pint, how many of the $\frac{1}{2}$-pint cartons can be filled from a 14-pint container?

64. Pieces of Pipe How many pieces of pipe that are $\frac{2}{3}$ foot long must be laid together to make a pipe 16 feet long?

Getting Ready for the Next Section

List the numbers from least to greatest.

65. $1, \frac{3}{2}, 0, \frac{1}{2}$

66. $-1, -\frac{3}{4}, -\frac{4}{3}, 2$

67. $\frac{1}{6}, \frac{5}{6}, \frac{1}{2}, \frac{1}{3}$

68. $-\frac{5}{4}, -5, 4, \frac{4}{5}$

FIND THE MISTAKE •

Each sentence below contains a mistake. Circle the mistake and write the correct word(s) or numbers(s) on the line provided.

1. Two numbers whose quotient is 1 are said to be reciprocals. _____

2. Dividing the fraction $\frac{12}{7}$ by $\frac{4}{9}$ is equivalent to $\frac{7}{12} \cdot \frac{9}{4}$. _____

3. To work the problem $\frac{22}{5} \div \frac{10}{3}$, multiply the first fraction by its reciprocal.

_____

4. The quotient of $\frac{14}{11}$ and $\frac{32}{6}$ is $\frac{224}{33}$. _____

ADDITION AND SUBTRACTION WITH FRACTIONS

 ## 4.5

In Las Vegas, the Stratosphere's hotel and casino has an attraction for thrill-seekers. SkyJump is a death-defying controlled free-fall from the 108th floor of the hotel to the ground. Jump Package 1 includes the jump cost plus a DVD of the jump for approximately $150. A jump without the DVD costs approximately $120. Suppose you are part of a group of people that schedules an appointment for the SkyJump. $\frac{2}{7}$ of the group buys Jump Package 1 and $\frac{3}{7}$ buys the jump without the DVD. The remaining $\frac{2}{7}$ of the group decides not to jump and instead buys the "Chicken" shirt available for purchase at the SkyJump store. What fraction represents the amount of people in the group that actually jumped? To answer this question, we must be able to add fractions with a common denominator.

 ● **OBJECTIVES** · · · · · · ·

A Add and subtract fractions with common denominators.

B Add and subtract fractions with unlike denominators.

● **KEY WORDS** · · · · · · ·

least common denominator

VIDEO EXAMPLES

SECTION 4.5

A Addition and Subtraction with Common Denominators

Let's start our discussion of adding and subtracting fractions with common denominators using a visualization of $\frac{2}{7}$ and $\frac{3}{7}$. We can visualize the process by using circles that are divided into 7 equal parts:

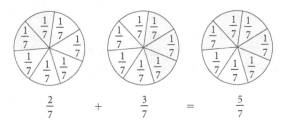

$$\frac{2}{7} \qquad + \qquad \frac{3}{7} \qquad = \qquad \frac{5}{7}$$

From the figure above, we can see that

$$\frac{2}{7} + \frac{3}{7} = \frac{5}{7}$$

$Note$ You may already know that we add fractions that have the same denominator by adding their numerators, but not their denominators. The reason why we add numerators but not denominators is because of the distributive property. That is what the discussion here is all about.

$Note$ In general, we can say that the fraction $\frac{a}{b}$ can always be written as $a \cdot \frac{1}{b}$, because

$$a \cdot \frac{1}{b} = \frac{a}{1} \cdot \frac{1}{b} = \frac{a}{b}$$

We can also see that we can add only numerators, but not denominators. We will now show that adding and subtracting fractions is actually just another application of the distributive property. The distributive property looks like this:

$$a(b + c) = a(b) + a(c) \qquad \text{or} \qquad a(b - c) = a(b) - a(c)$$

where a, b, and c may be whole numbers or fractions. We will want to apply this property to expressions like

$$\frac{2}{7} + \frac{3}{7}$$

But before we do, we must make one additional observation about fractions. The fraction $\frac{2}{7}$ can be written as $2 \cdot \frac{1}{7}$, because

$$2 \cdot \frac{1}{7} = \frac{2}{1} \cdot \frac{1}{7} = \frac{2}{7}$$

Likewise, the fraction $\frac{3}{7}$ can be written as $3 \cdot \frac{1}{7}$, because

$$3 \cdot \frac{1}{7} = \frac{3}{1} \cdot \frac{1}{7} = \frac{3}{7}$$

To add the fractions $\frac{2}{7}$ and $\frac{3}{7}$, we simply rewrite each of them as we have done above and apply the distributive property. Here is how it works:

$$\frac{2}{7} + \frac{3}{7} = 2 \cdot \frac{1}{7} + 3 \cdot \frac{1}{7} \qquad \textit{Rewrite each fraction.}$$

$$= (2 + 3) \cdot \frac{1}{7} \qquad \textit{Apply the distributive property.}$$

$$= 5 \cdot \frac{1}{7} \qquad \textit{Add 2 and 3 to get 5.}$$

$$= \frac{5}{7} \qquad \textit{Rewrite } 5 \cdot \frac{1}{7} \text{ as } \frac{5}{7}.$$

SUMMARY   **Addition and Subtraction of Fractions**

If a, b, and c are numbers, and c is not equal to 0, then

$$\frac{a}{c} + \frac{b}{c} = \frac{a + b}{c}$$

This rule holds for subtraction as well. That is,

$$\frac{a}{c} - \frac{b}{c} = \frac{a - b}{c}$$

In words: To add two fractions that have the same denominator, we add their numerators to get the numerator of the answer. The denominator in the answer is the same denominator as in the original fractions.

Example 1 Add or subtract.

a. $\frac{3}{8} + \frac{1}{8}$ **b.** $\frac{9}{5} - \frac{3}{5}$ **c.** $\frac{3}{7} + \frac{2}{7} + \frac{9}{7}$

Solution

a. $\frac{3}{8} + \frac{1}{8} = \frac{3+1}{8}$ Add numerators; keep the same denominator.

$= \frac{4}{8}$ The sum of 3 and 1 is 4.

$= \frac{1}{2}$ Reduce to lowest terms.

b. $\frac{9}{5} - \frac{3}{5} = \frac{9-3}{5}$ Subtract numerators; keep the same denominator.

$= \frac{6}{5}$ The difference of 9 and 3 is 6.

c. $\frac{3}{7} + \frac{2}{7} + \frac{9}{7} = \frac{3+2+9}{7}$ Add numerators; keep the same denominator.

$= \frac{14}{7}$ Add numerators; keep the same denominator.

$= 2$ Reduce to lowest terms.

Practice Problems

1. Add or subtract.

   a. $\frac{5}{12} + \frac{1}{12}$

   b. $\frac{3}{10} + \frac{7}{10}$

   c. $\frac{11}{6} - \frac{5}{6} - \frac{1}{6}$

B Addition and Subtraction with Unlike Denominators

We will now turn our attention to the process of adding fractions that have different denominators. In order to get started, we need the following definition:

> **DEFINITION** least common denominator
>
> The **least common denominator** (LCD) for a set of denominators is the smallest number that is exactly divisible by each denominator. (Note that we sometimes refer to the least common denominator as the least common multiple.)

In other words, all the denominators of the fractions involved in a problem must divide into the least common denominator exactly. That is, they divide it without leaving a remainder.

Example 2 Find the LCD for the fractions $\frac{5}{12}$ and $\frac{7}{18}$.

Solution The least common denominator for the denominators 12 and 18 must be the smallest number divisible by both 12 and 18. We can factor 12 and 18 completely and then build the LCD from these factors. Factoring 12 and 18 completely gives us

$$12 = 2 \cdot 2 \cdot 3 \qquad 18 = 2 \cdot 3 \cdot 3$$

Now, if 12 is going to divide the LCD exactly, then the LCD must have factors of $2 \cdot 2 \cdot 3$. If 18 is to divide it exactly, it must have factors of $2 \cdot 3 \cdot 3$. We don't need to repeat the factors that 12 and 18 have in common.

$$\left.\begin{array}{l} 12 = 2 \cdot 2 \cdot 3 \\ 18 = 2 \cdot 3 \cdot 3 \end{array}\right\} \qquad \text{LCD} = 2 \cdot 2 \cdot 3 \cdot 3 = 36$$

12 divides the LCD.
18 divides the LCD.

The LCD for 12 and 18 is 36.

2. Find the LCD for the fractions $\frac{7}{15}$ and $\frac{9}{25}$.

Note The ability to find least common denominators is very important in mathematics. The discussion here is a detailed explanation of how to find an LCD.

Answers

1. **a.** $\frac{1}{2}$ **b.** 1 **c.** $\frac{5}{6}$

2. 75

We can visualize the results in Example 2 with the diagram below. It shows that 36 is the smallest number that both 12 and 18 divide evenly. As you can see, 12 divides 36 exactly 3 times, and 18 divides 36 exactly 2 times.

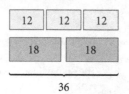

3. Add: $\frac{7}{15} + \frac{9}{25}$

Example 3   Add: $\frac{5}{12} + \frac{7}{18}$

Solution   We can add fractions only when they have the same denominators. In Example 2, we found the LCD for $\frac{5}{12}$ and $\frac{7}{18}$ to be 36. We change $\frac{5}{12}$ and $\frac{7}{18}$ to equivalent fractions that have 36 for a denominator by applying the multiplication property for fractions.

$$\frac{5}{12} = \frac{5 \cdot 3}{12 \cdot 3} = \frac{15}{36} \qquad \frac{7}{18} = \frac{7 \cdot 2}{18 \cdot 2} = \frac{14}{36}$$

We now add the numerators.

$$\frac{15}{36} + \frac{14}{36} = \frac{29}{36}$$

The sum of $\frac{5}{12}$ and $\frac{7}{18}$ is the fraction $\frac{29}{36}$.

4. Find the LCD for $\frac{7}{12}$ and $\frac{3}{8}$.

5. Add: $\frac{7}{12} + \frac{3}{8}$

Example 4   Find the LCD for $\frac{3}{4}$ and $\frac{1}{6}$.

Solution   We factor 4 and 6 into products of prime factors and build the LCD from these factors.

$$\left. \begin{array}{l} 4 = 2 \cdot 2 \\ 6 = 2 \cdot 3 \end{array} \right\} \quad \text{LCD} = 2 \cdot 2 \cdot 3 = 12$$

The LCD is 12. Both denominators divide it exactly; 4 divides 12 exactly 3 times, and 6 divides 12 exactly 2 times.

$\mathcal{Note}$ We can visualize the work in Example 5 using circles and shading.

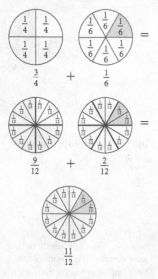

Example 5   Add: $\frac{3}{4} + \frac{1}{6}$

Solution   In Example 4, we found that the LCD for these two fractions is 12. We begin by changing $\frac{3}{4}$ and $\frac{1}{6}$ to equivalent fractions with denominator 12.

$$\frac{3}{4} = \frac{3 \cdot 3}{4 \cdot 3} = \frac{9}{12}$$

$$\frac{1}{6} = \frac{1 \cdot 2}{6 \cdot 2} = \frac{2}{12}$$

To complete the problem, we add numerators.

$$\frac{9}{12} + \frac{2}{12} = \frac{11}{12}$$

The sum of $\frac{3}{4}$ and $\frac{1}{6}$ is $\frac{11}{12}$.

Answers

3. $\frac{62}{75}$

4. 24

5. $\frac{23}{24}$

Example 6   Subtract: $\dfrac{7}{15} - \dfrac{3}{10}$

6. Subtract: $\dfrac{3}{4} - \dfrac{5}{12}$

Solution   Let's factor 15 and 10 completely and use these factors to build the LCD.

$$\left.\begin{array}{l} 15 = 3 \cdot 5 \\ 10 = 2 \cdot 5 \end{array}\right\} \text{LCD} = 2 \cdot 3 \cdot 5 = 30$$

Changing to equivalent fractions and subtracting, we have

$$\dfrac{7}{15} - \dfrac{3}{10} = \dfrac{7 \cdot 2}{15 \cdot 2} - \dfrac{3 \cdot 3}{10 \cdot 3} \quad \textit{Rewrite as equivalent fractions with the LCD for the denominator.}$$

$$= \dfrac{14}{30} - \dfrac{9}{30}$$

$$= \dfrac{5}{30} \qquad\qquad \textit{Subtract numerators; keep the LCD.}$$

$$= \dfrac{1}{6} \qquad\qquad \textit{Reduce to lowest terms.}$$

> *Note*   Always reduce your answers to lowest terms if possible.

As a summary of what we have done so far, and as a guide to working other problems, we now list the steps involved in adding and subtracting fractions with different denominators.

HOW TO   **Add or Subtract Any Two Fractions with Unlike Denominators**

Step 1:   Factor each denominator completely, and use the factors to build the LCD. (Remember, the LCD is the smallest number divisible by each of the denominators in the problem.)

Step 2:   Rewrite each fraction as an equivalent fraction with the LCD. This is done by multiplying both the numerator and the denominator of the fraction in question by the appropriate whole number.

Step 3:   Add or subtract the numerators of the fractions produced in Step 2. This is the numerator of the sum or difference. The denominator of the sum or difference is the LCD.

Step 4:   Reduce the fraction produced in Step 3 to lowest terms if it is not already in lowest terms.

We can only add or subtract fractions that have the same denominators. If the fractions we are trying to add or subtract do not have the same denominators, we rewrite each of them as an equivalent fraction with the LCD for a denominator.

Here are some additional examples of sums and differences of fractions:

Example 7   Subtract: $\dfrac{3}{5} - \dfrac{1}{6}$

7. Subtract: $\dfrac{1}{2} - \dfrac{3}{10}$

Solution   The LCD for 5 and 6 is their product, 30. We begin by rewriting each fraction with this common denominator.

$$\dfrac{3}{5} - \dfrac{1}{6} = \dfrac{3 \cdot 6}{5 \cdot 6} - \dfrac{1 \cdot 5}{6 \cdot 5}$$

$$= \dfrac{18}{30} - \dfrac{5}{30}$$

$$= \dfrac{13}{30}$$

Answers

6. $\dfrac{1}{3}$

7. $\dfrac{1}{5}$

8. Add: $\frac{1}{3} + \frac{3}{8} + \frac{1}{4}$

Example 8 Add: $\frac{1}{6} + \frac{1}{8} + \frac{1}{4}$

Solution We begin by factoring the denominators completely and building the LCD from the factors that result.

$$\left. \begin{array}{l} 6 = 2 \cdot 3 \\ 8 = 2 \cdot 2 \cdot 2 \\ 4 = 2 \cdot 2 \end{array} \right\} \qquad \text{LCD} = 2 \cdot 2 \cdot 2 \cdot 3 = 24$$

We then change to equivalent fractions and add.

$$\frac{1}{6} + \frac{1}{8} + \frac{1}{4} = \frac{1 \cdot 4}{6 \cdot 4} + \frac{1 \cdot 3}{8 \cdot 3} + \frac{1 \cdot 6}{4 \cdot 6}$$

$$= \frac{4}{24} + \frac{3}{24} + \frac{6}{24}$$

$$= \frac{13}{24}$$

9. Subtract: $4 - \frac{5}{7}$

Example 9 Subtract: $3 - \frac{5}{6}$

Solution Writing 3 as $\frac{3}{1}$, we see that we need to find the LCD for 1 and 6. The smallest number divisible by both 1 and 6 is 6.

$$3 - \frac{5}{6} = \frac{3}{1} - \frac{5}{6}$$

$$= \frac{3 \cdot 6}{1 \cdot 6} - \frac{5}{6}$$

$$= \frac{18}{6} - \frac{5}{6}$$

$$= \frac{13}{6}$$

We could write our answer as an improper fraction, $\frac{13}{6}$, or a mixed number, $2\frac{1}{6}$.

Here are some examples that involve addition with negative numbers.

10. Add: $\frac{4}{5} + \left(-\frac{2}{5}\right)$

Example 10 Add: $\frac{3}{8} + \left(-\frac{1}{8}\right)$

Solution Notice

$$\frac{3}{8} + \left(-\frac{1}{8}\right) = \frac{3}{8} - \frac{1}{8}$$

The answer will be positive, because $\frac{3}{8}$ is larger than $\frac{1}{8}$. We will now subtract the numerators and reduce to lowest terms.

$$\frac{3}{8} - \frac{1}{8} = \frac{2}{8} = \frac{1}{4}$$

Answers

8. $\frac{23}{24}$

9. $\frac{23}{7}$

10. $\frac{2}{5}$

Example 11 Add: $\dfrac{1}{10} + \left(-\dfrac{4}{5}\right) + \left(-\dfrac{3}{20}\right)$

Solution To begin, change each fraction to an equivalent fraction with an LCD of 20. Then we add from left to right.

$$\dfrac{1}{10} + \left(-\dfrac{4}{5}\right) + \left(-\dfrac{3}{20}\right) = \dfrac{1\cdot 2}{10\cdot 2} + \left(-\dfrac{4\cdot 4}{5\cdot 4}\right) + \left(-\dfrac{3}{20}\right)$$

$$= \dfrac{2}{20} + \left(-\dfrac{16}{20}\right) + \left(-\dfrac{3}{20}\right)$$

$$= -\dfrac{14}{20} + \left(-\dfrac{3}{20}\right)$$

$$= -\dfrac{17}{20}$$

11. Add: $\dfrac{5}{12} + \left(-\dfrac{5}{6}\right) + \left(-\dfrac{5}{24}\right)$

Example 12 Find the difference of $-\dfrac{3}{5}$ and $\dfrac{2}{5}$.

Solution Recall, difference means subtract.

$$-\dfrac{3}{5} - \dfrac{2}{5} = -\dfrac{3}{5} + \left(-\dfrac{2}{5}\right)$$

$$= -\dfrac{5}{5}$$

$$= -1$$

12. Find the difference of $-\dfrac{5}{8}$ and $\dfrac{3}{8}$.

Comparing Fractions

As we have shown previously, we can compare fractions to see which is larger or smaller when they have the same denominator. Now that we know how to find the LCD for a set of fractions, we can use the LCD to write equivalent fractions with the intention of comparing them.

Example 13 Find the LCD for the fractions below, then write each fraction as an equivalent fraction with the LCD for a denominator. Then write them in order from smallest to largest.

$$\dfrac{5}{8} \qquad \dfrac{5}{16} \qquad \dfrac{3}{4} \qquad \dfrac{1}{2}$$

13. Write the fractions from smallest to largest.

$$\dfrac{3}{4}, \dfrac{7}{12}, \dfrac{5}{8}, \dfrac{13}{16}$$

Solution The LCD for the four fractions is 16. We begin by writing each fraction as an equivalent fraction with denominator 16.

$$\dfrac{5}{8} = \dfrac{10}{16} \qquad \dfrac{5}{16} = \dfrac{5}{16} \qquad \dfrac{3}{4} = \dfrac{12}{16} \qquad \dfrac{1}{2} = \dfrac{8}{16}$$

Writing them in order from smallest to largest we have

$$\dfrac{5}{16} \quad < \quad \dfrac{8}{16} \quad < \quad \dfrac{10}{16} \quad < \quad \dfrac{12}{16}$$

$$\dfrac{5}{16} \quad < \quad \dfrac{1}{2} \quad < \quad \dfrac{5}{8} \quad < \quad \dfrac{3}{4}$$

Answers

11. $-\dfrac{5}{8}$

12. $-\dfrac{8}{8} = -1$

13. $\dfrac{7}{12} < \dfrac{5}{8} < \dfrac{3}{4} < \dfrac{13}{16}$

Mixed Numbers and Improper Fractions

Earlier in the chapter, we explained how to convert a mixed number to an improper fraction. To do so, we multiply the whole number by the denominator of the fraction, and add the result to the numerator of the fraction. The result is the numerator of the improper fraction we are looking for. The denominator is the same as the original denominator. Now that we can add fractions, we can see why this method works.

To change $2\frac{1}{8}$ to an improper fraction, let's write $2\frac{1}{8}$ as $2 + \frac{1}{8}$ and add using a common denominator:

$$2\frac{1}{8} = 2 + \frac{1}{8} \qquad \text{\textit{Write as addition.}}$$

$$= \frac{2}{1} + \frac{1}{8} \qquad \text{\textit{Write the whole number 2 as a fraction.}}$$

$$= \frac{2 \cdot 8}{1 \cdot 8} + \frac{1}{8} \qquad \text{\textit{Change } \tfrac{2}{1} \text{ to a fraction with denominator 8.}}$$

$$= \frac{16}{8} + \frac{1}{8}$$

$$= \frac{17}{8} \qquad \text{\textit{Add the numerators}}$$

Notice the result is the same as the method we've used previously. This discussion tells us why that method works.

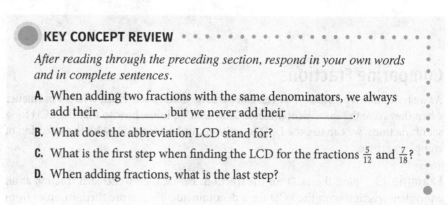

KEY CONCEPT REVIEW

After reading through the preceding section, respond in your own words and in complete sentences.

A. When adding two fractions with the same denominators, we always add their _____, but we never add their _____.

B. What does the abbreviation LCD stand for?

C. What is the first step when finding the LCD for the fractions $\frac{5}{12}$ and $\frac{7}{18}$?

D. When adding fractions, what is the last step?

EXERCISE SET 4.5 •

Problems

A Find the following sums and differences, and reduce to lowest terms. (Add or subtract as indicated.)

1. $\dfrac{3}{6} + \dfrac{1}{6}$

2. $\dfrac{2}{5} + \dfrac{3}{5}$

3. $\dfrac{5}{8} - \dfrac{3}{8}$

4. $\dfrac{6}{7} - \dfrac{1}{7}$

5. $\dfrac{3}{4} - \dfrac{1}{4}$

6. $\dfrac{9}{8} - \dfrac{1}{8}$

7. $-\dfrac{7}{9} + \dfrac{4}{9}$

8. $\dfrac{2}{3} + \left(-\dfrac{1}{3}\right)$

9. $\dfrac{1}{4} + \dfrac{2}{4} + \dfrac{3}{4}$

10. $\dfrac{2}{5} + \dfrac{3}{5} + \dfrac{4}{5}$

11. $-\dfrac{1}{2} + \left(-\dfrac{1}{2}\right)$

12. $-\dfrac{5}{4} - \dfrac{3}{4}$

13. $\dfrac{1}{10} + \dfrac{3}{10} + \dfrac{4}{10}$

14. $\dfrac{3}{20} + \dfrac{1}{20} + \dfrac{4}{20}$

15. $\dfrac{1}{3} + \dfrac{4}{3} + \dfrac{5}{3}$

16. $\dfrac{5}{4} + \dfrac{4}{4} + \dfrac{3}{4}$

B Complete the following tables.

17.

First Number a	Second Number b	The Sum of a and b $a + b$
$\dfrac{1}{2}$	$\dfrac{1}{3}$	
$\dfrac{1}{3}$	$\dfrac{1}{4}$	
$\dfrac{1}{4}$	$\dfrac{1}{5}$	
$\dfrac{1}{5}$	$\dfrac{1}{6}$	

18.

First Number a	Second Number b	The Sum of a and b $a + b$
1	$\dfrac{1}{2}$	
1	$\dfrac{1}{3}$	
1	$\dfrac{1}{4}$	
1	$\dfrac{1}{5}$	

19.

First Number a	Second Number b	The Sum of a and b $a + b$
$\dfrac{1}{12}$	$\dfrac{1}{2}$	
$\dfrac{1}{12}$	$\dfrac{1}{3}$	
$\dfrac{1}{12}$	$\dfrac{1}{4}$	
$\dfrac{1}{12}$	$\dfrac{1}{6}$	

20.

First Number a	Second Number b	The Sum of a and b $a + b$
$\dfrac{1}{8}$	$\dfrac{1}{2}$	
$\dfrac{1}{8}$	$\dfrac{1}{4}$	
$\dfrac{1}{8}$	$\dfrac{1}{16}$	
$\dfrac{1}{8}$	$\dfrac{1}{24}$	

Find the LCD for each of the following, then use the methods developed in this section to add or subtract as indicated.

21. $\frac{4}{9} + \frac{1}{3}$

22. $\frac{1}{2} + \frac{1}{4}$

23. $2 + \frac{1}{3}$

24. $3 + \frac{1}{2}$

25. $\frac{3}{4} + 1$

26. $\frac{3}{4} + 2$

27. $\frac{1}{2} + \frac{2}{3}$

28. $\frac{1}{8} + \frac{3}{4}$

29. $\frac{1}{4} - \frac{1}{5}$

30. $\frac{1}{3} - \frac{1}{5}$

31. $\frac{1}{2} + \frac{1}{5}$

32. $\frac{1}{2} - \frac{1}{5}$

33. $\frac{5}{12} + \frac{3}{8}$

34. $\frac{9}{16} + \frac{7}{12}$

35. $\frac{8}{30} - \frac{1}{20}$

36. $\frac{9}{40} - \frac{1}{30}$

37. $\frac{3}{10} - \left(-\frac{1}{100}\right)$

38. $\frac{9}{100} - \left(-\frac{7}{10}\right)$

39. $\frac{10}{36} + \frac{9}{48}$

40. $\frac{12}{28} + \frac{9}{20}$

41. $\frac{17}{30} + \frac{11}{42}$

42. $\frac{19}{42} + \frac{13}{70}$

43. $\frac{25}{84} - \left(-\frac{41}{90}\right)$

44. $-\frac{23}{70} - \frac{29}{84}$

45. $-10 + \frac{2}{9}$

46. $-9 + \frac{3}{5}$

47. $4 - \frac{2}{3}$

48. $5 + \left(-\frac{3}{4}\right)$

49. $-\frac{1}{6} - \frac{5}{6}$

50. $-\frac{4}{7} - \frac{3}{7}$

51. $-\frac{13}{70} - \frac{23}{42}$

52. $-\frac{17}{60} - \frac{17}{90}$

53. $\frac{13}{126} + \left(-\frac{13}{180}\right)$ **54.** $\frac{17}{84} + \left(-\frac{17}{90}\right)$ **55.** $\frac{3}{4} + \frac{1}{8} + \frac{5}{6}$ **56.** $\frac{3}{8} + \frac{2}{5} + \frac{1}{4}$

57. $\frac{3}{10} + \frac{5}{12} + \frac{1}{6}$ **58.** $\frac{5}{21} + \frac{1}{7} + \frac{3}{14}$ **59.** $\frac{1}{2} + \frac{1}{3} + \frac{1}{4} + \frac{1}{6}$ **60.** $\frac{1}{8} + \frac{1}{4} - \left(-\frac{1}{5}\right) + \frac{1}{10}$

61. $\frac{1}{10} + \frac{4}{5} - \frac{3}{20}$ **62.** $\frac{1}{2} + \frac{3}{4} - \frac{5}{8}$ **63.** $\frac{1}{4} - \frac{1}{8} - \left(-\frac{1}{2}\right) - \frac{3}{8}$ **64.** $\frac{7}{8} + \left(-\frac{3}{4}\right) + \frac{5}{8} - \frac{1}{2}$

There are two ways to work the problems below. You can combine the fractions inside the parentheses first and then multiply, or you can apply the distributive property first, then add.

65. $15\left(\frac{2}{3} + \frac{3}{5}\right)$ **66.** $15\left(\frac{4}{5} - \frac{1}{3}\right)$ **67.** $4\left(\frac{1}{2} + \frac{1}{4}\right)$ **68.** $6\left(\frac{1}{3} + \frac{1}{2}\right)$

69. $4\left(3 - \frac{3}{4}\right)$ **70.** $6\left(5 - \frac{2}{3}\right)$ **71.** $9\left(\frac{1}{3} + \frac{1}{9}\right)$ **72.** $12\left(\frac{1}{3} + \frac{1}{4}\right)$

73. Write the fractions in order from smallest to largest.

$\frac{3}{4} \quad \frac{3}{8} \quad \frac{1}{2} \quad \frac{1}{4}$

74. Write the fractions in order from smallest to largest.

$\frac{1}{2} \quad \frac{1}{6} \quad \frac{1}{4} \quad \frac{1}{3}$

75. Find the sum of $\frac{3}{7}$, 2, and $\frac{1}{9}$.

76. Find the sum of 6, $\frac{6}{11}$, and 11.

77. Give the difference of $\frac{7}{8}$ and $\frac{1}{4}$.

78. Give the difference of $\frac{9}{10}$ and $\frac{1}{100}$.

Arithmetic Sequences An arithmetic sequence is a sequence in which each term comes from the previous term by adding the same number each time. For example, the sequence $1, \frac{3}{2}, 2, \frac{5}{2}, \ldots$ is an arithmetic sequence that starts with the number 1. Then each term after that is found by adding $\frac{1}{2}$ to the previous term. By observing this fact, we know that the next term in the sequence will be $\frac{5}{2} + \frac{1}{2} = \frac{6}{2} = 3$.

Find the next number in each arithmetic sequence below.

79. $1, \frac{4}{3}, \frac{5}{3}, 2, \ldots$

80. $1, \frac{5}{4}, \frac{3}{2}, \frac{7}{4}, \ldots$

81. $\frac{3}{2}, 2, \frac{5}{2}, \ldots$

82. $\frac{2}{3}, 1, \frac{4}{3}, \ldots$

Applying the Concepts

Some of the application problems below involve multiplication or division, while others involve addition or subtraction.

83. Capacity One carton of milk contains $\frac{1}{2}$ pint while another contains 4 pints. How much milk is contained in both cartons?

84. Baking A recipe calls for $\frac{2}{3}$ cup of flour and $\frac{3}{4}$ cup of sugar. What is the total amount of flour and sugar called for in the recipe?

85. Budget A family decides that they can spend $\frac{5}{8}$ of their monthly income on house payments. If their monthly income is $2,120, how much can they spend for house payments?

86. Savings A family saves $\frac{3}{16}$ of their income each month. If their monthly income is $1,264, how much do they save each month?

Reading a Pie Chart The pie chart below shows how the students at State College are distributed among the different schools at the university. Use the information in the pie chart to answer the following questions.

87. If the students in the Schools of Engineering and Business are combined, what fraction results?

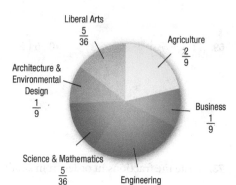

State College Enrollment

88. What fraction of the university's students are enrolled in the Schools of Agriculture, Engineering, and Business combined?

89. Final Exam Grades The table gives the fraction of students in a class of 40 that received grades of A, B, or C on the final exam. Fill in all the missing parts of the table.

Grade	Number of Students	Fraction of Students
A		$\frac{1}{8}$
B		$\frac{1}{5}$
C		$\frac{1}{2}$
Below C		
Total	40	1

90. Flu During a flu epidemic a company with 200 employees has $\frac{1}{10}$ of their employees call in sick on Monday and another $\frac{3}{10}$ call in sick on Tuesday. What is the total number of employees calling in sick during this 2-day period?

91. Subdivision A 6-acre piece of land is subdivided into $\frac{3}{5}$-acre lots. How many lots are there?

92. Cutting Wood A 12-foot piece of wood is cut into shelves. If each is $\frac{3}{4}$ foot in length, how many shelves are there?

Find the perimeter of each figure.

93.

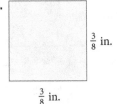

$\frac{3}{8}$ in.

$\frac{3}{8}$ in.

94.

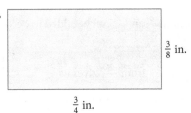

$\frac{3}{8}$ in.

$\frac{3}{4}$ in.

95.

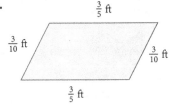

$\frac{3}{5}$ ft

$\frac{3}{10}$ ft

$\frac{3}{10}$ ft

$\frac{3}{5}$ ft

96.

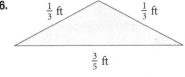

$\frac{1}{3}$ ft $\frac{1}{3}$ ft

$\frac{3}{5}$ ft

Getting Ready for the Next Section

Change to improper fractions.

97. $2\frac{3}{4}$ **98.** $3\frac{1}{5}$ **99.** $2\frac{4}{5}$ **100.** $5\frac{9}{10}$

Multiply or divide as indicated.

101. $\frac{11}{4} \cdot \frac{16}{5}$ **102.** $-\frac{2}{3}\left(\frac{9}{16}\right)$ **103.** $-\frac{8}{5} \div \frac{14}{5}$ **104.** $\frac{59}{10} \div (-2)$

105. Write as equivalent fractions with denominator 20.

    a. $\frac{1}{4}$ **b.** $\frac{3}{5}$ **c.** $\frac{9}{10}$ **d.** $\frac{1}{10}$

106. Write as equivalent fractions with denominator 12.

    a. $\frac{3}{4}$ **b.** $\frac{1}{3}$ **c.** $\frac{5}{6}$ **d.** $\frac{1}{4}$

Add or subtract the following fractions, as indicated.

107. $\frac{2}{3} + \frac{1}{5}$ **108.** $\frac{7}{10} - \frac{3}{5}$ **109.** $\frac{1}{4} + \frac{3}{5} + \frac{9}{10}$ **110.** $\frac{2}{3} - \frac{1}{4} - \frac{1}{6}$

FIND THE MISTAKE

Each sentence below contains a mistake. Circle the mistake and write the correct word(s) or numbers(s) on the line provided.

1. The fractions $\frac{a}{c}$ and $\frac{b}{c}$ can be added to become $\frac{a+b}{c}$ because they have different denominators.
_____

2. Subtracting $\frac{12}{21}$ from $\frac{18}{21}$, gives us $\frac{30}{21}$. _____

3. The least common denominator for a set of denominators is the smallest number that is exactly divisible by each numerator. _____

4. The LCD for the fractions $\frac{4}{6}$, $\frac{2}{8}$ and $\frac{3}{4}$ is 12. _____

Navigation Skills

Completing homework assignments in full is a key piece to succeeding in this class. To do this effectively, it's helpful to pay special attention to each set of instructions. When doing homework, you usually work a number of similar problems at a time. But the problems may vary on a test. It is very important to make a habit of paying attention to the instructions to elicit correct answers on a test. Secondly, to complete an assignment efficiently, being able to recall various definitions, properties, and formulas is important. There are many techniques for successful memorization. Here are a few:

- Spend some time rereading the definition.
- Say the definition out loud.
- Explain the definition to another person.
- Write the definition down on a separate sheet of notes.
- Create a mnemonic device using key words from the definition.
- Analyze how the definition applies to your homework problems.

The above suggestions are ways to engage the senses when memorizing an abstract concept. This will help anchor it in your memory. For instance, it is easier to remember explaining to a friend a difficult math formula, than it is to simply recall it from a single read of the chapter. Lastly, once you've completed an assignment, take any extra time allotted for studying to work more problems, and when you feel ready, read ahead and work problems you will encounter in the next section.

OPERATIONS WITH MIXED NUMBERS

4.6

The Appalachian Trail is a 2,190-mile hiking trail that stretches from Springer Mountain, Georgia to Katahdin, Maine. Nature lovers can plan day hikes, short overnight trips, or extended backpacking trips through a region of the trail, or they can hike the entire distance. Hiking the length of the trail, called a thru-hike, can take anywhere between five and seven months and requires extensive training and preparation.

Assume you plan a four-day, three-night backpacking trip along a section of the Appalachian Trail. Equipped with good hiking shoes, a tent, plenty of food and water and other gear for the journey, you begin your hike on the Art Loeb Trail in the North Carolina stretch of the trail. You pick this trail because it features waterfall side trips, 360-degree views, and ridgeline hiking. Your first day you hike 7 miles, and on the second day, you walk $8\frac{1}{2}$. Your last two days you complete $10\frac{1}{5}$ and $8\frac{1}{5}$ miles, respectively. How many miles did you hike over the course of four days? To solve this problem, we need to know how to add mixed numbers, which we will cover in this section.

OBJECTIVES

A Multiply mixed numbers.

B Divide mixed numbers.

C Add mixed numbers.

D Subtract mixed numbers.

VIDEO EXAMPLES

SECTION 4.6

A Multiplication with Mixed Numbers

Example 1   Multiply: $2\frac{3}{4} \cdot 3\frac{1}{5}$

Solution   We begin by changing each mixed number to an improper fraction.

$$2\frac{3}{4} = \frac{11}{4} \quad \text{and} \quad 3\frac{1}{5} = \frac{16}{5}$$

Using the resulting improper fractions, we multiply as usual. (That is, we multiply numerators and multiply denominators.)

$$\frac{11}{4} \cdot \frac{16}{5} = \frac{11 \cdot 16}{4 \cdot 5}$$

$$= \frac{11 \cdot 4 \cdot 4}{4 \cdot 5}$$

$$= \frac{44}{5} \quad \text{or} \quad 8\frac{4}{5}$$

Practice Problems

1. Multiply: $1\frac{1}{4} \cdot 2\frac{3}{5}$

Note   As you can see, once you have changed each mixed number to an improper fraction, you multiply the resulting fractions by multiplying the numerators and multiplying the denominators.

Answer

1. $3\frac{1}{4}$

263

2. Multiply: $6 \cdot 2\frac{1}{8}$

Example 2   Multiply: $3 \cdot 4\frac{5}{8}$

Solution   Writing each number as an improper fraction, we have

$$3 = \frac{3}{1} \quad \text{and} \quad 4\frac{5}{8} = \frac{37}{8}$$

Now we multiply.

$$3 \cdot 4\frac{5}{8} = \frac{3}{1} \cdot \frac{37}{8} \qquad \textit{Change to improper fractions.}$$

$$= \frac{111}{8} \qquad \textit{Multiply numerators and multiply denominators.}$$

$$= 13\frac{7}{8} \qquad \textit{Write the answer as a mixed number.}$$

B Division with Mixed Numbers

Dividing mixed numbers also requires that we change all mixed numbers to improper fractions before we actually do the division.

3. Divide: $3\frac{3}{4} \div 2\frac{1}{4}$

Example 3   Divide: $1\frac{3}{5} \div 2\frac{4}{5}$

Solution   We begin by rewriting each mixed number as an improper fraction.

$$1\frac{3}{5} = \frac{8}{5} \quad \text{and} \quad 2\frac{4}{5} = \frac{14}{5}$$

We then divide using the same method we used in previous sections. We multiply by the reciprocal of the divisor.

$$1\frac{3}{5} \div 2\frac{4}{5} = \frac{8}{5} \div \frac{14}{5} \qquad \textit{Change to improper fractions.}$$

$$= \frac{8}{5} \cdot \frac{5}{14} \qquad \textit{To divide by } \frac{14}{5}, \textit{ multiply by } \frac{5}{14}.$$

$$= \frac{8 \cdot 5}{5 \cdot 14} \qquad \textit{Multiply numerators and multiply denominators.}$$

$$= \frac{4 \cdot 2 \cdot 5}{5 \cdot 2 \cdot 7} \qquad \textit{Divide out factors common to the numerator and denominator.}$$

$$= \frac{4}{7} \qquad \textit{Answer in lowest terms.}$$

4. Divide: $8\frac{3}{4} \div 5$

Example 4   Divide: $5\frac{9}{10} \div 2$

Solution   We change to improper fractions and proceed as usual.

$$5\frac{9}{10} \div 2 = \frac{59}{10} \div \frac{2}{1} \qquad \textit{Write each number as an improper fraction.}$$

$$= \frac{59}{10} \cdot \frac{1}{2} \qquad \textit{Write division as multiplication by the reciprocal.}$$

$$= \frac{59}{20} \qquad \textit{Multiply numerators and multiply denominators.}$$

$$= 2\frac{19}{20} \qquad \textit{Change to a mixed number.}$$

Answers

2. $12\frac{3}{4}$

3. $1\frac{2}{3}$

4. $1\frac{3}{4}$

C Addition with Mixed Numbers

We will now present two methods for adding mixed numbers. The first method uses the definition of a mixed number.

5. Add: $2\frac{1}{3} + 3\frac{3}{4}$

Example 5   Add: $3\frac{2}{3} + 4\frac{1}{5}$

Solution   We begin by writing each mixed number showing the + sign. We then apply the commutative and associative properties to rearrange the order and grouping.

$$3\frac{2}{3} + 4\frac{1}{5} = 3 + \frac{2}{3} + 4 + \frac{1}{5}$$ Expand each number to show the + sign.

$$= 3 + 4 + \frac{2}{3} + \frac{1}{5}$$ Commutative property

$$= (3 + 4) + \left(\frac{2}{3} + \frac{1}{5}\right)$$ Associative property

$$= 7 + \left(\frac{2 \cdot 5}{3 \cdot 5} + \frac{1 \cdot 3}{5 \cdot 3}\right)$$ Add $3 + 4 = 7$, then multiply to get the LCD.

$$= 7 + \left(\frac{10}{15} + \frac{3}{15}\right)$$ Write each fraction with the LCD.

$$= 7 + \frac{13}{15}$$ Add the numerators.

$$= 7\frac{13}{15}$$ Write the answer in mixed-number notation.

As you can see, we obtain our result by adding the whole-number parts $(3 + 4 = 7)$ and the fraction parts $\left(\frac{2}{3} + \frac{1}{5} = \frac{13}{15}\right)$ of each mixed number. Knowing this, we can save ourselves some writing by doing the same problem in columns.

$$3\frac{2}{3} = 3\frac{2 \cdot 5}{3 \cdot 5} = 3\frac{10}{15}$$

$$+ 4\frac{1}{5} = 4\frac{1 \cdot 3}{5 \cdot 3} = 4\frac{3}{15}$$ Write each fraction with LCD 15

$$\overline{\phantom{+ 4\frac{1}{5} = 4\frac{1 \cdot 3}{5 \cdot 3} = }\; 7\frac{13}{15}}$$ Add whole numbers, then add fractions.

Example 6   Add: $5\frac{3}{4} + 9\frac{5}{6}$

6. Add: $3\frac{7}{12} + 1\frac{4}{9}$

Solution   The LCD for 4 and 6 is 12. Writing the mixed numbers in a column and then adding looks like this:

$$5\frac{3}{4} = 5\frac{3 \cdot 3}{4 \cdot 3} = 5\frac{9}{12}$$

$$+ 9\frac{5}{6} = 9\frac{5 \cdot 2}{6 \cdot 2} = 9\frac{10}{12}$$

$$\overline{\phantom{+ 9\frac{5}{6} = 9\frac{5 \cdot 2}{6 \cdot 2} = }\; 14\frac{19}{12}}$$

Note   Once you see how to change from a whole number and an improper fraction to a whole number and a proper fraction, you may be able to do this step without showing any work.

The fraction part of the answer is an improper fraction. We rewrite it as a whole number and a proper fraction.

$$14\frac{19}{12} = 14 + \frac{19}{12}$$ Write the mixed number with a + sign.

$$= 14 + 1\frac{7}{12}$$ Write $\frac{19}{12}$ as a mixed number.

$$= 15\frac{7}{12}$$ Add 14 and 1.

Answers

5. $6\frac{1}{12}$

6. $5\frac{1}{36}$

7. Add: $2\frac{2}{3} + 3\frac{1}{4} + 5\frac{5}{6}$

Example 7   Add: $3\frac{1}{4} + 2\frac{3}{5} + 1\frac{9}{10}$

Solution   The LCD is 20. We rewrite each fraction as an equivalent fraction with denominator 20 and add.

$$3\frac{1}{4} = 3\frac{1 \cdot 5}{4 \cdot 5} = 3\frac{5}{20}$$

$$2\frac{3}{5} = 2\frac{3 \cdot 4}{5 \cdot 4} = 2\frac{12}{20}$$

$$+ 1\frac{9}{10} = 1\frac{9 \cdot 2}{10 \cdot 2} = 1\frac{18}{20}$$
$$\overline{\phantom{+ 1\frac{9}{10} = 1\frac{9 \cdot 2}{10 \cdot 2} = }6\frac{35}{20}}$$

Notice $\frac{35}{20} = 1\frac{15}{20}$ which simplifies to $1\frac{3}{4}$. We regroup and combine the whole numbers, giving the solution $7\frac{3}{4}$.

- •

We should note here that we could have worked the last three examples by first changing each mixed number to an improper fraction and then adding as we did earlier in this chapter. To illustrate, if we were to work Example 7 this way, it would look like this:

$$3\frac{1}{4} + 2\frac{3}{5} + 1\frac{9}{10} = \frac{13}{4} + \frac{13}{5} + \frac{19}{10}$$ *Change to improper fractions.*

$$= \frac{13 \cdot 5}{4 \cdot 5} + \frac{13 \cdot 4}{5 \cdot 4} + \frac{19 \cdot 2}{10 \cdot 2}$$ *LCD is 20.*

$$= \frac{65}{20} + \frac{52}{20} + \frac{38}{20}$$ *Equivalent fractions*

$$= \frac{155}{20}$$ *Add numerators.*

$$= 7\frac{15}{20} = 7\frac{3}{4}$$ *Change to a mixed number, and reduce.*

As you can see, the result is the same as the result we obtained in Example 7.

   There are advantages to both methods. The method just shown works well when the whole-number parts of the mixed numbers are small. The vertical method shown in Examples 5–7 works well when the whole-number parts of the mixed numbers are large.

D Subtraction with Mixed Numbers

Subtraction with mixed numbers is very similar to addition with mixed numbers.

8. Subtract: $4\frac{5}{8} - 1\frac{1}{8}$

Example 8   Subtract: $3\frac{9}{10} - 1\frac{3}{10}$

Solution   Because the denominators are the same, we subtract the whole numbers and subtract the fractions.

$$3\frac{9}{10}$$

$$- 1\frac{3}{10}$$
$$\overline{2\frac{6}{10}} = 2\frac{3}{5}$$ *Reduce to lowest terms.*

- •

Answers

7. $11\frac{3}{4}$

8. $3\frac{1}{2}$

Example 9 Subtract: $12\frac{7}{10} - 8\frac{3}{5}$

Solution The common denominator is 10. We must rewrite $8\frac{3}{5}$ as an equivalent fraction with denominator 10.

$$12\frac{7}{10} = 12\frac{7}{10} = 12\frac{7}{10}$$
$$\underline{-8\frac{3}{5} = -8\frac{3\cdot 2}{5\cdot 2} = -8\frac{6}{10}}$$
$$4\frac{1}{10}$$

9. Subtract: $8\frac{1}{2} - 3\frac{1}{6}$

Example 10 Subtract: $10 - 5\frac{2}{7}$

Solution In order to have a fraction from which to subtract $\frac{2}{7}$, we borrow 1 from 10 and rewrite the 1 we borrow as $\frac{7}{7}$. The process looks like this:

$$10 = 9\frac{7}{7} \qquad \textit{We rewrite 10 as } 9+1\textit{, which is } 9 + \frac{7}{7} = 9\frac{7}{7}.$$
$$\underline{-5\frac{2}{7} = -5\frac{2}{7}} \qquad \textit{Then we can subtract as usual.}$$
$$4\frac{5}{7}$$

10. Subtract: $12 - 8\frac{5}{9}$

Example 11 Subtract: $8\frac{1}{4} - 3\frac{3}{4}$

Solution Because $\frac{3}{4}$ is larger than $\frac{1}{4}$, we again need to borrow 1 from the whole number. The 1 that we borrow from the 8 is rewritten as $\frac{4}{4}$, because 4 is the denominator of both fractions.

$$8\frac{1}{4} = 7\frac{5}{4} \qquad \textit{Borrow 1 in the form } \frac{4}{4}\textit{; then } \frac{4}{4} + \frac{1}{4} = \frac{5}{4}.$$
$$\underline{-3\frac{3}{4} = -3\frac{3}{4}}$$
$$4\frac{2}{4} = 4\frac{1}{2} \qquad \textit{Reduce to lowest terms.}$$

11. Subtract: $12\frac{1}{6} - 5\frac{5}{6}$

Example 12 Subtract: $4\frac{3}{4} - 1\frac{5}{6}$

Solution We begin by rewriting each fraction with the common denominator 12.

$$4\frac{3}{4} = 4\frac{3\cdot 3}{4\cdot 3} = 4\frac{9}{12}$$
$$\underline{-1\frac{5}{6} = -1\frac{5\cdot 2}{6\cdot 2} = -1\frac{10}{12}}$$

12. Subtract: $9\frac{1}{3} - 3\frac{3}{4}$

Because $\frac{10}{12}$ is larger than $\frac{9}{12}$, we borrow 1 from 4 in the form $\frac{12}{12}$ before we subtract.

$$4\frac{9}{12} = 3\frac{21}{12} \qquad 4 = 3 + 1 = 3 + \frac{12}{12}, \text{ so } 4\frac{9}{12} = \left(3 + \frac{12}{12}\right) + \frac{9}{12}$$
$$\underline{-1\frac{10}{12} = -1\frac{10}{12}} \qquad\qquad\qquad\qquad = 3 + \left(\frac{12}{12} + \frac{9}{12}\right)$$
$$2\frac{11}{12} \qquad\qquad\qquad\qquad\qquad\qquad = 3 + \frac{21}{12}$$
$$\qquad\qquad\qquad\qquad\qquad\qquad\qquad = 3\frac{21}{12}$$

KEY CONCEPT REVIEW

After reading through the preceding section, respond in your own words and in complete sentences.

A. Dividing $5\frac{9}{10}$ by 2 is equivalent to multiplying $5\frac{9}{10}$ by what number?

B. Find $4\frac{5}{8}$ of 3.

C. Is it necessary to "borrow" when subtracting $1\frac{3}{10}$ from $3\frac{9}{10}$?

D. To subtract $11\frac{20}{30}$ from $15\frac{3}{30}$, it is necessary to rewrite $15\frac{3}{30}$ as what mixed number?

VOCABULARY REVIEW ·

Choose the correct words to fill in the blanks below.

improper fraction   mixed number   addition sign   columns   borrow

1. To multiply mixed numbers, first change each _____mixed num_____ to an improper fraction. Then multiply numerators and denominators.

2. Division of mixed numbers requires that we change all mixed numbers to ___Improper_____ before actually doing the dividing.

3. To add mixed numbers, we can rewrite them using the _____addition sign_____, and then apply the commutative and associative properties. Alternatively, we can use ____columns____ to add the whole numbers and fractions.

4. When subtracting mixed numbers, if the fraction in the second mixed number is larger than the fraction in the first mixed number, _____borrow_____ 1 from the whole number in the first mixed number.

Problems

Write your answers as proper fractions or mixed numbers, not as improper fractions.

A Find the following products. (Multiply.)

1. $3\frac{2}{5} \cdot 1\frac{1}{2}$

2. $2\frac{1}{3} \cdot 6\frac{3}{4}$

3. $5\frac{1}{8} \cdot 2\frac{2}{3}$

4. $1\frac{5}{6} \cdot 1\frac{4}{5}$

5. $2\frac{1}{10} \cdot 3\frac{3}{10}$

6. $4\frac{7}{10} \cdot 3\frac{1}{10}$

7. $\left(-1\frac{1}{4}\right)\left(-4\frac{2}{3}\right)$

8. $\left(-3\frac{1}{2}\right)\left(-2\frac{1}{6}\right)$

9. $-2 \cdot 4\frac{7}{8}$

10. $-10 \cdot 1\frac{1}{4}$

11. $\frac{3}{5} \cdot 5\frac{1}{3}$

12. $\frac{2}{3} \cdot 4\frac{9}{10}$

13. $2\frac{1}{2} \cdot 3\frac{1}{3} \cdot 1\frac{1}{2}$

14. $3\frac{1}{5} \cdot 5\frac{1}{6} \cdot 1\frac{1}{8}$

15. $\frac{3}{4} \cdot 7 \cdot \left(-1\frac{4}{5}\right)$

16. $\frac{7}{8} \cdot 6 \cdot \left(-1\frac{5}{6}\right)$

B Find the following quotients. (Divide.)

17. $3\frac{1}{5} \div 4\frac{1}{2}$

18. $1\frac{4}{5} \div 2\frac{5}{6}$

19. $6\frac{1}{4} \div 3\frac{3}{4}$

20. $8\frac{2}{3} \div 4\frac{1}{3}$

21. $10 \div 2\frac{1}{2}$

22. $12 \div 3\frac{1}{6}$

23. $-8\frac{3}{5} \div 2$

24. $-12\frac{6}{7} \div 3$

25. $\left(\dfrac{3}{4} \div 2\dfrac{1}{2}\right) \div (-3)$ **26.** $\dfrac{7}{8} \div \left[1\dfrac{1}{4} \div (-4)\right]$ **27.** $\left(8 \div 1\dfrac{1}{4}\right) \div (-2)$ **28.** $8 \div \left(1\dfrac{1}{4} \div 2\right)$

29. $2\dfrac{1}{2} \cdot \left(3\dfrac{2}{5} \div 4\right)$ **30.** $4\dfrac{3}{5} \cdot \left(2\dfrac{1}{4} \div 5\right)$

C, D Add and subtract the following mixed numbers as indicated.

31. $2\dfrac{1}{5} + 3\dfrac{3}{5}$ **32.** $8\dfrac{2}{9} + 1\dfrac{5}{9}$ **33.** $4\dfrac{3}{10} + 8\dfrac{1}{10}$ **34.** $5\dfrac{2}{7} + 3\dfrac{3}{7}$

35. $6\dfrac{8}{9} - 3\dfrac{4}{9}$ **36.** $12\dfrac{5}{12} + \left(-7\dfrac{1}{12}\right)$ **37.** $9\dfrac{1}{4} - \left(-5\dfrac{3}{4}\right)$ **38.** $3\dfrac{5}{8} - 2\dfrac{1}{4}$

39. $7\dfrac{9}{10} - 6\dfrac{3}{5}$ **40.** $11\dfrac{1}{3} + 2\dfrac{5}{6}$ **41.** $1\dfrac{5}{8} + 2\dfrac{1}{2}$ **42.** $7\dfrac{5}{12} - 3\dfrac{1}{3}$

43. $7\dfrac{3}{4} - 3\dfrac{5}{12}$ **44.** $11\dfrac{7}{8} - \left(-9\dfrac{1}{6}\right)$ **45.** $18\dfrac{1}{8} + \left(-6\dfrac{3}{4}\right)$ **46.** $10\dfrac{1}{3} - 4\dfrac{1}{6}$

47. $\begin{array}{r} 6\dfrac{1}{2} \\ + 2\dfrac{5}{14} \\ \hline \end{array}$ **48.** $\begin{array}{r} 9\dfrac{11}{12} \\ + 4\dfrac{1}{6} \\ \hline \end{array}$ **49.** $\begin{array}{r} 1\dfrac{5}{8} \\ + 1\dfrac{3}{4} \\ \hline \end{array}$ **50.** $\begin{array}{r} 7\dfrac{6}{7} \\ + 2\dfrac{3}{14} \\ \hline \end{array}$

51. $\begin{array}{r} 4\dfrac{2}{3} \\ + 5\dfrac{3}{5} \\ \hline \end{array}$ **52.** $\begin{array}{r} 9\dfrac{4}{9} \\ + 1\dfrac{1}{6} \\ \hline \end{array}$ **53.** $\begin{array}{r} 5\dfrac{4}{10} \\ - 3\dfrac{1}{3} \\ \hline \end{array}$ **54.** $\begin{array}{r} 12\dfrac{7}{8} \\ - 3\dfrac{5}{6} \\ \hline \end{array}$

Find the following sums. (Add.)

55. $1\frac{1}{4} + 2\frac{3}{4} + 5$

56. $6 + 5\frac{3}{5} + 8\frac{2}{5}$

57. $7\frac{1}{10} + 8\frac{3}{10} + 2\frac{7}{10}$

58. $5\frac{2}{7} + 8\frac{1}{7} + 3\frac{5}{7}$

59. $\frac{3}{4} + 8\frac{1}{4} + 5$

60. $\frac{5}{8} + 1\frac{1}{8} + 7$

61. $3\frac{1}{2} + 8\frac{1}{3} + 5\frac{1}{6}$

62. $4\frac{1}{5} + 7\frac{1}{3} + 8\frac{1}{15}$

Find the following differences. (Subtract.)

63. $8 - 1\frac{3}{4}$

64. $5 - 3\frac{1}{3}$

65. $15 - 5\frac{3}{10}$

66. $24 - 10\frac{5}{12}$

67. $8\frac{1}{4} - 2\frac{3}{4}$

68. $12\frac{3}{10} - 5\frac{7}{10}$

69. $9\frac{1}{3} - 8\frac{2}{3}$

70. $7\frac{1}{6} - 6\frac{5}{6}$

71. $4\frac{1}{4} - 2\frac{1}{3}$

72. $6\frac{1}{5} - 1\frac{2}{3}$

73. $9\frac{2}{3} - 5\frac{3}{4}$

74. $12\frac{5}{6} - 8\frac{7}{8}$

75. $16\frac{3}{4} - 10\frac{4}{5}$

76. $18\frac{5}{12} - 9\frac{3}{4}$

77. $10\frac{3}{10} - 4\frac{4}{5}$

78. $9\frac{4}{7} - 7\frac{2}{3}$

79. $13\frac{1}{6} - 12\frac{5}{8}$

80. $21\frac{2}{5} - 20\frac{5}{6}$

81. $19\frac{1}{4} - 8\frac{5}{6}$

82. $22\frac{7}{10} - 18\frac{4}{5}$

83. Find the product of $2\frac{1}{2}$ and 3.

84. Find the product of $\frac{1}{5}$ and $3\frac{2}{3}$.

85. What is the quotient of $2\frac{3}{4}$ and $3\frac{1}{4}$?

86. What is the quotient of $1\frac{1}{5}$ and $2\frac{2}{5}$?

87. Find the difference between $6\frac{1}{5}$ and $2\frac{7}{10}$.

88. Give the difference between $5\frac{1}{3}$ and $1\frac{5}{6}$.

89. Find $\frac{3}{4}$ of $1\frac{7}{9}$.

90. Find $\frac{5}{6}$ of $2\frac{4}{15}$.

91. Find the sum of $3\frac{1}{8}$ and $2\frac{3}{5}$.

92. Find the sum of $1\frac{5}{6}$ and $3\frac{4}{9}$.

Applying the Concepts

93. **Cooking** A certain recipe calls for $2\frac{3}{4}$ cups of sugar. If the recipe is to be doubled, how much sugar should be used?

94. **Cooking** If a recipe calls for $3\frac{1}{2}$ cups of flour, how much flour will be needed if the recipe is tripled?

95. **Cooking** If a recipe calls for $2\frac{1}{2}$ cups of sugar, how much sugar is needed to make $\frac{1}{3}$ of the recipe?

96. **Cooking** A recipe calls for $3\frac{1}{4}$ cups of flour. If Diane is using only half the recipe, how much flour should she use?

97. **Cost of Gasoline** If a gallon of gas costs $305\frac{1}{5}$¢, how much does 8 gallons cost?

98. **Cost of Gasoline** If a gallon of gas costs $308\frac{1}{5}$¢, how much does $\frac{1}{2}$ gallon cost?

99. **Distance Traveled** If a car can travel $32\frac{3}{4}$ miles on a gallon of gas, how far will it travel on 5 gallons of gas?

100. **Distance Traveled** If a new car can travel $20\frac{3}{10}$ miles on 1 gallon of gas, how far can it travel on $\frac{1}{2}$ gallon of gas?

Find the area of each figure.

101.

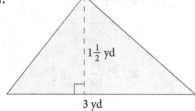

$1\frac{1}{2}$ yd

3 yd

102.

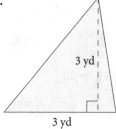

3 yd

3 yd

103. Write the numbers in order from smallest to largest.

$$2\frac{1}{8} \qquad \frac{5}{4} \qquad \frac{3}{4} \qquad 1\frac{1}{2}$$

104. Write the numbers in order from smallest to largest.

$$1\frac{3}{8} \qquad \frac{7}{8} \qquad \frac{7}{4} \qquad 1\frac{11}{16}$$

105. **Building** Two pieces of molding $5\frac{7}{8}$ inches and $6\frac{3}{8}$ inches long are placed end to end. What is the total length of the two pieces of molding together?

106. **Jogging** A jogger runs $2\frac{1}{2}$ miles on Monday, $3\frac{1}{4}$ miles on Tuesday, and $2\frac{2}{5}$ miles on Wednesday. What is the jogger's total mileage for this 3-day period?

107. Length of Jeans A pair of jeans is $32\frac{1}{2}$ inches long. How long are the jeans after they have been washed if they shrink $1\frac{1}{3}$ inches?

108. Manufacturing A clothing manufacturer has two rolls of cloth. One roll is $35\frac{1}{2}$ yards, and the other is $62\frac{5}{8}$ yards. What is the total number of yards in the two rolls?

Area and Perimeter The diagrams below show the dimensions of playing fields for the National Football League (NFL), the Canadian Football League, and arena football.

Football Fields

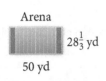

Arena

$28\frac{1}{3}$ yd

50 yd

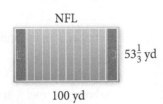

NFL

$53\frac{1}{3}$ yd

100 yd

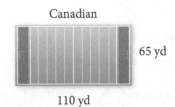

Canadian

65 yd

110 yd

109. Find the perimeter of each football field.

110. Find the area of each football field.

Getting Ready for the Next Section

Perform the indicated operations.

111. $4\left(\dfrac{3}{4}\right)$

112. $12\left(\dfrac{3}{4}\right)$

113. $\dfrac{11}{8} \cdot \dfrac{29}{8}$

114. $\dfrac{3}{4} + \dfrac{5}{8}$

115. $\dfrac{3}{4} \div \dfrac{5}{6}$

116. $\left(2\dfrac{1}{2}\right)\left(3\dfrac{2}{3}\right)$

117. $2\dfrac{3}{8} + 1\dfrac{1}{4}$

118. $10\dfrac{1}{3} \div 8\dfrac{2}{3}$

One Step Further

To find the square of a mixed number, we first change the mixed number to an improper fraction, and then we square the result. For example, $\left(2\dfrac{1}{2}\right)^2 = \left(\dfrac{5}{2}\right)^2 = \dfrac{25}{4}$. If we are asked to write our answer as a mixed number, we write it as $6\dfrac{1}{4}$.

Find each of the following squares, and write your answers as mixed numbers.

119. $\left(1\dfrac{1}{2}\right)^2$

120. $\left(3\dfrac{1}{2}\right)^2$

121. $\left(1\dfrac{3}{4}\right)^2$

122. $\left(2\dfrac{3}{4}\right)^2$

123. The length of one side of a square is $1\frac{1}{2}$ ft. Write the area of the square as a mixed number.

124. The length of one side of a square is $2\frac{1}{2}$ ft. Write the area of the square as a mixed number.

125. The volume of a cube is found by finding s^3 where s is the length of one side. If the length of one side of a cube is $1\frac{1}{2}$ ft., write the volume of the cube as a mixed number.

126. The volume of a cube is found by finding s^3 where s is the length of one side. If the length of one side of a cube is $1\frac{1}{3}$ ft., write the volume of the cube as a mixed number.

FIND THE MISTAKE •

Each sentence below contains a mistake. Circle the mistake and write the correct word(s) or numbers(s) on the line provided.

1. Multiplying $4\frac{3}{8}$ and $9\frac{2}{7}$ gives us the mixed number $45\frac{1}{3}$. _____

2. The answer to the division problem $3\frac{9}{14} \div 2$ written as a mixed number is $\frac{51}{28}$.

   _____

3. To begin adding $3\frac{9}{14}$ and $5\frac{1}{3}$, write each mixed number with the addition sign and then apply the commutative and associative properties, such that $\left(3 + \frac{2}{5}\right) + \left(5 + \frac{1}{3}\right)$. _____

4. The first step when subtracting $8 - 3\frac{2}{7} = 4\frac{5}{7}$ is to borrow 1 from 8 in the form of $\frac{8}{8}$. _____

LANDMARK REVIEW: CHECKING YOUR PROGRESS • • • • • • • • • • • • • • • •

Find the following sums and differences and reduce to lowest terms.

1. $\frac{7}{10} + \frac{3}{10}$

2. $\frac{2}{5} - \frac{1}{5}$

3. $\frac{2}{3} + \frac{3}{5}$

4. $\frac{1}{2} + \frac{3}{4}$

5. $\frac{3}{5} + \frac{2}{3} - \frac{4}{7}$

6. Find the sum of $\frac{2}{3}$, $\frac{1}{5}$, and $\frac{1}{2}$.

7. Find the difference of $\frac{7}{10}$ and $\frac{3}{5}$.

Change each mixed number to an improper fraction.

8. $3\frac{5}{8}$

9. $4\frac{2}{3}$

10. $10\frac{1}{2}$

11. $1\frac{1}{4}$

Change each improper fraction to a mixed number.

12. $\frac{14}{3}$

13. $\frac{23}{5}$

14. $\frac{7}{2}$

15. $\frac{42}{17}$

Perform the indicated operations.

16. $4\frac{1}{4} \cdot 5\frac{1}{2}$

17. $3\frac{1}{3} \cdot 2\frac{5}{6}$

18. $5\frac{1}{4} \div 4\frac{3}{8}$

19. $3\frac{7}{10} \div 1\frac{3}{5}$

20. $2\frac{1}{3} + 3\frac{2}{5}$

21. $7\frac{4}{5} + 2\frac{3}{8}$

22. $9\frac{4}{7} - 3\frac{1}{2}$

23. $8\frac{2}{3} - 2\frac{5}{6}$

ORDER OF OPERATIONS AND COMPLEX FRACTIONS

4.7

Each year, the coastal waters of Qingdao, China are infiltrated with a vibrant green algae bloom that covers more than 150 square miles. The algae thrive in high temperatures and in polluted waters caused by runoff from agriculture land and fish farms. The bloom sucks oxygen out of the water, threatening the local marine life. As it washes onshore and dries in the hot sun, it gives off a noxious odor that smells like rotten eggs. Soldiers and volunteers work tirelessly to clear the water and the beaches of the algae before the bloom drastically damages the local ecosystem.

Suppose you have volunteered to help clean up a portion of the algae-affected coast. The area of the beach you'll be responsible for has a width of $5\frac{1}{4}$ feet and a length of $10\frac{2}{3}$ feet. You also need to clean part of the water that measures 20 square feet. You wonder how large the total area is for which you are responsible. The total area is given by the following expression:

$$20 + \left(5\frac{1}{4}\right)\left(10\frac{2}{3}\right)$$

In this section, we will learn how to simplify expressions, such as the one above.

A Order of Operations

The order of operations that we used previously to simplify mathematical expressions will also apply to expressions that contain fractions. Here is the rule for the order of operations:

RULE Order of Operations

1. If the expression contains grouping symbols, such as parentheses ( ), brackets [ ], or a fraction bar, then we perform the operations inside the grouping symbols, or above and below the fraction bar, first.

2. Then we evaluate, or simplify, any numbers with exponents.

3. Then we do all multiplications and divisions in order, starting at the left and moving right.

4. Finally, we do all additions and subtractions, from left to right.

Practice Problems

1. Simplify the expression.

$$4 + \left(1\frac{1}{3}\right)\left(4\frac{1}{2}\right)$$

Example 1 Simplify the expression: $5 + \left(2\frac{1}{2}\right)\left(3\frac{2}{3}\right)$

Solution The order of operations indicates that we should multiply $2\frac{1}{2}$ times $3\frac{2}{3}$ and then add 5 to the result.

$$5 + \left(2\frac{1}{2}\right)\left(3\frac{2}{3}\right) = 5 + \left(\frac{5}{2}\right)\left(\frac{11}{3}\right) \qquad \text{Change the mixed numbers to improper fractions.}$$

$$= 5 + \frac{55}{6} \qquad \text{Multiply the improper fractions.}$$

$$= \frac{30}{6} + \frac{55}{6} \qquad \text{Write 5 as } \frac{30}{6} \text{ so both numbers have the same denominator.}$$

$$= \frac{85}{6} \qquad \text{Add fractions by adding their numerators.}$$

$$= 14\frac{1}{6} \qquad \text{Write the answer as a mixed number.}$$

2. Simplify: $\left(\frac{2}{3} + \frac{5}{6}\right)\left(3\frac{1}{4} - 1\frac{1}{2}\right)$

Example 2 Simplify: $\left(\frac{3}{4} + \frac{5}{8}\right)\left(2\frac{3}{8} + 1\frac{1}{4}\right)$

Solution We begin by combining the numbers inside the parentheses.

$$\frac{3}{4} + \frac{5}{8} = \frac{3 \cdot 2}{4 \cdot 2} + \frac{5}{8} \qquad \text{and} \qquad 2\frac{3}{8} = \quad 2\frac{3}{8} \quad = \quad 2\frac{3}{8}$$

$$= \frac{6}{8} + \frac{5}{8} \qquad\qquad\qquad\qquad +1\frac{1}{4} = +1\frac{1 \cdot 2}{4 \cdot 2} = +1\frac{2}{8}$$

$$= \frac{11}{8} \qquad\qquad\qquad\qquad\qquad\qquad\qquad\qquad 3\frac{5}{8}$$

Now that we have combined the expressions inside the parentheses, we can complete the problem by multiplying the results.

$$\left(\frac{3}{4} + \frac{5}{8}\right)\left(2\frac{3}{8} + 1\frac{1}{4}\right) = \left(\frac{11}{8}\right)\left(3\frac{5}{8}\right)$$

$$= \frac{11}{8} \cdot \frac{29}{8} \qquad \text{Change } 3\frac{5}{8} \text{ to an improper fraction.}$$

$$= \frac{319}{64} \qquad \text{Multiply fractions.}$$

$$= 4\frac{63}{64} \qquad \text{Write the answer as a mixed number.}$$

3. Simplify: $3\frac{5}{6} + \frac{1}{3}\left(4\frac{1}{3} + 2\frac{2}{3}\right)^2$

Example 3 Simplify: $\frac{3}{5} + \frac{1}{2}\left(3\frac{2}{3} + 4\frac{1}{3}\right)^2$

Solution We begin by combining the expressions inside the parentheses.

$$\frac{3}{5} + \frac{1}{2}\left(3\frac{2}{3} + 4\frac{1}{3}\right)^2 = \frac{3}{5} + \frac{1}{2}\,(8)^2 \qquad \text{The sum inside the parentheses is 8.}$$

$$= \frac{3}{5} + \frac{1}{2}\,(64) \qquad \text{The square of 8 is 64.}$$

$$= \frac{3}{5} + 32 \qquad \frac{1}{2}(64) = 32.$$

$$= 32\frac{3}{5} \qquad \text{The result is a mixed number.}$$

Answer

1. 10

2. $2\frac{5}{8}$

3. $20\frac{1}{6}$

B Complex Fractions

DEFINITION   complex fraction

A **complex fraction** is a fraction in which the numerator and/or the denominator are themselves fractions or combinations of fractions.

Each of the following is a complex fraction:

$$\frac{\frac{3}{4}}{\frac{5}{6}}, \qquad \frac{3 + \frac{1}{2}}{2 - \frac{3}{4}}, \qquad \frac{\frac{1}{2} + \frac{2}{3}}{\frac{3}{4} - \frac{1}{6}}$$

Example 4   Simplify: $\dfrac{\frac{3}{4}}{\frac{5}{6}}$

Solution   This is actually the same as the problem $\frac{3}{4} \div \frac{5}{6}$, because the fraction bar between $\frac{3}{4}$ and $\frac{5}{6}$ indicates division. Therefore, it must be true that

$$\frac{\frac{3}{4}}{\frac{5}{6}} = \frac{3}{4} \div \frac{5}{6}$$

$$= \frac{3 \cdot 6}{4 \cdot 5}$$

$$= \frac{18}{20}$$

$$= \frac{9}{10}$$

4. Simplify: $\dfrac{\frac{2}{3}}{\frac{5}{6}}$

As you can see, we continue to use properties we have developed previously when we encounter new situations. In the previous example, we use the fact that division by a number and multiplication by its reciprocal produce the same result. We are taking a new problem, simplifying a complex fraction, and thinking of it in terms of a problem we have done previously, division by a fraction.

Example 5   Simplify: $\dfrac{\frac{1}{2} + \frac{2}{3}}{\frac{3}{4} - \frac{1}{6}}$

Solution   Let's decide to call the numerator of this complex fraction the *top* of the fraction and its denominator the *bottom* of the complex fraction. The LCD for all the denominators on the top and bottom is 12, so we can multiply the top and bottom of this complex fraction by 12 and be sure all the denominators will divide it exactly. As we will show, this will leave us with only whole numbers on the top and bottom.

$$\frac{\frac{1}{2} + \frac{2}{3}}{\frac{3}{4} - \frac{1}{6}} = \frac{12 \left(\frac{1}{2} + \frac{2}{3} \right)}{12 \left(\frac{3}{4} - \frac{1}{6} \right)} \qquad \text{Multiply the top and bottom by the LCD.}$$

$$= \frac{12 \cdot \frac{1}{2} + 12 \cdot \frac{2}{3}}{12 \cdot \frac{3}{4} - 12 \cdot \frac{1}{6}} \qquad \text{Distributive property}$$

5. Simplify: $\dfrac{\frac{1}{4} + \frac{1}{3}}{\frac{1}{2} - \frac{1}{3}}$

Note   We are going to simplify this complex fraction by two different methods. This is the first method.

Answers

4. $\frac{4}{5}$

5. $3\frac{1}{2}$

$$= \frac{\dfrac{12}{2} + \dfrac{24}{3}}{\dfrac{36}{4} - \dfrac{12}{6}} \qquad \text{Multiply each fraction by 12.}$$

$$= \frac{6 + 8}{9 - 2} \qquad \text{Simplify.}$$

$$= \frac{14}{7} \qquad \text{Add on the top and subtract on the bottom.}$$

$$= 2 \qquad \text{Reduce to lowest terms.}$$

The previous problem can also be worked in another way. We can simplify the top and bottom of the complex fraction separately. Simplifying the top, we have

$$\frac{1}{2} + \frac{2}{3} = \frac{1 \cdot 3}{2 \cdot 3} + \frac{2 \cdot 2}{3 \cdot 2} = \frac{3}{6} + \frac{4}{6} = \frac{7}{6}$$

Simplifying the bottom, we have

$$\frac{3}{4} - \frac{1}{6} = \frac{3 \cdot 3}{4 \cdot 3} - \frac{1 \cdot 2}{6 \cdot 2} = \frac{9}{12} - \frac{2}{12} = \frac{7}{12}$$

We now write the original complex fraction again using the simplified expressions for the top and bottom. Then we proceed as we did in Example 4.

$$\frac{\dfrac{1}{2} + \dfrac{2}{3}}{\dfrac{3}{4} - \dfrac{1}{6}} = \frac{\dfrac{7}{6}}{\dfrac{7}{12}}$$

$$= \frac{7}{6} \div \frac{7}{12} \qquad \text{The divisor is } \tfrac{7}{12}.$$

$$= \frac{7}{6} \cdot \frac{12}{7} \qquad \text{Divide out a common factor of 7.}$$

$$= \frac{12}{6}$$

$$= 2 \qquad \text{Reduce to lowest terms.}$$

> **Note** The fraction bar that separates the numerator of the complex fraction from its denominator works like parentheses. If we were to rewrite this problem without it, we would write it like this:
>
> $$\left(\frac{1}{2} + \frac{2}{3} \right) \div \left(\frac{3}{4} - \frac{1}{6} \right)$$
>
> That is why we simplify the top and bottom of the complex fraction separately and then divide.

6. Simplify: $\dfrac{4 - \dfrac{1}{3}}{2 + \dfrac{1}{2}}$

Example 6   Simplify: $\dfrac{3 + \dfrac{1}{2}}{2 - \dfrac{3}{4}}$

Solution   One approach here is to multiply both the top and bottom by the LCD for all fractions, which is 4.

$$\frac{3 + \dfrac{1}{2}}{2 - \dfrac{3}{4}} = \frac{4\left(3 + \dfrac{1}{2} \right)}{4\left(2 - \dfrac{3}{4} \right)} \qquad \text{Multiply the top and bottom by 4.}$$

$$= \frac{4 \cdot 3 + 4 \cdot \dfrac{1}{2}}{4 \cdot 2 - 4 \cdot \dfrac{3}{4}} \qquad \text{Distributive property}$$

$$= \frac{12 + 2}{8 - 3} \qquad \text{Multiply each number by 4.}$$

$$= \frac{14}{5} \qquad \text{Add on the top and subtract on the bottom.}$$

$$= 2\frac{4}{5} \qquad \text{The result is a mixed number.}$$

Answer

6. $1\frac{7}{15}$

Example 7   Simplify: $\dfrac{10\frac{1}{3}}{8\frac{2}{3}}$

7. Simplify: $\dfrac{8\frac{3}{4}}{5\frac{1}{2}}$

Solution   One approach is to simplify this complex fraction by thinking of it as a division problem.

$$\dfrac{10\frac{1}{3}}{8\frac{2}{3}} = 10\frac{1}{3} \div 8\frac{2}{3}$$ Write with a ÷ symbol.

$$= \frac{31}{3} \div \frac{26}{3}$$ Change to improper fractions.

$$= \frac{31}{3} \cdot \frac{3}{26}$$ Write in terms of multiplication.

$$= \frac{31 \cdot 3}{3 \cdot 26}$$ Divide out the common factor 3.

$$= \frac{31}{26}$$

$$= 1\frac{5}{26}$$ Answer as a mixed number.

KEY CONCEPT REVIEW

After reading through the preceding section, respond in your own words and in complete sentences.

A. What is a complex fraction?

B. Rewrite $\dfrac{\frac{5}{6}}{\frac{1}{3}}$ as a multiplication problem.

C. True or false? The rules for order of operations tell us to work inside parentheses first.

D. True or false? We find the LCD when we add or subtract fractions, but not when we multiply them. Explain.

EXERCISE SET 4.7 . . . .

Problems

A Use the rule for order of operations to simplify each of the following.

1. $3 + \left(1\frac{1}{2}\right)\left(2\frac{2}{3}\right)$

2. $10 + \left(2\frac{4}{5}\right)\left(\frac{5}{7}\right)$

3. $7 - \left(1\frac{3}{5}\right)\left(2\frac{1}{2}\right)$

4. $8 - \left(\frac{6}{11}\right)\left(1\frac{5}{6}\right)$

5. $\frac{2}{3}\left(1\frac{1}{2}\right) + \frac{3}{4}\left(1\frac{1}{3}\right)$

6. $\frac{2}{5}\left(2\frac{1}{2}\right) + \frac{5}{8}\left(3\frac{1}{5}\right)$

7. $2\left(1\frac{1}{2}\right) + 5\left(6\frac{2}{5}\right)$

8. $4\left(5\frac{3}{4}\right) + 6\left(3\frac{5}{6}\right)$

9. $\left(\frac{2}{9} + \frac{1}{3}\right)\left(\frac{1}{5} + \frac{1}{10}\right)$

10. $\left(2 + \frac{2}{3}\right)\left(3 + \frac{1}{8}\right)$

11. $\left(3 - \frac{3}{4}\right)\left(3 + \frac{1}{3}\right)$

12. $\left(2 - \frac{1}{4}\right)\left(2 + \frac{1}{4}\right)$

13. $\frac{2}{3} + \frac{1}{3}\left(2\frac{1}{2} + \frac{1}{2}\right)^2$

14. $\frac{3}{5} + \frac{1}{4}\left(2\frac{1}{2} - \frac{1}{2}\right)^3$

15. $2\frac{3}{8} + \frac{1}{2}\left(\frac{1}{3} + \frac{5}{3}\right)^3$

16. $8\frac{2}{3} + \frac{1}{3}\left(\frac{8}{5} + \frac{7}{5}\right)^2$

17. $2\left(\frac{1}{2} + \frac{1}{3}\right) + 3\left(\frac{2}{3} + \frac{1}{4}\right)$

18. $5\left(\frac{1}{5} + \frac{3}{10}\right) + 2\left(\frac{1}{10} + \frac{1}{2}\right)$

B Simplify each complex fraction as much as possible.

19. $\dfrac{\frac{2}{3}}{\frac{3}{4}}$

20. $\dfrac{\frac{5}{6}}{\frac{3}{12}}$

21. $\dfrac{\frac{2}{3}}{\frac{4}{3}}$

22. $\dfrac{\frac{7}{9}}{\frac{5}{9}}$

23. $\dfrac{\frac{11}{20}}{\frac{5}{10}}$

24. $\dfrac{\frac{9}{16}}{\frac{3}{4}}$

25. $\dfrac{\frac{1}{2} + \frac{1}{3}}{\frac{1}{2} - \frac{1}{3}}$

26. $\dfrac{\frac{1}{4} + \frac{1}{5}}{\frac{1}{4} - \frac{1}{5}}$

27. $\dfrac{\frac{5}{8} - \frac{1}{4}}{\frac{1}{8} + \frac{1}{2}}$

28. $\dfrac{\frac{3}{4} + \frac{1}{3}}{\frac{2}{3} + \frac{1}{6}}$

29. $\dfrac{\frac{9}{20} - \frac{1}{10}}{\frac{1}{10} + \frac{9}{20}}$

30. $\dfrac{\frac{1}{2} + \frac{2}{3}}{\frac{3}{4} + \frac{5}{6}}$

31. $\dfrac{1 + \frac{2}{3}}{1 - \frac{2}{3}}$

32. $\dfrac{5 - \frac{3}{4}}{2 + \frac{3}{4}}$

33. $\dfrac{2 + \frac{5}{6}}{5 - \frac{1}{3}}$

34. $\dfrac{9 - \frac{11}{5}}{3 + \frac{13}{10}}$

35. $\dfrac{\frac{1}{3} + \frac{3}{4}}{2 - \frac{1}{6}}$

36. $\dfrac{3 + \frac{5}{2}}{\frac{5}{6} + \frac{1}{4}}$

37. $\dfrac{8 + \frac{3}{4}}{\frac{5}{8}}$

38. $\dfrac{\frac{5}{6}}{3 - \frac{1}{3}}$

Simplify each of the following complex fractions.

39. $\dfrac{2\frac{1}{2} + \frac{1}{2}}{3\frac{3}{5} - \frac{2}{5}}$

40. $\dfrac{5\frac{3}{8} + \frac{5}{8}}{4\frac{1}{4} + 1\frac{3}{4}}$

41. $\dfrac{2 + 1\frac{2}{3}}{3\frac{5}{6} - 1}$

42. $\dfrac{5 + 8\frac{3}{5}}{2\frac{3}{10} + 4}$

43. $\dfrac{3\frac{1}{4} - 2\frac{1}{2}}{5\frac{3}{4} + 1\frac{1}{2}}$

44. $\dfrac{9\frac{3}{8} + 2\frac{5}{8}}{6\frac{1}{2} + 7\frac{1}{2}}$

45. $\dfrac{3\frac{1}{4} + 5\frac{1}{6}}{2\frac{1}{3} + 3\frac{1}{4}}$

46. $\dfrac{8\frac{5}{6} + 1\frac{2}{3}}{7\frac{1}{3} + 2\frac{1}{4}}$

47. $\dfrac{6\frac{2}{3} + 7\frac{3}{4}}{8\frac{1}{2} + 9\frac{7}{8}}$

48. $\dfrac{3\frac{4}{5} - 1\frac{9}{10}}{6\frac{5}{6} - 2\frac{3}{4}}$

49. $\dfrac{4\frac{1}{3} - 1\frac{2}{3}}{8\frac{1}{4} - 5\frac{1}{2}}$

50. $\dfrac{3\frac{1}{2} + 2\frac{1}{6}}{2 - \frac{5}{6}}$

Applying the Concepts

51. What is twice the sum of $2\frac{1}{5}$ and $\frac{3}{6}$?

52. Find 3 times the difference of $1\frac{7}{9}$ and $\frac{2}{9}$.

53. Add $5\frac{1}{4}$ to the sum of $\frac{3}{4}$ and 2.

54. Subtract $\frac{7}{8}$ from the product of 2 and $3\frac{1}{2}$.

55. Manufacturing A dress manufacturer usually buys two rolls of cloth, one of $32\frac{1}{2}$ yards and the other of $25\frac{1}{3}$ yards, to fill his weekly orders. If his orders double one week, how much of the cloth should he order? (Give the total yardage.)

56. Body Temperature Suppose your normal body temperature is $98\frac{3}{5}°$ Fahrenheit. If your temperature goes up $3\frac{1}{5}°$ on Monday and then down $1\frac{4}{5}°$ on Tuesday, what is your temperature on Tuesday?

Getting Ready for the Next Section

Perform each of the indicated operations.

57. $\frac{5}{8} + \frac{3}{4}$

58. $\frac{5}{6} + \frac{2}{3}$

59. $8\left(\frac{3}{8}\right)$

60. $6\left(\frac{-5}{3}\right)$

61. $24\left(\frac{7}{8}x\right)$

62. $12\left(\frac{1}{3}x\right)$

Simplify.

63. $2(3a - 8)$

64. $4(2a - 5)$

65. $3(y - 5) + 6$

FIND THE MISTAKE •

Each sentence below contains a mistake. Circle the mistake and write the correct word(s) or numbers(s) on the line provided.

1. The first step to solving the problem $\frac{1}{4} - \left(2\frac{3}{8} - 1\frac{5}{8}\right)^2$ is to rewrite the problem so it looks like

$\frac{1}{4} + \left(-2\frac{3}{8} + -1\frac{5}{8}\right)^2$. _____

2. To simplify $5\frac{2}{3} + \left(10\frac{1}{3} \cdot \frac{2}{3}\right)$ you must first change $10\frac{1}{3}$ into the reciprocal $\frac{31}{3}$ before multiplying by $\frac{2}{3}$.

_____

3. A complex fraction is a fraction in which a fraction or combination of fractions appear in the denominator of the original fraction. _____

4. To simplify the complex fraction $\dfrac{\frac{1}{6} + \frac{2}{3}}{\frac{5}{6} + \frac{5}{12}}$, multiply the top and bottom of the fraction by 6. _____

SOLVING EQUATIONS INVOLVING FRACTIONS

4.8

The Rhind Papyrus is an ancient Egyptian document, created around 1650 BC, that contains some mathematical riddles. One problem on the Rhind Papyrus asked the reader to find a quantity such that when it is added to one-fourth of itself the sum is 15. The equation that describes this situation is

$$x + \frac{x}{4} = 15$$

The Papyrus also contained more difficult problems involving fractions, such as:

$$x + \frac{1}{3}x + \frac{1}{4}x = 2$$

OBJECTIVES · · · · · · ·

A Solve equations involving fractions.

KEY WORDS · · · · · ·

linear equation in one variable

least common denominator

VIDEO EXAMPLES

SECTION 4.8

Notice, the first equation contained $\frac{x}{4}$ whereas the second equation contained $\frac{1}{4}x$. We now know from our discussion of fractions that these are mathematically equivalent. In this section we will solve more equations using and involving fractions.

> **DEFINITION** linear equation in one variable
>
> A **linear equation in one variable** is any equation that can be put in the form $Ax + B = C$, where A, B, and C are real numbers and A is not zero.

A Linear Equations Involving Fractions

Before we solve any equations, recall the definition of a linear equation.

Here are some examples of linear equations in one variable that we have solved in previous chapters.

$$9 - x = 2 \qquad -7x = -42 \qquad 3(x + 2) = -9 \qquad 8(x + 5) - 6 = 18$$

You may have noticed that these equations are not in $Ax + B = C$ form. The key word in this definition is "can." Although these equations are not currently in that form, they could be rewritten that way.

In this section, we will solve linear equations involving fractions. In some cases, the answers will be fractions and in other cases, the equation may involve fractions. For the equations that involve fractions, we will strategically use the multiplication property of equality to eliminate those fractions.

Each of the equations we will solve in this section is a linear equation in one variable. The steps we use to solve a linear equation in one variable are listed here:

HOW TO   Strategy for Solving Linear Equations in One Variable

Step 1a: Use the distributive property to separate terms, if necessary.

1b: If fractions are present, consider multiplying both sides by the LCD to eliminate the fractions.

1c: Combine like terms on each side of the equation.

Step 2: Use the addition or subtraction property of equality to get all variable terms on one side of the equation and all constant terms on the other side. A variable term is a term that contains the variable. A constant term is a term that does not contain the variable.

Step 3: Use the multiplication or division property of equality to get x by itself on one side of the equation.

Step 4: Check your solution in the original equation.

As you work through the examples in this section, it is not always necessary to use all four steps when solving equations. The number of steps used depends on the equation. Let's look at an example.

Example 1   Solve: $-24x = 36$

Solution   In this problem, the terms are separated and no fractions are present. We will use the division property of equality to isolate x.

$$\frac{-24x}{-24} = \frac{36}{-24} \qquad \text{Divide both sides by } -24.$$

$$x = -\frac{36}{24}$$

$$x = -\frac{3}{2} \qquad \text{Reduce to lowest terms.}$$

We can write our answer as an improper fraction or as a mixed number, $x = -1\frac{1}{2}$. We can also check our solution by replacing x with $-\frac{3}{2}$.

$$-24\left(-\frac{3}{2}\right) = 36$$

$$-\frac{24}{1} \cdot -\frac{3}{2} = 36$$

$$\frac{72}{2} = 36$$

$$36 = 36 \qquad \text{A true statement}$$

Because the result is a true statement, we are confident that our solution $x = -\frac{3}{2}$ is the solution to $-24x = 36$.

Example 2   Solve: $\frac{1}{7}x - 4 = -8$

This is an example of an equation that involves a fraction. We can use the multiplication property of equality to eliminate the fraction. To do so, we use the LCD, which is 7, apply the distributive property, and simplify.

$$7\left(\frac{1}{7}x - 4\right) = 7(-8) \qquad \text{Multiply both sides by 7.}$$

$$7 \cdot \frac{1}{7}x - 7 \cdot 4 = 7(-8) \qquad \text{Distribute.}$$

$$x - 28 = -56 \qquad \text{Simplify.}$$

We will now use the addition property of equality to solve the remaining equation.

$$x - 28 + 28 = -56 + 28 \qquad \text{Add 28 to both sides.}$$

$$x = -28$$

We can check our solution to see that it's correct by substituting -28 for x.

$$\frac{1}{7}(-28) - 4 = -8$$

$$(-4) - 4 = -8$$

$$-8 = -8 \qquad \text{A true statement}$$

2. Solve: $\frac{1}{9}x + 5 = -10$

Example 3   Solve: $x - \frac{3}{4} = \frac{5}{8}$

Solution   We will multiply each side of the equation by the LCD, which is 8.

$$8\left(x - \frac{3}{4}\right) = 8\left(\frac{5}{8}\right) \qquad \text{Multiply both sides by 8.}$$

$$8x - 8 \cdot \frac{3}{4} = 8 \cdot \frac{5}{8} \qquad \text{Distribute.}$$

$$8x - 6 = 5 \qquad 8\left(\frac{3}{4}\right) = 6 \text{ and } 8\left(\frac{5}{8}\right) = 5.$$

We now solve the remaining equation.

$$8x - 6 + 6 = 5 + 6 \qquad \text{Add 6 to both sides.}$$

$$8x = 11 \qquad \text{Simplify.}$$

$$\frac{8x}{8} = \frac{11}{8} \qquad \text{Divide both sides by 8.}$$

$$x = \frac{11}{8}$$

We can leave our answer as an improper fraction or convert it to a mixed number, $x = 1\frac{3}{8}$.

3. Solve: $n - \frac{3}{5} = \frac{7}{10}$

4. Solve: $-\frac{3}{4}y = \frac{5}{20}$

Example 4   Solve: $-\frac{4}{5}x = \frac{8}{15}$

Solution   We multiply each side by the LCD, which is 15, and simplify.

$$15\left(\frac{-4}{5}x\right) = 15\left(\frac{8}{15}\right)$$ Multiply both sides by 15.

$$15 \cdot \frac{-4}{5}x = 15 \cdot \frac{8}{15}$$

$$-12x = 8$$ Simplify.

We solve the remaining equation by dividing both sides by -12 and reducing the result.

$$\frac{-12x}{-12} = \frac{8}{-12}$$ Divide both sides by -12.

$$x = -\frac{2}{3}$$ Reduce to lowest terms.

KEY CONCEPT REVIEW

After reading through the preceding section, respond in your own words and in complete sentences.

A. What is the first step in solving a linear equation containing parentheses?

B. When solving a linear equation, why should you get all variable terms on one side and all constant terms on the other before using the multiplication property of equality?

C. What is the last step in solving a linear equation?

VOCABULARY REVIEW ·

Choose the correct words to fill in the blanks below.

| LCD | original | subtraction | linear equations | multiplication |

To solve _____, we use the distributive property to separate terms, if necessary. If fractions are present, we multiply both sides by the _____ to eliminate the fractions. Then, combine like terms on each side of the equation. Use the addition or _____ property of equality to get all variable terms on one side of the equation and all constant terms on the other side. Use the _____ or division property of equality to get x by itself on one side of the equation. To verify that our work is correct, we can check the solution in the _____ equation.

Problems

A Solve each equation. You can check your solution by replacing the variable in the original equation.

1. $8x = 7$

2. $9x = 13$

3. $-10x = 15$

4. $12x = -20$

5. $5x = -\dfrac{1}{3}$

6. $4x = -\dfrac{3}{2}$

7. $\dfrac{5}{6}x = \dfrac{1}{12}$

8. $\dfrac{7}{8}x = \dfrac{3}{16}$

9. $-\dfrac{5}{7}x = \dfrac{3}{2}$

10. $\dfrac{8}{3}x = -\dfrac{4}{5}$

11. $5x - 3x = -\dfrac{2}{11}$

12. $4x - 7x = -\dfrac{3}{8}$

13. $a + \dfrac{1}{3} = -\dfrac{2}{3}$

14. $a + \dfrac{1}{4} = -\dfrac{3}{4}$

15. $x - \dfrac{3}{5} = \dfrac{4}{5}$

16. $x - \dfrac{7}{8} = \dfrac{3}{8}$

17. $\dfrac{x}{3} + \dfrac{x}{6} = 5$

18. $\dfrac{x}{2} - \dfrac{x}{4} = 3$

19. $\dfrac{x}{5} - x = 4$

20. $\dfrac{x}{3} + x = 8$

21. $3x + \dfrac{1}{2} = \dfrac{1}{4}$

22. $3x - \dfrac{1}{3} = \dfrac{1}{6}$

23. $\dfrac{x}{3} + \dfrac{1}{2} = -\dfrac{1}{2}$

24. $\dfrac{x}{2} + \dfrac{4}{3} = -\dfrac{2}{3}$

25. $1 = \dfrac{1}{2}(4x + 2)$

26. $1 = \dfrac{1}{3}(6x + 3)$

27. $\dfrac{1}{4}(16x - 8) = 2(3x + 9)$

28. $\dfrac{2}{3}(9x - 6) = 4(x - 2)$

29. $2(3x - 7) = -4(2x - 5)$

30. $3(4x - 1) = 8(2x - 3)$

31. $\dfrac{x}{3} + 8 = 10 + \dfrac{x}{4}$

32. $\dfrac{x}{2} + 8 = \dfrac{x}{5} + 14$

Applying the Concepts

33. Rhind Papyrus. Solve the following problem from the Rhind Papyrus.

$$x + \frac{1}{3}x + \frac{1}{4}x = 2$$

34. Rhind Papyrus. Solve the following problem from the Rhind Papyrus.

$$x + \frac{1}{2}x + \frac{1}{4}x = 10$$

35. Rhind Papyrus. The actual solution to the problem

$$x + \frac{1}{3}x + \frac{1}{4}x = 2$$

that was included in the Papyrus was

$$x = 1 + \frac{1}{6} + \frac{1}{12} + \frac{1}{114} + \frac{1}{228}$$

Show that your answer is mathematically equivalent.

36. Rhind Papyrus. The actual solution to the problem

$$x + \frac{1}{2}x + \frac{1}{4}x = 10$$

that was included in the Papyrus was

$$x = 5 + \frac{1}{2} + \frac{1}{7} + \frac{1}{14}$$

Show that your answer is mathematically equivalent.

37. Perimeter. The perimeter of a rectangle is 45 feet. If the width is one-third the length, what are the dimensions of the rectangle?

38. Perimeter. The perimeter of a rectangle is 33 meters. If the width is one-fifth the length, what are the dimensions of the rectangle?

39. Area. The area of the square below is 16 cm². Find x.

40. Area. The area of the square below is 36 in². Find x.

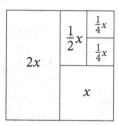

41. Test Average Justin earns scores of 75, 83, 77, and 81 on four tests in his math class. The final exam has twice the weight of a test. Justin wants to end the semester with an average of 80 for the course. Solving the equation below will give the lowest score Justin can earn on the final exam and still end the course with an 80 average. Solve the equation.

$$\frac{75 + 83 + 77 + 81 + 2x}{6} = 80$$

42. Test Average Rachel earns scores of 84, 73, 81, and 70 on four tests in her math class. The final exam has twice the weight of a test. Rachel wants to end the semester with an average of 80 for the course. Solving the equation below will give the lowest score Rachel can earn on the final exam and still end the course with an 80 average. Solve the equation.

$$\frac{84 + 73 + 81 + 70 + 2x}{6} = 80$$

Getting Ready for the Next Section

Check to see if the number to the right of each of the following equations is the solution to the equation.

43. $3 = 3x + 2; 2$

44. $5 = 3x + 2; 1$

45. $-4 = 3x + 2; -2$

Solve.

46. $2x + 3 = 6$

47. $4x - 7 = 8$

48. $2x - 10 = 20$

49. $2x - 0 = 20$

50. $3 = 2x - 1$

51. $7 = 2x - 1$

FIND THE MISTAKE ·

Each sentence below contains a mistake. Circle the mistake and write the correct word(s) or numbers(s) on the line provided.

1. The first step to solving the linear equation $\frac{2}{3}(9x - 6) = 4(x - 2)$ is to subtract $\frac{2}{3}$ from each side.

_____

2. In order to eliminate the fractions from the equation $3x - \frac{1}{3} = \frac{1}{6}$, we use the LCD, which is 3. _____

3. In order to eliminate the fractions from the equation $\frac{8}{3}x = -\frac{4}{5}$, we use the LCD, which is 3. _____

4. The solution to the equation $3x + \frac{1}{2} = \frac{1}{4}$ is $x = -12$. _____

4.9 THE RECTANGULAR COORDINATE SYSTEM AND LINEAR EQUATIONS

OBJECTIVES

A Determine whether an ordered pair is a solution to a linear equation in two variables.

B Find solutions to linear equations in two variables.

C Graph ordered pairs on a rectangular coordinate system.

KEY WORDS

linear equations in two variables

ordered pair

x-coordinate

y-coordinate

rectangular coordinate system

x-axis

y-axis

origin

quadrant

VIDEO EXAMPLES

SECTION 4.9

A robot named EMILY (Emergency Integrated Lifesaving Lanyard) patrols dangerous ocean waters off the coast of Malibu, California. Currently, a lifeguard controls EMILY by remote. However, developers are working to equip the robot with sonar and an autonomous system able to detect swimmers in distress without the help of a lifeguard on shore. EMILY's electric-powered impeller drives the robot through even the roughest surf at a speed 6 times faster than that of a human. A swimmer in distress can use EMILY as a flotation device until further help arrives, or EMILY can tow the swimmer back to shore.

Using the information about EMILY's speed, we can write the following equation, which uses two variables:

$$y = 6x$$

where x is a human's swimming speed and y is EMILY's speed. In this section, we will begin to investigate equations in two variables, such as the one above.

A Linear Equations in Two Variables

In the previous section we solved linear equations in one variable. In this section we will discuss linear equations in two variables.

> **DEFINITION** linear equation in two variables
>
> Any equation that can be put in the form $Ax + By = C$, where A, B, and C are real numbers and A and B are not both 0, is called a **linear equation in two variables.** The graph of any equation of this form is a straight line (that is why these equations are called "linear"). The form $Ax + By = C$ is called standard form.

An example of a linear equation in two variables is $2x + y = 3$. Because there are two variables, x and y, a solution to the equation will be a pair of numbers, one for x and one for y. These two numbers must make the equation a true statement. One pair of numbers that works is $x = 2$, $y = -1$ because when we substitute them for x and y in the equation, we get a true statement.

$$2(2) + (-1) \stackrel{?}{=} 3$$

$$4 - 1 = 3$$

$$3 = 3 \qquad \text{A true statement}$$

The pair of numbers $x = 2$, $y = -1$ is written as $(2, -1)$. This is called an **ordered pair** because it is a pair of numbers written in a specific order. The first number is always associated with the variable x, and the second number is always associated with the variable y. We call the first number in the ordered pair the **x-coordinate** and the second number the **y-coordinate** of the ordered pair.

Let's look back to the equation $2x + y = 3$. The ordered pair $(2, -1)$ is not the only solution. Another solution is $(0, 3)$ because when we substitute 0 for x and 3 for y we get

$$2(0) + 3 \stackrel{?}{=} 3$$

$$0 + 3 = 3$$

$$3 = 3 \qquad \text{A true statement}$$

Still another solution is the ordered pair $(5, -7)$ because

$$2(5) + (-7) \stackrel{?}{=} 3$$

$$10 - 7 = 3$$

$$3 = 3 \qquad \text{A true statement}$$

As a matter of fact, for any number we want to use for x, there is another number we can use for y that will make the equation a true statement. There is an infinite number of ordered pairs that satisfy (are solutions to) the equation $2x + y = 3$; we have listed just a few of them.

Example 1 Which of the ordered pairs $(2, 3)$, $(1, 5)$, and $(-2, -4)$ are solutions to the equation $y = 3x + 2$?

Solution If an ordered pair is a solution to the equation, then it must satisfy the equation; that is, when the coordinates are used in place of the variables in the equation, the equation becomes a true statement.

Try $(2, 3)$ in $y = 3x + 2$:

$$3 \stackrel{?}{=} 3(2) + 2$$

$$3 = 6 + 2$$

$$3 = 8 \qquad \text{A false statement}$$

Try $(1, 5)$ in $y = 3x + 2$:

$$5 \stackrel{?}{=} 3(1) + 2$$

$$5 = 3 + 2$$

$$5 = 5 \qquad \text{A true statement}$$

Try $(-2, -4)$ in $y = 3x + 2$:

$$-4 \stackrel{?}{=} 3(-2) + 2$$

$$-4 = -6 + 2$$

$$-4 = -4 \qquad \text{A true statement}$$

The ordered pairs $(1, 5)$ and $(-2, -4)$ are solutions to the equation $y = 3x + 2$, and $(2, 3)$ is not.

Practice Problems

1. Which of the following ordered pairs is a solution to $y = 4x + 1$? $(0, 1)$, $(3, 11)$, $(2, 9)$

Answers

1. $(0, 1)$ and $(2, 9)$

B Finding Ordered Pair Solutions

To find ordered pair solutions we substitute a value for x or y and then find the value for the remaining variable. We can check our work by substituting both values into the equation.

2. For the equation $2x + 5y = 10$, complete the ordered pairs $(0, \ )$, $(\ , 1)$, and $(5, \ )$.

Example 2   Given the equation $2x + 3y = 6$, complete the following ordered pairs so they will be solutions to the equation: $(0, \ )$, $(\ , 1)$, $(3, \ )$.

Solution   To complete the ordered pair $(0, \ )$, we substitute 0 for x in the equation and then solve for y.

$$2(0) + 3y = 6$$
$$3y = 6$$
$$y = 2$$

The ordered pair is $(0, 2)$.

To complete the ordered pair $(\ , 1)$, we substitute 1 for y in the equation and solve for x.

$$2x + 3(1) = 6$$
$$2x + 3 = 6$$
$$2x = 3$$
$$x = \frac{3}{2}$$

The ordered pair is $\left(\frac{3}{2}, 1\right)$.

To complete the ordered pair $(3, \ )$, we substitute 3 for x in the equation and solve for y.

$$2(3) + 3y = 6$$
$$6 + 3y = 6$$
$$3y = 0$$
$$y = 0$$

The ordered pair is $(3, 0)$.

We can check our work by substituting our values back into the original equation.

For $(0, 2)$:   For $\left(\frac{3}{2}, 1\right)$:   For $(3, 0)$:

$$2(0) + 3(2) = 6 \qquad 2\left(\frac{3}{2}\right) + 3(1) = 6 \qquad 2(3) + 3(0) = 6$$
$$0 + 6 = 6 \qquad\qquad 3 + 3 = 6 \qquad\qquad 6 + 0 = 6$$
$$6 = 6 \qquad\qquad\quad 6 = 6 \qquad\qquad\quad 6 = 6$$

In each case, the result was a true statement, so we can be confident that our work is correct.

Notice in each case that once we have used a number in place of one of the variables, the equation becomes a linear equation in one variable. We then solve for that variable.

Example 3   Complete the following table for the equation $2x - 5y = 20$.

x	0			−5
y		2	0	

Solution   Filling in the table is equivalent to completing the following ordered pairs: $(0,\ ), (\ , 2), (\ , 0), (-5,\ )$. So we proceed as in Example 2.

When $x = 0$, we have

$$2(0) - 5y = 20$$
$$0 - 5y = 20$$
$$-5y = 20$$
$$y = -4$$

When $y = 2$, we have

$$2x - 5(2) = 20$$
$$2x - 10 = 20$$
$$2x = 30$$
$$x = 15$$

When $y = 0$, we have

$$2x - 5(0) = 20$$
$$2x - 0 = 20$$
$$2x = 20$$
$$x = 10$$

When $x = -5$, we have

$$2(-5) - 5y = 20$$
$$-10 - 5y = 20$$
$$-5y = 30$$
$$y = -6$$

The completed table looks like this:

x	0	15	10	−5
y	−4	2	0	−6

The table above is equivalent to the ordered pairs $(0, -4)$, $(15, 2)$, $(10, 0)$, and $(-5, -6)$.

Example 4   Complete the following table for the equation $y = 2x - 1$.

x	0	5		
y			7	3

Solution   When $x = 0$, we have
$$y = 2(0) - 1$$
$$y = 0 - 1$$
$$y = -1$$

When $x = 5$, we have
$$y = 2(5) - 1$$
$$y = 10 - 1$$
$$y = 9$$

When $y = 7$, we have
$$7 = 2x - 1$$
$$8 = 2x$$
$$4 = x$$

When $y = 3$, we have
$$3 = 2x - 1$$
$$4 = 2x$$
$$2 = x$$

The completed table is

x	0	5	4	2
y	−1	9	7	3

3. Complete the table for $3x - 2y = 12$.

x	y
0	
	3
	0
−3	

Note   Tables of ordered pairs can be displayed vertically or horizontally. Here, we display them both ways.

4. Complete the table for $y = 3x - 2$.

x	y
0	
2	
	7
	3

Answers

3. $(0, -6), (6, 3), (4, 0), \left(-3, -\frac{21}{2}\right)$

4. $(0, -2), (2, 4), (3, 7), \left(\frac{5}{3}, 3\right)$

C Graphing Ordered Pairs

So far, we have seen that a solution to a linear equation in two variables is an ordered pair where the first number is the *x*-coordinate and the second number is the *y*-coordinate. Here is the formal definition for a graph's coordinates:

DEFINITION *x*-coordinate, *y*-coordinate

A pair of numbers enclosed in parentheses and separated by a comma, such as $(-2, 1)$, is called an **ordered pair** of numbers. The first number in the pair is called the **x-coordinate** of the ordered pair; the second number is called the **y-coordinate**. For the ordered pair $(-2, 1)$, the *x*-coordinate is -2 and the *y*-coordinate is 1.

To see the visual component of ordered pairs, we need the diagram shown in Figure 1. It is called the **rectangular coordinate system.** It is also sometimes referred to as the Cartesian coordinate system, named after the French philosopher René Descartes (1595–1650), who invented the system. As a philosopher, Descartes is responsible for the statement "I think, therefore I am." Until Descartes invented his coordinate system in 1637, algebra and geometry were treated as separate subjects. The rectangular coordinate system allows us to connect algebra and geometry by associating geometric shapes with algebraic equations.

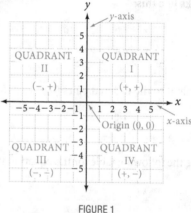

FIGURE 1

The rectangular coordinate system is built from two number lines oriented at a 90 degree angle. The horizontal number line is exactly the same as our real number line and is called the **x-axis.** The vertical number line is also the same as our real number line with the positive direction up and the negative direction down. It is called the **y-axis.** The point where the two axes intersect is called the **origin.** As you can see from Figure 1, the axes divide the plane into four **quadrants,** which are numbered I through IV in a counterclockwise direction.

To graph (a, b), we start at the origin and move *a* units right or left (right if *a* is positive and left if *a* is negative). Then we move *b* units up or down (up if *b* is positive, down if *b* is negative). The point where we end up is the graph of the ordered pair (a, b). To graph the ordered pair $(5, 2)$, we start at the origin and move 5 units to the right. Then, from that position, we move 2 units up.

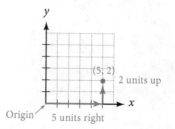

Note It is very important that you graph ordered pairs quickly and accurately. Remember, the first coordinate goes with the horizontal axis and the second coordinate goes with the vertical axis.

Example 5 Graph the ordered pairs (3, 4), (3, −4), (−3, 4), and (−3, −4).
Solution

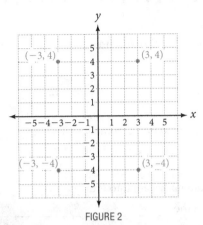

FIGURE 2

5. Graph the ordered pairs (2, 3), (2, −3), (−2, 3), and (−2, −3).

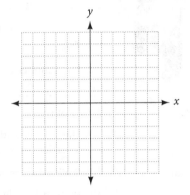

We can see in Figure 2 that when we graph ordered pairs, the *x*-coordinate corresponds to movement parallel to the *x*-axis (horizontal) and the *y*-coordinate corresponds to movement parallel to the *y*-axis (vertical).

• •

Example 6 Graph the ordered pairs (−1, 3), (2, 5), (0, 0), (0, −3), and (4, 0).
Solution

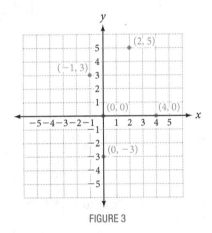

FIGURE 3

6. Graph the ordered pairs (−2, 1), (3, 5), (0, 2), (−5, 0), and (−3, −3).

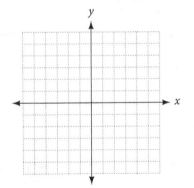

• •

Review the three points in Example 6 that contain a zero as either an *x*- or a *y*-coordinate. It is important to note that ordered pairs that sit on an axis or at the origin are not associated with any quadrant.

Note If we do not label the axes of a coordinate system, we assume that each square is one unit long and one unit wide.

 KEY CONCEPT REVIEW •

After reading through the preceding section, respond in your own words and in complete sentences.

A. How can you tell if an ordered pair is a solution to an equation?

B. How would you find a solution to $y = 3x − 5$?

C. Explain in words how you would graph the ordered pair (3, 4).

D. Where is the origin on a rectangular coordinate system and why is it important?

EXERCISE SET 4.9 ·

Problems

A For the following equations, tell which of the given ordered pairs are solutions.

1. $2x - 5y = 10$ $(2, 3), (0, -2), \left(\dfrac{5}{2}, 1\right)$

2. $3x + 7y = 21$ $(0, 3), (7, 0), (1, 2)$

3. $y = 7x - 2$ $(1, 5), (0, -2), (-2, -16)$

4. $y = 8x - 3$ $(0, 3), (5, 16), (1, 5)$

5. $y = 6x$ $(1, 6), (-2, 12), (0, 0)$

6. $y = -4x$ $(0, 0), (2, 4), (-3, 12)$

7. $x + y = 0$ $(1, 1), (2, -2), (3, 3)$

8. $x - y = 1$ $(0, 1), (0, -1), (1, 2)$

9. $x = 3$ $(3, 0), (3, -3), (5, 3)$

10. $y = -4$ $(3, -4), (-4, 4), (0, -4)$

B For each equation, complete the given ordered pairs.

11. $2x + y = 6$ $(0, \ ), (\ , 0), (\ , -6)$

12. $3x - y = 5$ $(0, \ ), (1, \ ), (\ , 5)$

13. $3x + 4y = 12$ $(0, \ ), (\ , 0), (-4, \ )$

14. $5x - 5y = 20$ $(0, \ ), (\ , -2), (1, \ )$

15. $y = 4x - 3$ $(1, \ ), (\ , 0), (5, \ )$

16. $y = 3x - 5$ $(\ , 13), (0, \ ), (-2, \ )$

17. $y = 7x - 1$ $(2, \ ), (\ , 6), (0, \ )$

18. $y = 8x + 2$ $(3, \ ), (\ , 0), (\ , -6)$

19. $x = -5$ $(\ , 4), (\ , -3), (\ , 0)$

20. $y = 2$ $(5, \ ), (-8, \ ), \left(\dfrac{1}{2}, \ \right)$

For each of the following equations, complete the given table.

21. $y = 3x$

x	y
1	
−3	
	12
	18

22. $y = -2x$

x	y
−4	
0	
	10
	12

23. $y = 4x$

x	y
0	
	−2
−3	
	12

24. $y = -5x$

x	y
3	
	0
−2	
	−20

25. $x + y = 5$

x	y
2	
3	
	0
	−4

26. $x - y = 8$

x	y
0	
4	
	−3
	−2

27. $2x - y = 4$

x	y
	2
1	
−3	

28. $3x - y = 9$

x	y
	−9
5	
−4	

29. $y = 6x - 1$

x	y
0	
	−7
−3	
	8

30. $y = 5x + 7$

x	y
0	
−2	
−4	
	−8

31. $y = -2x + 3$

x	y
0	
−2	
2	
	−7

32. $y = -3x + 1$

x	y
0	
	7
	−5
−3	

C Graph the following ordered pairs.

33. $(3, 2)$ **34.** $(3, -2)$ **35.** $(-3, 2)$ **36.** $(-3, -2)$ **37.** $(5, 1)$ **38.** $(5, -1)$

39. $(1, 5)$ **40.** $(1, -5)$ **41.** $(-1, 5)$ **42.** $(-1, -5)$ **43.** $\left(2, \dfrac{1}{2}\right)$ **44.** $\left(3, \dfrac{3}{2}\right)$

45. $\left(-4, -\dfrac{5}{2}\right)$ **46.** $\left(-5, -\dfrac{3}{2}\right)$ **47.** $(3, 0)$ **48.** $(-2, 0)$ **49.** $(0, 5)$ **50.** $(0, 0)$

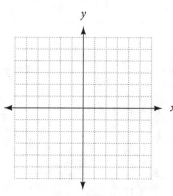 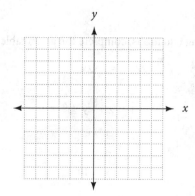

ODD-NUMBERED PROBLEMS   EVEN-NUMBERED PROBLEMS

Give the coordinates of each numbered point in the figure and list which quadrant each point is in.

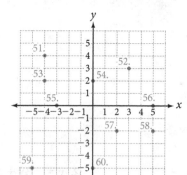

51.   **52.**

53.   **54.**

55.   **56.**

57.   **58.**

59.   **60.**

Graph the points $(4, 3)$ and $(-4, -1)$, and draw a straight line that passes through both of them. Then answer the following questions.

61. Does the graph of $(2, 2)$ lie on the line?

62. Does the graph of $(-2, 0)$ lie on the line?

63. Does the graph of $(0, -2)$ lie on the line?

64. Does the graph of $(-6, 2)$ lie on the line?

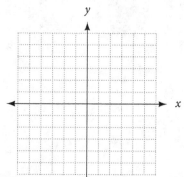

Graph the points $(-2, 4)$ and $(2, -4)$, and draw a straight line that passes through both of them. Then answer the following questions.

65. Does the graph of $(0, 0)$ lie on the line?

66. Does the graph of $(-1, 2)$ lie on the line?

67. Does the graph of $(2, -1)$ lie on the line?

68. Does the graph of $(1, -2)$ lie on the line?

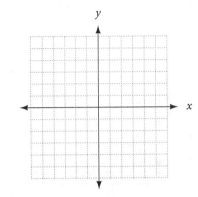

Draw a straight line that passes through the points $(3, 4)$ and $(3, -4)$. Then answer the following questions.

69. Is the graph of $(3, 0)$ on this line?

70. Is the graph of $(0, 3)$ on this line?

71. Is there any point on this line with an x-coordinate other than 3?

72. If you extended the line, would it pass through a point with a y-coordinate of 10?

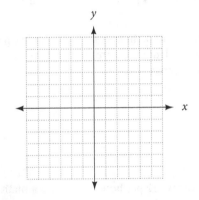

Draw a straight line that passes through the points $(3, 4)$ and $(-3, 4)$. Then answer the following questions.

73. Is the graph of $(4, 0)$ on this line?

74. Is the graph of $(0, 4)$ on this line?

75. Is there any point on this line with a y-coordinate other than 4?

76. If you extended the line, would it pass through a point with an x-coordinate of 10?

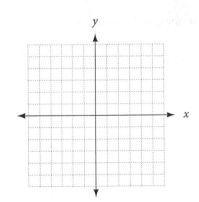

Applying the Concepts

77. Hourly Wages Jane takes a job at the local Marcy's department store. Her job pays $8.00 per hour. The graph shows how much Jane earns for working from 0 to 40 hours in a week.

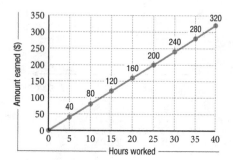

a. List three ordered pairs that lie on the line graph.

b. How much will she earn for working 40 hours?

c. If her check for one week is $240, how many hours did she work?

d. She works 35 hours one week, but her paycheck before deductions are subtracted out is for $260. Is this correct? Explain.

78. Hourly Wages Judy takes a job at Gigi's boutique. Her job pays $6.00 per hour plus $50 per week in commission. The graph shows how much Judy earns for working from 0 to 40 hours in a week.

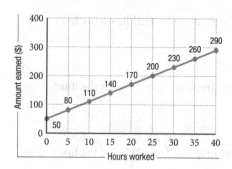

a. List three ordered pairs that lie on the line graph.

b. How much will she earn for working 40 hours?

c. If her check for one week is $230, how many hours did she work?

d. She works 35 hours one week, but her paycheck before deductions are subtracted out is for $260. Is this correct? Explain.

79. Janai earns $12 per hour working as a math tutor. We can express the amount she earns each week, y, for working x hours with the equation $y = 12x$. Indicate with a yes or no which of the following could be one of Janai's paychecks before deductions are taken out. If you answer no, explain your answer.

a. $60 for working five hours

b. $100 for working nine hours

c. $80 for working seven hours

d. $168 for working 14 hours

80. Erin earns $15 per hour working as a graphic designer. We can express the amount she earns each week, y, for working x hours with the equation $y = 15x$. Indicate with a yes or no which of the following could be one of Erin's paychecks before deductions are taken out. If you answer no, explain your answer.

a. $75 for working five hours

b. $125 for working nine hours

c. $90 for working six hours

d. $500 for working 35 hours

81. The equation $V = -45,000t + 600,000$, can be used to find the value, V, of a small crane at the end of t years.

   a. What is the value of the crane at the end of five years?

   b. When is the crane worth $330,000?

   c. Is it true that the crane with be worth $150,000 after nine years?

   d. How much did the crane cost?

82. The equation $V = -400t + 2,500$, can be used to find the value, V, of a notebook computer at the end of t years.

   a. What is the value of the notebook computer at the end of four years?

   b. When is the notebook computer worth $1,700?

   c. Is it true that the notebook computer will be worth $100 after five years?

   d. How much did the notebook computer cost?

83. Baseball Attendance The graph gives the attendance at Major League Baseball games over a ten-year period. If x represents the year in question and y represents attendance in millions, write six ordered pairs that describe the information in the table.

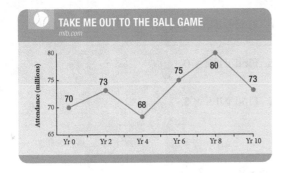

84. FIFA World Cup Goals The graph shows the number of goals scored by the US Men's National Team in FIFA World Cup competition. Write five ordered pairs that lie on the graph.

85. Right triangle ABC has legs of length 5. Point C is the ordered pair $(6, 2)$. Find the coordinates of A and B.

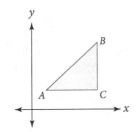

86. Right triangle ABC has legs of length 7. Point C is the ordered pair $(-8, -3)$. Find the coordinates of A and B.

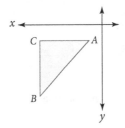

87. Rectangle *ABCD* has a length of 5 and a width of 3. Point *D* is the ordered pair (7, 2). Find points *A*, *B*, and *C*.

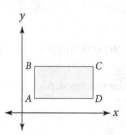

88. Rectangle *ABCD* has a length of 5 and a width of 3. Point *D* is the ordered pair (−1, 1). Find points *A*, *B*, and *C*.

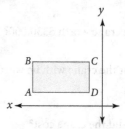

Getting Ready for the Next Section

89. Let $2x + 3y = 6$.
  a. Find *x* if $y = 4$.

  b. Find *x* if $y = -2$.

  c. Find *y* if $x = 3$.

  d. Find *y* if $x = 9$.

90. Let $2x - 5y = 20$.
  a. Find *x* if $y = 0$.

  b. Find *x* if $y = -6$.

  c. Find *y* if $x = 0$.

  d. Find *y* if $x = 5$.

91. Let $y = 2x - 1$.
  a. Find *x* if $y = 7$.

  b. Find *x* if $y = 3$.

  c. Find *y* if $x = 0$.

  d. Find *y* if $x = 5$.

92. Let $y = 3x - 2$.
  a. Find *x* if $y = 4$.

  b. Find *x* if $y = 3$.

  c. Find *y* if $x = 2$.

  d. Find *y* if $x = -3$.

93. Find *y* when *x* is 4 in the formula $3x + 2y = 6$.

94. Find *y* when *x* is 0 in the formula $3x + 2y = 6$.

95. Find *y* when *x* is 0 in $y = -\dfrac{1}{3}x + 2$.

96. Find *y* when *x* is 3 in $y = -\dfrac{1}{3}x + 2$.

97. Find *y* when *x* is 2 in $y = \dfrac{3}{2}x - 3$.

98. Find *y* when *x* is 4 in $y = \dfrac{3}{2}x - 3$.

99. Solve $5x + y = 4$ for y.

100. Solve $-3x + y = 5$ for y.

101. Solve $3x - 2y = 6$ for y.

102. Solve $2x - 3y = 6$ for y.

FIND THE MISTAKE •

Each sentence below contains a mistake. Circle the mistake and write the correct word(s) or numbers(s) on the line provided.

1. A solution to a linear equation in two variables will be a single number that makes the equation a true statement. _____

2. A solution to the equation $5x - 2y = 11$ is $(-3, 2)$ _____

3. An ordered pair is not a solution to an equation if it satisfies the equation. _____

4. In the ordered pair $(-3, 6)$, the x–coordinate is 6. _____

5. To graph the ordered pair $(7, 3)$, start at the origin, move 7 units to the left, and 3 units up. _____

6. The ordered pair $(-2, 5)$ appears in the fourth quadrant. _____

4.10

GRAPHING STRAIGHT LINES

• • • OBJECTIVES • • •

A Graph a linear equation in two variables.

B Graph horizontal lines, vertical lines, and lines through the origin.

• • • KEY WORDS • • •

horizontal

vertical

origin

VIDEO EXAMPLES

SECTION 4.10

Practice Problems

1. Graph the equation $x + y = 3$.

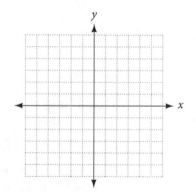

Business managers and owners can use trends in sales, profits, and expenses to predict company performance in the future. For example, assume a new business sells 150 units of their product in the first month, 300 units in the second month, and 450 units in the third month. Assuming the trend will continue, the company can use this information to predict sales in the coming months. Often businesses use the graphs of linear equations, the topic of this section, to visualize these trends.

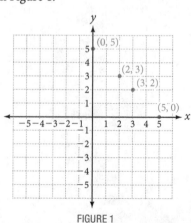

A Graphing Linear Equations

In this section we will use the rectangular coordinate system introduced in the previous section to obtain a visual picture of *all* solutions to a linear equation in two variables. The process we use to obtain a visual picture of all solutions to an equation is called graphing. The picture itself is called the graph of the equation.

Example 1 Graph the solution set for $x + y = 5$.

Solution We know from the previous section that an infinite number of ordered pairs are solutions to the equation $x + y = 5$. We can't possibly list them all. What we can do is list a few of them and see if there is any pattern to their graphs.

Some ordered pairs that are solutions to $x + y = 5$ are $(0, 5)$, $(2, 3)$, $(3, 2)$, $(5, 0)$. The graph of each is shown in Figure 1.

FIGURE 1

Now, by passing a straight line through these points we can graph the solution set for the equation $x + y = 5$. Linear equations in two variables always have graphs that are straight lines. The graph of the solution set for $x + y = 5$ is shown in Figure 2.

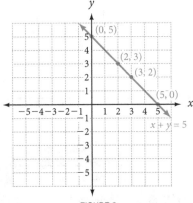

FIGURE 2

Every ordered pair that satisfies $x + y = 5$ has its graph on the line, and any point on the line has coordinates that satisfy the equation. So there is a one-to-one correspondence between points on the line and solutions to the equation. To summarize, the set of all points of a graph that satisfy an equation is the equation's solution set.

To graph a linear equation in two variables, as we did in Example 1, we simply graph its solution set; that is, we draw a line through all the points whose coordinates satisfy the equation. Here are the steps to follow:

HOW TO   **Graph a Linear Equation in Two Variables**

Step 1: Find any three ordered pairs that satisfy the equation. This can be done by using a convenient number for one variable and solving for the other variable.

Step 2: Graph the three ordered pairs found in step 1. Actually, we need only two points to graph a straight line. The third point serves as a check. If all three points do not line up, there is a mistake in our work.

Step 3: Draw a straight line through the three points graphed in step 2.

Example 2   Graph the equation $y = 3x - 1$.

Solution   Because $y = 3x - 1$ can be put in the form $Ax + By = C$, it is a linear equation in two variables. Hence, the graph of its solution set is a straight line. We can find some specific solutions by substituting numbers for x and then solving for the corresponding values of y. We are free to choose any numbers for x, so let's use 0, 2, and -1.

For $x = 0$: $y = 3(0) - 1$ For $x = 2$: $y = 3(2) - 1$ For $x = -1$: $y = 3(-1) - 1$

$\qquad\qquad\quad y = 0 - 1 \qquad\qquad\qquad\quad y = 6 - 1 \qquad\qquad\qquad\quad\; y = -3 - 1$

$\qquad\qquad\quad y = -1 \qquad\qquad\qquad\qquad y = 5 \qquad\qquad\qquad\qquad\;\; y = -4$

Thus our ordered pairs are $(0, -1)$, $(2, 5)$, and $(-1, -4)$. In table form:

x	0	2	-1
y	-1	5	-4

2. Graph the equation $y = 2x + 3$.

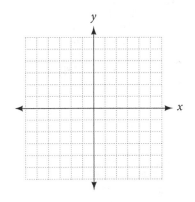

$\mathcal{Note}$ It may seem
that we have simply picked the
numbers 0, 2, and -1 out of the
air and used them for x. In fact
we have done just that. Could
we have used numbers other
than these? The answer is yes,
we can substitute any number
for x; for a linear equation in
two variables, there will always
be a value of y to go with it.

Next, we graph the ordered pairs $(0, -1)$, $(2, 5)$, $(-1, -4)$ and draw a straight line through them. The line we have drawn in Figure 3 is the graph of $y = 3x - 1$.

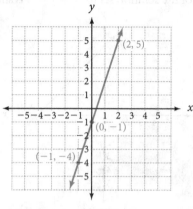

FIGURE 3

3. Graph $y = \dfrac{3}{2}x - 3$.

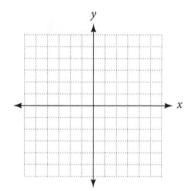

$\mathcal{Note}$ In Example 3
the values of x we used, -3,
0, and 3, are referred to as
convenient values of x because
they are easier to work with
than some other numbers. For
instance, if we let $x = 2$ in our
original equation, we would
have to add $-\frac{2}{3}$ and 2 to find
the corresponding value of y.
Not only would the arithmetic
be more difficult but also
the ordered pair we obtained
would have a fraction for its
y-coordinate, making it more
difficult to graph accurately.

Example 3   Graph the equation $y = -\dfrac{1}{3}x + 2$.

Solution   We need to find three ordered pairs that satisfy the equation. To do so, we can let x equal any numbers we choose and find corresponding values of y. But, every value of x we substitute into the equation is going to be multiplied by $-\frac{1}{3}$. For our convenience, let's use numbers for x that are divisible by 3, like -3, 0, and 3. That way, when we multiply them by $-\frac{1}{3}$, the result will be an integer.

For $x = -3$:
$$y = -\tfrac{1}{3}(-3) + 2$$
$$y = 1 + 2$$
$$y = 3$$

For $x = 0$:
$$y = -\tfrac{1}{3}(0) + 2$$
$$y = 0 + 2$$
$$y = 2$$

For $x = 3$:
$$y = -\tfrac{1}{3}(3) + 2$$
$$y = -1 + 2$$
$$y = 1$$

Our ordered pairs are $(-3, 3)$, $(0, 2)$, and $(3, 1)$. In table form:

x	-3	0	3
y	3	2	1

Graphing the ordered pairs $(-3, 3)$, $(0, 2)$, and $(3, 1)$ and drawing a straight line through their graphs, we have the graph of the equation $y = -\frac{1}{3}x + 2$, as shown in Figure 4.

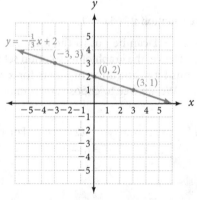

FIGURE 4

Example 4   Graph the solution set for $3x - 2y = 6$.

Solution   It will be easier to find convenient values of x to use in the equation if we first solve the equation for y. To do so, we subtract $3x$ from each side and divide each term by -2.

$3x - 2y = 6$	Original equation
$-2y = -3x + 6$	Subtract $3x$ from each side.
$\dfrac{-2y}{-2} = \dfrac{-3x}{-2} + \dfrac{6}{-2}$	Divide each term by -2.
$y = \dfrac{3}{2}x - 3$	Simplify each side.

Now, because each value of x will be multiplied by $\frac{3}{2}$, it will be to our advantage to choose values of x that are divisible by 2. That way, we will obtain values of y that do not contain fractions. This time, let's use 0, 2, and 4 for x.

For $x = 0$: $y = \frac{3}{2}(0) - 3$ For $x = 2$: $y = \frac{3}{2}(2) - 3$ For $x = 4$: $y = \frac{3}{2}(4) - 3$

$\qquad\qquad\quad y = 0 - 3 \qquad\qquad\qquad\qquad y = 3 - 3 \qquad\qquad\qquad\qquad y = 6 - 3$

$\qquad\qquad\quad y = -3 \qquad\qquad\qquad\qquad\quad y = 0 \qquad\qquad\qquad\qquad\quad y = 3$

Thus our ordered pairs are $(0, -3)$, $(2, 0)$, and $(4, 3)$. In table form:

x	0	2	4
y	-3	0	3

Graphing the ordered pairs $(0, -3)$, $(2, 0)$, and $(4, 3)$ and drawing a line through them, we have the graph shown in Figure 5.

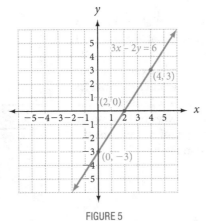

FIGURE 5

4. Graph the solution set for $2x - 4y = 8$.

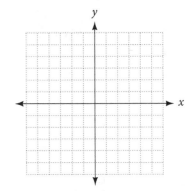

Note   After reading through Example 4, you may wonder why we didn't use -2 for x when we were finding ordered pairs that were solutions to the original equation. The answer is, we could have. If we were to let $x = -2$, the corresponding value of y would have been -6. As you can see by looking at the graph in Figure 5, the ordered pair $(-2, -6)$ is on the graph.

B Horizontal and Vertical Lines; Lines Through The Origin

We will now present three special cases of linear equations.

5. Graph each of the following lines.

a. $y = \dfrac{2}{3}x$

b. $x = 3$

c. $y = -2$

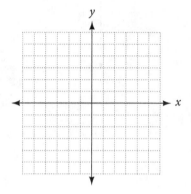

Example 5   Graph each of the following lines.

a. $y = \dfrac{1}{2}x$ **b.** $x = 3$ **c.** $y = -2$

Solution

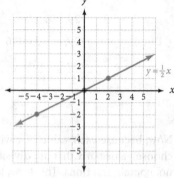

a. The line $y = \frac{1}{2}x$ passes through the origin because $(0, 0)$ satisfies the equation. To sketch the graph we need at least one more point on the line. When x is 2, we obtain the point $(2, 1)$, and when x is -4, we obtain the point $(-4, -2)$. The graph of $y = \frac{1}{2}x$ is shown in Figure 6A.

FIGURE 6A

b. The line $x = 3$ is the set of all points whose x-coordinate is 3. The variable y does not appear in the equation, so the y-coordinate can be any number. Note that we can write our equation as a linear equation in two variables by writing it as $x + 0y = 3$. Because the product of 0 and y will always be 0, y can be any number. The graph of $x = 3$ is the vertical line shown in Figure 6B.

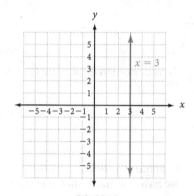

FIGURE 6B

c. The line $y = -2$ is the set of all points whose y-coordinate is -2. The variable x does not appear in the equation, so the x-coordinate can be any number. Again, we can write our equation as a linear equation in two variables by writing it as $0x + y = -2$. Because the product of 0 and x will always be 0, x can be any number. The graph of $y = -2$ is the horizontal line shown in Figure 6C.

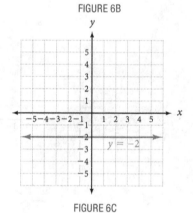

FIGURE 6C

SUMMARY   Special Equations and Their Graphs

For the equations below, m, a, and b are real numbers.

Through the Origin

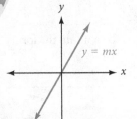

Vertical Line

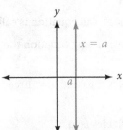

Horizontal Line

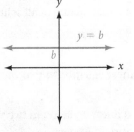

FIGURE 7A *Any equation of the form $y = mx$ has a graph that passes through the origin.*

FIGURE 7B *Any equation of the form $x = a$ has a vertical line for its graph.*

FIGURE 7C *Any equation of the form $y = b$ has a horizontal line for its graph.*

KEY CONCEPT REVIEW

After reading through the preceding section, respond in your own words and in complete sentences.

A. What type of equation has a line that passes through the origin?

B. Explain how to find points on a line.

C. How do we use a solution set to graph a linear equation in two variables?

D. Why do you think we frequently find the value of y when $x = 0$ when graphing a line?

VOCABULARY REVIEW ·

Choose the correct words to fill in the blanks below.

vertical   graphing   graph   horizontal
linear   ordered pairs   straight line

1. The process of obtaining a visual picture of all solutions to an equation is called _____.

2. A _____ equation in two variables is any equation that can be put into the form
   $Ax + By = C$.

3. The first step to graph a linear equation in two variables is to find any three _____
   that satisfy the equation.

4. The second step to graph a linear equation in two variables is to _____ the
   three ordered pairs that satisfy the equation.

5. The third step to graph a linear equation in two variables is to draw a _____
   through the three ordered pairs that satisfy the equation.

6. Any equation of the form $y = b$ has a _____ line for its graph, whereas any
   equation of the form $x = a$ has a _____ line for its graph.

Problems

A, B For the following equations, complete the given ordered pairs, and use the results to graph the solution set for the equation.

1. $x + y = 4$ $(0,\ ), (2,\ ), (\ , 0)$

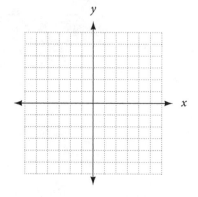

2. $x - y = 3$ $(0,\ ), (2,\ ), (\ , 0)$

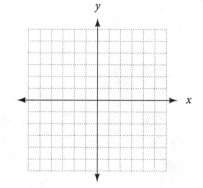

3. $x + y = 3$ $(0,\ ), (2,\ ), (\ , -1)$

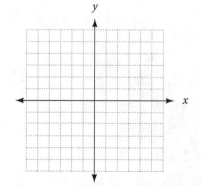

4. $x - y = 4$ $(1,\ ), (-1,\ ), (\ , 0)$

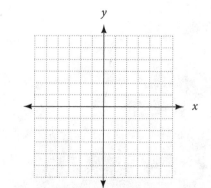

5. $y = 2x$ $(0, \ )$, $(-2, \ )$, $(2, \ )$

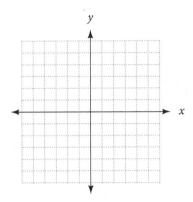

6. $y = \frac{1}{2}x$ $(0, \ )$, $(-2, \ )$, $(2, \ )$

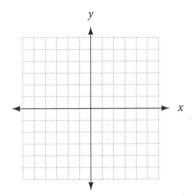

7. $y = \frac{1}{3}x$ $(-3, \ )$, $(0, \ )$, $(3, \ )$

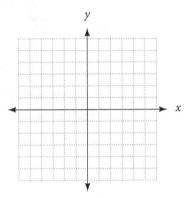

8. $y = 3x$ $(-2, \ )$, $(0, \ )$, $(2, \ )$

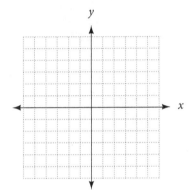

9. $y = 2x + 1$ $(0, \ )$, $(-1, \ )$, $(1, \ )$

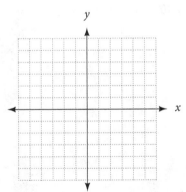

10. $y = -2x + 1$ $(0, \ )$, $(-1, \ )$, $(1, \ )$

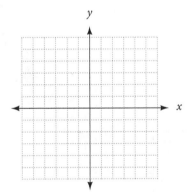

11. $y = 4$ $(0, \ )$, $(-1, \ )$, $(2, \ )$

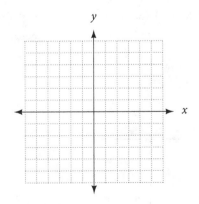

12. $x = 3$ $(\ , -2)$, $(\ , 0)$, $(\ , 5)$

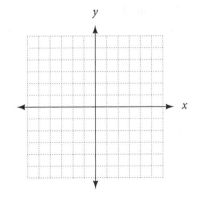

13. $y = \frac{1}{2}x + 3$ $(-2,\ ),(0,\ ),(2,\ )$

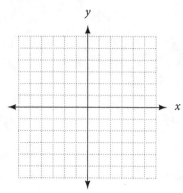

14. $y = \frac{1}{2}x - 3$ $(-2,\ ),(0,\ ),(2,\ )$

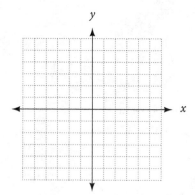

15. $y = -\frac{2}{3}x + 1$ $(-3,\ ),(0,\ ),(3,\ )$

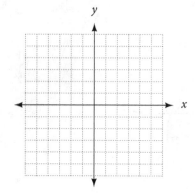

16. $y = -\frac{2}{3}x - 1$ $(-3,\ ),(0,\ ),(3,\ )$

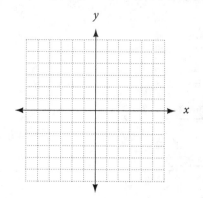

A Solve each equation for y. Then, complete the given ordered pairs, and use them to draw the graph.

17. $2x + y = 3$ $(-1,\ ),(0,\ ),(1,\ )$

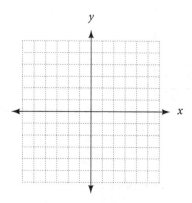

18. $3x + y = 2$ $(-1,\ ),(0,\ ),(1,\ )$

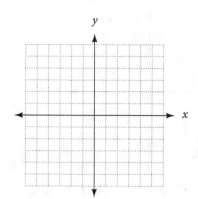

19. $3x + 2y = 6$ $(0,\ ),(2,\ ),(4,\ )$

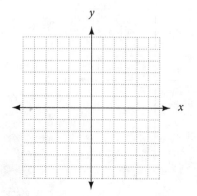

20. $2x + 3y = 6$ $(0,\ ),(3,\ ),(6,\ )$

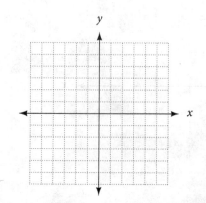

21. $-x + 2y = 6$ $(-2,\ ), (0,\ ), (2,\ )$

22. $-x + 3y = 6$ $(-3,\ ), (0,\ ), (3,\ )$

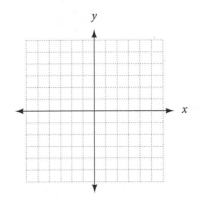

Find three solutions to each of the following equations, and then graph the solution set.

23. $y = -\dfrac{1}{2}x$

24. $y = -2x$

25. $y = 3x - 1$

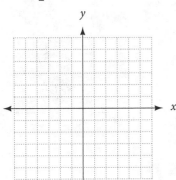
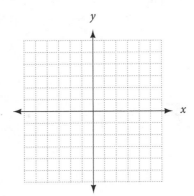
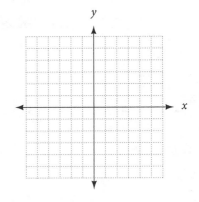

26. $y = -3x - 1$

27. $-2x + y = 1$

28. $-3x + y = 1$

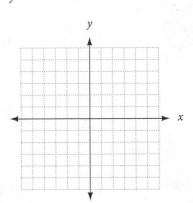
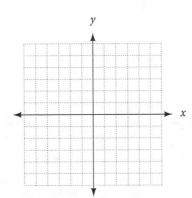
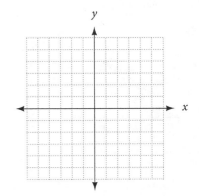

29. $3x + 4y = 8$

30. $3x - 4y = 8$

31. $x = -2$

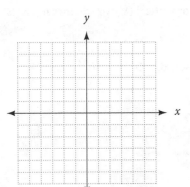
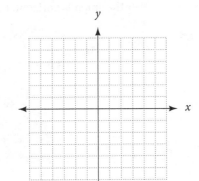
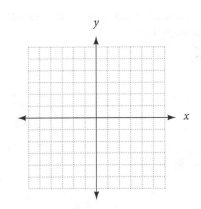

32. $y = 3$

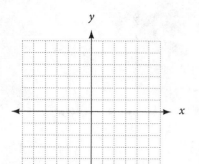

33. $y = 2$

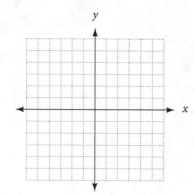

34. $x = -3$

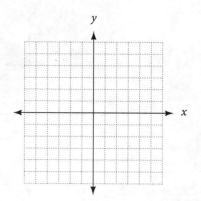

Graph each equation.

35. $y = \dfrac{3}{4}x + 1$

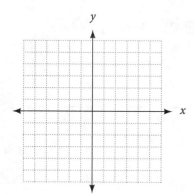

36. $y = \dfrac{2}{3}x + 1$

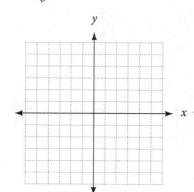

37. $y = \dfrac{1}{3}x + \dfrac{2}{3}$

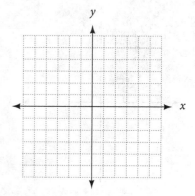

38. $y = \dfrac{1}{2}x + \dfrac{1}{2}$

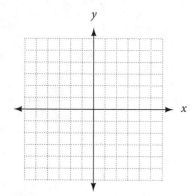

39. $y = \dfrac{2}{3}x + \dfrac{2}{3}$

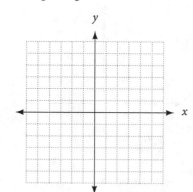

40. $y = -\dfrac{3}{4}x + \dfrac{3}{2}$

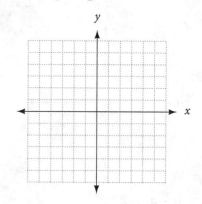

B For each equation in each table below, indicate whether the graph is horizontal (H), or vertical (V), or whether it passes through the origin (O).

41.

Equation	H, V, and/or O
$x = 3$	
$y = 3$	
$y = 3x$	
$y = 0$	

42.

Equation	H, V, and/or O
$x = \dfrac{1}{2}$	
$y = \dfrac{1}{2}$	
$y = \dfrac{1}{2}x$	
$x = 0$	

43.

Equation	H, V, and/or O
$x = -\dfrac{3}{5}$	
$y = -\dfrac{3}{5}$	
$y = -\dfrac{3}{5}x$	
$x = 0$	

44.

Equation	H, V, and/or O
$x = -4$	
$y = -4$	
$y = -4x$	
$y = 0$	

45. Use the graph to complete the table.

x	y
	−3
−2	
0	
	0
6	

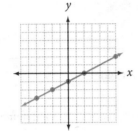

46. Use the graph at the right to complete the table. (*Hint:* Some parts have two answers.)

x	y
−3	
	4
0	3
	1
6	

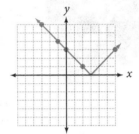

FIND THE MISTAKE •

Each sentence below contains a mistake. Circle the mistake and write the correct word(s) or numbers(s) on the line provided.

1. To graph a linear equation in two variables, you must find only one solution. _____

2. The line $y = \dfrac{1}{2}x$ crosses the x–axis but not the y–axis. _____

3. A horizontal line is given by the form $x = a$. _____

4. All lines require three points to define them. _____

piece of graph paper

4 colored pens or pencils

Trail Guide Project

Working with Fractions

This project will provide a visual approach for working with the multiplication and division of fractions. You will need a piece of graph paper and 4 colored pens or pencils.

1. On your graph paper, draw two squares each with a side length of 20 boxes. Fill in the boxes of your first square using your pens or pencils. You may choose any pattern as long as you use all four colors and fill in every box in your square.

2. Assign each color to a number (1-4).

   Color 1 _____   Color 2 _____

   Color 3 _____   Color 4 _____

3. Find the area of your first square. This will give you the total number of boxes in your square. Total area _____

4. Count the total number of boxes for each color. Enter these quantities in the second column of the table titled, "Number of Boxes."

Colors	Number of boxes	Fraction (not reduced)	Fraction (reduced)	Multiplied by $\frac{2}{3}$	Multiplied by $\frac{3}{4}$

5. In the third column, "Fraction (not reduced)," show the number of boxes for each color in the form of a fraction.

6. Reduce each fraction, if possible, and write the reduced fraction in the fourth column of the table.

7. Multiply each of the reduced fractions for Color 1 and Color 2 by $\frac{2}{3}$. Write these new fractions in the fifth column of the table.

8. Multiply each of the reduced fractions for Color 3 and Color 4 by $\frac{3}{4}$. Write these new fractions in the sixth column of the table.

9. Suppose the fractions in the fifth and sixth columns of your table now represent new quantities of boxes per color. Fill in your second square with these new quantities. Round to the nearest whole number. How many boxes are left over? Write this number as a fraction.

CHAPTER 4 SUMMARY . . . .

Definition of Fractions [4.1]

A fraction is any number that can be written in the form $\frac{a}{b}$, where a and b are numbers and b is not 0. The number a is called the numerator, and the number b is called the denominator.

1. Each of the following is a fraction:

$$\frac{1}{2}, \quad \frac{3}{4}, \quad \frac{8}{1}, \quad \frac{7}{3}$$

Properties of Fractions [4.1]

Multiplying the numerator and the denominator of a fraction by the same nonzero number will produce an equivalent fraction. The same is true for dividing the numerator and denominator by the same nonzero number. In symbols the properties look like this:
If a, b, and c are numbers and b and c are not 0, then

$$\text{Multiplication property for fractions} \quad \frac{a}{b} = \frac{a \cdot c}{b \cdot c}$$

$$\text{Division property for fraction} \quad \frac{a}{b} = \frac{a \div c}{b \div c}$$

2. Change $\frac{3}{4}$ to an equivalent fraction with denominator 12.

$$\frac{3}{4} = \frac{3 \cdot 3}{4 \cdot 3} = \frac{9}{12}$$

Fractions and the Number 1 [4.1]

If a represents any number, then

$$\frac{a}{1} = a \quad \text{and} \quad \frac{a}{a} = 1 \quad \text{(where a is not 0)}$$

3. $\frac{5}{1} = 5, \frac{5}{5} = 1$

Changing Mixed Numbers to Improper Fractions [4.1]

To change a mixed number to an improper fraction, we multiply the whole number by the denominator of the fraction, and add the result to the numerator of the fraction. The result is the numerator of the improper fraction we are looking for. The denominator is the same as the original denominator.

4. $4\frac{2}{3} = \frac{(3 \cdot 4) + 2}{3} = \frac{14}{3}$

↑   ↑
Mixed number   Improper fraction

Changing an Improper Fraction to a Mixed Number [4.1]

To change an improper fraction to a mixed number, divide the denominator into the numerator. The quotient is the whole-number part of the mixed number. The fraction part is the remainder over the divisor.

5. Change $\frac{14}{3}$ to a mixed number.

Quotient

$$3\overline{)14} \qquad \frac{14}{3} = 4\frac{2}{3}$$
$$\underline{12}$$
$$2$$

Divisor

Remainder

Reducing Fractions to Lowest Terms [4.2]

To reduce a fraction to lowest terms, factor the numerator and the denominator, and then divide both the numerator and denominator by any factors they have in common.

6. $\dfrac{90}{588} = \dfrac{2 \cdot 3 \cdot 3 \cdot 5}{2 \cdot 2 \cdot 3 \cdot 7 \cdot 7}$

$$= \frac{3 \cdot 5}{2 \cdot 7 \cdot 7}$$

$$= \frac{15}{98}$$

7. $\dfrac{3}{5} \cdot \dfrac{4}{7} = \dfrac{3 \cdot 4}{5 \cdot 7} = \dfrac{12}{35}$

Multiplying Fractions [4.3]

To multiply fractions, multiply numerators and multiply denominators.

The Area of a Triangle [4.3]

8. If the base of a triangle is 10 inches and the height is 7 inches, then the area is

$A = \dfrac{1}{2}bh$

$\quad = \dfrac{1}{2} \cdot 10 \cdot 7$

$\quad = 5 \cdot 7$

$\quad = 35$ square inches

The formula for the area of a triangle with base b and height h is

$$A = \dfrac{1}{2}bh$$

Reciprocals [4.4]

9. The reciprocal of $\dfrac{2}{3}$ is $\dfrac{3}{2}$.

$\dfrac{2}{3} \cdot \dfrac{3}{2} = 1$

Any two numbers whose product is 1 are called reciprocals. The reciprocal of a is $\dfrac{1}{a}$ because their product is 1.

Division with Fractions [4.4]

10. $\dfrac{3}{8} \div \dfrac{1}{3} = \dfrac{3}{8} \cdot \dfrac{3}{1} = \dfrac{9}{8}$

To divide by a fraction, you must multiply by its reciprocal. That is, the quotient of two fractions is defined to be the product of the first fraction with the reciprocal of the second fraction (the divisor).

Least Common Denominator (LCD) [4.5]

The least common denominator (LCD) for a set of denominators is the smallest number that is exactly divisible by each denominator.

Addition and Subtraction of Fractions [4.5]

11. $\dfrac{1}{8} + \dfrac{3}{8} = \dfrac{1+3}{8}$

$\quad = \dfrac{4}{8}$

$\quad = \dfrac{1}{2}$

To add (or subtract) two fractions with a common denominator, add (or subtract) numerators and use the common denominator. *In symbols*: If a, b, and c are numbers with c not equal to 0, then

$$\dfrac{a}{c} + \dfrac{b}{c} = \dfrac{a+b}{c} \quad \text{and} \quad \dfrac{a}{c} - \dfrac{b}{c} = \dfrac{a-b}{c}$$

Additional Facts about Fractions

1. Every whole number can be written as a fraction with a denominator of 1.

2. The commutative, associative, and distributive properties are true for fractions.

3. The word *of* as used in the expression "$\dfrac{2}{3}$ *of* 12" indicates that we are to multiply $\dfrac{2}{3}$ and 12.

4. Two fractions with the same value are called equivalent fractions.

Mixed-Number Notation [4.1, 4.6]

A mixed number is the sum of a whole number and a fraction. The $+$ sign is not shown when we write mixed numbers; it is implied. The mixed number $4\frac{2}{3}$ is actually the sum $4 + \frac{2}{3}$.

Multiplication and Division with Mixed Numbers [4.6]

To multiply or divide two mixed numbers, change each to an improper fraction and multiply or divide as usual.

12. $2\frac{1}{3} \cdot 1\frac{3}{4} = \frac{7}{3} \cdot \frac{7}{4} = \frac{49}{12} = 4\frac{1}{12}$

Addition and Subtraction with Mixed Numbers [4.6]

To add or subtract two mixed numbers, add or subtract the whole-number parts and the fraction parts separately. This is best done with the numbers written in columns.

13.
$$
\begin{array}{rcl}
3\frac{4}{9} & = 3\frac{4}{9} & = 3\frac{4}{9} \\
+ 2\frac{2}{3} & = 2\frac{2 \cdot 3}{3 \cdot 3} & = 2\frac{6}{9} \\
\hline
 & & 5\frac{10}{9} = 6\frac{1}{9}
\end{array}
$$

Common denominator | Add fractions.

Add whole numbers.

Borrowing in Subtraction with Mixed Numbers [4.6]

It is sometimes necessary to borrow when doing subtraction with mixed numbers. We always change to a common denominator before we actually borrow.

14.
$$
\begin{array}{rcll}
4\frac{1}{3} = & 4\frac{2}{6} = & 3\frac{8}{6} \\
- 1\frac{5}{6} = & - 1\frac{5}{6} = & - 1\frac{5}{6} \\
\hline
 & & 2\frac{3}{6} = 2\frac{1}{2}
\end{array}
$$

Complex Fractions [4.7]

A fraction that contains a fraction in its numerator or denominator is called a complex fraction.

15.
$$
\frac{4 + \frac{1}{3}}{2 - \frac{5}{6}} = \frac{6\left(4 + \frac{1}{3}\right)}{6\left(2 - \frac{5}{6}\right)}
$$

$$
= \frac{6 \cdot 4 + 6 \cdot \frac{1}{3}}{6 \cdot 2 - 6 \cdot \frac{5}{6}}
$$

$$
= \frac{24 + 2}{12 - 5}
$$

$$
= \frac{26}{7} = 3\frac{5}{7}
$$

Linear Equations with Fractions [4.8]

HOW TO   Strategy for Solving Linear Equations in One Variable

Step 1a: Use the distributive property to separate terms, if necessary.

1b: If fractions are present, consider multiplying both sides by the LCD to eliminate the fractions.

1c: Combine like terms on each side of the equation.

Step 2: Use the addition or subtraction property of equality to get all variable terms on one side of the equation and all constant terms on the other side. A variable term is a term that contains the variable (for example, $5x$). A constant term is a term that does not contain the variable (the number 3, for example).

Step 3: Use the multiplication or division property of equality to get x (that is, $1x$) by itself on one side of the equation.

Step 4: Check your solution in the original equation to be sure that you have not made a mistake in the solution process.

Linear Equation in Two Variables [4.9]

16. The equation $3x + 2y = 6$ is an example of a linear equation in two variables.

A linear equation in two variables is any equation that can be put in the form $Ax + By = C$. The graph of every linear equation is a straight line.

Ordered Pairs and Graphing [4.10]

A pair of numbers enclosed in parentheses and separated by a comma, such as $(-2, 1)$, is called an ordered pair of numbers. The first number in the pair is called the x-coordinate of the ordered pair; the second number is called the y-coordinate.

To graph the ordered pair (a, b), we start at the origin and move a units right or left (right if a is positive and left if a is negative). Then we move b units up or down (up if b is positive, down if b is negative). The point where we end up is the graph of the ordered pair (a, b).

Strategy for Graphing Linear Equations in Two Variables By Plotting Points [4.10]

17. The graph of $y = -\frac{2}{3}x - 1$ is shown below.

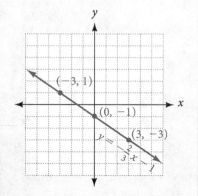

Step 1: Find any three ordered pairs that satisfy the equation. This can be done by using a convenient number for one variable and solving for the other variable.

Step 2: Graph the three ordered pairs found in step 1. Actually, we need only two points to graph a straight line. The third point serves as a check. If all three points do not line up, there is a mistake in our work.

Step 3: Draw a straight line through the three points graphed in step 2.

COMMON MISTAKES

1. A common mistake made with division of fractions occurs when we multiply by the reciprocal of the first fraction instead of the reciprocal of the divisor. For example,

$$\frac{2}{3} \div \frac{5}{6} \neq \frac{3}{2} \cdot \frac{5}{6}$$

Remember, we perform division by multiplying by the reciprocal of the divisor (the fraction to the right of the division symbol).

2. The most common mistake when working with fractions occurs when we try to add two fractions without using a common denominator. For example,

$$\frac{2}{3} + \frac{4}{5} \neq \frac{2+4}{3+5}$$

If the two fractions we are trying to add don't have the same denominators, then we *must* rewrite each one as an equivalent fraction with a common denominator. *We never add denominators when adding fractions.*

Note We do *not* need a common denominator when multiplying fractions.

3. A common mistake when working with mixed numbers is to confuse mixed-number notation for multiplication of fractions. The notation $3\frac{2}{5}$ does *not* mean 3 *times* $\frac{2}{5}$. It means 3 *plus* $\frac{2}{5}$.

4. Another mistake occurs when multiplying mixed numbers. The mistake occurs when we don't change the mixed number to an improper fraction before multiplying and instead try to multiply the whole numbers and fractions separately.

$$2\frac{1}{2} \cdot 3\frac{1}{3} = (2 \cdot 3) + \left(\frac{1}{2} \cdot \frac{1}{3}\right) \qquad \text{Mistake}$$
$$= 6 + \frac{1}{6}$$
$$= 6\frac{1}{6}$$

Remember, the correct way to multiply mixed numbers is to first change to improper fractions and then multiply numerators and multiply denominators. This is correct:

$$2\frac{1}{2} \cdot 3\frac{1}{3} = \frac{5}{2} \cdot \frac{10}{3} = \frac{50}{6} = 8\frac{2}{6} = 8\frac{1}{3} \qquad \text{Correct}$$

Reduce to lowest terms. [4.2]

1. $\dfrac{75}{105}$

2. $\dfrac{72}{192}$

3. $\dfrac{64}{208}$

4. $\dfrac{176}{330}$

Perform the indicated operations. Reduce all answers to lowest terms. [4.3, 4.4, 4.5]

5. $\dfrac{1}{3} \cdot \dfrac{6}{7}$

6. $\dfrac{2}{5} \cdot \dfrac{3}{8}$

7. $6 \cdot \dfrac{7}{12}$

8. $\dfrac{4}{15}\left(\dfrac{5}{8}\right)$

9. $-\dfrac{3}{7} \cdot \dfrac{4}{9}$

10. $-\dfrac{9}{4}\left(\dfrac{1}{3}\right)$

11. $-\dfrac{7}{4} \cdot \dfrac{8}{3}\left(-\dfrac{9}{14}\right)$

12. $\dfrac{6}{5}\left(-\dfrac{15}{7}\right)\left(-\dfrac{3}{9}\right)$

13. $\dfrac{7}{9} \div \dfrac{2}{3}$

14. $\dfrac{8}{5} \div \dfrac{2}{3}$

15. $-\dfrac{9}{16} \div \dfrac{3}{12}$

16. $\dfrac{4}{3} \div (-16)$

17. $15 \div \dfrac{3}{5}$

18. $\dfrac{24}{14} \div \dfrac{6}{7}$

Simplify each of the following as much as possible. [4.3, 4.4]

19. $\dfrac{8}{5} \cdot \dfrac{3}{4} \div \dfrac{9}{10}$

20. $\dfrac{12}{7} \div 3 \cdot \dfrac{5}{6}$

21. $\left(\dfrac{3}{14}\right)\left(\dfrac{4}{6}\right) \div \dfrac{1}{3}$

22. $\left(\dfrac{2}{3}\right)^3 \cdot \dfrac{9}{16}$

23. $\dfrac{4}{9} \div \dfrac{2}{7} \div \dfrac{1}{3}$

24. $\dfrac{8}{9} \div \left(\dfrac{4}{6}\right)^2$

25. $\dfrac{1}{6} \div \left[\dfrac{15}{18}\left(-\dfrac{9}{25}\right)\right]$

26. $\dfrac{5}{9} \cdot \dfrac{6}{7} \div \left(-\dfrac{20}{14}\right)$

27. $\left(\dfrac{4}{21}\right)\left(\dfrac{3}{8}\right) \div \dfrac{1}{6}$

28. $\left(\dfrac{3}{7} \div \dfrac{9}{14}\right)\left(\dfrac{6}{7}\right)$

29. Find the area of the triangle. [4.3]

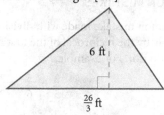

6 ft

$\dfrac{26}{3}$ ft

30. Sewing A dress requires $\dfrac{7}{4}$ yards of material to make. If you have 14 yards of material, how many dresses can you make? [4.4]

The illustration shows the results of a survey in which participants were asked how they stream movies on the internet.

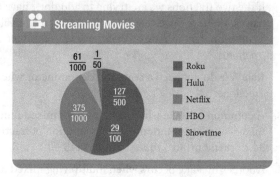

Streaming Movies

$\dfrac{61}{1000}$ $\dfrac{1}{50}$

$\dfrac{127}{500}$

$\dfrac{375}{1000}$

$\dfrac{29}{100}$

Roku
Hulu
Netflix
HBO
Showtime

31. Write the fraction of participants who stream movies via Netflix. [4.2]

32. Write the fraction of participants who stream movies via Roku as an equivalent fraction with a denominator of 1000. [4.1]

Perform the indicated operations. Reduce all answers to lowest terms. [4.3, 4.4, 4.5, 4.6]

33. $\dfrac{7}{9} + \dfrac{5}{9}$

34. $\dfrac{7}{12} - \dfrac{1}{2}$

35. $4 + \dfrac{4}{5}$

36. $\dfrac{3}{8} - \left(-\dfrac{1}{4}\right)$

37. $\dfrac{1}{2} + \dfrac{7}{12} + \dfrac{3}{20}$

38. $9\dfrac{2}{3} + 2\dfrac{3}{5}$

39. $6\dfrac{2}{5} - 4\dfrac{3}{10}$

40. $9 + \left(-\dfrac{3}{5}\right)$

41. $\dfrac{5}{8} - \dfrac{3}{16}$

42. $\dfrac{7}{8} + \dfrac{3}{4} + 4$

43. $\dfrac{9}{24} - \dfrac{1}{8}$

44. $2\dfrac{5}{6} + \left(-3\dfrac{1}{3}\right)$

45. $12\frac{5}{7} - \frac{3}{14}$

46. $\frac{4}{9} - \frac{5}{18}$

47. $5\frac{7}{12} - 1\frac{3}{8}$

48. $10\frac{9}{16} - \left(-\frac{7}{8}\right)$

49. $11\frac{2}{3} + 5\frac{5}{6}$

50. $4\frac{1}{4} + 3\frac{5}{8} - 1\frac{7}{12}$

51. Sewing A dress that is $24\frac{3}{8}$ inches long is shortened by $4\frac{3}{4}$ inches. What is the new length of the dress? [4.6]

52. Find the perimeter of the triangle below. [4.6]

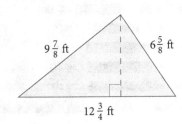

$9\frac{7}{8}$ ft $6\frac{5}{8}$ ft

$12\frac{3}{4}$ ft

Simplify each of the following as much as possible. [4.6, 4.7]

53. $7 + 3\left(2\frac{4}{5}\right)$

54. $\left(5\frac{7}{12} - \frac{1}{3}\right)\left(3 - 2\frac{5}{8}\right)$

55. $\dfrac{\frac{5}{16} - \frac{1}{4}}{\frac{1}{2} - \frac{3}{8}}$

56. $8 - 2\left(2\frac{5}{8}\right)$

57. $\left(5\frac{3}{8} - 2\frac{1}{4}\right)\left(6\frac{7}{12} - 2\frac{1}{3}\right)$

58. $\left(\frac{5}{4}\right)^2 - \frac{17}{24}$

59. $\left(\frac{2}{9}\right)\left(3\frac{3}{5}\right) - \frac{3}{10}$

60. $\dfrac{4\frac{3}{16}}{2\frac{7}{8}}$

61. $\dfrac{\frac{7}{12}}{6\frac{3}{4}}$

62. $\dfrac{4\frac{5}{8} - 2\frac{7}{12}}{5\frac{1}{3} - 1\frac{1}{4}}$

Solve each equation. [4.8]

63. $x - \frac{7}{8} = \frac{3}{8}$

64. $3(6x - 9) = -3(8x - 17)$

65. $2(4x - 7) - 3 = 3x + 9$

66. $\frac{2}{5}(10x - 15) = 2(4x + 9)$

67. $-\frac{4}{5}x = -\frac{8}{15}$

68. $\frac{x}{2} + \frac{4}{3} = -\frac{2}{3}$

The chart shows iPhone distribution around the world. Use the information to answer the following questions. [4.5]

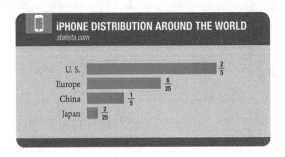

69. What is the fraction of iPhones found in Europe and Japan combined?

70. What is the fraction of iPhones found in the U.S. and Europe combined?

Graph the ordered pairs. [4.9]

71. $(3, -2)$

72. $(-1, -4)$

73. $(-3, 5)$

74. $(0, 6)$

75. $(0, 0)$

76. $(-5, 0)$

77. Fill in the following ordered pairs for the equation $2x - 5y = 10$. [4.9]

$\left(3, \quad\right), \left(-2, \quad\right), \left(\quad, \frac{2}{3}\right), \left(\frac{1}{2}, \quad\right)$

78. For $y = -2x + 1$, complete the ordered pairs [4.9]

$(0, \ ), (-1, \ ), (1, \ )$

Graph each line. [4.10]

79. $x - y = 8$

80. $y = -3$

81. $y = \frac{1}{3}x + 2$

82. $x = 5$

83. $3x + 4y = 12$

84. $-x + 4y = 8$

Reduce to lowest terms.

1. $\dfrac{27}{36}$

2. $\dfrac{30}{45}$

3. $\dfrac{51}{68}$

4. $\dfrac{135}{216}$

5. Change $5\dfrac{18}{19}$ to an improper fraction.

6. Change $\dfrac{319}{23}$ to a mixed number.

Simplify.

7. $\dfrac{7}{12} - \dfrac{5}{12}$

8. $23\dfrac{9}{14} - 7\dfrac{13}{21}$

9. $\dfrac{4}{9} \cdot \dfrac{12}{20}$

10. $7^2 - 3^3$

11. $6 \div \dfrac{1}{2}$

12. $512 \div 16 \div 8$

13. $\dfrac{46}{13}$

14. $\dfrac{170}{306}$

15. 14^2

16. $(9 + 13) - (8 - 4)$

17. $\dfrac{2}{5} + \dfrac{1}{3}$

18. $2{,}074(304)$

19. $\dfrac{4}{16} \div \dfrac{3}{8}$

20. $8 + 4^2 - 4 \cdot 5 + 7$

21. $\dfrac{2}{3} \cdot 4\dfrac{9}{10}$

22. $\left(\dfrac{6}{5}\right)^2 \cdot \left(\dfrac{2}{3}\right)^3$

23. $7{,}482 - 594$

24. $\dfrac{4\frac{2}{3}}{3\frac{1}{9}}$

25. $\left(\dfrac{3}{8} + \dfrac{7}{24}\right) + \left(-\dfrac{13}{48}\right)$

26. $4 + \dfrac{4}{9} \div \dfrac{2}{3}$

27. Find the sum of $\dfrac{5}{6}$, $\dfrac{3}{4}$, and $\dfrac{1}{5}$.

28. Write the fraction $\dfrac{7}{15}$ as an equivalent fraction with a denominator of $60x$.

29. Add $\dfrac{2}{3}$ to half of $\dfrac{6}{7}$.

30. Three times the difference of 8 and 3 is decreased by 3. What number results?

The chart shows the number of Twitter followers for some celebrities. Use the information to answer the following questions.

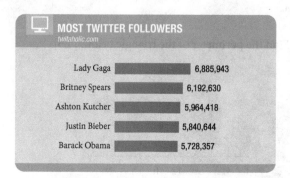

31. How many followers do Ashton Kutcher and Lady Gaga have together?

32. How many more followers does Britney Spears have than Justin Bieber?

33. $\dfrac{20}{72} \cdot \dfrac{42}{18} \div \dfrac{20}{16}$

34. $18 \div \left(\dfrac{3}{4}\right)^2 + 49 \div \left(\dfrac{7}{9}\right)^2$

35. $\dfrac{1}{2} + \dfrac{3}{4} - \dfrac{5}{8}$

36. $12\left(\dfrac{1}{3} + \dfrac{1}{4}\right)$

Simplify.

37. $8 \div \left(1\dfrac{1}{4} \div 2\right)$

38. $11\dfrac{7}{8} - \left(-9\dfrac{1}{6}\right)$

39. $\dfrac{5 - \frac{3}{4}}{2 + \frac{3}{4}}$

40. $4\dfrac{1}{5} + 7\dfrac{1}{3} + 8\dfrac{1}{15}$

Reduce to lowest terms.

1. $\dfrac{15}{70}$

2. $\dfrac{255}{340}$

Perform the indicated operations. Reduce all answers to lowest terms.

3. $\dfrac{2}{3} \cdot \dfrac{5}{7}$

4. $3 \cdot \dfrac{5}{8}$

5. $\dfrac{7}{5}\left(-\dfrac{1}{14}\right)$

6. $\dfrac{1}{2}\left(-\dfrac{3}{8}\right)\left(-\dfrac{4}{5}\right)$

7. $\dfrac{8}{5} \div \dfrac{2}{5}$

8. $\dfrac{8}{15} \div \left(-\dfrac{2}{3}\right)$

9. $\dfrac{3}{5} \div (-9)$

10. $\dfrac{36}{18} \div \dfrac{9}{2}$

Simplify each of the following as much as possible.

11. $\dfrac{2}{3} \cdot \dfrac{1}{2} \div \dfrac{5}{6}$

12. $\left(\dfrac{3}{4}\right)^2 \cdot \dfrac{1}{3}$

13. $-\dfrac{1}{5} \div \left(\dfrac{2}{3} \cdot \dfrac{4}{5}\right)$

14. $\left(\dfrac{5}{18}\right)\left(\dfrac{4}{5}\right) \div \dfrac{10}{9}$

15. Find the area of the triangle.

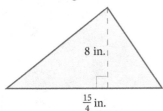

8 in.

$\dfrac{15}{4}$ in.

16. Sewing A dress requires $\dfrac{6}{5}$ yards of material to make. If you have 12 yards of material, how many dresses can you make?

Perform the indicated operations. Reduce all answers to lowest terms.

17. $5 + \dfrac{5}{8}$

18. $\dfrac{5}{6} - \left(-\dfrac{2}{3}\right)$

19. $\dfrac{3}{8} + \dfrac{7}{12} + \dfrac{1}{3}$

20. $5\dfrac{1}{5} + 4\dfrac{3}{4}$

21. $4\dfrac{1}{3} - 2\dfrac{7}{9}$

22. $4 + \left(-\dfrac{7}{8}\right)$

23. $\dfrac{7}{18} - \dfrac{1}{6}$

24. $1\dfrac{5}{8} + \left(-2\dfrac{1}{4}\right)$

25. $9\dfrac{1}{4} - \left(-\dfrac{7}{12}\right)$

26. $3\dfrac{5}{8} + 4\dfrac{1}{6} - 2\dfrac{4}{9}$

Simplify each of the following as much as possible.

27. $\left(4\dfrac{3}{4} + \dfrac{1}{2}\right)\left(6\dfrac{5}{6} - 4\dfrac{1}{3}\right)$

28. $\dfrac{\dfrac{1}{12} + \dfrac{3}{4}}{\dfrac{5}{6} - \dfrac{1}{3}}$

29. $\left(\dfrac{4}{3}\right)^2 - \dfrac{5}{6}$

30. $\dfrac{\dfrac{9}{16}}{5\dfrac{1}{4}}$

Solve each equation.

31. $4(5x - 7) = -4(3x + 6)$

32. $\dfrac{x}{3} + \dfrac{5}{4} = -\dfrac{7}{4}$

Graph the ordered pairs.

33. $(2, -1)$

34. $(-4, 3)$

35. $(-3, -2)$

36. $(0, -4)$

37. Fill in the following ordered pairs for the equation $3x - 2y = 6$.

$(0, \quad) \ (\quad, 0) \ (4, \quad) \ (\quad, -6)$

38. Which of the following ordered pairs are solutions to $y = -3x + 7$?

$(0, 7) \ (2, -1) \ (4, -5) \ (-5, -3)$

Graph each line.

39. $y = -\dfrac{1}{2}x + 4$

40. $x = -3$

The illustration shows recent smartphone sales worldwide.

SMARTPHONE SALES

- China
- Western Europe
- North America
- Asia-Pacific
- Other

$\frac{1}{5}$ $\frac{1}{3}$ $\frac{1}{5}$ $\frac{1}{6}$ $\frac{1}{8}$

41. Write the fraction of sales for Western Europe as an equivalent fraction with denominator 24.

42. Write the fraction of sales for China as an equivalent fraction with denominator 36.

DECIMALS

5

Stonehenge, located outside Wiltshire, England is one of the world's most well-known prehistoric monuments. Construction of the formation, a set of standing stones arranged in a circular shape, dates back as far as 3000 BC. Each stone measures approximately 4.1 meters high and 2.1 meters wide, each weighing around 25 tons. The configuration is an extraordinary feat for its time considering the technology that was available to move the stones into place. The purpose of Stonehenge is still debated today. Some believe it is a symbol of unification while others believe it to be a burial ground or a sacred area.

The distance across a circle is called the diameter while the distance around a circle is called the circumference. The diameter of the Stonehenge configuration is approximately 32.9 meters. To find the area, we need to use the formula

$$A = \pi r^2$$

where r is the radius or half the diameter. The symbol π represents the irrational number pi, the ratio of the circumference of a circle to the diameter. An approximation for π is 3.14. Finding the area of Stonehenge requires operations with decimals, a concept we will cover in this chapter.

circumference

radius

diameter

YOU ARE HERE

1 · · · 2 · · · 3 · · · 4 · · · 5 · · · 6 · · · 7 · · · 8 · · · 9

5.1

 DECIMAL NOTATION, PLACE VALUE, AND ROUNDING

OBJECTIVES

A Write decimals with fractions and with words.

B Round decimals to be given place values.

C Compare decimals.

KEY WORDS

decimals

decimal point

place value

VIDEO EXAMPLES

SECTION 5.1

A person's handwriting is extremely difficult to mimic. To make copying signatures of the world's elite businessmen and women even more impossible, a company based in Germany has produced a pen with plant DNA embedded in the ink. Each pen sold has a distinctively different type of DNA, making words written with the pen distinguishable from words written with other pens. A forensic test is needed to view the plant DNA, but uniqueness of each pen gives peace of mind that a forgery is less likely to happen.

Each pen containing plant DNA sells for $15,850. If this pen sold in California, the sales tax would be an additional $1,386.88. In this chapter, we will focus our attention on decimals. Anyone who has used money in the United States has likely worked with decimals already. For example, the sales tax on the pen contains a decimal:

$$\$1386.88$$

— Decimal point

What is interesting and useful about decimals is their relationship to fractions and to powers of ten. The work we have done up to now—especially our work with fractions—can be used to develop the properties of decimal numbers.

A Decimal Notation and Place Value

Previously you have used the idea of place value for the digits in a whole number. The name and the **place value** of each of the first seven columns in our number system is shown here:

Millions Place	Hundred Thousands Place	Ten Thousands Place	Thousands Place	Hundreds Place	Tens Place	Ones Place
1,000,000	100,000	10,000	1,000	100	10	1

As we move from right to left, we multiply by 10 each time. The value of each column is 10 times the value of the column on its right, with the rightmost column being 1. Up until now we have always looked at place value as increasing by a factor of 10 each time we move one column to the left.

328

Ten Thousands		Thousands		Hundreds		Tens		Ones
10,000	←	1,000	←	100	←	10	←	1
	Multiply by 10		Multiply by 10		Multiply by 10		Multiply by 10	

To understand the idea behind decimal numbers, we notice that moving in the opposite direction, from left to right, we *divide* by 10 each time.

Ten Thousands		Thousands		Hundreds		Tens		Ones
10,000	→	1,000	→	100	→	10	→	1
	Divide by 10		Divide by 10		Divide by 10		Divide by 10	

If we keep going to the right, the next column will have to be

$$1 \div 10 = 1 \cdot \frac{1}{10} = \frac{1}{10} \qquad \text{Tenths}$$

The next one after that will be

$$\frac{1}{10} \div 10 = \frac{1}{10} \cdot \frac{1}{10} = \frac{1}{100} \qquad \text{Hundredths}$$

After that, we have

$$\frac{1}{100} \div 10 = \frac{1}{100} \cdot \frac{1}{10} = \frac{1}{1000} \qquad \text{Thousandths}$$

We could continue this pattern as long as we wanted. We simply divide by 10 to move one column to the right. (Remember, dividing by 10 gives the same result as multiplying by $\frac{1}{10}$.) We use a **decimal point** between the ones column and the tenths column.

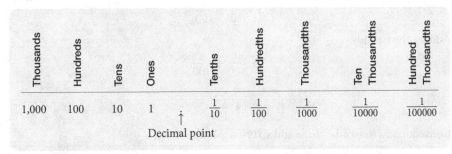

Thousands	Hundreds	Tens	Ones		Tenths	Hundredths	Thousandths	Ten Thousandths	Hundred Thousandths
1,000	100	10	1		$\frac{1}{10}$	$\frac{1}{100}$	$\frac{1}{1000}$	$\frac{1}{10000}$	$\frac{1}{100000}$

Decimal point

Note Because the digits to the right of the decimal point have fractional place values, numbers with digits to the right of the decimal point are called *decimal fractions*. In this book, we will also call them *decimal numbers*, or simply *decimals* for short.

The ones column can be thought of as the middle column, with columns larger than 1 to the left and columns smaller than 1 to the right. The first column to the right of the ones column is the tenths column, the next column to the right is the hundredths column, the next is the thousandths column, and so on. The decimal point is always written between the ones column and the tenths column.

Extending this concept, we can see that a digit one place to the right, such as 0.3, represents $\frac{3}{10}$ or "three tenths." We can now use the place value of decimal fractions to write them in expanded form.

Example 1   Write 423.576 in expanded form, using fractions.

Solution $423.576 = 400 + 20 + 3 + \frac{5}{10} + \frac{7}{100} + \frac{6}{1000}$

Practice Problems

1. Write 18.439 in expanded form.

Answers

1. $10 + 8 + \frac{4}{10} + \frac{3}{100} + \frac{9}{1000}$

2. Write each number in words.
   a. 0.7
   b. 0.07
   c. 0.007

> *Note*   Sometimes we name decimal numbers by simply reading the digits from left to right and using the word "point" to indicate where the decimal point is. For example, using this method the number 5.04 is read "five point zero four."

3. Write each number in words.
   a. 4.2
   b. 4.02
   c. 4.002

4. Write 10.805 in words.

5. Write 14.0836 in words.

Example 2   Write each number in words.
   a. 0.4   **b.** 0.04   **c.** 0.004
Solution

a. Because 0.4 is one place to the right of the decimal, it represents $\frac{1}{10}$ four times. Therefore, in words, 0.4 is "four tenths."

b. Because 0.04 is two places to the right of the decimal, it represents $\frac{1}{100}$ four times. Therefore, in words, 0.04 is "four hundredths."

c. Because 0.004 is three places to the right of the decimal, it represents $\frac{1}{1000}$ four times. Therefore, in words, 0.004 is "four thousandths."

When a decimal number contains digits to the left of the decimal point, we use the word "and" to indicate where the decimal point is when writing the number in words.

Example 3   Write each number in words.
   a. 5.4   **b.** 5.04   **c.** 5.004
Solution

a. 5.4 is "five and four tenths."

b. 5.04 is "five and four hundredths."

c. 5.004 is "five and four thousandths."

Example 4   Write 3.64 in words.
Solution   The place values of the digits are as follows:

$$\underset{3\ ones}{\overset{\uparrow}{3}} \quad . \quad \underset{6\ tenths}{\overset{\uparrow}{6}} \quad \underset{4\ hundredths}{\overset{\nwarrow}{4}}$$

In expanded form

$$3 + \frac{6}{10} + \frac{4}{100}$$

Adding the fractions

$$3 + \frac{60}{100} + \frac{4}{100}$$

$$3 + \frac{64}{100}$$

Consequently, in words "three and sixty-four hundredths."

Example 5   Write 25.4936 in words.
Solution   Using the idea given in Example 4, we write 25.4936 in words as "twenty-five and four thousand, nine hundred thirty-six ten thousandths."

In order to understand addition and subtraction of decimals, we need to be able to convert decimal numbers to fractions or mixed numbers.

Answers

2. a. Seven tenths
   b. Seven hundredths
   c. Seven thousandths
3. a. Four and two tenths
   b. Four and two hundredths
   c. Four and two thousandths
4. Ten and eight hundred five thousandths.
5. Fourteen and eight hundred thirty-six ten thousandths.

Example 6 Write each number as a fraction or a mixed number. Do not reduce to lowest terms.

a. 0.004   **b.** 3.64   **c.** 25.4936

Solution

a. Because 0.004 is 4 thousandths, we write

$$0.004 = \frac{4}{1000}$$

b. Looking over the work in Example 4, we can write

$$3.64 = 3\frac{64}{100}$$

c. From the way in which we wrote 25.4936 in words in Example 5, we have

$$25.4936 = 25\frac{4936}{10000}$$

6. Write each number as a fraction or mixed number. Do not reduce to lowest terms.
a. 0.08
b. 4.206
c. 12.5814

B Rounding Decimal Numbers

Rounding decimal numbers is similar to rounding whole numbers. If the digit in the column to the right of the one we are rounding to is 5 or more, we add 1 to the digit in the column we are rounding to; otherwise, we do not change the value. We then replace all digits to the right of the column we are rounding to with zeros. Let's look at what happens when we do this. Say we just rounded a number to

$$3.60$$

Writing this decimal as a fraction, we have

$$3 + \frac{60}{100} = 3 + \frac{6}{10}$$

Converting back to decimal notation, we have 3.6. Consequently, we see that we can delete zeros at the end of a decimal. Table 1 illustrates the procedure.

Table 1

Rounded to the Nearest

Number	Whole Number	Tenth	Hundredth
24.785	25	24.8	24.79
2.3914	2	2.4	2.39
0.98243	1	1.0	0.98
14.0942	14	14.1	14.09
0.545	1	0.5	0.55

Example 7 Round 9,235.492 to the nearest hundred.

Solution Notice we are rounding to the hundreds, not hundredths. The number next to the hundreds column is 3, which is less than 5. We change all digits to the right to 0, and we can drop all digits to the right of the decimal point, so we write

$$9,200$$

7. Round 8,456.085 to the nearest hundred.

Answers
6. a. $\frac{8}{100}$ **b.** $4\frac{206}{1000}$ **c.** $12\frac{5814}{10000}$
7. 8,500

8. Round 8,456.085 to the nearest hundredth.

Example 8   Round 0.00346 to the nearest ten thousandth.

Solution   Because the number to the right of the ten thousandths column is more than 5, we add 1 to the 4 and get

$$0.0035$$

C Comparing Decimals

To compare decimals, we rewrite each decimal using the same number of decimal places. This is the equivalent to rewriting fractions with common denominators, as we'll see in the next example.

9. Determine which is larger, 0.6 or 0.19.

Example 9   Determine which is larger, 0.7 or 0.83.

Solution   We will start by writing 0.7 as 0.70 so that both numbers are written using the hundredths place. Now we can write each decimal as a fraction

$$0.7 = 0.70 = \frac{70}{100} \quad \text{and} \quad 0.83 = \frac{83}{100}$$

Because $\frac{83}{100}$ is larger than $\frac{70}{100}$, we can conclude that 0.83 is larger than 0.7.

10. Order 9.01, 9, 7.8, and 9.001 from least to greatest.

Example 10   Order 10.02, 10.002, 10, and 9.8 from least to greatest.

Solution   We know that 9.8 is the smallest number in this set, followed by 10. We will compare 10.02 and 10.002. We will rewrite 10.02 using the thousandths place: 10.020. Writing 10.020 and 10.002 as a fraction, we have

$$10.02 = 10.020 = 10\frac{20}{1000} \quad \text{and} \quad 10.002 = 10\frac{2}{1000}$$

From this we can see that 10.002 is less than 10.020. Therefore, listing the numbers from least to greatest, we have:

$$9.8, 10, 10.002, 10.02$$

 KEY CONCEPT REVIEW

After reading through the preceding section, respond in your own words and in complete sentences.

A. Write 754.326 in expanded form.

B. Write $400 + 70 + 5 + \frac{1}{10} + \frac{3}{100} + \frac{7}{1000}$ in decimal form.

C. Write seventy-two and three tenths in decimal form.

D. How many places to the right of the decimal point is the hundredths column?

E. Which is larger, 0.03 or 0.3?

Answers

8. 8,456.09

9. 0.6

10. 7.8, 9, 9.001, 9.01

VOCABULARY REVIEW ·

Choose the correct words to fill in the blanks below.

hundredths   fractional   decimal point   left
tenths   place value   thousandths   right

1. Digits to the right of a decimal point have _____ place values.

2. A _____ is used to separate the ones column and the tenths column.

3. In the decimal number 0.036, the 6 is in the _____ column.

4. In the decimal number 4.169, the 1 is in the _____ column.

5. In the decimal number 10.0977, the 9 is in the _____ column.

6. We use _____ of decimal fractions to write them in expanded form.

7. When a decimal number contains digits to the _____ of the decimal point, we use the word *and* to indicate where the decimal point is when writing the number in words.

8. When rounding decimal numbers, if the digit in the column to the _____ of the one we are rounding to is 5 or more, we add 1 to the digit in the column to which we are rounding.

Problems

A Write out the name of each number in words.

1. 0.3   **2.** 0.03   **3.** 0.015   **4.** 0.0015

5. 3.4   **6.** 2.04   **7.** 52.7   **8.** 46.8

Write each number as a fraction or a mixed number. Do not reduce your answers.

9. 405.36   **10.** 362.78   **11.** 9.009   **12.** 60.06

13. 1.023   **14.** 12.045   **15.** 14.0037   **16.** 2.00106

Give the place value of the 5 in each of the following numbers.

17. 458.327   **18.** 327.458   **19.** 29.52   **20.** 25.92   **21.** 0.00375

22. 0.00532   **23.** 275.01   **24.** 0.356   **25.** 539.76   **26.** 0.123456

Write each of the following as a decimal number.

27. Fifty-five hundredths

28. Two hundred thirty-five ten thousandths

29. Six and nine tenths

30. Forty-five thousand and six hundred twenty-one thousandths

31. Eleven and eleven hundredths

32. Twenty-six thousand, two hundred forty-five and sixteen hundredths

33. One hundred and two hundredths

34. Seventy-five and seventy-five hundred thousandths

35. Three thousand and three thousandths

36. One thousand, one hundred eleven and one hundred eleven thousandths

B Complete the following table.

	Rounded to the Nearest			
Number	Whole Number	Tenth	Hundredth	Thousandth
37. 47.5479				
38. 100.9256				
39. 0.8175				
40. 29.9876				
41. 0.1562				
42. 128.9115				
43. 2,789.3241				
44. 0.8743				
45. 99.9999				
46. 71.7634				

C In each of the following pairs of numbers, determine which number is larger.

47. 0.52, 0.5
48. 2.9, 2.94
49. 0.004, 0.04
50. 7.01, 7.001

51. 8.012, 8.12
52. 13.091, 13.0091
53. 12.87, 12.807
54. 24.318, 24.38

Order each set of numbers from least to greatest.

55. 5.01, 5.001, 5.1, 5
56. 3.002, 3.02, 3.2, 3
57. 11.29, 11.3, 11.02, 11.03
58. 23.07, 23.71, 23.8, 23.08

59. 4.98, 4.08, 4.8, 4
60. 18.09, 18.29, 18.9, 18
61. 19.3, 19.431, 19.134, 19.34
62. 26.721, 26.27, 26.172, 26.2

Applying the Concepts

63. Penny Weight If you have a penny dated anytime from 1959 through 1982, its original weight was 3.11 grams. If the penny has a date of 1983 or later, the original weight was 2.5 grams. Write the two weights in words.

64. Javelin Throw The chart shows the results for some of the leading javelin throws for women at the 2016 Summer Olympics in Rio de Janeiro. Use the information to answer the following questions.

Participant	Country	Mark
Kathryn Mitchell	Australia	64.36
Barbora Spotakola	Czech Republic	64.8
Christina Obergfoll	Germany	62.92
Sara Kolak	Croatia	66.18

a. Write Katherine Mitchell's result in words and expanded form.

b. Whose mark was higher, Barbora Spotakola or Kathryn Mitchell?

65. Nutrition A 50-gram egg contains 0.15 milligram of riboflavin. Write 0.15 in words.

66. Nutrition One medium banana contains 0.64 milligram of Vitamin B6. Write 0.64 in words.

67. Gasoline Prices The bar chart below was created from a survey by the U.S. Department of Energy's Energy Information Administration during four weeks in 2011. It gives the average price of regular gasoline for the United States on each Monday throughout the four-week period. Use the information in the chart to fill in the table.

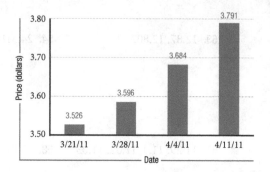

Price of 1 Gallon of Regular Gasoline	
Date	Price (Dollars)
3/21/11	
3/28/11	
4/4/11	
4/11/11	

68. Speed and Time The bar chart below was created from data given by *Car and Driver* magazine. It gives the minimum time in seconds for a Toyota Echo to reach various speeds from a complete stop. Use the information in the chart to fill in the table.

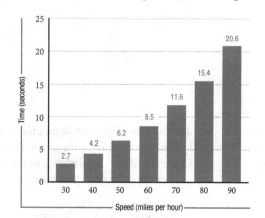

Speed (miles per hour)	Time (seconds)
30	
40	
50	
60	
70	
80	
90	

69. Which of the following numbers will round to 7.5?

7.451   7.449   7.54   7.56

70. Which of the following numbers will round to 3.2?

3.14999   3.24999   3.279   3.16111

Change each decimal to a fraction, and then reduce to lowest terms.

71. 0.25

72. 0.75

73. 0.125

74. 0.375

75. 0.625

76. 0.0625

77. 0.875

78. 0.1875

Estimating   For each pair of numbers, choose the number that is closest to 10.

79. 9.9 and 9.99

80. 8.5 and 8.05

81. 10.5 and 10.05

82. 10.9 and 10.99

Estimating   For each pair of numbers, choose the number that is closest to 0.

83. 0.5 and 0.05

84. 0.10 and 0.05

85. 0.01 and 0.02

86. 0.1 and 0.01

Getting Ready for the Next Section

Find each of the following sums and differences using common denominators. (Add or subtract.)

87. $4\frac{3}{10} + 2\frac{1}{100}$

88. $5\frac{35}{100} + 2\frac{3}{10}$

89. $8\frac{5}{10} - 2\frac{4}{100}$

90. $6\frac{3}{100} - 2\frac{125}{1000}$

91. $5\frac{1}{10} + 6\frac{2}{100} + 7\frac{3}{1000}$

92. $4\frac{27}{100} + 6\frac{3}{10} + 7\frac{123}{1000}$

FIND THE MISTAKE

Each sentence below contains a mistake. Circle the mistake and write the correct word(s) or numbers(s) on the line provided.

1. To move a place value from the tens column to the hundreds column, you must divide by ten.
_____

2. The decimal 0.09 can be written as the fraction $\frac{9}{10}$. _____

3. The decimal 142.9643 written as a mixed number is $142\frac{9643}{1000}$. _____

4. Rounding the decimal 0.06479 to the nearest tenth gives us 0.065. _____

Navigation Skills

Using a group of classmates or friends to study and review course concepts is a great way to prepare for assignments in this class. Make sure to keep your group size small to make sure each person gets the attention he or she needs. During these sessions, talk openly about the concepts you are studying and the difficulties you may be having. Here are a few examples to make your group study sessions as effective as possible:

- Choose a regular time and place to meet.
- Attend every meeting and pull your weight. Showing up and helping others will, in turn, help you in this course.
- Make flashcards of definitions, properties, and formulas and quiz each other.
- Recite definitions or formulas out loud.
- Take turns explaining concepts to the group. Try to use mathematical vocabulary as often as possible.
- Discuss how concepts learned in previous chapters are incorporated into the concepts you are currently studying.
- Role play where one person is the instructor verbally guiding another person as the student through a problem.
- Predict test questions and quiz each other.

5.2

ADDITION AND SUBTRACTION WITH DECIMALS

OBJECTIVES

A Add decimals.

B Subtract decimals.

VIDEO EXAMPLES

SECTION 5.2

The Olympic Games is the world's premier sports competition. Nearly every nation sends athletes to compete in the games. As a result, the symbol for the games is five overlapping circles representing the unity of the five continents. The colors of these rings were selected because every nation has at least one of these colors in their flag.

Today's summer Olympic competition still includes events that were held at the ancient games. This includes running and combat events as well as a version of the pentathlon, a combination of five different sports. The chart shows the top finishing times for the 400-meter race during the 2016 Summer Olympic Games. In order to analyze the different finishing times, we need to be able to add and subtract decimals, which is what we will cover in this section.

Runner (Country)	Time (seconds)
Wayde Van Niekerk (South Africa)	43.03
Kirani James (Grenada)	43.76
Lashawn Merrit (United States)	43.85

A Addition of Decimals

Suppose you are earning $8.50 an hour and you receive a raise of $1.25 an hour. Let's find your new hourly rate. To add the two rates of pay, we align the decimal points, and then add in columns.

$$
\begin{array}{r}
\$8.50 \\
+ \$1.25 \\
\hline
\$9.75
\end{array}
$$

Notice, the decimal point in the answer is directly below the decimals in the problem. To see why adding decimals like this is true in general, we can use mixed-number notation.

$$8.50 = 8\frac{50}{100}$$

$$+ 1.25 = 1\frac{25}{100}$$

$$9\frac{75}{100} = 9.75$$

338

We can visualize the mathematics above by thinking in terms of money.

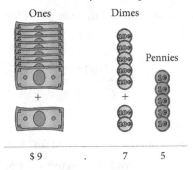

Ones   Dimes

Pennies

$9 . 7 5

Example 1 Add: 8 + 0.002 + 3.1 + 0.04

Solution   In order to add the numbers, we want them to have the same number of decimal places. This is the equivalent of finding the common denominator for the fractional parts. Because 0.002 is written to the thousandths place, we will write the other numbers to the thousandths place.

$$8 = 8.000$$

$$3.1 = 3.100$$

$$0.04 = 0.040$$

Recall, this doesn't change the value of any of the numbers, and it makes our task easier. Now we have

$$\begin{array}{r} 8.000 \\ 0.002 \\ 3.100 \\ + \ 0.040 \\ \hline 11.142 \end{array}$$

Practice Problems

1. Add: 9 + 1.05 + 8.7 + 3.86

B Subtraction of Decimals

The same thing would happen if we were to subtract two decimal numbers. We can use these facts to summarize what we've learned about addition and subtraction of decimal numbers.

SUMMARY Addition (or Subtraction) of Decimal Numbers

To add (or subtract) decimal numbers, we line up the decimal points and add (or subtract) as usual. The decimal point in the result is written directly below the decimal points in the problem.

We will use this rule for the rest of the examples in this section.

Example 2 Subtract: 39.812 − 14.236

Solution   We write the numbers vertically, with the decimal points lined up, and subtract as usual.

$$\begin{array}{r} 39.812 \\ - \ 14.236 \\ \hline 25.576 \end{array}$$

2. Subtract: 42.809 − 13.658

Answers

1. 22.61
2. 29.151

3. Subtract: $3.7 - 1.9034$

Example 3 Subtract: $5.9 - 3.0814$

Solution In this case, it is very helpful to write 5.9 as 5.9000, since we will have to borrow in order to subtract.

$$\begin{array}{r} 5.9000 \\ -\ 3.0814 \\ \hline 2.8186 \end{array}$$

4. Subtract 8.92 from the sum of 12 and 5.01.

Example 4 Subtract 3.09 from the sum of 9 and 5.472.

Solution Writing the problem in symbols, and using the order of operations, we have

$$(9 + 5.472) - 3.09 = 14.472 - 3.09$$
$$= 11.382$$

5. Add: $-3.5 + (-1.25)$

Example 5 Add: $-4.75 + (-2.25)$

Solution Because both signs are negative, we add absolute values.

$$\begin{array}{r} 4.75 \\ +\ 2.25 \\ \hline 7.00 \end{array}$$

The sum of two negative numbers is a negative number. Therefore,

$$-4.75 + (-2.25) = -7.00$$

6. Add: $6.58 + (-10.47)$

Example 6 Add: $3.42 + (-6.89)$

Solution The signs are different, so we subtract the smaller absolute value from the larger absolute value.

$$\begin{array}{r} 6.89 \\ -\ 3.42 \\ \hline 3.47 \end{array}$$

Because 6.89 is larger than 3.42 and the sign in front of 6.89 is negative, the answer will be negative. Therefore, $3.42 + (-6.89) = -3.47$.

 KEY CONCEPT REVIEW

After reading through the preceding section, respond in your own words and in complete sentences.

A. When adding numbers with decimals, why is it important to line up the decimal points?

B. Write 379.6 in mixed-number notation.

C. Why do we line up the decimals when we add or subtract vertically?

D. How many quarters does the decimal 0.75 represent?

Answers
3. 1.7966
4. 8.09
5. −4.75
6. −3.89

VOCABULARY REVIEW •

Choose the correct words to fill in the blanks below.

zeros   columns   decimal point   value

1. To add two decimal numbers, align the decimal points and then add in _____.

2. When adding or subtracting decimal numbers, the _____ in the answer is directly below the decimals in the problems.

3. It is important to write _____ to the right of the rightmost digits to keep the digits in the correct columns.

4. Writing zeros to the right of the rightmost digits does not change the _____ of any of the numbers.

Problems

A Find each of the following sums. (Add.)

1. 2.91 + 3.28

2. 8.97 + 2.04

3. 0.04 + 0.31 + 0.78

4. 0.06 + 0.92 + 0.65

5. −3.89 + 2.4

6. 7.65 + 3.8

7. 4.532 + 1.81 + 2.7

8. 9.679 + 3.49 + 6.5

9. 0.081 + 5 + 2.94

10. 0.396 + 7 + 3.96

11. 5.0003 + 6.78 + 0.004

12. 27.0179 + 7.89 + 0.009

13.
```
  7.123
  8.12
+ 9.1
```

14.
```
  5.432
  4.32
+ 3.2
```

15.
```
  9.001
  8.01
+ 7.1
```

16.
```
  6.003
  5.02
+ 4.1
```

17.
```
   89.7854
    3.4
   65.35
+ 100.006
```

18.
```
   57.4698
    9.89
   32.032
+ 572.0079
```

19.
```
  543.21
+ 123.45
```

20.
```
  987.654
+ 456.789
```

B Find each of the following differences. (Subtract.)

21. 99.34 − 88.23

22. 47.69 − 23.41

23. 5.97 − 2.04

24. 9.87 − 1.04

25. 6.3 − 2.08

26. 7.5 − 3.04

27. $-28.96 - (-149.37)$

28. $-32.68 - (-796.45)$

29. $45 - 0.067$

30. $48 - 0.075$

31. $8 - 0.327$

32. $12 - 0.962$

33. $765.432 - 234.567$

34. $654.321 - 123.456$

35. $100.42 - 56.87$

36. $200.34 - 12.76$

37. $10 - 4.082$

38. $20 - 5.86$

Subtract.

39.
$$\begin{array}{r} 34.07 \\ -\ 6.18 \\ \hline \end{array}$$

40.
$$\begin{array}{r} 25.008 \\ -\ 3.119 \\ \hline \end{array}$$

41.
$$\begin{array}{r} 40.04 \\ -\ 4.4 \\ \hline \end{array}$$

42.
$$\begin{array}{r} 50.05 \\ -\ 5.5 \\ \hline \end{array}$$

43.
$$\begin{array}{r} 768.436 \\ -\ 356.998 \\ \hline \end{array}$$

44.
$$\begin{array}{r} 495.237 \\ -\ 247.668 \\ \hline \end{array}$$

Add and subtract as indicated.

45. $(7.8 - 4.3) + 2.5$

46. $(8.3 - 1.2) + 3.4$

47. $7.8 - (4.3 + 2.5)$

48. $8.3 - (1.2 + 3.4)$

49. $(9.7 - 5.2) - 1.4$

50. $(7.8 - 3.2) - 1.5$

51. $9.7 - (5.2 - 1.4)$

52. $7.8 - (3.2 - 1.5)$

53. $5 - (4 - 2.3)$

54. $10 - (3 - 1.06)$

55. $12.2 - (9.1 + 0.3)$

56. $15.6 - (4.9 + 3.87)$

57. $-9.01 - 2.4$

58. $-8.23 - 5.4$

59. $-0.89 - 1.01$

60. $-0.42 - 2.04$

61. $-3.4 - 5.6 - 8.5$

62. $-2.1 - 3.1 - 4.1$

63. Subtract 5 from the sum of 8.2 and 0.072.

64. Subtract 8 from the sum of 9.37 and 2.5.

65. What number is added to 0.035 to obtain 4.036?

66. What number is added to 0.043 to obtain 6.054?

Applying the Concepts

67. Shopping A family buying school clothes for their two children spends $25.37 at one store, $39.41 at another, and $52.04 at a third store. What is the total amount spent at the three stores?

68. Expenses A 4-H Club member is raising a lamb to take to the county fair. If she spent $75 for the lamb, $25.60 for feed, and $35.89 for shearing tools, what was the total cost of the project?

69. Take-Home Pay A college professor making $2,105.96 per month has deducted from her check $311.93 for federal income tax, $158.21 for retirement, and $64.72 for state income tax. How much does the professor take home after the deductions have been taken from her monthly income?

70. Take-Home Pay A cook making $1,504.75 a month has deductions of $157.32 for federal income tax, $58.52 for Social Security, and $45.12 for state income tax. How much does the cook take home after the deductions have been taken from his check?

71. Rectangle The logo on a business letter is rectangular. The rectangle has a width of 0.84 inches and a length of 1.41 inches. Find the perimeter.

72. Rectangle A small sticky note is a rectangle. It has a width of 21.4 millimeters and a length of 35.8 millimeters. Find the perimeter.

73. Change A person buys $4.57 worth of candy. If he pays for the candy with a $10 bill, how much change should he receive?

74. Checking Account A checking account contains $342.38. If purchases are made for $25.04, $36.71, and $210, how much money is left in the account?

Downhill Skiers The table shows the fastest times for the 2016 women's Ironman World Championship triathlon in Kona, Hawaii. Use the information to answer the following questions.

75. How much faster was Mirinda Carfrae than Heather Jackson?

76. How much faster was Daniela Ryf than Mirinda Carfrae? (Hint: you will regroup 1 minute as 60 seconds and 1 hour as 60 minutes.)

Athlete (Country)	Time (hrs : mins : secs)
Daniela Ryf (Czech Republic)	8:46:46
Mirinda Carfrae (Australia)	9:10:30
Heather Jackson (United States)	9:11:32

77. App Sales The table shows the top grossing iPhone mobile gaming apps by daily revenue in the U. S. in millions as of July 2017. Use the information to answer the following questions.

Game	Revenue
Pokemon Go	2.07
Candy Crush Saga	1.55
Clash Royale	1.91
Game of War: Fire Age	0.81

a. How much more revenue is generated daily from the sale of Pokemon Go than Candy Crush Saga?

b. How much more revenue is generated daily from the sale of Pokemon Go than Game of War: Fire Age?

c. Write the revenue of each app in standard form.

78. Movie Tickets The chart shows the increase in movie ticket prices. Use the information to answer the following questions.

a. Were movie ticket prices above $7.50 in 2008?

b. Were ticket prices above $8.00 in 2015?

c. What is the change in ticket prices from 2007 and 2016?

79. Geometry A rectangle has a perimeter of 9.5 inches. If the length is 2.75 inches, find the width.

80. Geometry A rectangle has a perimeter of 11 inches. If the width is 2.5 inches, find the length.

81. Change Suppose you eat dinner in a restaurant and the bill comes to $16.76. If you give the cashier a $20 bill and a penny, how much change should you receive? List the bills and coins you should receive for change.

82. Change Suppose you buy some tools at the hardware store and the bill comes to $37.87. If you give the cashier two $20 bills and 2 pennies, how much change should you receive? List the bills and coins you should receive for change.

Sequences Find the next number in each sequence.

83. 2.5, 2.75, 3, . . .

84. 3.125, 3.375, 3.625, . . .

Getting Ready for the Next Section

Multiply the fractions. Do not reduce.

85. $\dfrac{7}{10} \cdot \dfrac{3}{10}$

86. $\dfrac{21}{10} \times \dfrac{7}{100}$

87. $9 \cdot \dfrac{7}{10}$

88. $\dfrac{7}{10} \times \dfrac{1}{10}$

89. Change Problem 85 to a decimal.

90. Change Problem 86 to a decimal.

91. Change Problem 87 to a decimal.

92. Change Problem 88 to a decimal.

Simplify.

93. $5(42 + 3)$

94. $\dfrac{1}{4}(6 + 10)$

95. $48 + 12(3)^2$

96. $\left(\dfrac{1}{3}\right)^2 (12)^2$

FIND THE MISTAKE •

Each sentence below contains a mistake. Circle the mistake and write the correct word(s) or numbers(s) on the line provided.

1. To add 32.69 and 4.837, align the rightmost digit of each number and add in columns.

_____

2. To add $0.004 + 5.06 + 32$ by first changing each decimal to a fraction would give us the problem $\dfrac{4}{1000} + \dfrac{5}{600} + 32$. _____

3. When subtracting $8.7 - 2.0163$, we make sure to keep the digits in the correct columns by writing 8.7 as 8.0007. _____

4. Subtracting 4.367 from the sum of 12.1 and 0.036 gives us 11.3333. _____

5.3 MULTIPLICATION WITH DECIMALS

• • OBJECTIVES • •

A Multiply with decimals.

B Simplify expressions with decimals using the order of operations.

VIDEO EXAMPLES

SECTION 5.3

The mystery of the roving rocks in Racetrack Playa of Death Valley, California has been puzzling scientists for decades. Water from winter rains wash down the slopes of the surrounding mountains and form a small lake in the Playa. During the summer, the lake evaporates and the muddy bed dries up, cracking into a mosaic of hexagonal clay tiles. Scientists have been trying to discover what causes large stones to move across the lakebed and leave behind tracks. One hypothesis suggests that as night temperatures fall below freezing, ice forms around each tile. Frequent winds up to 90 miles per hour can move this ice, allowing for a conveyor belt of sorts to move the rocks. To date, no one has ever witnessed the rocks moving, but scientists believe they may move at half the jogging speed of a human. Let's suppose a person is jogging at 6.5 miles per hour. If a rock in Racetrack Playa was moving at half the jogger's rate, it would be moving at 3.25 miles per hour. Therefore, it must be true that

$$\frac{1}{2} \text{ of } 6.5 \text{ is } 3.25$$

But because $\frac{1}{2}$ can be written as 0.5 and *of* translates to multiply, we can write this problem again as

$$0.5 \times 6.5 = 3.25$$

If we were to ignore the decimal points in this problem and simply multiply 5 and 65, the result would be 325.

A Multiplication with Decimals

Multiplication with decimal numbers is similar to multiplication with whole numbers. The difference lies in deciding where to place the decimal point in the answer. To find out how this is done, we can use fraction notation.

Example 1 Change each decimal to a fraction and multiply.

$$0.5 \times 0.3$$

Solution Changing each decimal to a fraction and multiplying, we have

$$0.5 \times 0.3 = \frac{5}{10} \times \frac{3}{10} \qquad \textit{Change to fractions.}$$

$$= \frac{15}{100} \qquad \textit{Multiply numerators and multiply denominators.}$$

$$= 0.15 \qquad \textit{Write the answer in decimal form.}$$

The result is 0.15, which has two digits to the right of the decimal point.

What we want to do now is find an alternative method that will allow us to multiply decimals without first having to change each decimal number to a fraction. Let's look at another example.

Example 2 Change each decimal to a fraction and multiply: 0.05×0.003.
Solution

$$0.05 \times 0.003 = \frac{5}{100} \times \frac{3}{1000} \qquad \textit{Change to fractions.}$$

$$= \frac{15}{100000} \qquad \textit{Multiply numerators and multiply denominators.}$$

$$= 0.00015 \qquad \textit{Write the answer in decimal form.}$$

The result is 0.00015, which has a total of five digits to the right of the decimal point.

Looking over these first two examples, we can see that the digits in the result are just what we would get if we simply forgot about the decimal points and multiplied; that is, $3 \times 5 = 15$. The decimal point in the result is placed so that the total number of digits to its right is the same as the total number of digits to the right of both decimal points in the original two numbers. The reason this is true becomes clear when we look at the denominators after we have changed from decimals to fractions.

Example 3 Multiply: 2.1×0.07
Solution

$$2.1 \times 0.07 = 2\frac{1}{10} \times \frac{7}{100} \qquad \textit{Change to fractions.}$$

$$= \frac{21}{10} \times \frac{7}{100} \qquad \textit{Write } 2\frac{1}{10} \textit{ as an improper fraction.}$$

$$= \frac{147}{1000} \qquad \textit{Multiply numerators and multiply denominators.}$$

$$= 0.147 \qquad \textit{Write the answer as a decimal.}$$

Again, the digits in the answer come from multiplying $21 \times 7 = 147$. The decimal point is placed so that there are three digits to its right, because that is the total number of digits to the right of the decimal points in 2.1 and 0.07.

Practice Problems

1. Change each decimal to a fraction and multiply.

$$0.4 \times 0.08$$

2. Change each decimal to a fraction and multiply.

$$0.08 \times 0.009$$

3. Multiply: 3.2×0.09

Answers
1. 0.032
2. 0.00072
3. 0.288

We summarize this discussion with the following rule:

SUMMARY **Multiplication with Decimal Numbers**

To multiply two decimal numbers, follow these steps:

1. Multiply as you would if the decimal points were not there.

2. Place the decimal point in the answer so that the number of digits to its right is equal to the total number of digits to the right of the decimal points in the original two numbers in the problem.

4. How many digits will be to the right of the decimal point in the following product?

$$4.632 \times 0.0008$$

Example 4 How many digits will be to the right of the decimal point in the following product?

$$2.987 \times 24.82$$

Solution There are three digits to the right of the decimal point in 2.987 and two digits to the right in 24.82. Therefore, there will be $3 + 2 = 5$ digits to the right of the decimal point in their product.

5. Multiply: 2.16×3.05

Example 5 Multiply: 3.05×4.36

Solution We can set this up as if it were a multiplication problem with whole numbers. We multiply and then place the decimal point in the correct position in the answer.

$$
\begin{array}{r}
3.05 \quad \longleftarrow \quad \textit{2 digits to the right of decimal point} \\
\times\ 4.36 \quad \longleftarrow \quad \textit{2 digits to the right of decimal point} \\
\hline
1830 \\
9150 \\
+\ 12\ 2000 \\
\hline
13.2980 \\
\end{array}
$$

The decimal point is placed so that there are $2 + 2 = 4$ digits to its right.

6. Simplify each expression.
   a. $(-4)(1.2)$
   b. $(-0.2)(-0.5)$

Example 6 Simplify each expression.

a. $(-5)(3.4)$ **b.** $(-0.4)(-0.8)$

Solution Our properties for multiplying negative numbers still hold for decimals.

a. $(-5)(3.4) = -17.0$ **b.** $(-0.4)(-0.8) = 0.32$

As you can see, multiplying decimal numbers is just like multiplying whole numbers, except that we must place the decimal point in the result in the correct position.

Estimating

Look back to Example 5. We could have placed the decimal point in the answer by rounding the two numbers to the nearest whole number and then multiplying them. Because 3.05 rounds to 3 and 4.36 rounds to 4, and the product of 3 and 4 is 12, we estimate that the answer to 3.05×4.36 will be close to 12. Then, we place the decimal point in the product 132980 between the 3 and the 2 in order to make it into a number close to 12. Estimating is useful in checking our answers.

Answers
4. Seven
5. 6.588
6. a. -4.8 **b.** 0.10

Example 7   Estimate the answer to each of the following products.

a. 29.4×8.2 **b.** 68.5×172 **c.** $(6.32)^2$

Solution

a. Because 29.4 is approximately 30 and 8.2 is approximately 8, we estimate this product to be about $30 \times 8 = 240$. (If we were to multiply 29.4 and 8.2, we would find the product to be exactly 241.08.)

b. Rounding 68.5 to 70 and 172 to 170, we estimate this product to be $70 \times 170 = 11,900$. (The exact answer is 11,782.) Note here that we do not always round the numbers to the nearest whole number when making estimates. The idea is to round to numbers that will be easy to multiply.

c. Because 6.32 is approximately 6 and $6^2 = 36$, we estimate our answer to be close to 36. (The actual answer is 39.9424.)

7. Estimate the answer to each of the following products.

  a. 39.6×9.1

  b. 58.7×141.3

  c. $(9.84)^2$

Note   Recall, the order of operations is:

  parentheses
  exponents
  multiplication and division
  addition and subtraction

B Order of Operations with Decimals

We can use the rule for order of operations to simplify expressions involving decimal numbers and addition, subtraction, and multiplication.

Example 8   Perform the indicated operations: $0.05(4.2 + 0.03)$

Solution   We begin by adding inside the parentheses.

$$0.05(4.2 + 0.03) = 0.05(4.23) \quad \text{Add.}$$
$$= 0.2115 \quad \text{Multiply.}$$

Notice that we could also have used the distributive property first, and the result would be unchanged.

$$0.05(4.2 + 0.03) = 0.05(4.2) + 0.05(0.03) \quad \text{Distributive property}$$
$$= 0.210 + 0.0015 \quad \text{Multiply.}$$
$$= 0.2115 \quad \text{Add.}$$

8. Perform the indicated operations.

  $0.07(3.9 + 6.05)$

Example 9   Simplify: $4.8 + 12(3.2)^2$

Solution   According to the rule for order of operations, we must first evaluate the number with an exponent, then multiply, and finally add.

$$4.8 + 12(3.2)^2 = 4.8 + 12(10.24) \quad (3.2)^2 = 10.24$$
$$= 4.8 + 122.88 \quad \text{Multiply.}$$
$$= 127.68 \quad \text{Add.}$$

9. Simplify: $9.5 + 11(2.3)^2$

10. How much will Sally from Example 10 make if she works 48 hours in one week?

Note To estimate the answer to Example 10 before doing the actual calculations, we would do the following:

$6(40) + 9(6) = 240 + 54 = 294$

Applications

Example 10   Sally earns $6.32 for each of the first 36 hours she works in one week, and $9.48 in overtime pay for each additional hour she works in the same week. How much money will she make if she works 42 hours in one week?

Solution   The difference between 42 and 36 is 6 hours of overtime pay. The total amount of money she will make is

Pay for the first   Pay for the
36 hours   next 6 hours

$6.32(36) \quad + \quad 9.48(6) = 227.52 + 56.88$

$$= 284.40$$

She will make $284.40 for working 42 hours in one week.

KEY CONCEPT REVIEW

After reading through the preceding section, respond in your own words and in complete sentences.

A. If you multiply 34.76 and 0.072, how many digits will be to the right of the decimal point in your answer?

B. To simplify the expression 0.053(9) + 67.42, what would be the first step according to the rule for order of operations?

C. What is the purpose of estimating?

D. What are some applications of decimals that we use in our everyday lives?

EXERCISE SET 5.3 ....

Problems

A Find each of the following products. (Multiply.)

1. 0.7×0.4

2. 0.8×0.3

3. 0.07×0.4

4. 0.8×0.03

5. 0.03×0.09

6. 0.07×0.002

7. $-2.6(0.3)$

8. $-8.9(0.2)$

9. 0.9×0.88

10. 0.8×0.99

11. 3.12×0.005

12. 4.69×0.006

13.
$$\begin{array}{r} 4.003 \\ \times\ 6.07 \\ \hline \end{array}$$

14.
$$\begin{array}{r} 7.0001 \\ \times\ \ 3.04 \\ \hline \end{array}$$

15.
$$\begin{array}{r} -0.006 \\ \times\ \ \ -5 \\ \hline \end{array}$$

16.
$$\begin{array}{r} -0.005 \\ \times\ \ \ -7 \\ \hline \end{array}$$

17. 75.14×2.5

18. 963.8×0.24

19. 0.1×0.02

20. 0.3×0.02

21.
$$\begin{array}{r} -2.796 \\ \times\ \ -10 \\ \hline \end{array}$$

22.
$$\begin{array}{r} -97.531 \\ \times\ -100 \\ \hline \end{array}$$

23.
$$\begin{array}{r} 0.0043 \\ \times\ \ \ 100 \\ \hline \end{array}$$

24.
$$\begin{array}{r} 12.345 \\ \times\ 1,000 \\ \hline \end{array}$$

25.
$$\begin{array}{r} -1000 \\ \times\ 49.94 \\ \hline \end{array}$$

26.
$$\begin{array}{r} -10,000 \\ \times 157.02 \\ \hline \end{array}$$

27.
$$\begin{array}{r} 987.654 \\ \times -10,000 \\ \hline \end{array}$$

28.
$$\begin{array}{r} -100,000 \\ \times\ \ \ \ 1.23 \\ \hline \end{array}$$

B Perform the following operations according to the rule for order of operations.

29. $2.1(3.5 - 2.6)$

30. $5.4(9.9 - 6.6)$

31. $0.05(0.02 + 0.03)$

32. $-0.04(0.07 + 0.09)$

33. $2.02(0.03 + 2.5)$

34. $-4.04(0.05 + 6.6)$

35. $(2.1 + 0.03)(3.4 + 0.05)$

36. $(9.2 + 0.01)(3.5 + 0.03)$

37. $(2.1 - 0.1)(2.1 + 0.1)$

38. $(9.6 - 0.5)(9.6 + 0.5)$

39. $3.08 - 0.2(5 + 0.03)$

40. $4.09 + 0.5(6 + 0.02)$

41. $4.23 - 5(0.04 + 0.09)$

42. $7.89 - 2(0.31 + 0.76)$

43. $2.5 + 10(4.3)^2$

44. $3.6 + 15(2.1)^2$

45. $100(1 + 0.08)^2$

46. $500(1 + 0.12)^2$

47. $(-1.5)^2 + (2.5)^2 + (-3.5)^2$ **48.** $(1.1)^2 + (-2.1)^2 + (3.1)^2$

Applying the Concepts

Evaluate each expression for $a = 0.4$.

49. $6a + 7.9$

50. $8a + 2.8$

51. $4(1.7 + a)$

52. $8(2.2 + a)$

53. $4.9 - 0.2a$

54. $15.4 - 0.1a$

55. $a^2 + 14.2$

56. $a^2 + 28.3$

Simplify each expression.

57. $3.2x + 7.8 - 14.6x$

58. $28.7x - 9.5 - 4.3x$

59. $4.7(1.2x - 3.8)$

60. $6.8(1.9x - 2.1)$

61. $-3.4(2.37x + 5.6) - 4.9$

62. $-2.9(3.81x + 4.3) - 9.6$

63. $3(2.9x + 3) - 5(2.81)$

64. $4(3.7x + 5) - 6(9.71)$

Solve each of the following word problems. Note that not all of the problems are solved by simply multiplying the numbers in the problems. Many of the problems involve addition and subtraction as well as multiplication.

65. Number Problem What is the product of 6 and the sum of 0.001 and 0.02?

66. Number Problem Find the product of 8 and the sum of 0.03 and 0.002.

67. Number Problem What does multiplying a decimal number by 100 do to the decimal point?

68. Number Problem What does multiplying a decimal number by 1,000 do to the decimal point?

69. Home Mortgage On a certain home mortgage, there is a monthly payment of $9.66 for every $1,000 that is borrowed. What is the monthly payment on this type of loan if $143,000 is borrowed?

70. Caffeine Content If 1 cup of regular coffee contains 105 milligrams of caffeine, how much caffeine is contained in 3.5 cups of coffee?

71. Price of Gasoline If gasoline costs $2.48 per gallon when you pay with a credit card, but $0.03 per gallon less if you pay with cash, how much do you save by filling up a 17-gallon tank and paying with cash?

72. Price of Gasoline If gasoline costs $3.05 per gallon when you pay with a credit card, but $0.06 per gallon less if you pay with cash, how much do you save by filling up a 12-gallon tank and paying for it with cash?

73. Car Rental Suppose it costs $15 per day and $0.12 per mile to rent a car. What is the total bill if a car is rented for 2 days and is driven 120 miles?

74. Car Rental Suppose it costs $20 per day and $0.08 per mile to rent a car. What is the total bill if the car is rented for 2 days and is driven 120 miles?

75. Wages A man earns $5.92 for each of the first 36 hours he works in one week and $8.88 in overtime pay for each additional hour he works in the same week. How much money will he make if he works 45 hours in one week?

76. Wages A student earns $8.56 for each of the first 40 hours she works in one week and $12.84 in overtime pay for each additional hour she works in the same week. How much money will she make if she works 44 hours in one week?

77. Rectangle A rectangle has a width of 33.5 millimeters and a length of 254 millimeters. Find the area.

78. Rectangle A rectangle has a width of 2.56 inches and a length of 6.14 inches. Find the area rounded to the nearest hundredth.

79. Rectangle The logo on a business letter is rectangular. The rectangle has a width of 0.84 inches and a length of 1.41 inches. Find the area rounded to the nearest hundredth.

80. Rectangle A small sticky note is a rectangle. It has a width of 21.4 millimeters and a length of 35.8 millimeters. Find the area.

Getting Ready for the Next Section

Perform the following operations.

81. 3,758 ÷ 2

82. 9,900 ÷ 22

83. 50,032 ÷ 33

84. 90,902 ÷ 5

85. 20)‾5,960

86. 30)‾4,620

87. 4 × 8.7

88. 5 × 6.7

89. 27 × 1.848

90. 35 × 32.54

91. 38)‾31,350

92. 25)‾377,800

Improving Your Quantitative Literacy

93. Containment System Holding tanks for hazardous liquids are often surrounded by containment tanks that will hold the hazardous liquid if the main tank begins to leak. We see that the center tank has a height of 16 feet and a radius of 6 feet. The outside containment tank has a height of 4 feet and a radius of 8 feet. The formula to calculate the volume of a tank is $V = \pi r^2 h$. Use 3.14 as an estimate for π. If the center tank is full of heating fuel and develops a leak at the bottom, will the containment tank be able to hold all the heating fuel that leaks out?

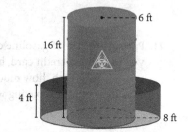

FIND THE MISTAKE •

Each sentence below contains a mistake. Circle the mistake and write the correct word(s) or numbers(s) on the line provided.

1. To multiply 18.05 by 3.5, multiply as if the numbers were whole numbers and then place the decimal in the answer with two digits to its right. _____

2. To estimate the answer for 24.9 × 7.3, round 24.9 to 20 and 7.3 to 7. _____

3. To simplify (8.43 + 1.002) − (0.05)(3.2), first subtract the product of 0.05 and 3.2 from 1.002 before adding 8.43. _____

4. Lucy pays $1.52 a pound for the first three pounds of candy she buys at a candy store, and pays $3.27 for each additional pound. To find how much she will pay if she buys 5.2 pounds of candy, we must solve the problem 1.52(3) + 3.27(5.2). _____

DIVISION WITH DECIMALS

5.4

A coffeemaker company announced the development of their new home espresso machine that scans your fingerprint to take an order. The new device can distinguish between six different housemates based on a scan of each fingerprint and its matching preferences (e.g., strength, froth, etc.). The current estimated selling price for the espresso machine is $3,200.

Suppose you and your three roommates have decided to purchase one of these espresso machines selling for $3,199.99. If you decide to split the bill equally, how much does each person owe? To find out, you will have to divide 3199.99 by 4. In this section, we will find out how to do division with any combination of decimal numbers.

OBJECTIVES

A Divide decimal numbers with exact answers.

B Divide decimal numbers with rounded answers.

C Solve application problems involving decimals.

VIDEO EXAMPLES

SECTION 5.4

A Dividing Decimal Numbers (Exact Answers)

Example 1   Divide: 5,974 ÷ 20

Solution   We will divide as we have done previously.

$$
\begin{array}{r}
298 \\
20\overline{)5974} \\
-40\downarrow \\
\hline
197 \\
-180\downarrow \\
\hline
174 \\
-160 \\
\hline
14
\end{array}
$$

Practice Problems

1. Divide: 4,870 ÷ 50

Note   We can estimate the answer to Example 1 by rounding 5,974 to 6,000 and dividing by 20:

$$\frac{6,000}{20} = 300$$

Answer

1. 97.4

355

In the past, we have written this answer as $298\frac{14}{20}$ or, after reducing the fraction, $298\frac{7}{10}$. Because $\frac{7}{10}$ can be written as 0.7, we could also write our answer as 298.7. This last form of our answer is exactly the same result we obtain if we write 5,974 as 5,974.0 and continue the division until we have no remainder. Here is how it looks:

$$
\begin{array}{r}
298.7 \\
20\overline{)5974.0} \\
-40 \\
\hline
197 \\
-180 \\
\hline
174 \\
-160 \\
\hline
140 \\
-140 \\
\hline
0
\end{array}
$$

Notice that we place the decimal point in the answer directly above the decimal point in the problem.

Let's try another division problem. This time one of the numbers in the problem will be a decimal.

2. Divide: 56.8 ÷ 4

Example 2   Divide: 34.8 ÷ 4

Solution   We can use the ideas from Example 1 and divide as usual. The decimal point in the answer will be placed directly above the decimal point in the problem.

$$
\begin{array}{r}
8.7 \\
4\overline{)34.8} \\
-32 \\
\hline
28 \\
-28 \\
\hline
0
\end{array}
\qquad
\begin{array}{r}
Check:\quad 8.7 \\
\times\ 4 \\
\hline
34.8
\end{array}
$$

The answer is 8.7.

$\mathcal{Note}$ We can always check our work from a division problem using multiplication.

We can use these facts to write a rule for dividing decimal numbers.

RULE   Division with Decimal Numbers

To divide a decimal by a whole number, we do the usual long division as if there were no decimal point involved. The decimal point in the answer is placed directly above the decimal point in the problem.

Here are some more examples to illustrate the procedure:

3. Divide: 53.625 ÷ 25

Example 3   Divide: 49.896 ÷ 27

Solution

$$
\begin{array}{r}
1.848 \\
27\overline{)49.896} \\
-27 \\
\hline
22\,8 \\
-21\,6 \\
\hline
1\,29 \\
-1\,08 \\
\hline
216 \\
-216 \\
\hline
0
\end{array}
\qquad
\begin{array}{r}
Check:\quad 1.848 \\
\times\ \ 27 \\
\hline
12\,936 \\
36\,960 \\
\hline
49.896
\end{array}
$$

Answers
2. 14.2
3. 2.145

We can write as many zeros as we choose after the rightmost digit in a decimal number without changing the value of the number. For example,

$$6.91 = 6.910 = 6.9100 = 6.91000$$

There are times when this can be very useful, as Example 4 shows.

Example 4   Divide: $1{,}138.9 \div 35$

4. Divide: $1{,}105.8 \div 15$

Solution

```
        32.54
  35)1138.90
    −105↓│││
        88│││
       −70↓││
        189││
       −175↓│
        140│
       −140↓
          0
```

Write 0 after the 9. It doesn't change the original number, but it gives us another digit to bring down.

Check:
```
      32.54
   ×     35
     162 70
     976 20
   1,138.90
```

Until now we have considered only division by whole numbers. Extending division to include division by decimal numbers is a matter of knowing what to do about the decimal point in the divisor. We will develop the procedure for these types of problems in the next example.

Example 5   Divide: $31.35 \div 3.8$

5. Divide: $46.354 \div 4.9$

Solution   In fraction form, this problem is equivalent to

$$\frac{31.35}{3.8}$$

If we want to write the divisor as a whole number, we can multiply the numerator and the denominator of this fraction by 10:

$$\frac{31.35 \times 10}{3.8 \times 10} = \frac{313.5}{38}$$

So, since this fraction is equivalent to the original fraction, our original division problem is equivalent to $313.5 \div 38$. This is the same as moving the decimal in the divisor and the decimal in the dividend one place to the right. Now we will divide:

```
        8.25
  38)313.50
    −304 ↓
       95│
      −76↓
       190
      −190
         0
```

Put 0 after the last digit.

Note   We do not always use the rules for rounding numbers to make estimates. This is especially true with division because we want to find compatible numbers. For example, to estimate the answer in Example 5, $31.35 \div 3.8$, we can get a rough estimate of the answer by reasoning that 3.8 is close to 4 and 31.35 is close to 32. Therefore, our answer will be approximately $32 \div 4 = 8$.

6. Divide: 2.975 ÷ 35

Example 6   Divide and round to the nearest tenth: 2.184 ÷ 28

Solution   We will solve this problem like the others in this section:

$$
\begin{array}{r}
.078 \\
28\overline{)2.184} \\
-196 \\
\hline
224 \\
-224 \\
\hline
0
\end{array}
$$

Notice, the decimal point in the answer is directly above the decimal point in the problem. Also, the decimal point is followed by a 0 because 28 does not go into 21.

We can summarize division with decimal numbers by listing the following points, as illustrated in the previous examples.

SUMMARY Division with Decimals

1. We divide decimal numbers by the same process used to divide whole numbers. The decimal point in the answer is placed directly above the decimal point in the dividend.

2. We are free to write as many zeros after the last digit in a decimal number as we need.

3. If the divisor is a decimal, we can change it to a whole number by moving the decimal point to the right as many places as necessary so long as we move the decimal point in the dividend the same number of places.

B Dividing Decimal Numbers (Rounded Answers)

7. Divide, and round the answer to the nearest hundredth.

0.3849 ÷ 0.49

Example 7   Divide, and round the answer to the nearest hundredth.

$$0.3778 \div 0.25$$

Solution   First, we move the decimal point two places to the right.

$$0.25\overline{\smash{).}37.78}$$

Moving the decimal point two places in both the divisor and the dividend is justified like this:

$$\frac{0.3778 \times 100}{0.25 \times 100} = \frac{37.78}{25}$$

In the remaining examples we will move the decimal in the divisor to the right to change it to a whole number. We will also move the decimal in the dividend to the right the same number of places.

Answers
6. 0.085
7. 0.79

Then we divide, using long division.

$$
\begin{array}{r}
1.5112 \\
25\overline{)37.7800} \\
-25 \\
\hline
12\,7 \\
-12\,5 \\
\hline
28 \\
-25 \\
\hline
30 \\
-25 \\
\hline
50 \\
-50 \\
\hline
0
\end{array}
$$

Rounding to the nearest hundredth, we have 1.51. We actually did not need to have this many digits to round to the hundredths column. We could have stopped at the thousandths column and rounded off.

Example 8   Divide and round to the nearest tenth: $17 \div 0.03$.

Solution   Because we are rounding to the nearest tenth, we will continue dividing until we have a digit in the hundredths column. We don't have to go any further to round to the tenths column.

$$
\begin{array}{r}
5\,66.66 \\
0.03.\overline{)17.00.00} \\
-15 \\
\hline
20 \\
-18 \\
\hline
20 \\
-18 \\
\hline
20 \\
-18 \\
\hline
20 \\
-18 \\
\hline
2
\end{array}
$$

Rounding to the nearest tenth, we have 566.7.

C Applications

Example 9   If a man earning \$5.26 an hour receives a paycheck for \$170.95 before deductions, how many hours did he work?

Solution   To find the number of hours the man worked, we divide \$170.95 by \$5.26.

$$
\begin{array}{r}
32.5 \\
5.26.\overline{)170.95.0} \\
-157\,8 \\
\hline
13\,15 \\
-10\,52 \\
\hline
2\,63\,0 \\
-2\,63\,0 \\
\hline
0
\end{array}
$$

The man worked 32.5 hours.

8. Divide, and round to the nearest tenth.

$$19 \div 0.07$$

9. If you earn \$8.30 per hour and receive a paycheck for \$311.25 before deductions, how many hours did you work?

Answers

8. 271.4
9. 37.5 hours

10. Repeat Example 10 if the call costs $13.63.

Example 10   A telephone company charges $0.43 for the first minute and then $0.33 for each additional minute for calls made when outside the U.S. If a call costs $3.07, how many minutes was the call?

Solution   To solve this problem we need to find the number of additional minutes for the call. To do so, we first subtract the cost of the first minute from the total cost, and then we divide the result by the cost of each additional minute. Without showing the actual arithmetic involved, the solution looks like this:

$$\text{The number of additional minutes} = \frac{\overbrace{3.07}^{\text{Total cost of the call}} - \overbrace{0.43}^{\text{Cost of the first minute}}}{\underbrace{0.33}_{\text{Cost of each additional minute}}} = \frac{2.64}{0.33} = 8$$

The call was 9 minutes long. (The number 8 is the number of additional minutes past the first minute.)

DESCRIPTIVE STATISTICS

Grade Point Average

As a college student, your academic performance is often measured by your grade point average (GPA). This is a measure of your average letter grade over time. Assume you earn the following grades during your first semester:

Class	Units	Grade
Biology	5	C
Algebra	4	B
Psychology	3	B
Humanities	3	A

Let's calculate your GPA, which is a weighted average. To calculate your grade point average, you must first calculate the number of grade points you have earned in each class that you have completed. The number of grade points for a class is the product of the number of units the class is worth times the value of the grade received. The table below shows the value that is traditionally assigned to each grade.

Grade	Value
A	4
B	3
C	2
D	1
F	0

For example you earned a C in Biology, a 5-unit class, earning you 5 × 2 = 10 grade points. A grade of B in Algebra earned you 4 × 3 = 12 grade points. After finding the grade points for Psychology and Humanities, divide by the total number of units (5 + 4 + 3 + 3). Round your answer to the nearest tenth. This is your GPA for your first semester of college.

Answer

10. 41 minutes

Example 11   Below is a set of grades for a given semester. Calculate the student's GPA.

Solution   We begin by creating two more columns: one for the value of each grade (4 for an A, 3 for a B, 2 for a C, 1 for a D, and 0 for an F), and another for the grade points earned for each class. To fill in the grade points column, we multiply the number of units by the value of the grade.

Class	Units	Grade	Value	Grade Points
Algebra	5	B	3	$5 \times 3 = 15$
Chemistry	4	C	2	$4 \times 2 = 8$
English	3	A	4	$3 \times 4 = 12$
History	3	B	3	$3 \times 3 = 9$
Total Units	15			Total Grade Points: 44

To find her grade point average, we divide 44 by 15 and round (if necessary) to the nearest hundredth.

$$\text{Grade point average} = \frac{44}{15} = 2.93$$

11. Calculate the grade-point average.

Class	Units	Grade
Algebra	4	A
Biology	3	B
English	3	B
History	3	C
PE	1	A

KEY CONCEPT REVIEW

After reading through the preceding section, respond in your own words and in complete sentences.

A. The answer to the division problem in Example 1 is $298\frac{7}{10}$. Write this number in decimal notation.

B. In Example 4, we place a 0 at the end of a number without changing the value of the number. Why is the placement of this 0 helpful?

C. The expression $0.3778 \div 0.25$ is equivalent to the expression $37.78 \div 25$ because each number was multiplied by what?

D. Briefly explain how to divide with decimals.

Answer

11. 3.14

Spotlight on Success

A Message from the Author

Dear Student,

Now that you are close to finishing this course, I want to pass on a couple of things that have helped me a great deal with my career. I'll introduce each one with a quote:

Do something for the person you will be 5 years from now. I have always made sure that I arranged my life so that I was doing something for the person I would be 5 years later. For example, when I was 20 years old, I was in college. I imagined that the person I would be at 25 years old would want to have a college degree, so I made sure I stayed in school. That's all there is to this. It is not a hard, rigid philosophy. It is a soft, behind the scenes, foundation. It does not include ideas such as "Five years from now I'm going to graduate at the top of my class from the best college in the country." Instead, you think, "five years from now I will have a college degree, or I will still be in school working towards it."

This philosophy led to a community college teaching job, writing textbooks, doing videos with the textbooks, then to MathTV and the book you are reading right now. Along the way there were many other options and directions that I didn't take, but all the choices I had were due to keeping the person I would be in 5 years in mind.

It's easier to ride a horse in the direction it is going. I started my college career thinking that I would become a dentist. I enrolled in all the courses that were required for dental school. When I completed the courses, I applied to a number of dental schools, but wasn't accepted. I kept going to school, and applied again the next year, again, without success. My life was not going in the direction of dental school, even though I had worked hard to put it in that direction. So I did a little inventory of the classes I had taken and the grades I earned, and realized that I was doing well in mathematics. My life was actually going in that direction so I decided to see where that would take me. It was a good decision.

It is a good idea to work hard toward your goals, but it is also a good idea to take inventory every now and then to be sure you are headed in the direction that is best for you.

I wish you good luck with the rest of your college years, and with whatever you decide you want to do as a career.

Pat McKeague

EXERCISE SET 5.4 ....

Problems

A Perform each of the following divisions.

1. $394 \div 20$

2. $486 \div 30$

3. $248 \div 40$

4. $440 \div 80$

5. $5\overline{)26}$

6. $8\overline{)36}$

7. $25\overline{)276}$

8. $50\overline{)253}$

9. $28.8 \div 6$

10. $15.5 \div 5$

11. $-77.6 \div 8$

12. $-31.48 \div 4$

13. $35\overline{)92.05}$

14. $26\overline{)146.38}$

15. $45\overline{)190.8}$

16. $55\overline{)342.1}$

17. $86.7 \div 34$

18. $411.4 \div 44$

19. $29.7 \div (-22)$

20. $488.4 \div (-88)$

21. $4.5\overline{)29.25}$

22. $3.3\overline{)21.978}$

23. $0.11\overline{)1.089}$

24. $0.75\overline{)2.40}$

25. $2.3\overline{)0.115}$

26. $6.6\overline{)0.198}$

27. $0.012\overline{)0.11748}$

28. $0.052\overline{)0.23712}$

29. $-2.42 \div (-1.1)$

30. $-7.26 \div (-2.2)$

31. $0.8848 \div 0.014$

32. $9.652 \div 0.38$

B Carry out each of the following divisions only so far as needed to round the results to the nearest hundredth.

33. $26\overline{)35}$ **34.** $18\overline{)47}$ **35.** $3.3\overline{)56}$ **36.** $4.4\overline{)75}$

37. $0.1234 \div 0.5$ **38.** $-0.543 \div 2.1$ **39.** $19 \div 7$ **40.** $16 \div (-6)$

41. $0.059\overline{)0.69}$ **42.** $0.048\overline{)0.49}$ **43.** $1.99 \div 0.5$ **44.** $0.99 \div 0.5$

45. $2.99 \div 0.5$ **46.** $3.99 \div (-0.5)$ **47.** $-3.82 \div 0.9$ **48.** $1.79 \div 0.08$

C Solve the following application problems that involve operations with decimals.

49. Wages If you earn $49.50 for working 6 hours, how much do you earn per hour?

50. Wages How many hours does a person making $9.25 per hour have to work in order to earn $351.50?

51. Gas Mileage If a car travels 336 miles on 15 gallons of gas, how far will the car travel on 1 gallon of gas?

52. Gas Mileage If a car travels 392 miles on 16 gallons of gas, how far will the car travel on 1 gallon of gas?

53. Wages Suppose you earn $8.65 an hour for the first 36 hours you work in a week and then $12.98 an hour in overtime for each additional hour you work in the same week. If you make $376.30 in one week, how many hours did you work overtime?

54. Wages Suppose you earn $9.30 an hour for the first 36 hours you work in a week and then $13.15 an hour in overtime for each additional hour you work in the same week. If you make $440 in one week, how many hours did you work overtime?

55. Stocks Suppose a stockbroker charges buyers $7 when they purchase stocks. You want to purchase a stock that costs $7.15 per share. If you have $150 to invest, how many shares can you purchase?

56. Stocks Suppose a stockbroker charges buyers $8 when they purchase stocks. You want to purchase a stock that costs $12.25 per share. If you have $400 to invest, how many shares can you purchase?

Grade Point Average The following grades were earned by Steve during his first term in college. Use these data to answer Problems 57–60.

57. Calculate Steve's GPA.

58. If his grade in chemistry had been a B instead of a C, by how much would his GPA have increased?

59. If his grade in health had been a C instead of a B, by how much would his grade point average have dropped?

Class	Units	Grade
Basic mathematics	3	A
Health	2	B
History	3	B
English	3	C
Chemistry	4	C

60. If his grades in both English and chemistry had been Bs, what would his GPA have been?

Applying the Concepts

Evaluate each expression for $a = 3.8$.

61. $a \div 0.4$

62. $a \div 0.8$

63. $2.3 + 11.4 \div a$

64. $9.7 + 22.8 \div a$

Simplify each expression.

65. $\dfrac{54.28x}{23}$

66. $\dfrac{65.86x}{37}$

67. $\dfrac{2.48x}{1.6}$

68. $\dfrac{3.51x}{1.5}$

69. Hot Air Balloon Since the pilot of a hot air balloon can only control the balloon's altitude, he relies on the winds for travel. To ride on the jet streams, a hot air balloon must rise as high as 12 kilometers. Convert this to miles by dividing by 1.61. Round your answer to the nearest tenth of a mile.

70. Hot Air Balloon December and January are the best times for traveling in a hot-air balloon because the jet streams in the Northern Hemisphere are the strongest. They reach speeds of 400 kilometers per hour. Convert this to miles per hour by dividing by 1.61. Round to the nearest whole number.

71. Women's Golf The table below gives the top five earners for the Ladies' Professional Golf Association (LPGA) in 2016. Fill in the last column of the table by finding the average earning per tournament for each golfer.

Rank	Name	Number of Tournaments	Total Earnings	Average per Tournament
1.	Ariya Jutanugarn	28	$2,550,947	
2.	Lydia Ko	24	$2,493,059	
3.	Brooke M. Henderson	31	$1,724,420	
4.	In Gee Chun	19	$1,501,102	
5.	Shanshan Feng	21	$1,458,579	

72. Men's Golf The table below gives the top five earners for the men's Professional Golf Association (PGA) in 2016. Fill in the last column of the table by finding the average earnings per tournament for each golfer.

Rank	Name	Number of Tournaments	Total Earnings	Average per Tournament
1.	Dustin Johnson	24	$9,472,185	
2.	Jason Day	20	$8,045,112	
3.	Adam Scott	21	$6,590,590	
4.	Patrick Reed	32	$6,152,075	
5.	Rory McIlroy	19	$5,790,585	

Calculator Problems Work each of the following problems on your calculator. If rounding is necessary, round to the nearest hundred thousandth.

73. $7 \div 9$

74. $11 \div 13$

75. $243 \div 0.791$

76. $67.8 \div 37.92$

77. $0.0503 \div 0.0709$

78. $429.87 \div 16.925$

Getting Ready for the Next Section

Reduce to lowest terms.

79. $\dfrac{75}{100}$

80. $\dfrac{220}{1000}$

81. $\dfrac{12}{18}$

82. $\dfrac{15}{30}$

83. $\dfrac{75}{200}$

84. $\dfrac{220}{2000}$

85. $\dfrac{38}{100}$

86. $\dfrac{75}{1000}$

Write each fraction as an equivalent fraction with denominator 100.

87. $\dfrac{3}{5}$

88. $\dfrac{1}{2}$

89. $\dfrac{5}{1}$

90. $\dfrac{17}{20}$

Write each fraction as an equivalent fraction with denominator 15.

91. $\dfrac{4}{5}$

92. $\dfrac{2}{3}$

93. $\dfrac{4}{1}$

94. $\dfrac{2}{1}$

95. $\dfrac{6}{5}$

96. $\dfrac{7}{3}$

Divide.

97. $3 \div 4$

98. $3 \div 5$

99. $7 \div 8$

100. $3 \div 8$

FIND THE MISTAKE •

Each sentence below contains a mistake. Circle the mistake and write the correct word(s) or numbers(s) on the line provided.

1. The answer to the problem 25)‾70.75 will have a decimal point placed with four digits to its right. _____

2. To work the problem 27.468 ÷ 8.4, multiply 8.4 by 10 and then divide. _____

3. To divide 0.6778 by 0.54, multiply both numbers by 10 to move the decimal point two places to the right. _____

4. Samantha earns $10.16 an hour as a cashier. She received a paycheck for $309.88. To find out how many hours she worked, you must solve the problem 10.16 ÷ 309.88. _____

LANDMARK REVIEW: CHECKING YOUR PROGRESS • • • • • • • • • • • •

Write each of the following in words.

1. 1.15   **2.** 45.08   **3.** 0.005   **4.** 245.157

Write each of the following as a decimal number.

5. Sixty-seven ten thousandths   **6.** Five and six tenths   **7.** Twenty-three and fourteen thousandths   **8.** Two thousand thirteen and fifteen hundredths

Find each of the following sums and differences.

9. $24.13 + 4.15$ **10.** $6.000014 + 3.15$ **11.** $100.00001 + 24.1583$ **12.** $5.387 + 6.412$

13. $8.3 - 5.2$ **14.** $14.2 - 7.13$ **15.** $27.57 - 14.24$ **16.** $92.42 - 14.05$

Perform each of the following operations.

17. $4.735(10)$ **18.** $0.075(0.03)$ **19.** $1.4 ÷ 0.07$ **20.** $0.24 ÷ 0.6$

Perform the following operations according to the rule for order of operations.

21. $4.3(3.8 - 2.6)$ **22.** $(2.85 - 1.7)(5.67 + 4.2)$ **23.** $5.5 + 2.2(14 - 12.5)$ **24.** $(1.3)^2 + (5.1)^2 + (2.4)^2$

5.5

 FRACTIONS AND DECIMALS

• • OBJECTIVES • •

A Convert between fractions and decimals.

B Simplify expressions involving both fractions and decimals.

• • • KEY WORDS • • •

convert

VIDEO EXAMPLES

SECTION 5.5

Practice Problems

1. Write $\frac{5}{8}$ as a decimal.

If you are shopping for clothes and a store has a sale advertising $\frac{1}{3}$ off the regular price, how much can you expect to pay for a pair of pants that normally sells for $31.95? If the sale price of the pants is $22.30, have they really been marked down by $\frac{1}{3}$? To answer questions like these, we need to know how to solve problems that involve fractions and decimals together.

We begin this section by showing how to convert back and forth between fractions and decimals.

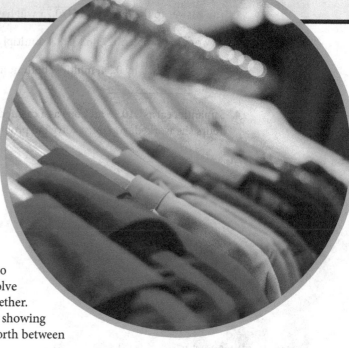

A Converting Fractions to Decimals

You may recall that the notation we use for fractions can be interpreted as implying division. That is, the fraction $\frac{3}{4}$ can be thought of as meaning "3 divided by 4." We can use this idea to convert fractions to decimals.

Example 1 Write $\frac{3}{4}$ as a decimal.

Solution Dividing 3 by 4, we have

$$
\begin{array}{r}
.75 \\
4\overline{)3.00} \\
-28 \\
\hline
20 \\
-20 \\
\hline
0
\end{array}
$$

The fraction $\frac{3}{4}$ is equal to the decimal 0.75.

• •

This will be our general approach to converting fractions to decimals. We will write the fraction using division and then long divide. The numerator will always be the dividend and the denominator will be the divisor. Let's look at two more examples.

Answer

1. 0.625

368

Example 2   Write $\frac{7}{12}$ as a decimal rounded to the thousandths place.

Solution   Because we want the decimal to be rounded to the thousandths place, we divide to the ten thousandths place and round off to the thousandths place.

$$
\begin{array}{r}
.5833 \\
12\overline{)7.0000} \\
-6\,0 \\
\hline
1\,00 \\
-96 \\
\hline
40 \\
-36 \\
\hline
40 \\
-36 \\
\hline
4
\end{array}
$$

Rounding off to the thousandths place, we have 0.583. Because $\frac{7}{12}$ is not exactly the same as 0.583, we write

$$\frac{7}{12} \approx 0.583$$

where the symbol $\approx$ is read "is approximately equal to."

If we wrote more zeros after 0.583 in Example 2, the pattern of 3s would continue for as many places as we choose to divide. When we get a sequence of digits that repeat like this, 0.58333 . . . , we can indicate the repetition by writing

$$0.58\overline{3}$$ *The bar over the 3 indicates that the 3 repeats from there on.*

Example 3   Write $\frac{3}{11}$ as a decimal.

Solution   Dividing 3 by 11, we have

$$
\begin{array}{r}
.272727 \\
11\overline{)3.000000} \\
-2\,2 \\
\hline
80 \\
-77 \\
\hline
30 \\
-22 \\
\hline
80 \\
-77 \\
\hline
30 \\
-22 \\
\hline
80 \\
-77 \\
\hline
3
\end{array}
$$

No matter how long we continue the division, the remainder will never be 0, and the pattern will continue. We write the decimal form of $\frac{3}{11}$ as $0.\overline{27}$, where

$$0.\overline{27} = 0.272727 . . .$$ *The dots mean "and so on."*

Converting Decimals to Fractions

To convert decimals to fractions, we take advantage of the place values we assigned to the digits to the right of the decimal point.

2. Write $\frac{5}{7}$ as a decimal rounded to the thousandths place.

3. Write $\frac{5}{6}$ as a decimal.

Note   The bar over the 2 and the 7 in $0.\overline{27}$ is used to indicate that the pattern repeats itself indefinitely.

Answers

2. 0.714

3. $0.8\overline{3}$

4. Write 0.76 as a fraction in lowest terms.

Example 4   Write 0.38 as a fraction in lowest terms.

Solution   0.38 is 38 hundredths, or

$$0.38 = \frac{38}{100}$$

$$= \frac{19}{50} \qquad \textit{Reduce to lowest terms by dividing the numerator and denominator by 2.}$$

The decimal 0.38 is equal to the fraction $\frac{19}{50}$.

We could check our work here by converting $\frac{19}{50}$ back to a decimal. We do this by dividing 19 by 50. That is,

$$
\begin{array}{r}
.38 \\
50\overline{)19.00} \\
-15\,0 \\
\hline
4\,00 \\
-4\,00 \\
\hline
0
\end{array}
$$

5. Convert 0.045 to a fraction.

Example 5   Convert 0.075 to a fraction.

Solution   We have 75 thousandths, or

$$0.075 = \frac{75}{1000}$$

$$= \frac{3}{40} \qquad \textit{Reduce to lowest terms by dividing the numerator and denominator by 25.}$$

6. Write 12.08 as a mixed number.

Example 6   Write 15.6 as a mixed number.

Solution   Converting 0.6 to a fraction, we have

$$0.6 = \frac{6}{10} = \frac{3}{5} \qquad \textit{Reduce to lowest terms.}$$

Since $0.6 = \frac{3}{5}$, we have $15.6 = 15\frac{3}{5}$.

B Problems Containing Both Fractions and Decimals

We continue this section by working some problems that involve both fractions and decimals. Remember, when simplifying expressions with multiple operations, we need to follow the order of operations.

7. Simplify: $\frac{12}{25}(1.41 - 0.56)$

Example 7   Simplify: $\frac{19}{50}(1.32 + 0.48)$

Solution   In Example 4, we found that $0.38 = \frac{19}{50}$. Therefore, we can rewrite the problem as

$$\frac{19}{50}(1.32 + 0.48) = 0.38(1.32 + 0.48) \qquad \textit{Convert all numbers to decimals.}$$

$$= 0.38(1.80) \qquad \textit{Add: 1.32 + 0.48}$$

$$= 0.684 \qquad \textit{Multiply: 0.38 × 1.80}$$

Answers

4. $\frac{19}{25}$

5. $\frac{9}{200}$

6. $12\frac{2}{25}$

7. 0.408

Example 8　Simplify: $\frac{1}{2} + (0.75)\left(\frac{2}{5}\right)$

Solution　We could do this problem one of two different ways. First, we could convert all fractions to decimals and then simplify.

$$\frac{1}{2} + (0.75)\left(\frac{2}{5}\right) = 0.5 + 0.75(0.4) \qquad \textit{Convert to decimals.}$$

$$= 0.5 + 0.300 \qquad \textit{Multiply: } 0.75 \times 0.4$$

$$= 0.8 \qquad \textit{Add.}$$

Or, we could convert 0.75 to $\frac{3}{4}$ and then simplify.

$$\frac{1}{2} + (0.75)\left(\frac{2}{5}\right) = \frac{1}{2} + \frac{3}{4}\left(\frac{2}{5}\right) \qquad \textit{Convert decimals to fractions.}$$

$$= \frac{1}{2} + \frac{3}{10} \qquad \textit{Multiply. Reduce to lowest terms.}$$

$$= \frac{5}{10} + \frac{3}{10} \qquad \textit{The common denominator is 10.}$$

$$= \frac{8}{10} \qquad \textit{Add numerators.}$$

$$= \frac{4}{5} \qquad \textit{Reduce to lowest terms.}$$

The answers are equivalent. That is, $0.8 = \frac{8}{10} = \frac{4}{5}$. Either of these methods can be used with problems of this type.

8. Simplify: $\frac{3}{4} + \frac{2}{3}(0.66)$

Note　At first it may be difficult to determine whether you should convert the problem to decimals or fractions. Often it's best to use whichever method you're comfortable with. Also, sometimes the directions will indicate which method should be used.

Example 9　Simplify: $\left(\frac{1}{2}\right)^3 (2.4) + \left(\frac{1}{4}\right)^2 (3.2)$

Solution　In this problem we will show how an expression can sometimes be simplified without any conversions between fractions and decimals. To begin, we evaluate all numbers that contain exponents. Then we multiply. After that, we add.

$$\left(\frac{1}{2}\right)^3 (2.4) + \left(\frac{1}{4}\right)^2 (3.2) = \frac{1}{8}(2.4) + \frac{1}{16}(3.2) \qquad \textit{Evaluate exponents.}$$

$$= \frac{2.4}{8} + \frac{3.2}{16} \qquad \textit{Multiply.}$$

$$= 0.3 + 0.2 \qquad \textit{Divide.}$$

$$= 0.5 \qquad \textit{Add.}$$

9. Simplify: $\left(\frac{1}{3}\right)^2 (0.81) + \left(\frac{1}{2}\right)^3 (1.2)$

Applications

Example 10　If a shirt that normally sells for $27.99 is on sale for $\frac{1}{3}$ off, what is the sale price of the shirt?

Solution　To find out how much the shirt is marked down, we must find $\frac{1}{3}$ of 27.99. That is, we multiply $\frac{1}{3}$ and 27.99, which is the same as dividing 27.99 by 3.

$$\frac{1}{3}(27.99) = \frac{27.99}{3} = 9.33$$

The shirt is marked down $9.33. The sale price is $9.33 less than the original price.

$$\text{Sale price} = 27.99 - 9.33 = 18.66$$

The sale price is $18.66.

10. A pair of jeans that normally sell for $38.60 are on sale for $\frac{1}{4}$ off. What is the sale price of the jeans?

Note　We also could have solved this problem by simply multiplying the original price by $\frac{2}{3}$, since, if the shirt is marked $\frac{1}{3}$ off, then the sale price must be $\frac{2}{3}$ of the original price. Multiplying by $\frac{2}{3}$ is the same as dividing by 3 and then multiplying by 2. The answer would be the same.

Answers

8. 1.19
9. 0.24
10. $28.95

KEY CONCEPT REVIEW

After reading through the preceding section, respond in your own words and in complete sentences.

A. To convert fractions to decimals, do we multiply or divide the numerator by the denominator?

B. The decimal 0.13 is equivalent to what fraction?

C. Write 36 thousandths in decimal form and in fraction form.

D. Explain how to write the fraction $\frac{84}{1000}$ in lowest terms.

Spotlight on Success

GORDON, student instructor

Math takes time. This fact holds true in the smallest of math problems as much as it does in the most math-intensive careers. I see proof in each video I make. My videos get progressively better with each take, though I still make mistakes and find aspects I can improve on with each new video. In order to keep trying to improve in spite of any failures or lack of improvement, something else is needed. For me it is the sense of a specific goal in sight, to help me maintain the desire to put in continued time and effort.

When I decided on the number one university I wanted to attend, I wrote the name of that school in bold block letters on my door, written to remind myself daily of my ultimate goal. Stuck in the back of my head, this end result pushed me little by little to succeed and meet all of the requirements for the university I had in mind. And now I can say I'm at my dream school bringing with me that skill.

I recognize that others may have much more difficult circumstances than my own to endure, with the goal of improving or escaping those circumstances, and I deeply respect that. But that fact demonstrates to me how easy but effective it is, in comparison, to "stay with the problems longer" with a goal in mind of something much more easily realized, like a good grade on a test. I've learned to set goals, small or big, and to stick with them until they are realized.

Problems

A Each circle below is divided into 8 equal parts. The number below each circle indicates what fraction of the circle is shaded. Convert each fraction to a decimal.

1.

$\dfrac{1}{8}$

2.

$\dfrac{3}{8}$

3.

$\dfrac{5}{8}$

4.

$\dfrac{7}{8}$

Complete the following tables by converting each fraction to a decimal.

5.

Fraction	$\frac{1}{5}$	$\frac{2}{5}$	$\frac{3}{5}$	$\frac{4}{5}$	$\frac{5}{5}$
Decimal					

6.

Fraction	$\frac{1}{6}$	$\frac{2}{6}$	$\frac{3}{6}$	$\frac{4}{6}$	$\frac{5}{6}$	$\frac{6}{6}$
Decimal						

Convert each of the following fractions to a decimal.

7. $\dfrac{1}{2}$

8. $-\dfrac{12}{25}$

9. $\dfrac{14}{25}$

10. $\dfrac{14}{32}$

11. $-\dfrac{18}{32}$

12. $\dfrac{9}{16}$

13. $-\dfrac{21}{5}$

14. $-\dfrac{13}{8}$

Write each fraction as a decimal rounded to the hundredths place.

15. $\dfrac{12}{13}$

16. $\dfrac{17}{19}$

17. $-\dfrac{5}{11}$

18. $-\dfrac{6}{17}$

19. $\dfrac{3}{28}$

20. $\dfrac{2}{23}$

21. $-\dfrac{12}{43}$

22. $-\dfrac{15}{51}$

Complete the following table by converting each decimal to a fraction.

23.

Decimal	0.125	0.250	0.375	0.500	0.625	0.750	0.875
Fraction							

24.

Decimal	0.1	0.2	0.3	0.4	0.5	0.6	0.7	0.8	0.9
Fraction									

Write each decimal as a fraction in lowest terms.

25. 0.15   **26.** 0.45   **27.** −0.08   **28.** −0.06   **29.** 0.375   **30.** 0.475

Write each decimal as a mixed number.

31. 5.6   **32.** 8.4   **33.** 5.06   **34.** 8.04   **35.** −1.22   **36.** −2.11

B Simplify each of the following as much as possible, and write all answers as decimals.

37. $\frac{1}{2}(2.3 + 2.5)$

38. $\frac{3}{4}(1.8 + 7.6)$

39. $\dfrac{1.99}{\frac{1}{2}}$

40. $\dfrac{2.99}{\frac{1}{2}}$

41. $3.4 - \frac{1}{2}(0.76)$

42. $6.7 - \frac{1}{5}(0.45)$

43. $\frac{2}{5}(0.3) + \frac{3}{5}(0.3)$

44. $\frac{1}{8}(0.7) + \frac{3}{8}(0.7)$

45. $6\left(\frac{3}{5}\right)(0.02)$

46. $8\left(\frac{4}{5}\right)(0.03)$

47. $\frac{5}{8} + 0.35\left(\frac{1}{2}\right)$

48. $\frac{7}{8} + 0.45\left(\frac{3}{4}\right)$

49. $\left(\frac{1}{3}\right)^2(5.4) + \left(\frac{1}{2}\right)^3(3.2)$

50. $\left(\frac{1}{5}\right)^2(7.5) + \left(\frac{1}{4}\right)^2(6.4)$

51. $(0.25)^2 + \left(\frac{1}{4}\right)^2(3)$

52. $(0.75)^2 + \left(\frac{1}{4}\right)^2(7)$

Paying Attention to Instructions Find each of the following. Carefully read the directions to help you select the appropriate operation.

53. **a.** Find the sum of $\frac{1}{3}$ and 0.75.

  b. Find the difference of $\frac{1}{3}$ and 0.75.

  c. Find the product of $\frac{1}{3}$ and 0.75.

  d. Find the quotient of $\frac{1}{3}$ and 0.75.

54. **a.** Find the sum of $-\frac{1}{2}$ and 1.5.

  b. Find the difference of $-\frac{1}{2}$ and 1.5.

  c. Find the product of $-\frac{1}{2}$ and 1.5.

  d. Find the quotient of $-\frac{1}{2}$ and 1.5.

Applying the Concepts

55. Price of Beef If each pound of beef costs $2.59, how much does $3\frac{1}{4}$ pounds cost?

56. Price of Gasoline What does it cost to fill a $15\frac{1}{2}$-gallon gas tank if the gasoline is priced at 305.2¢ per gallon? Convert your answer to dollars.

57. Sale Price A dress that costs $57.36 is on sale for $\frac{1}{4}$ off. What is the sale price of the dress?

58. Sale Price A suit that normally sells for $121 is on sale for $\frac{1}{4}$ off. What is the sale price of the suit?

59. Perimeter of the Sierpinski Triangle The diagram shows one stage of what is known as the Sierpinski triangle. Each triangle in the diagram has three equal sides. The large triangle is made up of 4 smaller triangles. If each side of the large triangle is 2 inches, and each side of the smaller triangles is 1 inch, what is the perimeter of the shaded region?

60. Perimeter of the Sierpinski Triangle The diagram shows another stage of the Sierpinski triangle. Each triangle in the diagram has three equal sides. The largest triangle is made up of a number of smaller triangles. If each side of the large triangle is 2 inches, and each side of the smallest triangles is 0.5 inch, what is the perimeter of the shaded region?

61. Average Gain in Stock Price The table below shows the amount of gain each day of one week for the price of a stock. Complete the table by converting each fraction to a decimal and rounding to the nearest hundredth if necessary.

Change in Stock Price		
Day	Gain ($)	As a Decimal ($) (to the nearest hundredth)
Monday	$\frac{3}{5}$	
Tuesday	$\frac{1}{2}$	
Wednesday	$\frac{1}{25}$	
Thursday	$\frac{1}{5}$	
Friday	$\frac{1}{10}$	

62. Average Gain in Stock Price The table below shows the amount of gain each day of one week for the price of a stock. Complete the table by converting each fraction to a decimal and rounding to the nearest hundredth, if necessary.

Change in Stock Price		
Day	Gain	As a Decimal ($) (to the nearest hundredth)
Monday	$\frac{3}{10}$	
Tuesday	$\frac{3}{50}$	
Wednesday	$\frac{2}{25}$	
Thursday	$\frac{1}{10}$	
Friday	0	

63. **Nutrition** If 1 ounce of ground beef contains 50.75 calories and 1 ounce of halibut contains 27.5 calories, what is the difference in calories between a $4\frac{1}{2}$-ounce serving of ground beef and a $4\frac{1}{2}$-ounce serving of halibut?

64. **Nutrition** If a 1-ounce serving of baked potato contains 48.3 calories and a 1-ounce serving of chicken contains 24.6 calories, how many calories are in a meal of $5\frac{1}{4}$ ounces of chicken and a $3\frac{1}{3}$-ounce baked potato?

Taxi Ride The Texas Junior College Teachers Association annual conference was held in Austin, Texas. At that time, a taxi ride in Austin was $1.25 for the first $\frac{1}{5}$ of a mile and $0.25 for each additional $\frac{1}{5}$ of a mile. The charge for a taxi to wait is $12.00 per hour. Use this information for Problems 65 through 68.

65. If the distance from one of the convention hotels to the airport is 7.5 miles, how much will it cost to take a taxi from that hotel to the airport?

66. If you were to tip the driver of the taxi in Problem 65 $1.50, how much would it cost to take a taxi from the hotel to the airport?

67. Suppose the distance from one of the hotels to one of the western dance clubs in Austin is 12.4 miles. If the fare meter in the taxi gives the charge for that trip as $16.50, is the meter working correctly?

68. Suppose that the distance from a hotel to the airport is 8.2 miles, and the ride takes 20 minutes. Is it more expensive to take a taxi to the airport or to just sit in the taxi?

Getting Ready for the Next Section

69. Add: $8.7 + 3.5$

70. Divide: $-3.32 \div 4$

71. Multiply: $2(6.4)$

72. Add: $-0.89 + (-0.61)$

73. Multiply: $100(1.18x + 0.24)$

74. Multiply: $100(0.84x - 0.78)$

75. Divide: $14.40 \div 0.16$

76. Simplify: $0.05x + 0.10(x + 7)$

77. Add: $104.89 + (-49.99)$

78. Divide: $54.90 \div 0.45$

FIND THE MISTAKE •

Each sentence below contains a mistake. Circle the mistake and write the correct word(s) or numbers(s) on the line provided.

1. The correct way to write $\frac{6}{11}$ as a decimal is 0.54.... _____

2. Writing 14.3 as a fraction gives us $14 \cdot \frac{3}{10} = \frac{42}{10} = \frac{21}{5}$. _____

3. The simplified answer to the problem $\frac{12}{45(0.256 + 0.14)}$ contains both fractions and decimals. _____

4. Simplifying the problem $\left(\frac{3}{2}\right)(0.5) + \left(\frac{1}{2}\right)^2(6.7)$ by first converting all decimals to fractions gives us $\left(\frac{3}{2}\right)\left(\frac{1}{2}\right) + \left(\frac{1}{2}\right)^2\left(\frac{67}{100}\right)$. _____

EQUATIONS WITH DECIMALS

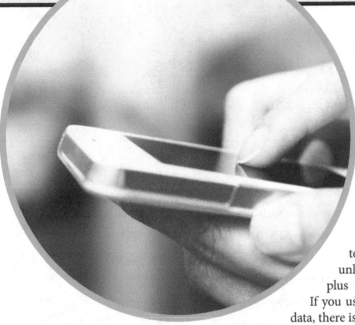

Cell phone providers offer several different monthly plans. Your choice of plan depends on how much time you spend talking, how many text messages you send, and how much data you typically use.

For $49.99 per month (excluding taxes and service charges), you can get unlimited minutes to make phone calls and unlimited texting capabilities plus 2,000 megabytes of data. If you use more than your allotted data, there is a charge of 10¢ per megabyte, for every megabyte over 2,000 used. If you receive a bill for $104.89, by how many megabytes did you exceed your allowance? To answer questions like this, we need to be able to solve equations containing decimals.

OBJECTIVES

A   Solve equations containing decimals.

B   Solve applications involving equations containing decimals.

VIDEO EXAMPLES

SECTION 5.6

A Solving Equations Containing Decimals

Example 1   Solve the equation $x - 3.5 = 8.7$.

Solution We use the addition property of equality to add 3.5 to each side of the equation.

$$x - 3.5 = 8.7$$
$$x - 3.5 + 3.5 = 8.7 + 3.5 \qquad \text{Add 3.5 to each side.}$$
$$x = 12.2$$

Example 2   Solve: $4y = -3.32$

Solution   We use the division property of equality to divide each side of the equation by 4.

$$4y = -3.32$$
$$\frac{4y}{4} = \frac{-3.32}{4} \qquad \text{Divide each side by 4.}$$
$$y = -0.83$$

Practice Problems

1. Solve the equation $x - 4.7 = 9.9$.

2. Solve: $3y = -6.93$

Answers
1. $x = 14.6$
2. $y = -2.31$

3. Solve: $\frac{1}{3}x - 4.38 = 8.42$

Example 3   Solve: $\frac{1}{2}x - 2.59 = 3.81$

Solution   We will solve for x using the addition property of equality and multiplication property of equality.

$$\frac{1}{2}x - 2.59 = 3.81$$

$$\frac{1}{2}x - 2.59 + 2.59 = 3.81 + 2.59 \qquad \text{Add 2.59 to both sides.}$$

$$\frac{1}{2}x = 6.4$$

$$2\left(\frac{1}{2}x\right) = 2(6.4) \qquad \text{Multiply each side by 2.}$$

$$x = 12.8$$

4. Solve: $4a + 0.73 = -2a - 1.22$

Example 4   Solve: $7a + 0.61 = -5a - 0.89$

Solution   We will start by moving the variables to one side of the equation.

$$7a + 0.61 = -5a - 0.89$$

$$7a + 5a + 0.61 = -5a + 5a - 0.89 \qquad \text{Add 5a to both sides.}$$

$$12a + 0.61 = -0.89$$

$$12a + 0.61 - 0.61 = -0.89 - 0.61 \qquad \text{Subtract 0.61 from both sides.}$$

$$12a = -1.50$$

$$\frac{12a}{12} = \frac{-1.50}{12} \qquad \text{Divide each side by 12.}$$

$$a = -0.125 \qquad -1.50 \div 12 = -0.125$$

Previously, our approach to solving equations involving fractions was to first multiply by the least common denominator in order to clear the equation of fractions. If you prefer to work with integers rather than decimals, you can do the same thing with equations involving decimals. We simply use the multiplication property of equality to multiply by the power of 10 (10, 100, 1,000, and so on) that will clear the equation of decimals.

5. Solve: $2.44x + 0.48 = 1.28x - 0.6$

Example 5   Solve: $1.18x + 0.24 = 0.84x - 0.78$

Solution   This time we begin by clearing the equation of decimals. Because multiplying each decimal by 100 would result in integer values, we will multiply each side of the equation by 100.

$$100(1.18x + 0.24) = 100(0.84x - 0.78) \qquad \text{Multiply each side by 100.}$$

$$118x + 24 = 84x - 78 \qquad \text{Apply the distributive property.}$$

$$118x - 84x + 24 = 84x - 84x - 78 \qquad \text{Subtract 84x from both sides.}$$

$$34x + 24 - 24 = -78 - 24 \qquad \text{Subtract 24 from both sides.}$$

$$34x = -102 \qquad \text{Simplify.}$$

$$x = -3 \qquad \text{Divide both sides by 34.}$$

Answers

3. $x = 38.4$

4. $a = -0.325$

5. $x = -1$

B Application Problems Involving Decimals

As a guide to solving this application problem and the ones that follow, we use the Blueprint for Problem Solving that we developed in Chapter 3.

BLUEPRINT FOR PROBLEM SOLVING

Step 1: *Read* the problem, and then mentally *list* the items that are known and the items that are unknown.

Step 2: *Assign a variable to* one of the unknown items. Then *translate the other information* in the problem to expressions involving the variables.

Step 3: *Reread* the problem, and then *write an equation,* using the items and the variable listed in Steps 1 and 2.

Step 4: *Solve the equation* found in Step 3.

Step 5: *Write* your *answer* using a complete sentence.

Step 6: *Reread* the problem, and *check* your solution with the original words in the problem. *Verify* that your answer makes sense.

Example 6 A car rental company charges $11 per day and 16 cents per mile for their cars. If a car were rented for 1 day and the charge was $25.40, how many miles was the car driven?

Solution

Step 1 *Read and list.*

> *Known items:* Charges are $11 per day and 16 cents per mile. Car is rented for 1 day. Total charge is $25.40.

> *Unknown items:* How many miles the car was driven

Step 2 *Assign a variable and translate information.* If we let x represent the number of miles driven, then the charge for the number of miles driven will be $0.16x$, the cost per mile times the number of miles.

Step 3 *Reread and write an equation.* To find the total cost to rent the car, we add 11 to $0.16x$. Here is the equation that describes the situation:

$$\underbrace{\substack{\$11 \text{ per} \\ \text{day}}}_{11} \; + \; \underbrace{\substack{16 \text{ cents} \\ \text{per mile}}}_{0.16x} \; = \; \underbrace{\text{Total cost}}_{25.40}$$

Step 4 *Solve the equation.* To solve the equation, we subtract 11 from each side and then divide each side by 0.16.

$$11 - 11 + 0.16x = 25.40 - 11 \qquad \text{Subtract 11 from each side.}$$
$$0.16x = 14.40$$
$$\frac{0.16x}{0.16} = \frac{14.40}{0.16} \qquad \text{Divide each side by 0.16.}$$
$$x = 90$$

Step 5 *Write the answer.* The car was driven 90 miles.

Step 6 *Reread and check.* The charge for 1 day is $11, and driving 90 miles adds $90(\$0.16) = \$14.40$ to the 1-day charge. Adding these values together makes the total $\$11 + \$14.40 = \$25.40$, which checks with the total charge given in the problem.

6. A car rental company charges $29.95 per day and 11 cents per mile for their cars. If a car were rented for 1 day and the charge was $42.27, how many miles was the car driven?

Answer

6. 112 miles

7. Fred has $1.20 in dimes and nickels. If he has 9 more nickels than dimes, how many of each coin does he have?

Example 7   Diane has $1.60 in dimes and nickels. If she has 7 more dimes than nickels, how many of each coin does she have?

Solution

Step 1 *Read and list.*

> Known items: Diane has dimes and nickels. There are 7 more dimes than nickels, and the total value of the coins is $1.60.
> Unknown items: How many of each type of coin Diane has

Step 2 *Assign a variable and translate information.* We let x represent the number of nickels. Because Diane has 7 more dimes than nickels, the number of dimes must be $x + 7$. Because each nickel is worth 5 cents, the amount of money she has in nickels is $0.05x$. Similarly, because each dime is worth 10 cents, the amount of money she has in dimes is $0.10(x + 7)$. Here is a table that summarizes what we have so far:

	Nickels	Dimes
Number of	x	$x + 7$
Value of	$0.05x$	$0.10(x + 7)$

Step 3 *Reread and write an equation.* Because the total value of all the coins is $1.60, the equation that describes this situation is

Amount of money in nickels	+	Amount of money in dimes	=	Total amount of money
$0.05x$	+	$0.10(x + 7)$	=	1.60

Step 4 *Solve the equation.* This time, let's show only the essential steps in the solution.

$$0.05x + 0.10x + 0.70 = 1.60 \qquad \text{Apply the distributive property.}$$
$$0.15x + 0.70 = 1.60 \qquad \text{Combine like terms.}$$
$$0.15x = 0.90 \qquad \text{Subtract 0.70 from each side.}$$
$$x = 6 \qquad \text{Divide each side by 0.15.}$$

Step 5 *Write the answer.* Because x represents the number of nickels and we found that $x = 6$, Diane has 6 nickels. To find the number of dimes, we add 7 to the number of nickels (she has 7 more dimes than nickels). The number of dimes is $6 + 7 = 13$.

Step 6 *Reread and check.* Here is a check of our results.

$$\begin{aligned} 6 \text{ nickels are worth } 6(\$0.05) &= \$0.30 \\ 13 \text{ dimes are worth } 13(\$0.10) &= \$1.30 \end{aligned}$$

> The total value is $1.60

Note We could also begin Step 4 by multiplying both sides by 100 to clear the equation of decimals, as we did in Example 5.

Example 8   A cell phone service provider charges $49.99 a month for a plan with unlimited calling and texting, plus 2,000 megabytes of data. If you use more than this allotted data, there is a charge of 10¢ per megabyte over 2,000 used. If a customer receives a bill for $104.89, by how many megabytes of data did he exceed his allowance?

Solution

Step 1 *Read and list.*

Known items: Charge is $49.99 a month plus $0.10 for each megabyte over 2,000. Bill is for 1 month. Total bill is $104.89.

Unknown items: How many extra megabytes of data were used

Step 2 *Assign a variable and translate information.* If we let x equal the number of megabytes of data over 2,000, then the charge for the extra megabytes will be $0.10x$, the cost per megabyte times the number of additional megabytes used.

Step 3 *Reread and write an equation.* To find the total monthly bill, we add 49.99 to $0.10x$. Here is the equation that describes the situation.

$49.99 per month	$+$	$0.10 per extra megabyte	$=$	Total monthly bill
49.99	$+$	$0.10x$	$=$	104.89

Step 4 *Solve the equation.* To solve the equation, we subtract 49.99 from each side and then divide each side by 0.10.

$$49.99 - 49.99 + 0.10x = 104.89 - 49.99 \qquad \text{Subtract 49.99 from each side.}$$

$$0.10x = 54.90$$

$$\frac{0.10x}{0.10} = \frac{54.90}{0.10} \qquad \text{Divide each side by 0.10.}$$

$$x = 549 \qquad 54.90 \div 0.10 = 549$$

Step 5 *Write the answer.* The customer used 549 extra megabytes of data.

Step 6 *Reread and check.* The charge for 1 month is $49.99. The 549 extra megabytes add $0.10(549) = $54.90 to the monthly charge. The total is $49.99 + $54.90 = $104.89, which checks with the total bill given in the problem.

KEY CONCEPT REVIEW

After reading through the preceding section, respond in your own words and in complete sentences.

A. Why should we multiply both sides of the equation in Example 5 by 100 and not 10?

B. Repeat Example 1, but multiply both sides of the original equation by 10 for your first step. Does your answer match the answer shown in Example 1?

C. If x is the number of nickels in a cash register, how can we represent the value of those nickels?

D. If it costs $0.45 a minute to talk on your cell phone, write an expression representing the charge for talking x minutes.

8. A cell phone service provider charges $69.99 a month for unlimited texting and data and 1,000 voice minutes. The cost is $0.09 for each minute of talking over that number. If the customer receives a bill for $101.22, by how many minutes did she exceed her allowance?

Answer

8. 347 minutes

EXERCISE SET 5.6 ···

Problems

A Solve each equation.

1. $x - 2.9 = 7.8$

2. $x - 0.47 = 0.65$

3. $x + 4.6 = 3.5$

4. $x + 21.2 = -5.6$

5. $-6n = 2.4$

6. $5n = -3.8$

7. $4n = 15.2$

8. $7n = 0.56$

9. $0.4x = 0.28$

10. $-0.8x = -0.72$

11. $-0.02x = 0.36$

12. $0.5x = -0.08$

13. $2y + 2.7 = 9.3$

14. $-3y - 8.2 = 5.6$

15. $\frac{1}{2}x + 3.9 = 2.6$

16. $-\frac{2}{3}x + 4.88 = 5.66$

17. $-\frac{1}{5}x + 3.54 = -5.46$

18. $\frac{1}{4}x - 0.06 = -0.02$

19. $8a - 2.5 = 5a - 5.8$

20. $-4a + 4.33 = -6a + 5.63$

21. $0.1y + 0.5(y - 10) = 2.5$

22. $0.6y - 0.1(y + 20) = 11$

23. $-0.07x + 0.03(x + 4,000) = 320$

24. $0.03x + 0.12(x - 6,000) = -270$

For Problems 25-28, solve each equation using the technique illustrated in Example 5 of this section.

25. $0.5x - 1.2 = 0.3x + 4.5$

26. $1.35x + 0.88 = -2.15x - 0.87$

27. $0.75x - 1.37 = 0.42x - 0.05$

28. $1.8x + 0.7 = 1.1x - 1.4$

B Applying the Concepts

29. Car Rental A car rental company charges $10 a day and 16 cents per mile for their cars. If a car was rented for 1 day for a total charge of $23.92, how many miles was it driven?

30. Car Rental A car rental company charges $12 a day and 18 cents per mile to rent their cars. If the total charge for a 1-day rental were $33.78, how many miles was the car driven?

31. Car Rental A rental company charges $9 per day and 15 cents a mile for their cars. If a car was rented for 2 days for a total charge of $40.05, how many miles was it driven?

32. Car Rental A car rental company charges $11 a day and 18 cents per mile to rent their cars. If the total charge for a 2-day rental were $61.60, how many miles was it driven?

33. Coin Problem Mary has $2.20 in dimes and nickels. If she has 10 more dimes than nickels, how many of each coin does she have?

34. Coin Problem Bob has $1.65 in dimes and nickels. If he has 9 more nickels than dimes, how many of each coin does he have?

35. Coin Problem Suppose you have $9.60 in dimes and quarters. How many of each coin do you have if you have twice as many quarters as dimes?

36. Coin Problem A collection of dimes and quarters has a total value of $2.75. If there are 3 times as many dimes as quarters, how many of each coin is in the collection?

37. Cell Phone Plan Jay signed up for a monthly cell phone plan that costs $39.99 for unlimited texting, calls, and 2,500 megabytes of data. For each additional megabyte of data he uses, there is a charge of 5¢. If his most recent bill was for $54.99, how many additional megabytes of data did he use?

38. Cell Phone Plan Monica has a cell phone plan that costs $55.99 for unlimited texting, calls, and 4,200 megabytes of data. For each additional megabyte of data she uses, there is a charge of 15¢. If her most recent bill was for $175.99, how many additional megabytes of data did she use?

39. Airport Parking Airport parking costs $4.99 for each of the first two hours and then $3.80 for each additional hour. If the total bill was $21.38, how long were you parked at the airport?

40. Bowling Bowling by the hour costs $24.16 for the first hour and then $16.28 for each additional hour. If the total bill was $56.72, how long did you and your friends bowl?

Getting Ready for the Next Section

Expand and simplify.

41. 6^2

42. 8^2

43. 5^2

44. 10^2

45. 5^3

46. 2^5

47. 3^2

48. 2^3

49. $\left(\dfrac{1}{3}\right)^4$

50. $\left(\dfrac{3}{4}\right)^3$

51. $\left(\dfrac{5}{6}\right)^2$

52. $\left(\dfrac{3}{5}\right)^3$

53. $(0.5)^2$

54. $(0.1)^3$

55. $(1.2)^2$

56. $(2.1)^2$

57. $3^2 + 4^2$

58. $5^2 + 12^2$

59. $6^2 + 8^2$

60. $2^2 + 3^2$

FIND THE MISTAKE •

Each sentence below contains a mistake. Circle the mistake and write the correct word(s) or numbers(s) on the line provided.

1. If you multiply the equation $0.23x = 1.2$ by 10, that would clear the decimals. _____

2. If you decide not to multiply by a factor of 10 to solve the equation $0.23x = 1.2$, then you should divide both sides by 23 to find x. _____

3. When you use the distributive property, $0.2(x + 5.2) = 0.2x + 5.4$. _____

4. To solve the equation $x - 5.15 = 2.3$, add 5.15 to 2.3 to get $x = 5.38$. _____

SQUARE ROOTS AND THE PYTHAGOREAN THEOREM

5.7

Imagine you are a seasoned backpacker and decide to hike through Evolution Valley in Kings Canyon National Park, California. You hike directly east along one leg of a trail for 6 miles, then turn north and hike for 8 more miles. If you were to draw a straight line from where you began to where you are now, what would be the distance?

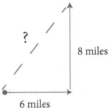

? / 8 miles
6 miles

In this section we will learn how to find this distance, but first we have to discuss square roots.

A Square Roots

Previously, we did some work with exponents. In particular, we spent some time finding squares of numbers. For example, we considered expressions like this:

$$5^2 = 5 \cdot 5 = 25$$
$$7^2 = 7 \cdot 7 = 49$$
$$x^2 = x \cdot x$$

We say that "the square of 5 is 25" and "the square of 7 is 49." To square a number, we multiply it by itself. When we ask for the **square root** of a given number, we want to know what number we square in order to obtain the given number. We say that the square root of 49 is 7, because 7 is the number we square to get 49. Likewise, the square root of 25 is 5, because $5^2 = 25$. The symbol we use to denote square root is $\sqrt{}$, which is also called a **radical sign.** Here is the precise definition of square root:

DEFINITION **square root**

The **square root** of a positive number a, written $\sqrt{a}$, is the number we square to get a.

If $\sqrt{a} = b$ then $b^2 = a$.

OBJECTIVES

A Simplify expressions involving square roots.

B Find square roots using a calculator.

C Solve problems using the Pythagorean theorem.

KEY WORDS

square root

radical sign

perfect squares

irrational number

right triangle

hypotenuse

Pythagorean theorem

spiral of roots

VIDEO EXAMPLES

SECTION 5.7

Note The square root we are describing here is actually the principal or positive square root. There is another square root that is a negative number. We won't see it in this book, but, if you go on to take an another algebra course, you may see it there.

385

We list some common square roots in Table 1.

Table 1

Statement	In Words	Reason
$\sqrt{0} = 0$	The square root of 0 is 0	Because $0^2 = 0$
$\sqrt{1} = 1$	The square root of 1 is 1	Because $1^2 = 1$
$\sqrt{4} = 2$	The square root of 4 is 2	Because $2^2 = 4$
$\sqrt{9} = 3$	The square root of 9 is 3	Because $3^2 = 9$
$\sqrt{16} = 4$	The square root of 16 is 4	Because $4^2 = 16$
$\sqrt{25} = 5$	The square root of 25 is 5	Because $5^2 = 25$
$\sqrt{36} = 6$	The square root of 36 is 6	Because $6^2 = 36$

Numbers like 1, 4, 9, 16, and 25, whose square roots are whole numbers, are called **perfect squares**. To find the square root of a perfect square, we look for the whole number that is squared to get the perfect square. The following examples involve square roots of perfect squares.

Practice Problems

1. Simplify: $5\sqrt{81}$

Example 1   Simplify: $7\sqrt{64}$

Solution   The expression $7\sqrt{64}$ means 7 times $\sqrt{64}$. To simplify this expression, we write $\sqrt{64}$ as 8 because $8^2 = 64$. Then we multiply.

$$7\sqrt{64} = 7 \cdot 8 = 56$$

2. Simplify: $\sqrt{25} + \sqrt{36}$

Example 2   Simplify: $\sqrt{9} + \sqrt{16}$

Solution   We write $\sqrt{9}$ as 3 and $\sqrt{16}$ as 4. Then we add.

$$\sqrt{9} + \sqrt{16} = 3 + 4 = 7$$

3. Simplify: $\sqrt{\frac{36}{49}}$

Example 3   Simplify: $\sqrt{\frac{25}{81}}$

Solution   We are looking for the number we square to get $\frac{25}{81}$. We know that when we multiply two fractions, we multiply the numerators and multiply the denominators. Because $5^2 = 25$ and $9^2 = 81$, the square root of $\frac{25}{81}$ must be $\frac{5}{9}$.

$$\sqrt{\frac{25}{81}} = \frac{5}{9} \quad \text{because} \quad \left(\frac{5}{9}\right)^2 = \frac{5}{9} \cdot \frac{5}{9} = \frac{25}{81}$$

So far in this section we have been concerned only with square roots of perfect squares. The next question is, "What about square roots of numbers that are not perfect squares, like $\sqrt{7}$, for example?" We know that

$$\sqrt{4} = 2 \quad \text{and} \quad \sqrt{9} = 3$$

And because 7 is between 4 and 9, $\sqrt{7}$ should be between $\sqrt{4}$ and $\sqrt{9}$. That is, $\sqrt{7}$ should be between 2 and 3. But what is it exactly? The answer is, we cannot write it exactly in decimal or fraction form. Because of this, it is called an **irrational number.** We can approximate it with a decimal, but we can never write it exactly with a decimal.

Answers

1. 45

2. 11

3. $\frac{6}{7}$

Table 2 gives some decimal approximations for $\sqrt{7}$. The decimal approximations were obtained by using a calculator. We could continue the list to any accuracy we desired. However, we would never reach a number in decimal form whose square was exactly 7.

Table 2

Approximations for the Square Root of 7

Accurate to the nearest	The square root of 7 is	Check by squaring
Tenth	$\sqrt{7} = 2.6$	$(2.6)^2 = 6.76$
Hundredth	$\sqrt{7} = 2.65$	$(2.65)^2 = 7.0225$
Thousandth	$\sqrt{7} = 2.646$	$(2.646)^2 = 7.001316$
Ten thousandth	$\sqrt{7} = 2.6458$	$(2.6458)^2 = 7.00025764$

B Using Calculators to Find Square Roots

Example 4 Give a decimal approximation for the expression $5\sqrt{12}$ that is accurate to the nearest ten thousandth.

Solution For a more accurate answer, let's agree not to round to the nearest ten thousandth until we have first done all the calculations. Using a calculator, we find $\sqrt{12} \approx 3.4641016$. Therefore,

$$5\sqrt{12} \approx 5(3.4641016) \quad \text{Find } \sqrt{12} \text{ on calculator.}$$
$$= 17.320508 \quad \text{Multiply.}$$
$$= 17.3205 \quad \text{Round to the nearest ten thousandth.}$$

4. Give a decimal approximation for the expression $6\sqrt{10}$ that is accurate to the nearest thousandth.

Example 5 Approximate $\sqrt{301} + \sqrt{137}$ to the nearest hundredth.

Solution Using a calculator to approximate the square roots, we have

$$\sqrt{301} + \sqrt{137} \approx 17.349352 + 11.704700 = 29.054052$$

To the nearest hundredth, the answer is 29.05.

5. Approximate $\sqrt{245} - \sqrt{131}$ to the nearest thousandth.

Example 6 Approximate $\sqrt{\dfrac{7}{11}}$ to the nearest thousandth.

Solution Because we are using calculators, we first change $\frac{7}{11}$ to a decimal and then find the square root.

$$\sqrt{\frac{7}{11}} \approx \sqrt{0.6363636} \approx 0.7977240$$

To the nearest thousandth, the answer is 0.798.

6. Approximate $\sqrt{\dfrac{9}{26}}$ to the nearest ten thousandth.

Answers
4. 18.974
5. 4.207
6. 0.5883

C The Pythagorean Theorem

 FACTS FROM GEOMETRY

Pythagorean Theorem

A **right triangle** is a triangle that contains a 90° (or right) angle. The longest side in a right triangle is called the **hypotenuse**, and we use the letter c to denote it. The two shorter sides are denoted by the letters a and b. The Pythagorean theorem states that the sum of the squares of the two legs of a right triangle equals the square of the hypotenuse. In symbols, we have

$$a^2 + b^2 = c^2$$

Using the rules of algebra, we could derive and then use the following formulas. In this section, though, we will use the formula above.

$$c = \sqrt{a^2 + b^2}$$
$$a = \sqrt{c^2 - b^2}$$

---

7. Find the length of the hypotenuse in the right triangle.

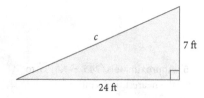

24 ft

Example 7 Find the length of the hypotenuse in each right triangle. If the result is an irrational number, use a calculator to approximate the length to the hundredths place.

a.

b.

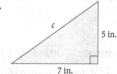

Solution

a. Substituting $a = 3$ and $b = 4$ into the formula, we have:

$$3^2 + 4^2 = c^2$$

$$9 + 16 = c^2 \qquad \text{Evaluate exponents.}$$

$$25 = c^2 \qquad \text{Simplify.}$$

Because c represents the length of the side of a triangle, the value for c must be positive. Also, because c^2 must be 25, it follows that $c = 5$ meters.

b. Substituting $a = 5$ and $b = 7$, we have:

$$5^2 + 7^2 = c^2$$

$$25 + 49 = c^2$$

$$74 = c^2$$

Therefore, $c = \sqrt{74}$. Using a calculator, $c \approx 8.60$ inches.

Answer

7. 25

Example 8   Find the length of the missing side in each right triangle. Use a calculator to round to the nearest hundredth.

a.

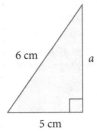

6 cm   *a*

5 cm

b.

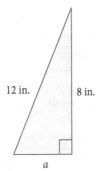

12 in.   8 in.

a

8. Find the length of the missing side of the right triangle.

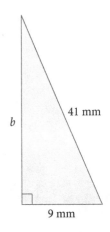

41 mm

b

9 mm

Solution We will substitute the values into the formula and solve for *a*.

a. When $b = 5$ and $c = 6$, then

$$a^2 + 5^2 = 6^2$$

$$a^2 + 25 = 36 \qquad \text{Simplify.}$$

$$a^2 + 25 - 25 = 36 - 25 \qquad \text{Subtract 25 from each side.}$$

$$a^2 = 11 \qquad \text{Simplify.}$$

$$a = \sqrt{11}$$

$$a \approx 3.32 \text{ cm} \qquad \text{Approximate using a calculator.}$$

b. When $b = 8$ and $c = 12$, then

$$a^2 + 8^2 = 122$$

$$a^2 + 64 = 144 \qquad \text{Simplify.}$$

$$a^2 + 64 - 64 = 144 - 64 \qquad \text{Subtract 64 from each side.}$$

$$a^2 = 80 \qquad \text{Simplify.}$$

$$a \approx 8.94 \text{ inches} \qquad \text{Approximate using a calculator.}$$

Example 9   A ladder is leaning against a barn to reach a hayloft 6 feet above the barn floor. If the bottom of the ladder is 8 feet from the wall, how long is the ladder?

Solution   A picture of the situation is shown in Figure 2. We let *c* denote the length of the ladder. Applying the Pythagorean theorem, we have

$$6^2 + 8^2 = c^2$$

$$36 + 64 = c^2$$

$$100 = c^2$$

$$\sqrt{100} = c$$

$$10 = c$$

The ladder is 10 feet long.

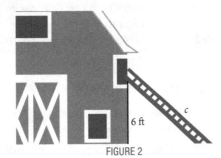

c

6 ft

FIGURE 2

9. A rope is tied from the top of a 12-foot pole to the ground 5 feet from the base of the pole. If there is no slack in the rope, how long is the rope?

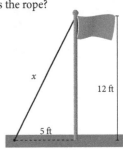

x

12 ft

5 ft

FIGURE 1

Answers

8. 40 mm

9. 13 ft

FACTS FROM GEOMETRY

The Spiral of Roots

The diagram showed here is called the **spiral of roots**. It is constructed using the Pythagorean theorem and it gives us a way to visualize positive square roots. The table below gives us the decimal equivalents (some of which are approximations) of the first 10 square roots in the spiral. The line graph can be constructed from the table or from the spiral.

Approximate length of diagonals

Number	Positive Square Root
1	1
2	1.41
3	1.73
4	2
5	2.24
6	2.45
7	2.65
8	2.83
9	3
10	3.16

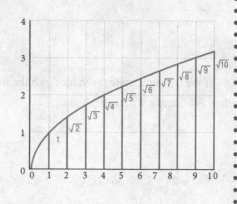

To visualize the square roots of the counting numbers, we can construct the spiral of roots another way. To begin, we draw two line segments, each of length 1, at right angles to each other. Then we use the Pythagorean theorem to find the length of the diagonal. Figure 3 illustrates:

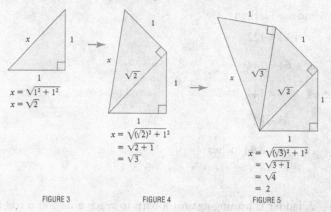

FIGURE 3   FIGURE 4   FIGURE 5

Next, we construct a second triangle by connecting a line segment of length 1 to the end of the first diagonal so that the angle formed is a right angle. We find the length of the second diagonal using the Pythagorean theorem. Figure 4 illustrates this procedure. As we continue to draw new triangles by connecting line segments of length 1 to the end of each previous diagonal, so that the angle formed is a right angle, the spiral of roots begins to appear (see Figure 5).

KEY CONCEPT REVIEW

After reading through the preceding section, respond in your own words and in complete sentences.

A. Which number is larger, the square of 10 or the square root of 10?

B. Give a definition for the square root of a number.

C. What two numbers will the square root of 20 fall between?

D. What is the Pythagorean theorem?

Choose the correct words to fill in the blanks below.

right   hypotenuse   irrational   perfect squares

square root   radical sign   Pythagorean theorem

1. The _____ of a positive number a is the number we square to get a.

2. The symbol we use to denote a square root is called a _____.

3. Numbers whose square roots are whole numbers are called_____.

4. An _____ number, such as $\sqrt{7}$, is a number that can be approximated with a decimal number but can never be written exactly as a decimal or fraction.

5. A _____ triangle is a triangle that contains a 90 degree angle.

6. The longest side of a right triangle is called the _____.

7. The _____ states that the hypotenuse is the square root of the sum of the squares of the two shorter sides.

Problems

A Find each of the following square roots without using a calculator.

1. $\sqrt{64}$

2. $\sqrt{100}$

3. $\sqrt{81}$

4. $\sqrt{49}$

5. $\sqrt{36}$

6. $\sqrt{144}$

7. $\sqrt{25}$

8. $\sqrt{169}$

Simplify each of the following expressions without using a calculator.

9. $3\sqrt{25}$

10. $9\sqrt{49}$

11. $6\sqrt{64}$

12. $11\sqrt{100}$

13. $15\sqrt{9}$

14. $8\sqrt{36}$

15. $16\sqrt{9}$

16. $9\sqrt{16}$

17. $\sqrt{49} + \sqrt{64}$

18. $\sqrt{1} + \sqrt{0}$

19. $\sqrt{16} - \sqrt{9}$

20. $\sqrt{25} - \sqrt{4}$

21. $3\sqrt{25} + 9\sqrt{49}$

22. $6\sqrt{64} + 11\sqrt{100}$

23. $15\sqrt{9} - 9\sqrt{16}$

24. $7\sqrt{49} - 2\sqrt{4}$

25. $\sqrt{\dfrac{16}{49}}$ **26.** $\sqrt{\dfrac{100}{121}}$ **27.** $\sqrt{\dfrac{36}{64}}$ **28.** $\sqrt{\dfrac{81}{144}}$

29. $\sqrt{\dfrac{4}{9}}$ **30.** $\sqrt{\dfrac{25}{16}}$ **31.** $\sqrt{\dfrac{1}{16}}$ **32.** $\sqrt{\dfrac{1}{100}}$

Indicate whether each of the statements in Problems 33–36 is *True* or *False*.

33. $\sqrt{4} + \sqrt{9} = \sqrt{4 + 9}$ **34.** $\sqrt{\dfrac{16}{25}} = \dfrac{\sqrt{16}}{\sqrt{25}}$

35. $\sqrt{25 \cdot 9} = \sqrt{25} \cdot \sqrt{9}$ **36.** $\sqrt{100} - \sqrt{36} = \sqrt{100 - 36}$

Calculator Problems

B Use a calculator to work problems 37 through 56.

Approximate each of the following square roots to the nearest ten thousandth.

37. $\sqrt{125}$ **38.** $\sqrt{1250}$ **39.** $\sqrt{1.25}$ **40.** $\sqrt{12.5}$

Approximate each of the following expressions to the nearest hundredth.

41. $2\sqrt{3}$ **42.** $3\sqrt{2}$ **43.** $5\sqrt{5}$ **44.** $5\sqrt{3}$

45. $\dfrac{\sqrt{3}}{3}$ **46.** $\dfrac{\sqrt{2}}{2}$ **47.** $\sqrt{\dfrac{1}{3}}$ **48.** $\sqrt{\dfrac{1}{2}}$

Approximate each of the following expressions to the nearest thousandth.

49. $\sqrt{12} + \sqrt{75}$ **50.** $\sqrt{18} + \sqrt{50}$ **51.** $\sqrt{87}$ **52.** $\sqrt{68}$

53. $2\sqrt{3} + 5\sqrt{3}$ **54.** $3\sqrt{2} + 5\sqrt{2}$ **55.** $7\sqrt{3}$ **56.** $8\sqrt{2}$

C Find the length of the missing side in each right triangle. Round to the nearest hundredth, if rounding is necessary.

57.
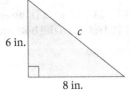
6 in.
8 in.
c

58.
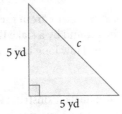
5 yd
5 yd
c

59.
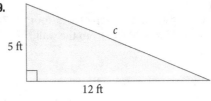
5 ft
12 ft
c

60.
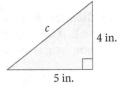
c
4 in.
5 in.

61.
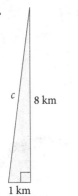
c
8 km
1 km

62.
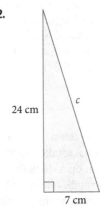
24 cm
c
7 cm

63.
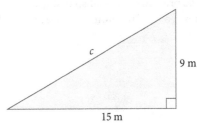
c
9 m
15 m

64.
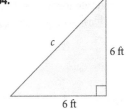
c
6 ft
6 ft

65.

5 m
a
4 m

66.
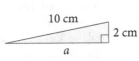
10 cm
2 cm
a

67.
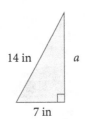
14 in
a
7 in

68.
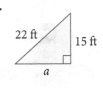
22 ft
15 ft
a

69.
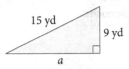
15 yd
9 yd
a

70.
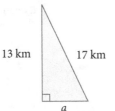
13 km
17 km
a

Applying the Concepts

71. Geometry One end of a wire is attached to the top of a 24-foot pole; the other end of the wire is anchored to the ground 18 feet from the bottom of the pole. If the pole makes an angle of 90° with the ground, find the length of the wire.

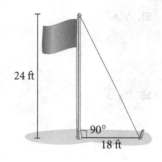

24 ft

90°
18 ft

72. Geometry Two children are trying to cross a stream. They want to use a log that goes from one bank to the other. If the left bank is 5 feet higher than the right bank and the stream is 12 feet wide, how long must a log be to just barely reach the other bank?

5 ft

12 ft

73. Geometry A ladder is leaning against the top of a 15-foot wall. If the bottom of the ladder is 20 feet from the wall, how long is the ladder?

74. Geometry A wire from the top of a 24-foot pole is fastened to the ground by a stake that is 10 feet from the bottom of the pole. How long is the wire?

75. Spiral of Roots Construct your own spiral of roots by using a ruler. Draw the first triangle by using two 1-inch lines. The first diagonal will have a length of $\sqrt{2}$ inches. Each new triangle will be formed by drawing a 1-inch line segment at the end of the previous diagonal so that the angle formed is 90°. Draw your spiral until you have at least six right triangles.

76. Spiral of Roots Construct a spiral of roots by using line segments of length 2 inches. The length of the first diagonal will be $2\sqrt{2}$ inches. The length of the second diagonal will be $2\sqrt{3}$ inches. What will be the length of the third diagonal?

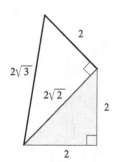

2

$2\sqrt{3}$

$2\sqrt{2}$

2

2

Use a calculator to work problems 77 and 78.

77. Lighthouse Problem The higher you are above the ground, the farther you can see. If your view is unobstructed, then the distance in miles that you can see from h feet above the ground is given by the formula

$$d = \sqrt{\dfrac{3h}{2}}$$

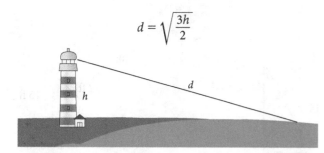

d

h

78. Pendulum Problem The time (in seconds) it takes for the pendulum on a clock to swing through one complete cycle is given by the formula

$$T = \dfrac{11}{7}\sqrt{\dfrac{L}{2}}$$

where L is the length (in feet) of the pendulum. Use this formula and a calculator to complete the following table. Round your answers to the nearest hundredth.

T sec

The following figure shows a lighthouse with a door and windows at various heights. The preceding formula can be used to find the distance to the ocean horizon from these heights. Use the formula and a calculator to complete the following table. Round your answers to the nearest whole number.

Height h (feet)	Distance d (miles)
10	
50	
90	
130	
170	
190	

Length L (feet)	Time T (seconds)
1	
2	
3	
4	
5	
6	

Improving Your Quantitative Literacy

79. Super Bowl Viewers The chart shows the number of people who have watched the Super Bowl over a ten-year period. Use the information to answer the following questions.

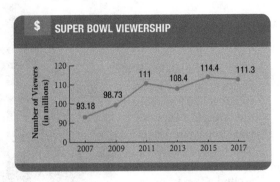

a. If the trend from 2013 to 2015 had continued, what would the viewership have been in 2017?

b. What is the difference between the predicted viewership you found in part a and the actual 2017 viewership?

Getting Ready for the Next Section

Simplify.

80. $\sqrt{36}$ **81.** $\sqrt{9}$ **82.** $\sqrt{25}$ **83.** $\sqrt{16}$

Factor each number into the product of prime factors.

84. 50   **85.** 45   **86.** 48   **87.** 180

FIND THE MISTAKE •

Each sentence below contains a mistake. Circle the mistake and write the correct word(s) or numbers(s) on the line provided.

1. The square root of a positive number x is the number we square to get $\sqrt{x}$. _____

2. The square root of 225 is 15, and can be written in symbols as $\sqrt{15} = 225$. _____

3. Simplifying the radical $\sqrt{\frac{196}{25}}$ gives us $\frac{98}{25}$ because $\left(\frac{98}{25}\right)^2 = \frac{98}{25} + \frac{98}{25} = \frac{196}{25}$. _____

4. The Pythagorean theorem states that $b = \sqrt{a^2 + c^2}$. _____

5.8

 SIMPLIFYING SQUARE ROOTS

OBJECTIVES

A Use the multiplication property to simplify square roots.

KEY WORDS

simplify

square root

perfect square

VIDEO EXAMPLES

SECTION 5.8

The observation deck of Seattle's Space Needle stands at 520 feet above the ground. Suppose you drop your wallet over the deck's railing and it plummets to the ground. The formula that gives the number of seconds t it takes for an object to reach the ground when dropped from a height h (in feet) is

$$t = \sqrt{\frac{h}{16}}$$

In this section, we will simplify square roots such as the one used in the above equation. We will also revisit this equation in a similar application later in the problem set. Then you can return to this problem and solve it.

A Simplifying Square Roots

Do you know that $\sqrt{50}$ and $5\sqrt{2}$ are the same number? One way to convince yourself that this is true is with a calculator. Using a calculator, we can find the approximation of $\sqrt{50}$.

$$\sqrt{50} = 7.0710678$$

To find the approximation of $5\sqrt{2}$, we find the value for $\sqrt{2}$ and then multiply by 5.

$$5\sqrt{2} = 5(1.41421356) = 7.0710678$$

Although a calculator will give the same result for both $\sqrt{50}$ and $5\sqrt{2}$, it does not tell us *why* the answers are the same. The discussion below shows why the results are the same.

First, notice that the expressions $\sqrt{4 \cdot 9}$ and $\sqrt{4} \cdot \sqrt{9}$ have the same value:

$$\sqrt{4 \cdot 9} = \sqrt{36} = 6 \qquad \text{and} \qquad \sqrt{4} \cdot \sqrt{9} = 2 \cdot 3 = 6$$

Both are equal to 6. When we are multiplying and taking square roots, we can either multiply first and then take the square root of what we get, or we can take square roots first and then multiply. This is called the multiplication property for square roots. In symbols, we write the property this way:

DEFINITION   multiplication property for square roots

If a and b are positive numbers, then

$$\sqrt{a \cdot b} = \sqrt{a} \cdot \sqrt{b}$$

In words: The square root of a product is the product of the square roots.

To see why $\sqrt{50}$ and $5\sqrt{2}$ have the same value, we need to review the definition of perfect squares. Recall, if a is a positive number, then a^2 is a perfect square. Here is a list of some perfect squares.

$$1, 4, 9, 16, 25 \ldots$$

Now, to simplify $\sqrt{50}$, we must find a factor of 50 that is a perfect square. We will use $50 = 25 \cdot 2$ because 25 is a perfect square. Rewriting $\sqrt{50}$ using this fact, we have

$$\sqrt{50} = \sqrt{25 \cdot 2} = \sqrt{25} \cdot \sqrt{2} = 5 \cdot \sqrt{2} = 5\sqrt{2}$$

Example 1   Simplify: $\sqrt{45}$

Solution   To begin, we factor 45 into a product involving a perfect square.

$$\sqrt{45} = \sqrt{9 \cdot 5} \qquad \text{Factor.}$$

$$= \sqrt{9} \cdot \sqrt{5} \qquad \text{Apply multiplication property.}$$

$$= 3 \cdot \sqrt{5} \qquad \text{Simplify.}$$

The expressions $\sqrt{45}$ and $3\sqrt{5}$ are equivalent. The expression $3\sqrt{5}$ is said to be in *simplified form* because the number under the radical no longer has any perfect squares as factors.

· ●

In our next example, a variable appears under the square root symbol. Before stating the next problem, let's discuss $\sqrt{x^2}$. Recall, $\sqrt{16} = 4$ because $4^2 = 16$. Similarly, if x is a positive number, $\sqrt{x^2} = x$ because $x \cdot x = x^2$. For these problems, we will also assume that x is always a positive number.

Example 2   Simplify: $\sqrt{18x^2}$

Solution   We factor $18x^2$ into $9 \cdot 2 \cdot x^2$. We use the product $9 \cdot 2$ because it involves a perfect square. Using $\sqrt{x^2} = x$, we have,

$$\sqrt{18x^2} = \sqrt{9 \cdot 2 \cdot x^2}$$

$$= \sqrt{9} \cdot \sqrt{2} \cdot \sqrt{x^2}$$

$$= 3 \cdot \sqrt{2} \cdot x$$

$$= 3x\sqrt{2}$$

You may be wondering if we can check this answer on a calculator. The answer is yes, but we need to substitute a value for x first. Suppose x is 5. Then

$$\sqrt{18x^2} = \sqrt{18 \cdot 25} = \sqrt{450} \approx 21.213203$$

and

$$3x\sqrt{2} = 3 \cdot 5 \cdot \sqrt{2} = 15\sqrt{2} \approx 15(1.4142136) = 21.213203$$

Practice Problems

1. Simplify: $\sqrt{63}$

2. Simplify: $\sqrt{45x^2}$

Answers
1. $3\sqrt{7}$
2. $3x\sqrt{5}$

3. Simplify: $\sqrt{300}$

Note We could have also used $180 = 36 \cdot 5$, giving us the same answer:

$$\sqrt{180} = \sqrt{36 \cdot 5}$$
$$= \sqrt{36} \cdot \sqrt{5}$$
$$= 6 \cdot \sqrt{5}$$
$$= 6\sqrt{5}$$

4. Simplify: $\sqrt{50x^2}$

Example 3   Simplify: $\sqrt{180}$

Solution   There are several perfect squares that are factors of 180. We can use any of these to simplify $\sqrt{180}$. Let's start with $4 \cdot 45 = 180$. Because we can write 45 using another perfect square, namely $9 \cdot 5$, we will write $\sqrt{180}$ as

$$\sqrt{180} = \sqrt{4 \cdot 9 \cdot 5}$$
$$= \sqrt{4} \cdot \sqrt{9} \cdot \sqrt{5}$$
$$= 2 \cdot 3 \cdot \sqrt{5}$$
$$= 6\sqrt{5}$$

Example 4   Simplify: $\sqrt{48x^2}$

Solution   Again, we will simplify using a product with a perfect square. Let's start with $4 \cdot 12 = 48$. Notice we can rewrite 12 using $4 \cdot 3$, another product involving a perfect square. Now we will use $4 \cdot 4 \cdot 3 = 48$ and use the fact $\sqrt{x^2} = x$.

$$\sqrt{48x^2} = \sqrt{4 \cdot 4 \cdot 3 \cdot x^2}$$
$$= \sqrt{4} \cdot \sqrt{4} \cdot \sqrt{3} \cdot \sqrt{x^2}$$
$$= 2 \cdot 2 \cdot \sqrt{3} \cdot x$$
$$= 4x\sqrt{3}$$

This is just one solution. We could also have used $16 \cdot 3 = 48$.

$$\sqrt{48x^2} = \sqrt{16 \cdot 3 \cdot x^2}$$
$$= \sqrt{16} \cdot \sqrt{3} \cdot \sqrt{x^2}$$
$$= 4 \cdot \sqrt{3} \cdot x$$
$$= 4x\sqrt{3}$$

KEY CONCEPT REVIEW • • • • • • • • • • • •

After reading through the preceding section, respond in your own words and in complete sentences.

A. What is the multiplication property for square roots?

B. How do you know if you can take a factor from under the radical sign?

C. What is a perfect square? Why are they important for simplifying square roots?

D. List ten perfect squares.

Answers

3. $10\sqrt{3}$

4. $5x\sqrt{2}$

EXERCISE SET 5.8 ···············

Problems

A Simplify each expression by taking as much out from under the radical as possible. You may assume that all variables represent positive numbers.

1. $\sqrt{12}$ **2.** $\sqrt{18}$ **3.** $\sqrt{20}$ **4.** $\sqrt{27}$

5. $\sqrt{72}$ **6.** $\sqrt{48}$ **7.** $\sqrt{98}$ **8.** $\sqrt{75}$

9. $\sqrt{28}$ **10.** $\sqrt{44}$ **11.** $\sqrt{200}$ **12.** $\sqrt{300}$

13. $\sqrt{12x^2}$ **14.** $\sqrt{18x^2}$ **15.** $\sqrt{50x^2}$ **16.** $\sqrt{45x^2}$

17. $\sqrt{75x^2}$ **18.** $\sqrt{8x^2}$ **19.** $\sqrt{50x^2}$ **20.** $\sqrt{45x^2}$

21. $\sqrt{32x^2y^2}$ **22.** $\sqrt{90x^2y^2}$ **23.** $\sqrt{243x^2}$ **24.** $\sqrt{288x^2}$

25. $\sqrt{72x^2y^2}$ **26.** $\sqrt{128x^2y^2}$ **27.** $\sqrt{12x^2y^2}$ **28.** $\sqrt{20x^2y^2}$

Applying the Concepts

The triangles below are called *isosceles* right triangles because the two shorter sides are the same length. In each case, use the Pythagorean theorem to find the length of the hypotenuse. Simplify your answers, but do not use a calculator to approximate them.

29.

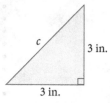

30.

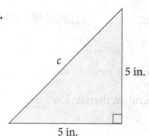

31.

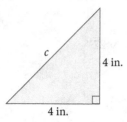

32.

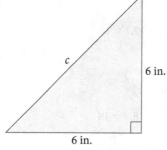

33.

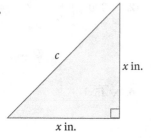

34.

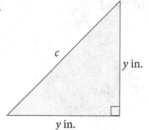

35. Falling Time The formula that gives the number of seconds *t* it takes for an object to reach the ground when dropped from a height of *h* feet is

$$t = \sqrt{\frac{h}{16}}$$

If a rock is dropped from the top of a building 25 feet high, how long will it take for the rock to hit the ground?

36. Falling Time Suppose a maintenance man doing work on the antennas on the top of the Space Needle drops a tool from a height of 529 feet. How long will it take for the tool to hit the ground?

Calculator Problems

Use a calculator to find decimal approximations for each of the following numbers. Round to the thousandths place.

37. $\sqrt{72}$ and $6\sqrt{2}$

38. $\sqrt{75}$ and $5\sqrt{3}$

Substitute $x = 5$ into each of the following expressions, and then use a calculator to obtain a decimal approximation of each. Round to the nearest thousandth.

39. $x\sqrt{x}$

40. $\sqrt{x^3}$

41. $x^2\sqrt{x}$

42. $\sqrt{x^5}$

Use a calculator to help complete the following tables. If an answer needs rounding, round to the nearest thousandth.

43.

x	$\sqrt{x}$	$2\sqrt{x}$	$\sqrt{4x}$
1			
2			
3			
4			

44.

x	$\sqrt{x}$	$2\sqrt{x}$	$\sqrt{4x}$
1			
4			
9			
16			

45.

x	$\sqrt{x}$	$3\sqrt{x}$	$\sqrt{9x}$
1			
2			
3			
4			

46.

x	$\sqrt{x}$	$3\sqrt{x}$	$\sqrt{9x}$
1			
4			
9			
16			

Getting Ready for the Next Section

Combine like terms.

47. $15x + 8x$

48. $6x + 20x$

49. $25y + 3y - y$

50. $12y + 4y - y$

51. $2ab + 5ab$

52. $3ab + 7ab$

53. $2xy - 9xy + 50x$

54. $2xy - 18xy + 3x$

FIND THE MISTAKE •

Each sentence below contains a mistake. Circle the mistake and write the correct word(s) or numbers(s) on the line provided.

1. The simplified form of $\sqrt{300}$ is $\sqrt{25 \cdot 4 \cdot 3} = 5 + 2\sqrt{3} = 7\sqrt{3}$. _____

2. $\sqrt{50}$ is in simplified form. _____

3. The hypotenuse of an isosceles right triangle is always twice the length of a leg. _____

4. To simplify a radical, we need to factor using prime factors. _____

5.9

 ADDING AND SUBTRACTING SQUARE ROOTS

 OBJECTIVES

A Add and subtract expressions containing square roots.

 KEY WORDS

distributive property

radical expression

like terms

simplify

VIDEO EXAMPLES

SECTION 5.9

The Blue Ridge Parkway is a 469-mile scenic highway that runs through Virginia and North Carolina. Situated in the Appalachian Mountains, this parkway is often the most visited unit of the National Park System. Along the parkway are a total of 26 vehicle tunnels, quite an impressive number as the majority of these tunnels were dug by hand in the 1930s when work on the parkway began.

Suppose a surveying team must choose between two mountains through which to dig a tunnel. To calculate the length of a tunnel, the team uses the Pythagorean theorem, so the length of a tunnel can be a square root. Because they are comparing two lengths, they could end up subtracting two square roots.

A Add and Subtract Expressions Containing Square Roots

Previously, we have combined like terms by applying the distributive property. Here are some examples that will remind you of that procedure. The middle step in each example shows the distributive property.

$$7x + 3x = (7 + 3)x = 10x$$

$$5a^2 - 2a^2 = (5 - 2)a^2 = 3a^2$$

$$6xy + 3xy = (6 + 3)xy = 9xy$$

$$4x + 3x - 2x = (4 + 3 - 2)x = 5x$$

The distributive property is the only property that allows us to combine like terms as we have done above. In order for the distributive property to be applied, the variable parts in each expression must be the same.

Let's revisit the tunnel problem from the introduction to this section. Look at figures 1 and 2 below.

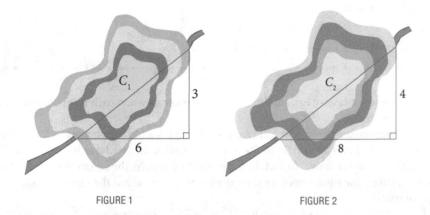

FIGURE 1   FIGURE 2

The surveying team will choose to dig one of the two tunnels, represented by the hypotenuse of c of each triangle. In order to determine the length of each hypotenuse, we need to apply the Pythagorean theorem, which involves square roots.

Hypotenuse for Figure 1   Hypotenuse for Figure 2

$$3^2 + 6^2 = c_1^{\,2}$$ $$4^2 + 8^2 = c_2^{\,2}$$

$$9 + 36 = c_1^{\,2}$$ $$16 + 64 = c_2^{\,2}$$

$$45 = c_1^{\,2}$$ $$80 = c_2^{\,2}$$

$$\sqrt{45} = c_1$$ $$\sqrt{80} = c_2$$

$$\sqrt{9 \cdot 5} = c_1$$ $$\sqrt{16 \cdot 5} = c_2$$

$$3\sqrt{5} = c_1$$ $$4\sqrt{5} = c_2$$

The hypotenuse for Figure 1 is $3\sqrt{5}$ miles long, and the hypotenuse for Figure 2 is $4\sqrt{5}$ miles long. Now we have our values to answer the question, "What is the difference in lengths of the two tunnels?" As you can see, both lengths contain a radical. We add and subtract radical expressions in the same way we add and subtract like terms, that is, by applying the distributive property. Here is how we use the distributive property to subtract $3\sqrt{5}$ from $4\sqrt{5}$:

$$4\sqrt{5} - 3\sqrt{5} = (4 - 3)\sqrt{5} \qquad \text{Distributive property}$$

$$= \sqrt{5} \qquad \text{Subtract 3 from 4.}$$

To understand the steps shown here, you must remember that $4\sqrt{5}$ means 4 times $\sqrt{5}$; the 4 and the $\sqrt{5}$ are not "stuck together."

Here is the formal definition for a radical expression:

DEFINITION radical expression

A **radical expression** is an expression that contains a radical, as well as any combination of numbers, variables, operation symbols, and grouping symbols. This definition includes the use of exponents and fractions.

Here are some more examples that will show how we use the distributive property to combine radical expressions. (Assume all variables represent positive numbers.)

Practice Problems

1. Use the distributive property to combine each of the following.

   a. $5\sqrt{3} - 2\sqrt{3}$

   b. $7\sqrt{y} + 3\sqrt{y}$

   c. $8\sqrt{5} - 2\sqrt{5} + 9\sqrt{5}$

$\mathcal{Note}$ You may be thinking "Why did they show us the wrong way to do the problem first?" The reason is simple: Many people will try to add $\sqrt{12}$ and $\sqrt{75}$ by adding 12 and 75—it is a natural thing to want to do. This gives the wrong answer, though, like we saw in the exercises in 5.7. One of the things you need to know about learning algebra is that your intuition may lead you to a mistake.

2. Combine, if possible:
   $\sqrt{27} + \sqrt{75} - \sqrt{12}$

Example 1   Combine using the distributive property. (Assume all variables represent positive numbers.)

a. $5\sqrt{6} - 2\sqrt{6} = (5 - 2)\sqrt{6} = 3\sqrt{6}$

b. $6\sqrt{x} + 3\sqrt{x} = (6 + 3)\sqrt{x} = 9\sqrt{x}$

c. $4\sqrt{3} + 3\sqrt{3} - 2\sqrt{3} = (4 + 3 - 2)\sqrt{3} = 5\sqrt{3}$

As you can see, it is easy to combine radical expressions when each term contains the same square root.

Next, suppose we try to add $\sqrt{12}$ and $\sqrt{75}$. How should we go about it? You may think we should add 12 and 75 to get $\sqrt{87}$, but notice that we have not done that in any of the examples above. In fact, in the previous example, the square root under the answer is the same square root we started with; we never added the number under the square roots.

A calculator can help us decide if $\sqrt{12} + \sqrt{75}$ is the same as $\sqrt{87}$. Here are the decimal approximations a calculator will give us:

$$\sqrt{12} + \sqrt{75} = 3.4641016 + 8.6602540 = 12.1243556$$

$$\sqrt{12} + \sqrt{75} = \sqrt{87} = 9.3273791$$

As you can see, the two results are quite different, so we can assume that it would be a mistake to add the numbers under the square roots. That is,

$$\sqrt{12} + \sqrt{75} \neq \sqrt{12 + 75}$$

The correct way to add $\sqrt{12}$ and $\sqrt{75}$ is to first simplify. Then, if the square roots in the resulting expressions are the same, we can add using the distributive property. Here is the way the problem is done correctly:

$$\sqrt{12} + \sqrt{75} = \sqrt{4 \cdot 3} + \sqrt{25 \cdot 3} \quad \text{Simplify each square root.}$$

$$= 2\sqrt{3} + 5\sqrt{3}$$

$$= (2 + 5)\sqrt{3} \quad \text{Apply the distributive property.}$$

$$= 7\sqrt{3} \quad \text{Add 2 and 5.}$$

On a calculator, $7\sqrt{3} = 7(1.7320508) = 12.1243556$, which matches the approximation a calculator gives for $\sqrt{12} + \sqrt{75}$.

Example 2   Combine, if possible: $\sqrt{18} + \sqrt{50} - \sqrt{8}$

Solution   First we simplify each term by taking as much out from under the square root as possible. Then we use the distributive property to combine terms if they contain the same square root.

$$\sqrt{18} + \sqrt{50} - \sqrt{8} = \sqrt{9 \cdot 2} + \sqrt{25 \cdot 2} - \sqrt{4 \cdot 2}$$

$$= 3\sqrt{2} + 5\sqrt{2} - 2\sqrt{2}$$

$$= (3 + 5 - 2)\sqrt{2}$$

$$= 6\sqrt{2}$$

Answers

1. a. $3\sqrt{3}$
   b. $10\sqrt{y}$
   c. $15\sqrt{5}$
2. $6\sqrt{3}$

Example 3   Combine, if possible: $5\sqrt{54} - 3\sqrt{24}$

Solution   Proceeding as we did in the previous example, we simplify each term first; then we subtract by applying the distributive property.

$$5\sqrt{54} - 3\sqrt{24} = 5\sqrt{9 \cdot 6} - 3\sqrt{4 \cdot 6}$$
$$= 5 \cdot 3\sqrt{6} - 3 \cdot 2\sqrt{6}$$
$$= 15\sqrt{6} - 6\sqrt{6}$$
$$= (15 - 6)\sqrt{6}$$
$$= 9\sqrt{6}$$

3. Combine, if possible:
$5\sqrt{45} - 3\sqrt{20}$

Example 4   Assume x is a positive number and combine, if possible:
$$5\sqrt{12x^2} - 3\sqrt{75x^2}$$

Solution   We simplify each square root, and then we subtract.

$$5\sqrt{12x^2} - 3\sqrt{75x^2} = 5\sqrt{4 \cdot 3 \cdot x^2} - 3\sqrt{25 \cdot 3 \cdot x^2}$$
$$= 5 \cdot 2 \cdot x\sqrt{3} - 3 \cdot 5 \cdot x\sqrt{3}$$
$$= 10x\sqrt{3} - 15x\sqrt{3}$$
$$= (10x - 15x)\sqrt{3}$$
$$= -5x\sqrt{3}$$

4. Combine, if possible:
$7\sqrt{18x^2} - 3\sqrt{50x^2}$

KEY CONCEPT REVIEW

After reading through the preceding section, respond in your own words and in complete sentences.

A. How is adding radical expressions the same thing as adding like terms?

B. What property is used to add $3\sqrt{x}$ and $7\sqrt{x}$?

C. Why is it wrong to add $\sqrt{12}$ and $\sqrt{75}$ to get $\sqrt{87}$?

D. What is the sum of $\sqrt{12}$ and $\sqrt{75}$?

Answers

3. $9\sqrt{5}$
4. $6x\sqrt{2}$

Problems

A Combine by applying the distributive property. Assume all variables represent positive numbers.

1. $2\sqrt{3} + 8\sqrt{3}$

2. $2\sqrt{3} - 8\sqrt{3}$

3. $7\sqrt{5} - 3\sqrt{5}$

4. $7\sqrt{5} + 3\sqrt{5}$

5. $9\sqrt{x} + 3\sqrt{x} - 5\sqrt{x}$

6. $6\sqrt{x} + 10\sqrt{x} - 3\sqrt{x}$

7. $8\sqrt{7} + \sqrt{7}$

8. $9\sqrt{7} + \sqrt{7}$

9. $2\sqrt{y} + \sqrt{y} + 3\sqrt{y}$

10. $7\sqrt{y} + \sqrt{y} + 2\sqrt{y}$

Simplify each square root, then combine if possible. Assume all variables represent positive numbers.

11. $\sqrt{18} + \sqrt{32}$

12. $\sqrt{12} + \sqrt{27}$

13. $\sqrt{75} + \sqrt{27}$

14. $\sqrt{50} + \sqrt{8}$

15. $2\sqrt{75} - 4\sqrt{27}$

16. $4\sqrt{50} - 5\sqrt{8}$

17. $2\sqrt{90} + 3\sqrt{40} - 4\sqrt{10}$

18. $5\sqrt{40} - 2\sqrt{90} + 3\sqrt{10}$

19. $\sqrt{72x^2} - \sqrt{50x^2}$

20. $\sqrt{98x^2} - \sqrt{72x^2}$

21. $4\sqrt{20x^2} + 3\sqrt{45x^2}$

22. $8\sqrt{48x^2} + 2\sqrt{12x^2}$

In each diagram below, find the distance from *A* to *B*. Simplify your answers, but do not use a calculator.

23.

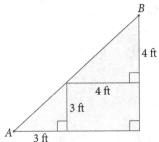

24.

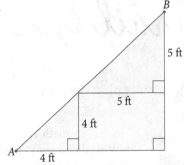

Calculator Problems

25. Use a calculator to show that $\sqrt{2} + \sqrt{3}$ is not the same as $\sqrt{5}$.

26. Use a calculator to show that $\sqrt{5} - \sqrt{2}$ is not the same as $\sqrt{3}$.

Use a calculator to help complete the following tables. If an answer needs rounding, round to the nearest thousandth.

27.

x	$\sqrt{x^2 + 9}$	$x + 3$
1		
2		
3		
4		
5		
6		

28.

x	$\sqrt{x^2 + 16}$	$x + 4$
1		
2		
3		
4		
5		
6		

29.

x	$\sqrt{x + 3}$	$\sqrt{x} + \sqrt{3}$
1		
2		
3		
4		
5		
6		

30.

x	$\sqrt{x + 4}$	$\sqrt{x} + 2$
1		
2		
3		
4		
5		
6		

FIND THE MISTAKE •

Each sentence below contains a mistake. Circle the mistake and write the correct word(s) or numbers(s) on the line provided.

1. $5\sqrt{2} + 3\sqrt{7} = 8\sqrt{9} = 8 \cdot 3 = 24$. _____

2. $5\sqrt{45} + 3\sqrt{20}$ cannot be combined, because what is under the radical is different.

_____

3. $\sqrt{16 + 25}$ is the same as $4 + 5$. _____

4. The notation $4\sqrt{5}$ assumes an addition symbol between the 4 and the $\sqrt{5}$, that is, $4 + \sqrt{5}$. _____

Trail Guide Project

Celebrating Pi

Since 1988, math enthusiasts around the world have spent March 14 celebrating the irrational number pi by eating pies and having discussions of the number's significance. Then in 2009, Congress passed a non-binding resolution that recognizes March 14 as National Pi Day. Pi, written using the Greek symbol π, represents the ratio of a circle's circumference to its diameter. Rounded to the nearest hundredth, π can be written as 3.14, which explains why National Pi Day occurs on the fourteenth day of the third month each year. However, since π is an irrational number, its digits will infinitely continue without repeating. Here are the first ten digits of π:

3.141592653

One of the activities often found on Pi Day is that of writing pi-kus. A pi-ku, the name derived from a short-form Japanese poem called haiku, is a short poem that uses the digits of pi to represent the syllables in each line. To write a pi-ku for the 3-digit approximation of pi, the first line of the poem contains three syllables, the second line one syllable, and the final line four syllables. For instance,

Today is	←	3 syllables
a	←	1 syllable
great day for math!	←	4 syllables

1. Write a pi-ku using the 3-digit approximation of π.

_____	←	3 syllables
_____	←	1 syllable
_____	←	4 syllables

2. Another style of writing known as Basic Pilish uses the digits of pi to represent the number of letters in each word. Here's an example:

But I gaze a while patiently at grassy hills and seven gorillas gallivant merrily...
3. 1 4 1 5 9 2 6 5 3 5 8 9 7

Break into groups. Each group will be assigned a different sequential set of pi's digits.

Group 1: 3.14159265358979...
Group 2: ...323846264338327...
Group 3: ...950288419716939...
Group 4: ...937510582097494...
Group 5: ...459230781640628...

For each digit, come up with a word that has the same number of letters as the digit. If the digit is 0, use a ten-letter word. The words should flow into sentences and tell a story. Punctuation may appear but is not counted as a digit. Each group should share its story with the class in the order the digits appear in pi (e.g., Group 1 shares first, then Group 2, and so on).

Hint: Use the stories as a mnemonic device to recite the digits of pi.

CHAPTER 5 SUMMARY . . . .

Place Value [5.1]

The place values for the first five places to the right of the decimal point are

Decimal Point	Tenths	Hundredths	Thousandths	Ten Thousandths	Hundred Thousandths
.	$\frac{1}{10}$	$\frac{1}{100}$	$\frac{1}{1000}$	$\frac{1}{10000}$	$\frac{1}{100000}$

1. The number 4.123 in words is "four and one hundred twenty-three thousandths."

Rounding Decimals [5.1]

If the digit in the column to the right of the one we are rounding to is 5 or more, we add 1 to the digit in the column we are rounding to; otherwise, we do not change the value. We then replace all digits to the right of the column we are rounding to with zeros if they are to the left of the decimal point; otherwise, we simply delete them.

2. 357.753 rounded to the nearest
Tenth: 357.8
Ten: 360

Addition and Subtraction with Decimals [5.2]

To add (or subtract) decimal numbers, we align the decimal points and add (or subtract) as if we were adding (or subtracting) whole numbers. The decimal point in the answer goes directly below the decimal points in the problem.

3.
$$\begin{array}{r} 3.400 \\ 25.060 \\ + 0.347 \\ \hline 28.807 \end{array}$$

Multiplication with Decimals [5.3]

To multiply two decimal numbers, we multiply as if the decimal points were not there. The decimal point in the product has as many digits to the right as there are total digits to the right of the decimal points in the two original numbers.

4. If we multiply 3.49×5.863, there will be a total of $2 + 3 = 5$ digits to the right of the decimal point in the answer.

Division with Decimals [5.4]

To begin a division problem with decimals, we make sure that the divisor is a whole number. If it is not, we move the decimal point in the divisor to the right as many places as it takes to make it a whole number. We must then be sure to move the decimal point in the dividend the same number of places to the right. Once the divisor is a whole number, we divide as usual. The decimal point in the answer is placed directly above the decimal point in the dividend.

5.
$$\begin{array}{r} 1.39 \\ 2.5.\overline{)3.4.75} \\ -25 \\ \hline 97 \\ -75 \\ \hline 225 \\ -225 \\ \hline 0 \end{array}$$

6. Write $\frac{5}{8}$ as a decimal.

Changing Fractions to Decimals [5.5]

To change a fraction to a decimal, we divide the numerator by the denominator.

Changing Decimals to Fractions [5.5]

7. $0.781 = \dfrac{781}{1000}$

To change a decimal to a fraction, we write the digits to the right of the decimal point over the appropriate power of 10.

Square Roots [5.7]

8. $\sqrt{49} = 7$ because
   $7^2 = 7 \cdot 7 = 49$

The square root of a positive number a, written $\sqrt{a}$, is the number we square to get a.

Pythagorean Theorem [5.7]

In any right triangle, the length of the longest side (the hypotenuse) is equal to the square root of the sum of the squares of the two shorter sides.

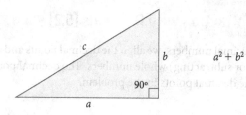

Multiplication Property for Square Roots [5.8]

If a and b are positive numbers, then

$$\sqrt{a \cdot b} = \sqrt{a} \cdot \sqrt{b}$$

In words: The square root of a product is the product of the square roots.

Simplifying Square Roots [5.8]

9. Simplify: $\sqrt{50}$
   $\sqrt{50} = \sqrt{25 \cdot 2}$
   $\phantom{\sqrt{50}} = \sqrt{25} \cdot \sqrt{2}$
   $\phantom{\sqrt{50}} = 5\sqrt{2}$

To simplify a square root, we factor the number under the square root symbol using perfect squares and then simplify.

Adding and Subtracting Roots [5.9]

10. $\sqrt{12} + \sqrt{75}$
   $= \sqrt{4 \cdot 3} + \sqrt{25 \cdot 3}$
   $= 2\sqrt{3} + 5\sqrt{3}$
   $= (2 + 5)\sqrt{3}$
   $= 7\sqrt{3}$

We add expressions containing square roots by first simplifying each square root and then, if the square roots in the resulting terms are the same, applying the distributive property.

1. Write the decimal number 6.302 in words. [5.1]

2. Write the decimal number 2.04 in words. [5.1]

3. Write the decimal number 2.00106 as a fraction or mixed number. [5.1]

4. Give the place value of the 6 in the number 23.4263. [5.1]

Write each of the following as a decimal number. [5.1]

5. Twenty-three and five thousand, six ten thousandths

6. Two hundred thirty-five ten thousandths

7. Seventy-five and seventy-five hundred thousandths

8. Round 72.1950 to the nearest hundredth. [5.1]

9. Round 128.9115 to the nearest whole number, tenth, hundredth, and thousandth. [5.1]

10. Write the following numbers in order from smallest to largest. [5.1]

    0.2   0.02   0.4   0.04   0.42   0.24

Change each decimal to a fraction, and then reduce to lowest terms. [5.1]

11. -0.75

12. 0.1875

Perform the following operations. Round to the nearest thousandth if necessary. [5.2, 5.3, 5.4]

13. $11 + 0.1 + 0.92$

14. $-14.002 + 6.098$

15. $8.3 - (1.2 - 3.4)$

16. $10 - (3 - 1.06)$

17. $\begin{array}{r} 57.4698 \\ 9.89 \\ 32.032 \\ + 572.0079 \\ \hline \end{array}$

18. $\begin{array}{r} 495.237 \\ -247.668 \\ \hline \end{array}$

19. $1.8(9.03)$

20. $11.913 \div (-4.8)$

21. $\begin{array}{r} 4.69 \\ \times 0.006 \\ \hline \end{array}$

22. $\begin{array}{r} 157.02 \\ \times 10{,}000 \\ \hline \end{array}$

23. $8.1 + 6.49$

24. $14.831 - 6.938$

25. $0.9(3.1)(-1.1)$

26. $12.364 \div 4$

27. $4.04(0.05 + 6.6)$

28. $4.09 + 0.5(6 + 0.02)$

29. $(1.1)^2 + (2.1)^2 + (3.1)^2$

30. $0.38\overline{)9.652}$

31. What number is added to -0.043 to obtain 6.054? [5.2]

32. A person purchases $7.23 worth of goods at a drugstore. If a $10 bill is used to pay for the purchases, how much change is received? [5.2]

33. If coffee sells for $5.29 per pound, how much will 4.5 pounds of coffee cost? [5.3]

34. If a person earns $540 for working 50 hours, what is the person's hourly wage? [5.4]

Convert each of the following fractions to a decimal. [5.5]

35. $\dfrac{17}{20}$

36. $-\dfrac{13}{8}$

37. Write 0.62 as a fraction in lowest terms. [5.5]

Simplify. [5.2, 5.3, 5.4, 5.5]

38. $6.8(3.9 + 0.37)$

39. $8.7 - 5(0.23)$

40. $46.918 - 6(4.92 + 0.086)$

41. $\dfrac{4}{3}(0.36) - \dfrac{7}{5}(0.3)$

42. $16.3 - 6(3.07 - 4.3)$

43. $\dfrac{1}{5}(0.38) + 7(9.1 - 2.7)$

Write each fraction as a decimal rounded to the hundredths place. [5.5]

44. $\dfrac{5}{11}$

45. $\dfrac{15}{51}$

46. Write 0.06 as a fraction in lowest terms. [5.5]

Simplify each of the following as much as possible, and write all answers as decimals. [5.5]

47. $8\left(\dfrac{4}{5}\right)(-0.03)$ **48.** $\left(\dfrac{1}{5}\right)^2(7.5) + \left(\dfrac{1}{4}\right)^2(6.4)$

Find each of the following square roots without using a calculator. [5.7]

49. $\sqrt{4}$ **50.** $\sqrt{121}$

51. $\sqrt{25} - \sqrt{4}$ **52.** $6\sqrt{64} - 11\sqrt{100}$

53. $\sqrt{\dfrac{25}{16}}$ **54.** $\sqrt{\dfrac{1}{100}}$

Simplify each of the following without using a calculator. [5.7]

55. $4\sqrt{81}$ **56.** $5\sqrt{25}$

Find the length of the hypotenuse in each right triangle. Round to the nearest hundredth if necessary. [5.7]

57.

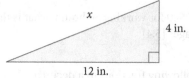

58.

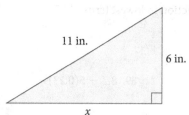

Simplify each expression by taking as much out from under the radical as possible. [5.8]

59. $\sqrt{12}$ **60.** $\sqrt{50}$ **61.** $\sqrt{20x^2}$

62. $\sqrt{16x^2}$ **63.** $\sqrt{18x^2y^2}$ **64.** $\sqrt{75x^2y^2}$

Combine. [5.9]

65. $8\sqrt{3} + 2\sqrt{3}$ **66.** $7\sqrt{6} + 10\sqrt{6}$

67. $4\sqrt{3} + \sqrt{3}$ **68.** $9\sqrt{2} + \sqrt{2}$

Simplify each square root, and then combine if possible. [5.9]

69. $\sqrt{24} + \sqrt{54}$ **70.** $\sqrt{18} + \sqrt{8}$

71. $3\sqrt{75} - 8\sqrt{27}$ **72.** $7\sqrt{20} - 2\sqrt{45}$

The diagram shows the annual sales for different brands of ice cream. Use the information to answer the following questions.

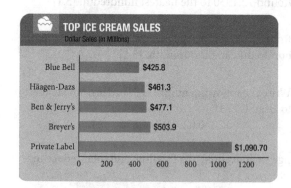

73. What are the average monthly sales for Ben & Jerry's ice cream? Round to the nearest hundredth.

74. What is the difference between Breyer's average monthly sales and Ben & Jerry's average monthly sales? Round to the nearest hundredth.

Solve each equation. [5.6]

75. $6n = -5.1$

76. $-4y - 7.9 = 4.9$

77. $\dfrac{1}{6}x - 0.08 = -0.01$

78. $0.7a - 0.2(a + 10) = 13$

Simplify.

1. $4{,}832 - (-459)$

2. $620 + (-476)$

3. $93(190)$

4. $4.390 - 1.57$

5. $6\overline{)921.41}$

6. $\dfrac{3}{7} + \dfrac{5}{6}$

7. $9.1(11.03)$

8. $1{,}178 \div 19$

9. $\dfrac{9}{14} \div \dfrac{6}{35}$

10. Twice the sum of 3 and 4 decreased by 14 results in what number?

11. Change $\frac{81}{5}$ to a mixed number.

12. Change $3\frac{7}{8}$ to an improper fraction.

13. Find the product of $3\frac{5}{8}$ and 7.

14. Change each decimal into a fraction.

Decimal	Fraction
0.125	
0.250	
0.375	
0.500	
0.625	
0.750	
0.875	
1	

15. Give the quotient of 72 and 18.

16. Translate into symbols: Four times the sum of two and three is twenty.

17. Translate into symbols: Seven times the sum of six and three is sixty-three.

18. Reduce $\dfrac{75}{130}$.

19. **True or False?** Adding the same number to the numerator and denominator of a fraction produces an equivalent fraction.

Simplify.

20. $48(3)^2 - 9(5)^2$

21. $\dfrac{3 + 7(5)}{10 + 9}$

22. $20\left(\dfrac{1}{4}\right) + 8\left(\dfrac{3}{8}\right)$

23. $\dfrac{3}{5}(0.65) + \dfrac{9}{10}(0.7)$

24. $\left(\dfrac{1}{3}\right)^3 + \left(\dfrac{1}{9}\right)^2$

25. $\left(5\dfrac{1}{8} - \dfrac{1}{3}\right)\left(3\dfrac{1}{4} + \dfrac{7}{8}\right)$

26. Suppose the temperature at 5 a.m. is 50 degrees Fahrenheit. If the temperature rises 40 degrees by 2 p.m., then decreases 4 degrees by 6 p.m., what is the temperature?

27. **Recipe** A muffin recipe calls for $4\frac{3}{4}$ cups of flour. If the recipe is doubled, how many cups of flour will be needed?

28. **Hourly Wage** If you earn $288.75 for working 35 hours, what is your hourly wage?

1. Write the decimal number 11.819 in words. [5.1]

2. Give the place value of the 8 in the number 61.8276. [5.1]

3. Write seventy-three and forty-six ten thousandths as a decimal number. [5.1]

4. Round 100.9052 to the nearest hundredth. [5.1]

Perform the following operations. [5.2, 5.3, 5.4]

5. $6 + 0.8 + 0.22$

6. $28.332 - 16.608$

7. $6.9(2.40)$

8. $96.4768 \div 16.52$

9. $6.8 + 3.3$

10. $16.47 - 8.58$

11. $0.5(3.7)(-1.8)$

12. $11.616 \div 52.8$

13. A person purchases $11.39 worth of goods at a drugstore. If a $10 bill and a $5 bill were used to pay for the purchases, how much change is received? [5.2]

14. If coffee sells for $3.29 per pound, how much will 5.5 pounds of coffee cost? [5.3]

15. If a person earns $489 for working 60 hours, what is the person's hourly wage? [5.4]

16. Write $\frac{17}{25}$ as a decimal. [5.5]

17. Write 0.38 as a fraction in lowest terms. [5.5]

Simplify. [5.2, 5.3, 5.4, 5.5]

18. $6.8(3.7 + 0.08)$

19. $6.1 - 4(0.93)$

20. $41.901 - 7(3.11 + 0.462)$

21. $\frac{7}{8}(0.11) + \frac{5}{6}(0.45)$

22. $23.4 - 8(6.01 - 4.2)$

23. $\frac{1}{5}(0.17) + 8(6.13 - 2.8)$

Find each of the following square roots without using a calculator. [5.7]

24. $\sqrt{100}$

25. $\sqrt{9}$

Simplify each of the following without using a calculator. [5.7]

26. $3\sqrt{25}$

27. $10\sqrt{9}$

Find the length of the hypotenuse in each right triangle. Round to the nearest hundredth if necessary. [5.7]

28.

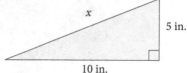

29.

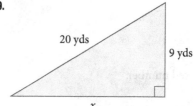

Simplify without using a calculator. [5.8]

30. $\sqrt{72}$

31. $\sqrt{48x^2}$

32. Combine $5\sqrt{7} + 3\sqrt{7}$. [5.9]

33. Simplify each square root, and then combine, if possible: $6\sqrt{12} - 5\sqrt{48}$. [5.9]

Solve each equation. [5.6]

34. $-8y - 3.1 = 29.7$

35. $\frac{1}{9}y - 0.13 = -0.01$

RATIO AND PROPORTION

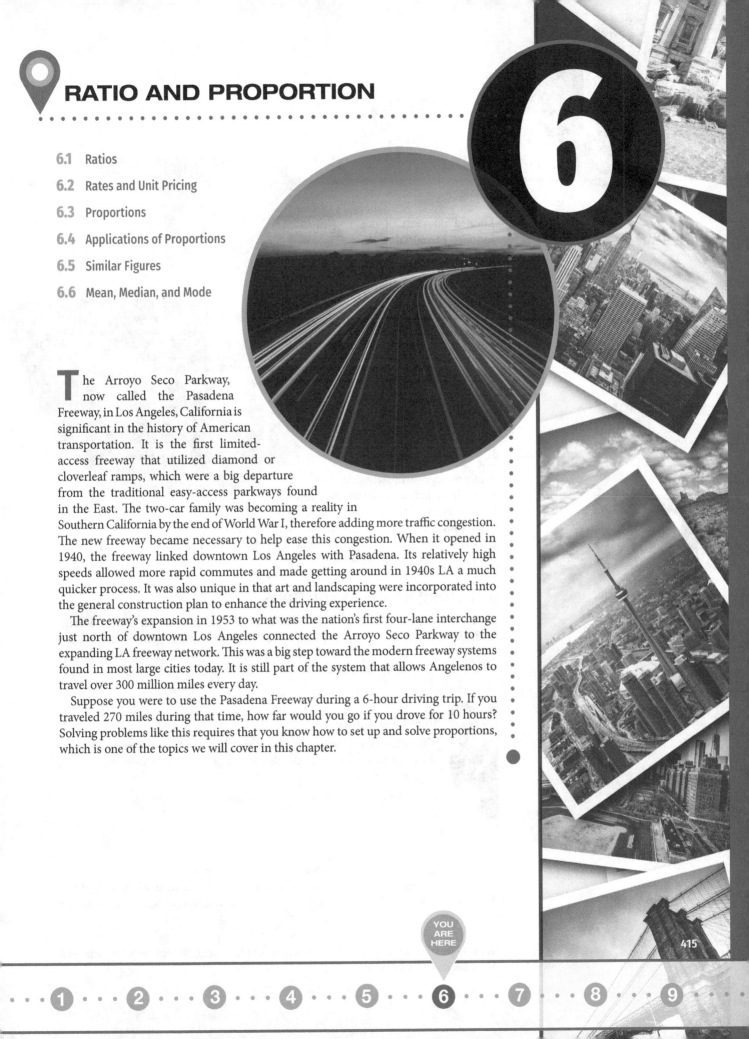

The Arroyo Seco Parkway, now called the Pasadena Freeway, in Los Angeles, California is significant in the history of American transportation. It is the first limited-access freeway that utilized diamond or cloverleaf ramps, which were a big departure from the traditional easy-access parkways found in the East. The two-car family was becoming a reality in Southern California by the end of World War I, therefore adding more traffic congestion. The new freeway became necessary to help ease this congestion. When it opened in 1940, the freeway linked downtown Los Angeles with Pasadena. Its relatively high speeds allowed more rapid commutes and made getting around in 1940s LA a much quicker process. It was also unique in that art and landscaping were incorporated into the general construction plan to enhance the driving experience.

The freeway's expansion in 1953 to what was the nation's first four-lane interchange just north of downtown Los Angeles connected the Arroyo Seco Parkway to the expanding LA freeway network. This was a big step toward the modern freeway systems found in most large cities today. It is still part of the system that allows Angelenos to travel over 300 million miles every day.

Suppose you were to use the Pasadena Freeway during a 6-hour driving trip. If you traveled 270 miles during that time, how far would you go if you drove for 10 hours? Solving problems like this requires that you know how to set up and solve proportions, which is one of the topics we will cover in this chapter.

YOU ARE HERE

6.1 RATIOS

OBJECTIVES

A Write ratios as fractions.

B Solve application problems involving ratios.

KEY WORDS

ratio

VIDEO EXAMPLES

SECTION 6.1

Located due east of the Lincoln Memorial and Reflecting Pool on the National Mall in the United States' capital city is the Washington Monument. A tribute to the military and presidential leadership of the nation's first president, George Washington, the monument remains both the world's tallest stone structure and tallest obelisk. The height of the structure measures approximately 555 feet while the base is approximately 55 feet long, adhering to the traditional Egyptian proportion for pyramids, 10 to 1. That is, the height is ten times the base. In order to understand and compare these measurements, we can use ratios, the topic of this section.

A Writing Ratios as Fractions

If we say that the ratio of two numbers is 2 to 1, then the first number is twice as large as the second number. For example, if there are 10 men and 5 women enrolled in a math class, then the ratio of men to women is 10 to 5. Because 10 is twice as large as 5, we can also say that the ratio of men to women is 2 to 1.

 **DEFINITION ratio**

The **ratio** of two numbers is a fraction, where the first number in the ratio is the numerator and the second number in the ratio is the denominator.

In symbols: If a and b are any two numbers ($b \neq 0$), then the ratio of a to b is $\frac{a}{b}$.

We can define the ratio of two numbers in terms of fractions.

We handle ratios the same way we handle fractions. For example, when we said that the ratio of 10 men to 5 women was the same as the ratio 2 to 1, we were actually saying

$$\frac{10}{5} = \frac{2}{1} \qquad \textit{Reduce to lowest terms.}$$

Because we have already studied fractions in detail, some of this introductory material on ratios may seem like review.

Example 1 Express the ratio of 16 to 48 as a fraction in lowest terms.

Solution Because the ratio is 16 to 48, the numerator of the fraction is 16 and the denominator is 48.

$$\frac{16}{48} = \frac{1}{3}$$

Notice that the first number in the ratio becomes the numerator of the fraction, and the second number in the ratio becomes the denominator.

Practice Problems

1. Express the ratio of 15 to 25 as a fraction in lowest terms.

Example 2 Write the ratio of $\frac{2}{3}$ to $\frac{4}{9}$ as a fraction in lowest terms.

Solution We begin by writing the ratio of $\frac{2}{3}$ to $\frac{4}{9}$ as a complex fraction. The numerator is $\frac{2}{3}$, and the denominator is $\frac{4}{9}$. Then we simplify.

$$\frac{\frac{2}{3}}{\frac{4}{9}} = \frac{2}{3} \div \frac{4}{9} \qquad \text{Write using division sign.}$$

$$= \frac{2}{3} \cdot \frac{9}{4} \qquad \text{Multiply by the reciprocal.}$$

$$= \frac{18}{12} \qquad \text{Multiply.}$$

$$= \frac{3}{2} \qquad \text{Reduce to lowest terms.}$$

2. Write the ratio of $\frac{3}{4}$ to $\frac{5}{8}$ as a fraction in lowest terms.

Example 3 Write the ratio of 0.08 to 0.12 as a fraction in lowest terms.

Solution When the ratio is in reduced form, it is customary to write it with whole numbers and not decimals. For this reason, we multiply the numerator and the denominator of the ratio by 100 to clear it of decimals. Then we reduce to lowest terms.

$$\frac{0.08}{0.12} = \frac{0.08 \times 100}{0.12 \times 100} \qquad \text{Multiply the numerator and the denominator by 100 to clear the ratio of decimals.}$$

$$= \frac{8}{12} \qquad \text{Multiply.}$$

$$= \frac{2}{3} \qquad \text{Reduce to lowest terms.}$$

3. Write the ratio of 0.16 to 0.20 as a fraction in lowest terms.

Note Another symbol used to denote ratio is the colon (:). The ratio of, say, 5 to 4 can be written as 5:4. Although we will not use it here, this notation is fairly common.

Table 1 shows several more ratios and their fractional equivalents. Notice that in each case the fraction has been reduced to lowest terms. Also, the ratio that contains decimals has been rewritten as a fraction that does not contain decimals.

Table 1			
Ratio	**Fraction**	**Fraction in lowest terms**	
25 to 35	$\frac{25}{35}$	$\frac{5}{7}$	
8 to 2	$\frac{8}{2}$	$\frac{4}{1}$	We can also write this as just 4.
$\frac{1}{4}$ to $\frac{3}{4}$	$\frac{\frac{1}{4}}{\frac{3}{4}}$	$\frac{1}{3}$	because $\frac{\frac{1}{4}}{\frac{3}{4}} = \frac{1}{4} \div \frac{3}{4} = \frac{1}{4} \cdot \frac{4}{3} = \frac{1}{3}$
0.6 to 1.7	$\frac{0.6}{1.7}$	$\frac{6}{17}$	because $\frac{0.6 \times 10}{1.7 \times 10} = \frac{6}{17}$

Answers

1. $\frac{3}{5}$

2. $\frac{6}{5}$

3. $\frac{4}{5}$

4. During a game, a baseball pitcher throws 50 strikes out of 80 pitches. Write the ratio of the strikes to total pitches as a fraction in lowest terms.

B Solving Application Problems

Example 4   During a game, a basketball player makes 12 out of the 18 free throws he attempts. Write the ratio of the number of free throws he makes to the number of free throws he attempts as a fraction in lowest terms.

Solution   Because he makes 12 out of 18, we want the ratio 12 to 18, or

$$\frac{12}{18} = \frac{2}{3}$$

Because the ratio is 2 to 3, we can say that, in this particular game, he made 2 out of every 3 free throws he attempted.

5. A solution of radiator fluid contains 2 pints antifreeze and 8 pints water. Find the ratio of antifreeze to water, water to antifreeze, antifreeze to total solution, and water to total solution.

Example 5   A solution of alcohol and water contains 15 milliliters of water and 5 milliliters of alcohol. Find the ratio of alcohol to water, water to alcohol, water to total solution, and alcohol to total solution. Write each ratio as a fraction and reduce to lowest terms.

Solution   There are 5 milliliters of alcohol and 15 milliliters of water, so there are 20 milliliters of solution (alcohol + water). The ratios are as follows:

The ratio of alcohol to water is 5 to 15, or

$$\frac{5}{15} = \frac{1}{3} \qquad \text{In lowest terms}$$

The ratio of water to alcohol is 15 to 5, or

$$\frac{15}{5} = \frac{3}{1} \qquad \text{In lowest terms}$$

The ratio of water to total solution is 15 to 20, or

$$\frac{15}{20} = \frac{3}{4} \qquad \text{In lowest terms}$$

The ratio of alcohol to total solution is 5 to 20, or

$$\frac{5}{20} = \frac{1}{4} \qquad \text{In lowest terms}$$

6. Using the information from Example 6, find the ratio of the price of the medium pizza to the large pizza. Then change the ratio to a decimal rounded to the nearest hundredth.

Example 6   Suppose a pizza restaurant advertised the following prices for their deep-dish pizza. Use the information to find the ratio of the cost of the large cheese pizza to the medium cheese pizza. Then change the ratio to a decimal rounded to the nearest tenth.

Size	Price
Medium 12" cheese	$12.00
Large 15" cheese	$16.50

Answers

4. $\frac{5}{8}$

5. $\frac{1}{4}, \frac{4}{1}, \frac{1}{5}, \frac{4}{5}$

6. $\frac{8}{11} \approx 0.73$

Solution The ratio of the large pizza to the medium is

$$\frac{16.5}{12.0} = \frac{16.5 \times 10}{12.0 \times 10}$$ Multiply the numerator and denominator by 10 to clear the ratio of decimals.

$$= \frac{165}{120}$$ Multiply.

$$= \frac{11}{8}$$ Reduce to lowest terms.

To convert to a decimal, we divide 11 by 8 and round to the nearest tenth.

$$\frac{11}{8} \approx 1.4$$

KEY CONCEPT REVIEW

After reading through the preceding section, respond in your own words and in complete sentences.

A. In your own words, write a definition for the ratio of two numbers.

B. What does a ratio compare?

C. What are some different ways of using mathematics to write the ratio of *a* to *b*?

D. When will the ratio of two numbers be a complex fraction?

EXERCISE SET 6.1 ···

VOCABULARY REVIEW •

Choose the correct words to fill in the blanks below.

| colon | numerator | fraction | denominator | ratio |

1. The ratio of two numbers is a _____, where the first number in the ratio is the numerator and second number in the ratio is the denominator.

2. When writing the ratio 6 to 8 as a fraction, 6 is the _____ and 8 is the _____.

3. If a and b are any two numbers, then the _____ of a to b is $\frac{a}{b}$.

4. A symbol used to denote a ratio is the _____.

Problems

A Write each of the following ratios as a fraction in lowest terms. None of the answers should contain decimals.

1. 8 to 6   **2.** 6 to 8   **3.** 64 to 12   **4.** 12 to 64

5. 100 to 250   **6.** 250 to 100   **7.** 13 to 26   **8.** 36 to 18

9. $\frac{3}{4}$ to $\frac{1}{4}$ **10.** $\frac{5}{8}$ to $\frac{3}{8}$ **11.** $\frac{7}{3}$ to $\frac{6}{3}$ **12.** $\frac{9}{5}$ to $\frac{11}{5}$

13. $\frac{6}{5}$ to $\frac{6}{7}$ **14.** $\frac{5}{3}$ to $\frac{5}{8}$ **15.** $2\frac{1}{2}$ to $3\frac{1}{2}$ **16.** $5\frac{1}{4}$ to $1\frac{3}{4}$

17. $2\frac{2}{3}$ to $\frac{5}{3}$ **18.** $\frac{1}{2}$ to $3\frac{1}{2}$ **19.** 0.05 to 0.15   **20.** 0.21 to 0.03

21. 0.3 to 3   **22.** 0.5 to 10   **23.** 1.2 to 10   **24.** 6.4 to 0.8

Use the figures to answer the following questions.

25. **a.** What is the ratio of shaded squares to nonshaded squares?

    b. What is the ratio of shaded squares to total squares?

    c. What is the ratio of nonshaded squares to total squares?

26. **a.** What is the ratio of shaded squares to nonshaded squares?

    b. What is the ratio of shaded squares to total squares?

    c. What is the ratio of nonshaded squares to total squares?

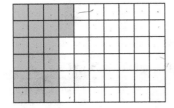

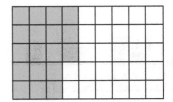

Applying the Concepts

27. **Family Budget** A family of four budgeted the amounts shown below for some of their monthly bills.

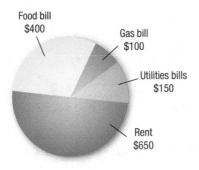

Food bill $400
Gas bill $100
Utilities bills $150
Rent $650

28. **Nutrition** One cup of breakfast cereal was found to contain the nutrients shown here.

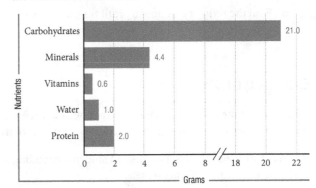

Carbohydrates 21.0
Minerals 4.4
Vitamins 0.6
Water 1.0
Protein 2.0

    a. What is the ratio of the rent to the food bill?

    b. What is the ratio of the gas bill to the food bill?

    c. What is the ratio of the utilities bills to the food bill?

    d. What is the ratio of the rent to the utilities bills?

    a. Find the ratio of water to protein.

    b. Find the ratio of carbohydrates to protein.

    c. Find the ratio of vitamins to minerals.

    d. Find the ratio of protein to vitamins and minerals.

29. **Pizza Prices** The price of several menu items from a pizza restaurant are shown in the table. Find the ratio of the prices for the following items.

    a. Large pizza to garlic bread

    b. Buffalo wings to medium pizza

    c. Garlic bread to buffalo wings

    d. Garlic bread to medium pizza

Item	Price
Large pizza with pepperoni	$18.25
Medium pizza with pepperoni	$12.75
Buffalo wings	$6.50
Garlic bread	$3.50

30. **Profit and Revenue** The following bar chart shows the profit and revenue of a company each quarter for one year.

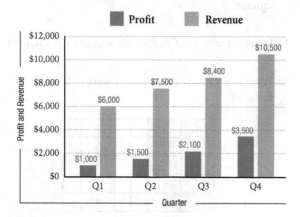

Find the ratio of revenue to profit for each of the following quarters. Write your answers in lowest terms.

a. Q1   **b.** Q2   **c.** Q3   **d.** Q4

e. Find the ratio of revenue to profit for the entire year.

31. **Geometry** In the diagram below, AC represents the length of the line segment that starts at A and ends at C. From the diagram we see that $AC = 8$.

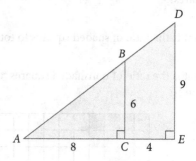

a. Find the ratio of BC to AC.

b. What is the length AE?

c. Find the ratio of DE to AE.

Calculator Problems

Write each of the following ratios as a fraction, and then use a calculator to change the fraction to a decimal. Round all decimal answers to the nearest hundredth. Do not reduce fractions.

Number of Students The total number of students attending a community college in the Midwest is 4,722. Of these students, 2,314 are male and 2,408 are female.

32. Give the ratio of males to females as a fraction and as a decimal.

33. Give the ratio of females to males as a fraction and as a decimal.

34. Give the ratio of males to total number of students as a fraction and as a decimal.

35. Give the ratio of total number of students to females as a fraction and as a decimal.

Getting Ready for the Next Section

Write as a decimal.

36. $\dfrac{90}{5}$

37. $\dfrac{120}{3}$

38. $\dfrac{125}{2}$

39. $\dfrac{2}{10}$

40. $\dfrac{1.23}{2}$

41. $\dfrac{1.39}{2}$

42. $\dfrac{88}{0.5}$

43. $\dfrac{1.99}{0.5}$

44. $\dfrac{46}{0.25}$

45. $\dfrac{9}{0.25}$

Divide. Round answers to the nearest thousandth.

46. $0.48 \div 5.5$ **47.** $0.75 \div 11.5$ **48.** $2.19 \div 46$ **49.** $1.25 \div 50$

Improving Your Quantitative Literacy

50. Stock Market One method of comparing stocks on the stock market is the price to earnings ratio, or P/E.

$$\text{P/E} = \frac{\text{Current Stock Price}}{\text{Earnings per Share}}$$

Most stocks have a P/E between 25 and 40. A stock with a P/E of less than 25 may be undervalued, while a stock with a P/E greater than 40 may be overvalued. Fill in the P/E for each stock listed in the table. Based on your results, are any of the stocks undervalued?

Stock	Price	Earnings Per Share	P/E
IBM	146.05	$6.35	
AOL	139.69	$0.61	
DIS	30.03	$0.91	
KM	15.64	$0.68	
GE	90.75	$2.75	
TOY	19.92	$1.66	

FIND THE MISTAKE •

Each sentence below contains a mistake. Circle the mistake and write the correct word(s) or numbers(s) on the line provided.

1. Writing the ratio of $\frac{2}{5}$ to $\frac{3}{8}$ is the same as writing $\frac{2}{5} \cdot \frac{3}{8}$.

_____

2. The ratio of 6 to 24 expressed in lowest terms is 4. _____

3. To write the ratio of 0.04 to 0.20 as a fraction in lowest terms, you must first multiply 0.20 by 10.

_____

4. A cleaning solution of bleach and water contains 100 milliliters of bleach and 150 milliliters of water. To find the ratio of water to the whole solution in lowest terms, you must write the ratio as $\frac{150}{100}$.

_____

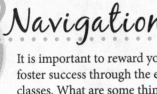

Navigation Skills

It is important to reward yourself for working hard in this class. Recognizing your achievement will help foster success through the end of this course, and enable you to carry over the skills you've learned to future classes. What are some things you can do to reward and celebrate yourself? Also, for future classes, you could decide on these rewards at the beginning of the course. Schedule smaller short-term rewards to work towards as you complete each chapter. Then have a long-term reward that you achieve at the end of the course to celebrate your overall success. You deserve it. Congratulations!

6.2

RATES AND UNIT PRICING

OBJECTIVES

A Convert ratios to rates.

B Calculate unit prices.

KEY WORDS

rate

unit pricing

VIDEO EXAMPLES

SECTION 6.2

A Rates

Iceland is located in the Nordic Island nation, approximately 2,700 kilometers from the North Pole. Travelers to Iceland have the opportunity to visit black sand beaches, tour crystal caves, and explore glacier lagoons. Between September and April, you can even see the Northern Lights. In addition to these natural wonders, you can also visit manmade attractions such as the Blue Lagoon hot springs and Hallgrínskirkja church.

The distance from New York City to Reykjavik, Iceland's most populous city, is approximately 4,100 kilometers. By airplane, this trip takes approximately 5 hours and 30 minutes or 5.5 hours. To determine how fast a plane on this route is traveling we can use a ratio. A ratio that compares two quantities, such as kilometers and time, is called a **rate**. The average speed of a plane traveling from New York to Reykjavik can be expressed as the ratio of kilometers to time.

$$\frac{4100 \text{ kilometers}}{5.5 \text{ hours}}$$

A rate is expressed in simplest form when the numerical part of the denominator is 1. To do this we use division. Because 4,100 divided by 5.5 is approximately 745.5, the speed of the plane is about 745.5 kilometers per hour or 745.5 kilometers/hour.

In this section, we will use this concept to find rates and unit prices.

Practice Problems

1. A car travels 238 miles in 3.5 hours. What is the car's rate in miles per hour?

Example 1   A train travels 125 miles in 2 hours. What is the train's rate in miles per hour?

Solution   The ratio of miles to hours is

$$\frac{125 \text{ miles}}{2 \text{ hours}} = 62.5 \frac{\text{miles}}{\text{hours}} \qquad \textit{Divide 125 by 2.}$$

$$= 62.5 \text{ miles/hour}$$

If the train travels 125 miles in 2 hours, then its average rate of speed is 62.5 miles per hour.

Answer

1. 68 miles per hour

Example 2 A car travels 90 miles on 5 gallons of gas. Give the ratio of miles to gallons as a rate.

Solution   The ratio of miles to gallons is

$$\frac{90 \text{ miles}}{5 \text{ gallons}} = 18 \frac{\text{miles}}{\text{gallon}} \qquad \text{Divide 90 by 5.}$$

$$= 18 \text{ miles/gallon}$$

The gas mileage of the car is 18 miles per gallon.

2. A car travels 357 miles on 8.5 gallons of gas. Give the ratio of miles to gallons as a rate.

B Unit Pricing

One kind of rate that is very common is **unit pricing.** Unit pricing is the cost per one unit. In other words, it is the ratio of price to quantity when the quantity is one unit. Suppose a 1-liter bottle of a certain soft drink costs $1.19, whereas a 2-liter bottle of the same drink costs $1.39. Which is the better buy? That is, which has the lower price per liter?

$$\frac{\$1.19}{1 \text{ liter}} = \$1.19 \text{ per liter} \qquad\qquad \frac{\$1.39}{2 \text{ liters}} = \$0.695 \text{ per liter}$$

The unit price for the 1-liter bottle is $1.19 per liter, whereas the unit price for the 2-liter bottle is 69.5¢ per liter. The 2-liter bottle is a better buy.

Example 3 A supermarket sells low-fat milk in three different containers at the following prices:

| 1 gallon | ½ gallon | 1 quart (1 quart = 0.25 gallon) |
| $3.59 | $1.99 | $1.29 |

Give the unit price in dollars per gallon for each one to decide which container has the highest and lowest unit price.

3. A store sells paper towels for $2.57 (4-pack) and $5.99 (10-pack). Find the unit price for each package to determine the cheapest unit price.

Solution   Because 1 quart = 0.25 gallon, we have

$$1\text{-gallon container} \quad \frac{\$3.59}{1 \text{ gallon}} = \$3.59 \text{ per gallon}$$

$$\tfrac{1}{2}\text{-gallon container} \quad \frac{\$1.99}{\tfrac{1}{2} \text{ gallon}} = \frac{\$1.99}{0.5 \text{ gallon}} = \$3.98 \text{ per gallon}$$

$$1\text{-quart container} \quad \frac{\$1.29}{1 \text{ quart}} = \frac{\$1.29}{0.25 \text{ gallon}} = \$5.16 \text{ per gallon}$$

The 1-gallon container has the lowest unit price, whereas the 1-quart container has the highest unit price.

● KEY CONCEPT REVIEW

After reading through the preceding section, respond in your own words and in complete sentences.

A. In your own words, explain what a rate is.

B. When is a rate written in simplest terms?

C. What is unit pricing?

D. Give some examples of rates not found in your textbook.

Spotlight on Success

LAUREN, student instructor

There are a lot of word problems in algebra and many of them involve topics that I don't know much about. I am better off solving these problems if I know something about the subject. So, I try to find something I can relate to. For instance, an example may involve the amount of fuel used by a pilot in a jet airplane engine. In my mind, I'd change the subject to something more familiar, like the mileage I'd be getting in my car and the amount spent on fuel, driving from my hometown to my college. Changing these problems to more familiar topics makes math much more interesting and gives me a better chance of getting the problem right. It also helps me to understand how greatly math affects and influences me in my everyday life. We really do use math more than we would like to admit—budgeting our income, purchasing gasoline, planning a day of shopping with friends—almost everything we do is related to math. So the best advice I can give with word problems is to learn how to associate the problem with something familiar to you.

You should know that I have always enjoyed math. I like working out problems and love the challenges of solving equations like individual puzzles. Although there are more interesting subjects to me, and I don't plan on pursuing a career in math or teaching, I do think it's an important subject that will help you in any profession.

EXERCISE SET 6.2 ··

Problems

A Solve each of the following word problems.

1. **Miles/Hour** A car travels 220 miles in 4 hours. What is the rate of the car in miles per hour?

2. **Miles/Hour** A train travels 360 miles in 5 hours. What is the rate of the train in miles per hour?

3. **Kilometers/Hour** It takes a car 3 hours to travel 252 kilometers. What is the rate in kilometers per hour?

4. **Kilometers/Hour** In 6 hours an airplane travels 4,200 kilometers. What is the rate of the airplane in kilometers per hour?

5. **Gallons/Second** The flow of water from a water faucet can fill a 3-gallon container in 15 seconds. Give the ratio of gallons to seconds as a rate in gallons per second.

6. **Gallons/Minute** A 225-gallon drum is filled in 3 minutes. What is the rate in gallons per minute?

7. **Liters/Minute** A gas tank which can hold a total of 56 liters contains only 8 liters of gas when the driver stops to refuel. If it takes 4 minutes to fill up the tank, what is the rate in liters per minute?

8. **Liters/Hour** The gas tank on a car holds 60 liters of gas. At the beginning of a 6-hour trip, the tank is full. At the end of the trip, it contains only 12 liters. What is the rate at which the car uses gas in liters per hour?

9. **Miles/Gallon** A car travels 95 miles on 5 gallons of gas. Give the ratio of miles to gallons as a rate in miles per gallon.

10. **Miles/Gallon** On a 384-mile trip, an economy car uses 8 gallons of gas. Give this as a rate in miles per gallon.

11. **Miles/Liter** The gas tank on a car has a capacity of 75 liters. On a full tank of gas, the car travels 325 miles. What is the gas mileage in miles per liter?

12. **Miles/Liter** A car pulling a trailer can travel 105 miles on 70 liters of gas. What is the gas mileage in miles per liter?

427

B Calculate unit pricing for the following problems.

13. **Cents/Ounce** A 6-ounce can of frozen orange juice costs 96¢. Give the unit price in cents per ounce.

14. **Cents/Liter** A 2-liter bottle of root beer costs $1.25. Give the unit price in cents per liter.

15. **Cents/Ounce** A 20-ounce package of frozen peas is priced at 99¢. Give the unit price in cents per ounce.

16. **Dollars/Pound** A 4-pound bag of cat food costs $8.12. Give the unit price in dollars per pound.

17. **Best Buy** Find the unit price in cents per diaper for each of the brands shown below. Round to the nearest tenth of a cent. Which is the better buy?

Dry Baby	*Happy Baby*
36 Diapers, $12.49	38 Diapers, $11.99

18. **Best Buy** Find the unit price in cents per pill for each of the brands shown below. Round to the nearest tenth of a cent. Which is the better buy?

Relief	*New Life*
100 Pills, $5.99	225 Pills, $13.96

19. **Carbon Footprint** A car produces 38.5 tons of carbon dioxide, CO_2, over a 5-year period. Find the tons of CO_2 produced per year.

20. **Pounds/Gallon** A car uses 5 gallons of gas on a trip and produces 101 pounds of carbon dioxide. Find the amount of CO_2 per gallon produced by the car.

21. **Cents/Day** If a 15-day supply of vitamins costs $1.62, what is the price in cents per day?

22. **Miles/Hour** A car travels 675.4 miles in $12\frac{1}{2}$ hours. Give the rate in miles per hour to the nearest hundredth.

23. **Miles/Gallon** A truck's odometer reads 15,208.3 at the beginning of a trip and 15,336.7 at the end of the trip. If the trip takes 13.8 gallons of gas, what is the gas mileage in miles per gallon? (Round to the nearest tenth.)

24. **Miles/Hour** At the beginning of a trip, the odometer on a car read 32,567.2 miles. At the end of the trip, it read 32,741.8 miles. If the trip took $4\frac{1}{4}$ hours, what was the rate of the car in miles per hour to the nearest tenth?

Getting Ready for the Next Section

Solve each equation by finding a number to replace *n* with that will make the equation a true statement.

25. $2n = 12$ **26.** $3n = 27$ **27.** $6n = 24$ **28.** $8n = 16$

29. $20 = 5n$ **30.** $35 = 7n$ **31.** $650 = 10n$ **32.** $630 = 7n$

Improving Your Quantitative Literacy

33. Unit Pricing An article in *USA Today* reported that the makers of Wisk liquid detergent cut the size of its popular midsize jug from 100 ounces (3.125 quarts) to 80 ounces (2.5 quarts). At the same time it lowered the price from $6.99 to $5.75. Fill in the table and use your results to decide which of the two sizes is the better buy.

Wisk laundry detergent		
	Old	New
Size	3.125 quarts	2.5 quarts
Container cost	$6.99	$5.75
Price per quart		

FIND THE MISTAKE •

Each sentence below contains a mistake. Circle the mistake and write the correct word(s) or numbers(s) on the line provided.

1. The rate in miles per hour for a plane traveling 3000 miles in 6 hours is 50 miles per hour.

_____

2. If a runner can run 16 miles in 2 hours, then her ratio of miles to hours is $\frac{1}{8}$ miles per hour.

_____

3. If a supermarket sells a package of 20 cookies for $4.27, then the unit price for each cookie is $4.68. _____

4. A supermarket sells 10 packages of oatmeal for $5.33. A wholesale store sells the same oatmeal for $8.86 for 24 packages of oatmeal. Given the information, we find that the supermarket has the lowest unit price. _____

6.3

 PROPORTIONS

OBJECTIVES

A Solve proportions.

KEY WORDS

proportion

term

extremes

means

VIDEO EXAMPLES

SECTION 6.3

The Elizabeth Tower at the north end of the Palace of Westminster in London, England is more commonly known as Big Ben. Although the nickname is supposed to be for the bell of the clock, the term is often used by locals and visitors to refer to the clock, the bell, and the tower together. The origin of the nickname is unknown; some speculate that it's for Sir Benjamin Hall, who lead the installation of the clock, while others argue that it's for Benjamin Caunt, an English boxing champion.

On a trip to London, the capital city of the United Kingdom, you visit Big Ben in addition to Buckingham Palace, the London Eye, and Downing Street. You pick up a miniature version of Big Ben in a gift shop as a souvenir. The model tower measures 9.4 inches tall and has a base of 2.4 inches. If you know the height of the actual tower is approximately 3,780 inches tall we can find the approximate measurement for the base using a proportion. To do so, we put the measurements of the model and the actual tower into ratios and set them equal to each other to solve for x.

$$\frac{x}{3780} = \frac{2.4}{9.4}$$

After reading this section, you will be able to find the value for x. First, let's formally define proportions.

A Solving Proportions Using the Fundamental Property

In this section, we will solve problems using proportions. As you will see later in this chapter, proportions can model a number of everyday applications.

DEFINITION proportion

A statement that two ratios are equal is called a **proportion**.
If $\frac{a}{b}$ and $\frac{c}{d}$ $(b, d \neq 0)$ are two equal ratios, then the statement

$$\frac{a}{b} = \frac{c}{d}$$

is called a proportion.

Each of the four numbers in a proportion is called a **term** of the proportion. We number the terms of a proportion as follows:

First term $\longrightarrow$ $\dfrac{a}{b}$ = $\dfrac{c}{d}$ $\longleftarrow$ Third term
Second term $\longrightarrow$ $\quad\quad$ $\longleftarrow$ Fourth term

The first and fourth terms of a proportion are called the **extremes,** and the second and third terms of a proportion are called the **means.**

Means $\longrightarrow$ $\dfrac{a}{b}$ = $\dfrac{c}{d}$ $\longleftarrow$ Extremes

In the fraction above, b and c are the means. The terms a and d are the extremes. Being able to identify these terms is important when solving proportions, which will be the focus of the rest of this section.

Practice Problems

1. In the proportion $\frac{5}{8} = \frac{15}{24}$, name the four terms, the means, and the extremes.

Example 1 In the proportion $\frac{3}{4} = \frac{6}{8}$, name the four terms, the means, and the extremes.

Solution The terms are numbered as follows:

First term = 3 $\quad\quad\quad$ Third term = 6
Second term = 4 $\quad\quad\quad$ Fourth term = 8

The means are 4 and 6; the extremes are 3 and 8.

The key thing we need to know about proportions is the following property.

PROPERTY Fundamental Property of Proportions

In any proportion, the product of the extremes is equal to the product of the means. In symbols, it looks like this:

If $\quad \dfrac{a}{b} = \dfrac{c}{d} \quad$ then $\quad ad = bc \quad$ for $b \neq 0$ and $d \neq 0$.

Sometimes we refer to these as crossproducts.

Example 2 Verify the fundamental property of proportions for the following proportions.

a. $\dfrac{3}{4} = \dfrac{6}{8}$

b. $\dfrac{17}{34} = \dfrac{1}{2}$

2. Verify the fundamental property of proportions for the following proportions.

a. $\frac{9}{10} = \frac{36}{40}$

b. $\frac{2}{3} = \frac{24}{36}$

Solution We verify the fundamental property by finding the product of the means and the product of the extremes in each case.

a. The product of the means is $4 \cdot 6 = 24$ and the product of the extremes is $3 \cdot 8 = 24$.

b. The product of the means is $34 \cdot 1 = 34$ and the product of the extremes is $17 \cdot 2 = 34$.

For each proportion the product of the means is equal to the product of the extremes.

Answers

1. First term = 5, second term = 8, third term = 15, fourth term = 24; means: 8 and 15; extremes: 5 and 24.

2. a. $9 \cdot 40 = 360$; $10 \cdot 36 = 360$
b. $2 \cdot 36 = 72$; $3 \cdot 24 = 72$

We can use the fundamental property of proportions to solve an equation that has the form of a proportion.

3. Solve $\frac{3}{10} = \frac{12}{x}$ for x.

Example 3   Solve for x.

$$\frac{2}{3} = \frac{4}{x}$$

Solution   Applying the fundamental property of proportions, we have

If $\frac{2}{3} = \frac{4}{x}$

then $2 \cdot x = 3 \cdot 4$ The product of the extremes equals the product of the means.

$2x = 12$ Multiply.

$x = 6$ Divide both sides by 2.

Note   In some of these problems you will be able to see what the solution is just by looking the problem over. In those cases it is still best to show all the work involved in solving the proportion. It is good practice for the more difficult problems.

The solution is 6. We can check our work by using the fundamental property of proportions.

$$\frac{2}{3} \diagup\!\!\!\!\diagdown \frac{4}{6}$$

12   12

Product of   Product of
the means   =   the extremes

Because the product of the means and the product of the extremes are equal, our work is correct.

· ●

4. Solve $\frac{7}{y} = \frac{14}{30}$ for y.

Example 4   Solve $\frac{5}{y} = \frac{10}{13}$ for y.

Solution   We apply the fundamental property and solve as we did in Example 3.

If $\frac{5}{y} = \frac{10}{13}$

then $5 \cdot 13 = y \cdot 10$ The product of the extremes equals the product of the means.

$65 = 10y$ Simplify.

$6.5 = y$ Divide both sides by 10.

The solution is $y = 6.5$. We could check our result by substituting 6.5 for y in the original proportion and then finding the product of the means and the product of the extremes.

· ●

5. Solve $\frac{n}{8} = \frac{0.5}{5}$ for n.

Example 5   Solve $\frac{n}{3} = \frac{0.4}{8}$ for n.

Solution   We proceed as we did in the previous two examples.

If $\frac{n}{3} = \frac{0.4}{8}$

then $n \cdot 8 = 3(0.4)$ The product of the extremes equals the product of the means.

$8n = 1.2$ Simplify.

$n = 0.15$ Divide both sides by 8.

Answers

3. $x = 40$

4. $y = 15$ The missing term is 0.15.

5. $n = 0.8$

· ●

Example 6   Solve $\dfrac{\frac{2}{3}}{5} = \dfrac{x}{6}$ for x.

Solution   We begin by multiplying the means and multiplying the extremes.

If $\qquad \dfrac{\frac{2}{3}}{5} = \dfrac{x}{6}$

then $\qquad \dfrac{2}{3} \cdot 6 = 5 \cdot x$ $\qquad$ *The product of the extremes equals the product of the means.*

$\qquad\qquad 4 = 5x$ $\qquad$ $\dfrac{2}{3} \cdot 6 = 4$

$\qquad\qquad \dfrac{4}{5} = x$ $\qquad$ *Divide both sides by 5.*

The missing term is $\frac{4}{5}$, or 0.8.

6. Solve $\dfrac{\frac{3}{4}}{6} = \dfrac{x}{10}$ for x.

Example 7   Solve $\dfrac{b}{15} = 2$ for b.

Solution   Since 2 can be written as the ratio of 2 to 1, we can write this equation as a proportion, and then solve as we have in the examples above.

$\qquad \dfrac{b}{15} = 2$

$\qquad \dfrac{b}{15} = \dfrac{2}{1}$ $\qquad$ *Write 2 as a ratio.*

$\qquad b \cdot 1 = 15 \cdot 2$ $\qquad$ *Product of the extremes equals the product of the means.*

$\qquad b = 30$ $\qquad$ *Simplify.*

Therefore, the missing term is 30.

7. Solve $\dfrac{a}{20} = 4$.

As we've seen from these examples, the procedure for finding a missing term in a proportion is always the same. We first apply the fundamental property of proportions to find the product of the extremes and the product of the means. Then we solve the resulting equation.

 KEY CONCEPT REVIEW

After reading through the preceding section, respond in your own words and in complete sentences.

A. In your own words, give a definition of a proportion.

B. In the proportion $\frac{2}{5} = \frac{4}{x}$, name the means and the extremes.

C. State the fundamental property of proportions in words and in symbols.

D. For the proportion $\frac{2}{5} = \frac{4}{x}$, find the product of the means and the product of the extremes.

Answers

6. $x = \frac{5}{4}$ or 1.25

7. $a = 80$

VOCABULARY REVIEW ·

Choose the correct words to fill in the blanks below.

product	proportion	term	fundamental property of proportions
first	second	third	fourth

1. If $\frac{a}{b}$ and $\frac{c}{d}$ are two equal ratios, then the statement $\frac{a}{b} = \frac{c}{d}$ is called a _____.

2. Each of the four numbers in a proportion is called a _____.

3. The _____ and _____ terms of a proportion are called the extremes.

4. The _____ and _____ terms of a proportion are called the means.

5. The fundamental property of proportions states that the _____ of the extremes is equal to the product of the means.

6. To find a missing term in a proportion, first apply the _____ and then solve the resulting equation.

Problems

A For each of the following proportions, name the means, name the extremes, and show that the product of the means is equal to the product of the extremes.

1. $\frac{1}{3} = \frac{5}{15}$

2. $\frac{6}{12} = \frac{1}{2}$

3. $\frac{10}{25} = \frac{2}{5}$

4. $\frac{5}{8} = \frac{10}{16}$

5. $\frac{\frac{1}{3}}{\frac{1}{2}} = \frac{4}{6}$

6. $\frac{2}{\frac{1}{4}} = \frac{4}{\frac{1}{2}}$

7. $\frac{0.5}{5} = \frac{1}{10}$

8. $\frac{0.3}{1.2} = \frac{1}{4}$

Find the missing term in each of the following proportions. Set up each problem like the examples in this section. For problems 30–36, write your answers in decimal form. For the other problems, write your answers as fractions in lowest terms.

9. $\dfrac{3}{5} = \dfrac{6}{x}$

10. $\dfrac{3}{8} = \dfrac{9}{x}$

11. $\dfrac{1}{y} = \dfrac{5}{12}$

12. $\dfrac{2}{y} = \dfrac{6}{10}$

13. $\dfrac{x}{4} = \dfrac{3}{8}$

14. $\dfrac{x}{5} = \dfrac{7}{10}$

15. $\dfrac{5}{9} = \dfrac{x}{2}$

16. $\dfrac{3}{7} = \dfrac{x}{3}$

17. $\dfrac{3}{7} = \dfrac{3}{x}$

18. $\dfrac{2}{9} = \dfrac{2}{x}$

19. $\dfrac{x}{2} = 7$

20. $\dfrac{x}{3} = 10$

21. $\dfrac{\frac{1}{2}}{y} = \dfrac{\frac{1}{3}}{12}$

22. $\dfrac{\frac{2}{3}}{y} = \dfrac{\frac{1}{3}}{15}$

23. $\dfrac{n}{12} = \dfrac{\frac{1}{4}}{\frac{1}{2}}$

24. $\dfrac{n}{10} = \dfrac{\frac{3}{5}}{\frac{3}{8}}$

25. $\dfrac{10}{20} = \dfrac{20}{n}$

26. $\dfrac{8}{4} = \dfrac{4}{n}$

27. $\dfrac{x}{10} = \dfrac{10}{2}$

28. $\dfrac{x}{12} = \dfrac{12}{48}$

29. $\dfrac{y}{12} = 0.25$

30. $\dfrac{y}{16} = 0.75$

31. $\dfrac{0.4}{1.2} = \dfrac{1}{x}$

32. $\dfrac{0.3}{1.5} = \dfrac{1}{x}$

33. $\dfrac{0.3}{0.18} = \dfrac{n}{0.6}$

34. $\dfrac{0.01}{0.1} = \dfrac{n}{10}$

35. $\dfrac{0.5}{x} = \dfrac{3.5}{0.7}$

36. $\dfrac{0.3}{x} = \dfrac{2.4}{0.8}$

Getting Ready for the Next Section

Divide.

37. $360 \div 18$

38. $2,700 \div 6$

39. $3,300 \div 11$

40. $1,440 \div 24$

Multiply.

41. $3.5(85)$

42. $4.75(105)$

43. $4.2(12)$

44. $1.25(34)$

Solve each equation.

45. $\dfrac{x}{10} = \dfrac{270}{6}$

46. $\dfrac{x}{45} = \dfrac{8}{18}$

47. $\dfrac{x}{25} = \dfrac{4}{20}$

48. $\dfrac{x}{3.5} = \dfrac{85}{1}$

FIND THE MISTAKE •

Each sentence below contains a mistake. Circle the mistake and write the correct word(s) or numbers(s) on the line provided.

1. A statement that two proportions are equal is called a ratio. _____

2. For the proportion $\dfrac{5}{6} = \dfrac{10}{x}$, the means are 5 and x. _____

3. To solve $\dfrac{7}{10} = \dfrac{n}{0.2}$, set the product of the first and third terms equal to the product of second and fourth terms. _____

4. Solving the proportion $\dfrac{8}{5} = \dfrac{n}{\frac{3}{10}}$ gives us $n = \dfrac{3}{16}$. _____

LANDMARK REVIEW: CHECKING YOUR PROGRESS •

Write each of the following ratios as a fraction in lowest terms.

1. 5 to 6

2. 10 to 1

3. 0.6 to 6

4. 0.25 to 0.75

Solve each of the following word problems.

5. A car travels 210 miles in 3 hours. What is the rate of the car in miles per hour?

6. An 8-ounce can of corn costs $1.16. Give the unit price in cents per ounce.

Find the missing term in each of the following proportions.

7. $\dfrac{3}{7} = \dfrac{9}{x}$

8. $\dfrac{x}{12} = 6$

9. $\dfrac{4}{3.6} = \dfrac{10}{x}$

10. $\dfrac{4}{15} = \dfrac{x}{6}$

Model railroads continue to be as popular today as they ever have been. One of the first things model railroaders ask each other is what scale they work with. The scale of a model train indicates its size relative to a full-size train. Each scale is associated with a ratio and a fraction, as shown in the table and bar chart below. An HO scale model train, a common model, has a ratio of 1 to 87, meaning it is $\frac{1}{87}$ as large as an actual train.

Scale	Ratio	As a Fraction
LGB	1 to 22.5	$\frac{1}{22.5}$
#1	1 to 32	$\frac{1}{32}$
O	1 to 43.5	$\frac{1}{43.5}$
S	1 to 64	$\frac{1}{64}$
HO	1 to 87	$\frac{1}{87}$
TT	1 to 120	$\frac{1}{120}$

How long is an actual boxcar that has an HO scale model 5 inches long? In this section we will solve this problem using proportions.

A Solving Application Problems Using Proportions

Proportions can be used to solve a variety of word problems. The examples that follow show some of these word problems. In each case we will translate the word problem into a proportion and then solve the proportion using the methods developed in this chapter.

Practice Problems

1. If you travel 310 miles in 5 hours, and continue at the same rate, how far will you travel in 12 hours?

$\mathcal{Note}$ In mathematics, the word "as" often indicates that a proportion or ratio should be used.

2. A baseball pitcher gives up 6 earned runs in 18 innings. If he continues at this rate, how many earned runs will he give up in 81 innings?

3. A solution contains 3.5 g salt in 40 ml of water. If another solution is to have the same ratio of salt to water and it must contain 220 ml of water, how much salt should it contain?

Answers

1. 744 miles
2. 27 earned runs
3. 19.25 g

Example 1   Suppose you drive your car 270 miles in 6 hours using the Pasadena Freeway. If you continue at the same rate, how far will you travel in 10 hours?

Solution   We let x represent the distance you travel in 10 hours. Using x, we translate the problem into the following proportion:

$$\text{Miles} \rightarrow \frac{x}{10} = \frac{270}{6} \leftarrow \text{Miles} \atop \text{Hours}$$

Notice that the two ratios in the proportion compare the same quantities. That is, both ratios compare miles to hours. In words, this proportion says

x miles is to 10 hours as 270 miles is to 6 hours

$$\frac{x}{10} = \frac{270}{6}$$

Next, we solve the proportion.

$$x \cdot 6 = 10 \cdot 270 \qquad \text{Fundamental property of proportions}$$
$$6x = 2{,}700 \qquad \text{Simplify.}$$
$$x = 450 \text{ miles} \qquad \text{Divide both sides by 6.}$$

If you continue at the same rate, you will travel 450 miles in 10 hours.

Example 2   A baseball player gets 8 hits in the first 18 games of the season. If he continues at the same rate, how many hits will he get in 45 games?

Solution   We let x represent the number of hits he will get in 45 games. Then

x is to 45 as 8 is to 18.

$$\text{Hits} \rightarrow \frac{x}{45} = \frac{8}{18} \leftarrow \text{Hits} \atop \text{Games}$$

Notice again that the two ratios are comparing the same quantities, hits to games. We solve the proportion as follows:

$$x \cdot 18 = 45 \cdot 8 \qquad \text{Fundamental property of proportions}$$
$$18x = 360 \qquad \text{Simplify.}$$
$$x = 20 \qquad \text{Divide both sides by 18.}$$

If he continues to hit at the rate of 8 hits in 18 games, he will get 20 hits in 45 games.

Example 3   A solution contains 4 milliliters of alcohol and 20 milliliters of water. If another solution is to have the same ratio of milliliters of alcohol to milliliters of water and must contain 25 milliliters of water, how much alcohol should it contain?

Solution   We let x represent the number of milliliters of alcohol in the second solution. The problem translates to

x milliliters is to 25 milliliters as 4 milliliters is to 20 milliliters.

$$\text{Alcohol} \rightarrow \frac{x}{25} = \frac{4}{20} \leftarrow \text{Alcohol} \atop \text{Water}$$

$$x \cdot 20 = 25 \cdot 4 \qquad \text{Fundamental property of proportions}$$
$$20x = 100 \qquad \text{Simplify.}$$
$$x = 5 \qquad \text{Divide both sides by 20.}$$

Therefore, 5 milliliters of alcohol would be combined with the 25 milliliters of water.

Example 4   The scale on a map indicates that 1 inch on the map corresponds to an actual distance of 85 miles. Two cities are 3.5 inches apart on the map. What is the actual distance between the two cities?

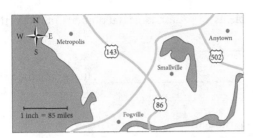

4. The scale on a map indicates that $\frac{1}{2}$ inch on the map corresponds to an actual distance of 70 miles. Two cities are $3\frac{1}{4}$ inches apart on the map. What is the actual distance between the two cities?

Solution   We let x represent the actual distance between the two cities. The proportion is

$$\text{Miles} \longrightarrow \frac{x}{3.5} = \frac{85}{1} \longleftarrow \text{Miles}$$
$$\text{Inches} \longrightarrow \qquad\qquad \longleftarrow \text{Inches}$$

$$x \cdot 1 = 3.5 \cdot 85 \qquad \text{Fundamental property of proportions}$$

$$x = 297.5 \text{ miles} \qquad \text{Simplify.}$$

  KEY CONCEPT REVIEW

After reading through the preceding section, respond in your own words and in complete sentences.

A. Give an example not found in the book of a proportion problem you may encounter.

B. Write a word problem for the proportion $\frac{2}{5} = \frac{4}{x}$.

C. What does it mean to translate a word problem into a proportion?

D. Name some jobs that may frequently require solving proportion problems.

EXERCISE SET 6.4 ······························

VOCABULARY REVIEW ·

Choose the correct words to fill in the blanks below.

proportion   quantities   word problems   fundamental property of proportions

1. Proportions can be used to solve _____.

2. When translating a word problem into a _____, make sure the two ratios in the proportion compare the same _____.

3. Once you translate a word problem into a proportion, use _____ to solve for the unknown term.

Problems

A Solve each of the following word problems by translating the statement into a proportion. Be sure to show the proportion used in each case.

1. Distance A woman drives her car 235 miles in 5 hours. At this rate how far will she travel in 7 hours?

2. Distance An airplane flies 1,260 miles in 3 hours. How far will it fly in 5 hours?

3. Basketball A basketball player scores 162 points in 9 games. At this rate how many points will he score in 20 games?

4. Football In the first 4 games of the season, a football team scores a total of 68 points. At this rate how many points will the team score in 11 games?

5. Mixture A solution contains 8 pints of antifreeze and 5 pints of water. How many pints of water must be added to 24 pints of antifreeze to get a solution with the same concentration?

6. Nutrition If 10 ounces of a certain breakfast cereal contains 3 ounces of sugar, how many ounces of sugar does 25 ounces of the same cereal contain?

7. Map Reading The scale on a map indicates that 1 inch corresponds to an actual distance of 95 miles. Two cities are 4.5 inches apart on the map. What is the actual distance between the two cities?

8. Map Reading A map is drawn so that every 2.5 inches on the map corresponds to an actual distance of 100 miles. If the actual distance between two cities is 350 miles, how far apart are they on the map?

9. Farming A farmer knows that of every 50 eggs his chickens lay, only 45 will be marketable. If his chickens lay 1,000 eggs in a week, how many of them will be marketable?

10. Manufacturing Of every 17 parts manufactured by a certain machine, 1 will be defective. How many parts were manufactured by the machine if 8 defective parts were found?

Model Trains In the introduction to this section, we indicated that the size of a model train relative to an actual train is referred to as its scale. Each scale is associated with a ratio as shown in the table. For example, an HO model train has a ratio of 1 to 87, meaning it is $\frac{1}{87}$ as large as an actual train.

Scale	Ratio
LGB	1 to 22.5
#1	1 to 32
O	1 to 43.5
S	1 to 64
HO	1 to 87
TT	1 to 120

11. **Boxcar** How long is an actual boxcar that has an HO scale model 5 inches long?
    Give your answer in inches, then divide by 12 to give the answer in feet.

12. **Length of a Flatcar** How long is an actual flatcar that has an LGB scale model 24 inches long? Give your answer in feet.

13. **Travel Expenses** A traveling salesman figures it costs 21¢ for every mile he drives his car. How much does it cost him a week to drive his car if he travels 570 miles a week?

14. **Travel Expenses** A family plans to drive their car during their annual vacation. The car can go 350 miles on a tank of gas, which is 18 gallons of gas. The vacation they have planned will cover 1,785 miles. How many gallons of gas will that take?

15. **Nutrition** A 6-ounce serving of grapefruit juice contains 159 grams of water. How many grams of water are in 10 ounces of grapefruit juice?

16. **Nutrition** If 100 grams of ice cream contains 13 grams of fat, how much fat is in 250 grams of ice cream?

17. **Travel Expenses** If a car travels 378.9 miles on 50 liters of gas, how many liters of gas will it take to go 692 miles if the car travels at the same rate? (Round to the nearest tenth.)

18. **Nutrition** If 125 grams of peas contains 26 grams of carbohydrates, how many grams of carbohydrates does 375 grams of peas contain?

19. **Elections** During a recent election, 47 of every 100 registered voters in a certain city voted. If there were 127,900 registered voters in that city, how many people voted?

20. **Map Reading** The scale on a map is drawn so that 4.5 inches corresponds to an actual distance of 250 miles. If two cities are 7.25 inches apart on the map, how many miles apart are they? (Round to the nearest tenth.)

21. **Nursing** Assume 85 mg of a drug is prescribed per 5 kg of a patient's weight. If a child weighs 16 kg, what dosage should be taken?

22. **Nursing** Assume 93 mg of a drug is prescribed per 3 kg of a patient's weight. If a child weighs 15 kg, what dosage should be taken?

23. **Nursing** Assume 22 mg of a drug is prescribed per $1 m^2$ of a patient's body surface area. If an adult has a body surface area of $1.7 \ m^2$, what dosage should be taken?

24. **Nursing** Assume 19 mg of a drug is prescribed per $1 m^2$ of a patient's body surface area. If an adult has a body surface area of $1.8 \ m^2$, what dosage should be taken?

Getting Ready for the Next Section

Simplify.

25. $\dfrac{320}{160}$

26. $21 \cdot 105$

27. $2{,}205 \div 15$

28. $\dfrac{48}{24}$

Solve each equation.

29. $\dfrac{x}{5} = \dfrac{28}{7}$

30. $\dfrac{x}{4} = \dfrac{6}{3}$

31. $\dfrac{x}{21} = \dfrac{105}{15}$

32. $\dfrac{b}{4.5} = 2$

FIND THE MISTAKE •

Each sentence below contains a mistake. Circle the mistake and write the correct word(s) or numbers(s) on the line provided.

1. A basketball player scores 112 points in 8 games. The proportion to find how many points the player will score in 14 games is $\dfrac{112}{8} = \dfrac{14}{x}$. _____

2. The scale of a map indicates that 2 inches corresponds to 250 miles in real life. If two cities on the map are 3.5 inches apart, they are 0.028 miles apart in real life. _____

3. A jellybean company knows that for every 100 jellybeans, 4 will be misshapen. The proportion needed to find how many jelly beans were made if 36 misshapen jelly beans are found is $\dfrac{4}{36} = \dfrac{x}{100}$. _____

4. If burning 1 gallon of gasoline produces 20.2 pounds of carbon dioxide, then burning 12 gallons of gasoline produces approximately 0.59 pounds of carbon dioxide. _____

SIMILAR FIGURES

6.5

In mathematics, when two or more objects have the same shape, but are different sizes, we say they are similar. If two figures are similar, then their corresponding sides are proportional.

By the time we complete this section, we will be using proportions to solve application problems. Before we do this, though, we will explore what is meant by corresponding sides of similar figures. Often it is helpful to label the parts of these figures, including triangles, as shown in the margin.

OBJECTIVES

A Use similar figures to solve for missing sides.

B Draw similar figures.

C Solve applications involving similar figures.

KEY WORDS

similar figures

corresponding sides

proportional

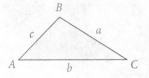
VIDEO EXAMPLES
SECTION 6.5

A Similar Triangles

Two triangles that have the same shape are similar when their corresponding sides are proportional, or have the same ratio. The triangles below are similar.

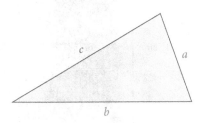
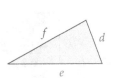

Corresponding Sides	**Ratio**
side a corresponds with side d	$\dfrac{a}{d}$
side b corresponds with side e	$\dfrac{b}{e}$
side c corresponds with side f	$\dfrac{c}{f}$

Because their corresponding sides are proportional, we write

$$\frac{a}{d} = \frac{b}{e} = \frac{c}{f}$$

Note One way to label the important parts of a triangle is to label the vertices with capital letters and the sides with lowercase letters.

Notice that side a is opposite vertex A, side b is opposite vertex B, and side c is opposite vertex C. Also, because each vertex is the vertex of one of the angles of the triangle, we refer to the three interior angles as A, B, and C.

Practice Problems

1. The two triangles below are similar. Find side x.

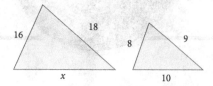

Example 1   The two triangles below are similar. Find side x.

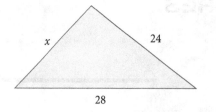
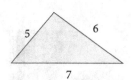

Solution   To find the length x, we set up a proportion of equal ratios. The ratio of x to 5 is equal to the ratio of 24 to 6 and to the ratio of 28 to 7. Algebraically, we have

$$\frac{x}{5} = \frac{24}{6} \quad \text{and} \quad \frac{x}{5} = \frac{28}{7}$$

We can solve either proportion to get our answer. The first gives us

$x \cdot 6 = 5 \cdot 24$	Fundamental property of proportions
$6x = 120$	Simplify.
$x = 20$	Divide both sides by 6.

Other Similar Figures

When one shape or figure is either a reduced or enlarged copy of the same shape or figure, we consider them similar. For example, video viewed over the Internet was once confined to a small "postage stamp" size. Now it is common to see larger video over the Internet. Although the width and height has increased, the shape of the video has not changed.

2. If the height of the larger drawing from Example 2 is expanded to 80 centimeters, what is the new width of the larger drawing?

Example 2   Suppose the width and height of the two similar drawings are proportional. Find the width, w, of the larger drawing.

16 cm.

32 cm.

12 cm.

w

Solution   We write our proportion as the ratio of the height of the larger drawing to the height of the smaller drawing is equal to the ratio of the width of the larger drawing to the width of the smaller drawing.

$$\frac{32}{16} = \frac{w}{12}$$

$32 \cdot 12 = 16 \cdot w$	Fundamental property of proportions
$384 = 16w$	Simplify.
$24 = w$	Divide both sides by 16.

The width of the larger drawing is 24 centimeters.

Answers

1. $x = 20$

2. 60 centimeters

B Drawing Similar Figures

Example 3   Draw a triangle similar to triangle *ABC*, if *AC* is proportional to *DF*. Make *E* the third vertex of the new triangle.

3. The base of a triangle is 4 squares of graph paper, and the height is 6 squares. If a similar triangle has a base of 6 squares, what is its height?

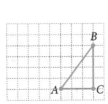 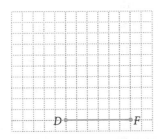

Solution   We see that *AC* is 3 units in length and *BC* has a length of 4 units. Since *AC* is proportional to *DF*, which has a length of 6 units, we set up a proportion to find the length *EF*.

$$\frac{EF}{BC} = \frac{DF}{AC}$$

$$\frac{EF}{4} = \frac{6}{3}$$

$$3EF = 24 \qquad \text{Fundamental property of proportions}$$

$$EF = 8 \qquad \text{Divide both sides by 3.}$$

Now we can draw *EF* with a length of 8 units, then complete the triangle by drawing line *DE*.

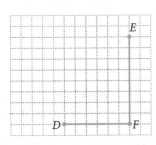 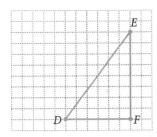

We have drawn triangle *DEF* similar to triangle *ABC*.

C Applications

Example 4   A building casts a shadow of 105 feet while a 21-foot flagpole casts a shadow that is 15 feet. Find the height of the building.

4. If the building from Example 4 is 175 feet high, how long would the shadow that is cast be?

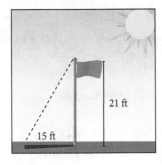 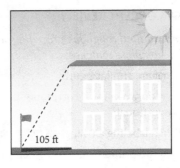

21 ft

15 ft

105 ft

Solution   The figure shows both the building and the flagpole, along with their respective shadows. From the figure we see that we have two similar triangles. Letting x represent the height of the building, we have

$$\frac{x}{21} = \frac{105}{15}$$

$$15x = 2{,}205 \qquad \textit{Fundamental property of proportions}$$

$$x = 147 \qquad \textit{Divide both sides by 15.}$$

The height of the building is 147 feet.

---

5. Suppose your chessboard has a side measuring 30 inches with a perimeter of 120 inches. The side of the life-sized board measures 150 inches. Use a proportion to determine the perimeter of the new board.

Example 5   Chessboards are square regardless of their size, which makes them proportional to each other. Suppose you have a chessboard with each side measuring 20 inches. Therefore, the perimeter of that board is 80 inches. Use the measurements of this board to design a life-sized chessboard for your local park. The park can accommodate a board with a side that is 240 inches long. Use a proportion to determine the perimeter

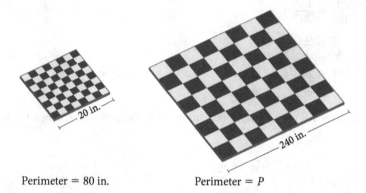

Perimeter = 80 in.   Perimeter = P

P of the new board.

Solution   Since the length of a chessboard is proportional to its perimeter, we can set up the following proportion to calculate the perimeter of the life-sized board.

$$\frac{20}{80} = \frac{240}{P}$$

$$20P = 19{,}200 \qquad \textit{Fundamental property of proportions}$$

$$P = 960 \text{ inches} \qquad \textit{Divide both sides by 20.}$$

The perimeter of the new board will be 960 inches.

> Note   We can only solve problems similar to Example 5 using proportions. We cannot use proportions to solve problems like this involving area.

KEY CONCEPT REVIEW

After reading through the preceding section, respond in your own words and in complete sentences.

A. What are similar figures?

B. How do we know if corresponding sides of two triangles are proportional?

C. When labeling a triangle ABC, how do we label the sides?

D. How are proportions used when working with similar figures?

Answer

5. 600 inches

EXERCISE SET 6.5 ·

Problems

A In problems 1–4, for each pair of similar triangles, use a proportion to find the unknown.

1.

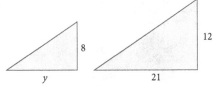

2.

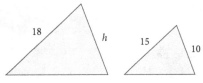

3.

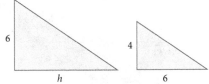

4.

In problems 5–10, for each pair of similar figures, use a proportion to find the unknown.

5.

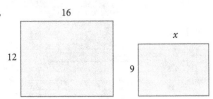

6.

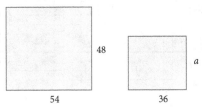

7.

8.

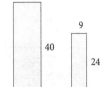

9.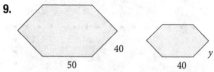

10.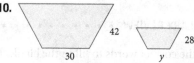

B For each problem, draw a figure on the grid on the right that is similar to the given figure.

11. *AC* is proportional to *DF*.

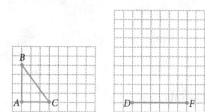

12. *AB* is proportional to *DE*.

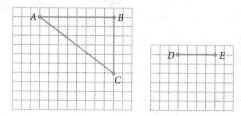

13. *BC* is proportional to *EF*.

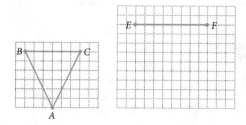

14. *AC* is proportional to *DF*.

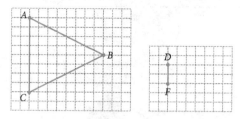

15. *DC* is proportional to *HG*.

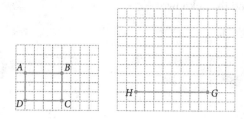

16. *AD* is proportional to *EH*.

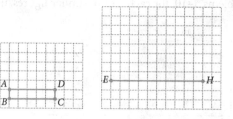

17. *AB* is proportional to *FG*.

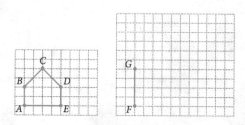

18. *BC* is proportional to *FG*.

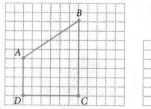

C Applying the Concepts

Recall that the perimeters of two chessboards are proportional to the length of each of their sides.

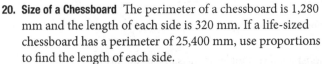

19. **Size of a Chessboard** The perimeter of a chessboard is 50 inches and the length of each side is 12.5 inches. If a life-sized chessboard has a perimeter of 1,000 inches, use proportions to find the length of each side.

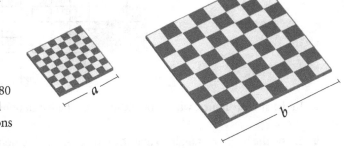

20. **Size of a Chessboard** The perimeter of a chessboard is 1,280 mm and the length of each side is 320 mm. If a life-sized chessboard has a perimeter of 25,400 mm, use proportions to find the length of each side.

21. **Video Resolution** A graphics card can increase the resolution of a computer's monitor. Suppose a monitor has a horizontal resolution of 800 pixels and a vertical resolution of 600 pixels. By adding a new graphics card, the resolutions remain in the same proportions, but the horizontal resolution increases to 1,280 pixels. What is the new vertical resolution?

22. **Video Resolution** A graphics card can increase the resolution of a computer's monitor. Suppose a monitor has a horizontal resolution of 640 pixels and a vertical resolution of 480 pixels. By adding a new graphics card, the resolutions remain in the same proportions, but the vertical resolution increases to 786 pixels. What is the new horizontal resolution?

23. **Screen Resolution** The display of the monitor of computer A is proportional to that of computer B. Computer A has a horizontal resolution of 1,680 pixels and a vertical resolution of 1,050 pixels. If computer B has a vertical resolution of 900 pixels, what is its horizontal resolution?

24. **Screen Resolution** The display of the monitor of computer A is proportional to that of computer B. Computer A has a horizontal resolution of 1,680 pixels and a vertical resolution of 1,050 pixels. If computer B has a horizontal resolution of 1,920 pixels, what is its vertical resolution?

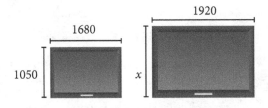

25. **Height of a Tree** A tree casts a shadow 38 feet long, while a 6-foot man casts a shadow 4 feet long. How tall is the tree?

26. **Height of a Building** A building casts a shadow 128 feet long, while a 24-foot flagpole casts a shadow 32 feet long. How tall is the building?

27. **Height of a Child** A water tower is 36 feet tall and casts a shadow 54 feet long, while a child casts a shadow 6 feet long. How tall is the child?

28. **Height of a Truck** A clock tower is 36 feet tall and casts a shadow 30 feet long, while a large truck next to the tower casts a shadow 15 feet long. How tall is the truck?

One Step Further

29. The rectangles shown here are similar.

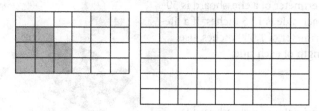

   a. In the smaller figure, what is the ratio of the shaded to nonshaded rectangles?

   b. Shade the larger rectangle so that the ratio of shaded to nonshaded rectangles is the same as in part a.

   c. For each of the figures, what is the ratio of the shaded rectangles to total rectangles?

Getting Ready for the Next Section

Simplify.

30. $\dfrac{187 + 293}{2}$

31. $\dfrac{488 + 397}{2}$

32. $\dfrac{25 + 47 + 33 + 12}{4}$

33. $\dfrac{333 + 122 + 435 + 80}{4}$

34. $100,493 - 54,392$

35. $594,332 - 412,609$

36. $\dfrac{33 + 12 + 15}{3}$

37. $\dfrac{54,493 + 12 + 11}{3}$

FIND THE MISTAKE •

Each sentence below contains a mistake. Circle the mistake and write the correct word(s) or numbers(s) on the line provided.

   1. The two triangles below are similar. The side x is equal to $\frac{4}{3}$. _____

   2. The two triangles below are similar. We can find x by solving the proportion $\frac{12}{x} = \frac{4}{2}$. _____

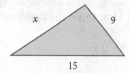

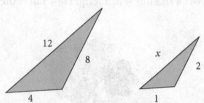

   3. The width of a rectangle on graph paper is 5 squares and the length is 7 squares. If a similar rectangle has a width of 10, then the length would be $\frac{7}{2}$. _____

   4. A pocket dictionary is similar to a regular dictionary. The pocket dictionary is 4 inches wide by 6 inches long. The width of the regular dictionary is 16 inches. You must solve the proportion $\frac{6}{4} = \frac{x}{16}$ to find the remaining side length of the regular dictionary. _____

MEAN, MEDIAN, AND MODE

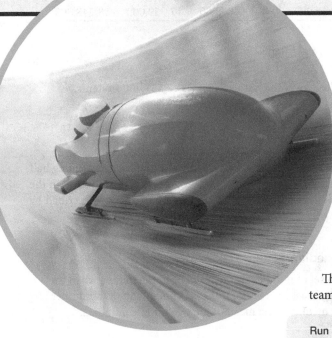

In the 2014 Winter Olympic Games, the United States four-man bobsleigh team took the bronze medal for their event. The team competed on a 1325-meter-long track. During four runs, the team logged a total time of 3:40:99 (read "3 minutes, 40 seconds, and 99 one hundredths of a second"). The following table shows the team's individual run times.

Run	Time
Run 1	54.89 seconds
Run 2	55.47 seconds
Run 3	55.30 seconds
Run 4	55.33 seconds

VIDEO EXAMPLES

SECTION 6.6

In this section, we will be discussing averages, which will give us the tools to further evaluate the bobsleigh team's times. For instance, we can calculate their mean run time as 55.25 seconds. We will discuss means and averages in greater depth in just a moment. For now, let's discuss sets.

A **set** is defined as a collection of objects or things, with the objects in the set called elements or members of the set. For example, the times above make up a set with four objects, each of the four times.

Many times we want to reduce the set to a single value called an **average** that summarizes or represents the general significance of a set. In statistics we refer to the mean and median as **measures of central tendency.** In everyday language, the word **average,** being used here as a noun, can refer to the mean, the median, or the mode.

A Mean

The mean is probably the most common measure of central tendency and it refers to the arithmetic average for a set of numbers. It is typically used to describe data sets such as test scores, salary, and various averages having to do with sports.

DEFINITION mean

The **mean**, denoted $\overline{x}$, for a set of values is the sum of the values divided by the number of values.
$$\overline{x} = \frac{x_1 + x_2 + x_3 + \ldots + x_n}{n}$$

Practice Problems

1. A runner training for an event runs 6 miles, 10 miles, 11 miles, 12 miles, and 5 miles during five days of training. What was the mean distance she trained over the five days? Round to the nearest tenth.

Example 1   Enrollment in college over a five-year period is shown by the following numbers. Find the mean enrollment over the five-year period.

16,911,000   17,272,000   17,487,000   17,759,000   18,248,000

Solution   We add the five enrollments and then divide by 5, the number of values in the set.

$$\text{Mean} = \frac{16{,}911{,}000 + 17{,}272{,}000 + 17{,}487{,}000 + 17{,}759{,}000 + 18{,}248{,}000}{5}$$

$$= \frac{87{,}677{,}000}{5} = 17{,}535{,}400$$

The mean enrollment in college over the last five years is 17,535,400 students.

B Median

The median for a set of numbers is the number in the middle of the data, meaning half the numbers in the set have a value less than the median, and half the numbers in the set have a value greater than the median. Housing prices are frequently described by using a median.

DEFINITION median

The **median** of a set of numbers is the number in the middle when the set is written from least to greatest. If the set contains an even number of elements, the median is the mean of the two middle numbers.

2. Find the median for the distances in Practice Problem 1.

Example 2   Find the median enrollment from the numbers in Example 1.

Solution   The numbers in Example 1 are already written from smallest to largest. Because there are an odd number of numbers in the set, the median is the middle number.

16,911,000   17,272,000   17,487,000   17,759,000   18,248,000
                                        ↑
                                     Median

The median enrollment for the five years is 17,487,000.

3. The selling prices of four apartments are given below. Find the median.
$860 $2,800 $750 $1,100

Example 3   These selling prices of four hybrid cars were listed on hybridcars.com.

$23,063 $31,700 $28,600 $24,650

Find the mean and the median for the four prices. Round to the nearest cent if necessary.

Solution   To find the mean, we add the four numbers and then divide by 4:

$$\frac{23{,}063 + 31{,}700 + 28{,}600 + 24{,}650}{4} = \frac{108{,}013}{4} = 27{,}003.25$$

To find the median, we write the numbers in order from smallest to largest. Then, because there is an even number of numbers, we average the middle two numbers to obtain the median.

$23,063 $24,650 $28,600 $31,700
               median
                  ↓

$$\frac{24{,}650 + 28{,}600}{2} = 26{,}625$$

The mean is $27,003.25, and the median is $26,625.

Answers
1. 8.8 miles
2. 10 miles
3. $980

C Mode

The **mode** is best used when we are looking for the most common eye color in a group of people, the most popular breed of dog in the United States, or the movie that was seen the most often. When we have a set of numbers in which one number occurs more often than the rest, that number is the mode. For example, consider the following set of golf caps:

Given the set of caps, the most popular color is green. We call this the mode.

DEFINITION mode

The mode for a set of numbers is the value that occurs most frequently. If more than one number occurs most often, there will be more than one mode. If all the numbers in the set occur the same number of times, there is no mode.

Example 4 A math class with 18 students had the grades shown below on their first test. Find the mean, the median, and the mode.

$$
\begin{array}{cccccc}
77 & 87 & 100 & 65 & 79 & 87 \\
79 & 85 & 87 & 95 & 56 & 87 \\
56 & 75 & 79 & 93 & 97 & 92
\end{array}
$$

Solution To find the mean, we add all the numbers and divide by 18.

$$\text{Mean} = \frac{77+87+100+65+79+87+79+85+87+95+56+87+56+75+79+93+97+92}{18}$$

$$= \frac{1476}{18} = 82$$

To find the median, we must put the test scores in order from smallest to largest; then, because there are an even number of test scores, we must find the mean of the middle two scores.

56 56 65 75 77 79 79 79 85 87 87 87 87 92 93 95 97 100

$$\text{Median} = \frac{85 + 87}{2} = 86$$

The mode is the most frequently occurring score. Because 87 occurs 4 times, and no other scores occur that many times, 87 is the mode.

The mean is 82, the median is 86, and the mode is 87.

4. The students in a small math class have the following scores on their final exam. Find the mean, mode, and median.

56 89 74 68 97
74 68 74 88 45

Vocabulary

When we used the word average in the beginning of this section, we used it as a noun. It can also be used as an adjective and a verb. If you are asked for the average of a set of numbers, the word average can represent the mean, the median, or the mode. When used in this way, the word average is a noun. However, if you are asked to average a set of numbers, then the word average is a verb, and you are being asked to find the mean of the numbers.

Answers

4. mean = 73.3, mode = 74, median = 74

D Range

The range of a set of data is the difference between the least and greatest values of the set. For example, the following table shows some of the minimum wages across the country.

State	Minimum Wage
Arkansas	$8.50
Connecticut	$10.10
Florida	$8.10
Massachusetts	$11.00
Rhode Island	$9.60
Wyoming	$5.15

Source: U.S. Department of Labor

From the information in the table, we see that the lowest minimum wage is found in Wyoming at $5.15 per hour and the highest minimum wage is found in Massachusetts at $11.00. The range for this set of data is the difference between these two numbers.

$$\$11.00 - \$5.15 = \$5.85$$

We say that this set of data has a range of $5.85.

> **DEFINITION   range**
>
> The **range** for a set of numbers is the difference between the largest number and the smallest number in the set.

5. Find the range of the exam scores given in Practice Problem 4.

Example 5   Find the range of the test scores given in Example 4.

Solution   The highest score is 100, and the lowest score is 56. The range is $100 - 56 = 44$.

 KEY CONCEPT REVIEW

After reading through the preceding section, respond in your own words and in complete sentences.

A. The word *average* can refer to what three mathematical concepts?

B. What is the median for a set of numbers?

C. What is the mode for a set of numbers?

D. What number must we use for x, if the average of 6, 8, and x is to be 8?

Answer

5. 52

VOCABULARY REVIEW ·

Choose the correct words to fill in the blanks below.

 mode   range   median   mean   average

1. An _____ can refer to the mean, the median, or the mode for a set of values.

2. The _____ for a set of numbers is the sum of the numbers divided by the number of values.

3. The _____ for a set of numbers is the number in the middle of the data.

4. The _____ for a set of numbers is the number that occurs most frequently.

5. The _____ for a set of numbers is the difference between the largest number and the smallest number.

Problems

A Find the mean for each set of numbers.

1. 1, 2, 3, 4, 5   **2.** 2, 4, 6, 8, 10   **3.** 1, 3, 9, 11   **4.** 5, 7, 9, 12, 12

5. 29,500, 10,650, 8,900, 15,120, 16,800   **6.** 8,040, 5,505, 4,121, 9,910   **7.** 12.5, 8.2, 1.8   **8.** 4.1, 6.9, 2.2, 3.6

B Find the median for each set of numbers.

9. 5, 9, 11, 13, 15   **10.** 42, 48, 50, 64   **11.** 10, 20, 50, 90, 100   **12.** 500, 800, 1200, 1300

13. 900, 700, 1100   **14.** 850, 100, 225, 480   **15.** 1.0, 6.5, 3.2, 1.7, 2.1, 4.6, 3.9   **16.** 2.7, 3.4, 1.8, 1.1, 2.3, 3.0

C Find the mode for each set of numbers.

17. 14, 18, 27, 36, 18, 73   **18.** 11, 27, 18, 11, 72, 11   **19.** 98, 87, 65, 73, 82, 87, 65, 97, 87, 77

20. 3.0, 3.2, 2.5, 4.0, 3.1, 3.1, 2.6, 1.9, 1.8, 3.4, 3.1, 2.0   **21.** 1, 1, 2, 3, 1, 3, 3, 2, 1, 2, 2, 3, 1   **22.** 5, 8, 9, 9, 6, 6, 7, 7, 5, 8, 6, 8, 9, 5, 8, 8, 9

D Determine the range of the given data.

23. 15, 34, 12, 25, 27   **24.** 2.6, 4.1, 5.4, 3.9, 0.6   **25.** 1.0, 3.9, 2.1, 3.6, 2.9, 3.8

26. 12,000, 13,500, 10,120, 14,250, 11,490   **27.** 52, 69, 84, 81, 79, 46, 81, 73, 68   **28.** 4080, 2900, 1650, 1800, 1925, 690

Applying the Concepts

29. Test Average A student's scores for four exams in a basic math class were 79, 62, 87, and 90. What is the student's mean and median test score?

30. Test Scores A first-year math student had grades of 79, 64, 78, and 95 on the first four tests. What is the student's mean and median test grade?

31. Average Salary Over a 3-year period a woman's annual salaries were $28,000, $31,000, and $34,000. What was her mean annual salary and median annual salary for this 3-year period?

32. Bowling If a person has scores of 205, 222, 174, 236, 185, and 215 for six games of bowling, what is the median score for the six games?

33. Average Suppose a basketball team has scores of 64, 76, 98, 55, 76, and 102 in their first six games.

a. Find the mean score.

b. Find the median score.

c. Find the mode of the scores.

34. Home Sales Below are listed the prices paid for 10 homes that sold during the month of February in a city in Texas.

    $210,000 $139,000 $122,000 $145,000 $120,000
    $540,000 $167,000 $125,000 $125,000 $950,000

a. Find the mean housing price for the month.

b. Find the median housing price for the month.

c. Find the mode of the housing prices for the month.

d. Which measure of "average" best describes the average housing price for the month? Explain your answer.

35. Cost of College The average cost of tuition for a 4-year public college varies by region. Suppose the cost of tuition for different regions of the United States is $8,602, $7,785, $7,565, $6,421, $5,428, and $5,412. What is the mean and median national cost to attend college? Round to the nearest cent.

36. Cost of College The net cost of tuition is the cost that students actually pay when financial aid is taken into account. If the net cost for a 4-year public college for four different years was $2,260, $2,210, $2,130, and $2,850, what was the mean and median net cost? Round to the nearest cent.

37. Federal Grants The following are the amounts of federal grants (in millions) that were given out over five years: $19,788, $20,304, $19,416, $19,472, $20,946. What was the mean and median amount given out in federal grants? Round to the nearest dollar.

38. Financial Aid The following are the amounts of all financial aid distributed including all grants, loans, and scholarships, for five years: $132,839, $143,694, $149,668, $154,044, $162,501. What was the mean and median amount of financial aid for these five years? Round to the nearest cent.

39. Basketball Find the range of the basketball game scores given in Problem 33.

40. Bowling Find the range of the bowling scores given in Problem 32.

41. Cost of College Find the range of the average costs of tuition given in Problem 35.

42. Cost of College Find the range of the net costs of tuition given in Problem 36.

43. Federal Grants Find the range of the amounts of federal grants given in Problem 37.

44. Financial Aid Find the range of the amounts of financial aid given in Problem 38.

FIND THE MISTAKE

Each sentence below contains a mistake. Circle the mistake and write the correct word(s) or numbers(s) on the line provided.

1. The following is a list of lunch prices at a school cafeteria. Based on the list, the mean cost of lunch is $20.10.

   $3.23 $1.50 $5.27 $4.30 $3.68 $2.12   _____

2. Suppose you collect 10 different leaves and measure their lengths. The following is a list of those measurements in inches.

   1.2 2.5 4.6 1.7 2.4 3.9 3.0 2.7 3.1 4.3

   You would find the median by adding 2.4 and 3.9, and then dividing by 2 to get 3.15 inches.

   _____

3. The mode for the following list of numbers is 808.

   808 12 32 7 91 808 64 7 12 91 64 32 12   _____

4. Suppose a basketball team scored 80 points during their highest scoring game, and 42 points during their lowest scoring game. The range of points scored is $80 + 42 = 122$. _____

Navigation Skills

The chapters in this course are organized such that each chapter builds on the previous chapters. So you already have learned the tools to master the final topics in this book and be successful on the final exam. However, studying for the final exam may still seem like an overwhelming task. To ease that anxiety, begin now to lay out a study plan. Dedicate time in your day to do the following:

- Stay calm and maintain a positive attitude.
- Scan each section of the book to review headers, graphics, definitions, rules, properties, formulas, italicized words, and margin notes. Take new notes as you scan.
- Review your notes and homework.
- Rework problems in each section and from your difficult problems list.
- Make and review flashcards of definitions, properties, or formulas.
- Explain concepts to a friend or out loud to yourself.
- Schedule time to meet with a study partner or group.
- Prepare a list of questions that you may have for your instructor.

Trail Guide Project

Olympic Rates

In 2014, the Winter Olympics were held in Sochi, Russia. The following is a list of some of the sports in which athletes competed during the 2014 Olympic Games:

Alpine skiing

Bobsleigh

Freestyle skiing

Luge

Ski jumping

Biathlon

Cross-country skiing

Ice hockey

Speed skating

Snowboarding

Working in groups, choose a sport from the above list. Research the sport, as well as the 2014 race details and results. Explain how rates and proportions can be used to describe the details of each sport's race and results. Present your findings to the class.

EXAMPLES · · · · ·

Ratio [6.1]

The ratio of a to b is $\frac{a}{b}$. The ratio of two numbers is a way of comparing them using fraction notation.

1. The ratio of 6 to 8 is $\frac{6}{8}$ which can be reduced to $\frac{3}{4}$.

Rates [6.2]

A ratio that compares two different quantities, like miles and hours, gallons and seconds, etc., is called a rate.

2. If a car travels 150 miles in 3 hours, then the ratio of miles to hours is considered a rate.

$$\frac{150 \text{ miles}}{3 \text{ hours}} = 50 \frac{\text{miles}}{\text{hour}}$$

$$= 50 \text{ miles per hour}$$

Unit Pricing [6.2]

The unit price of an item is the ratio of price to quantity when the quantity is one unit.

3. If a 10-ounce package of frozen peas costs 69¢, then the price per ounce, or unit price, is

$$\frac{69 \text{ cents}}{10 \text{ ounces}} = 6.9 \frac{\text{cents}}{\text{ounce}}$$

$$= 6.9 \text{ cents per ounce}$$

Proportion [6.3]

A proportion is an equation that indicates that two ratios are equal.
The numbers in a proportion are called terms and are numbered as follows:

First term $\longrightarrow \dfrac{a}{b} = \dfrac{c}{d} \longleftarrow$ Third term
Second term $\longrightarrow$ $\phantom{\dfrac{a}{b}}$ $\longleftarrow$ Fourth term

4. The following is a proportion:

$$\frac{6}{8} = \frac{3}{4}$$

The first and fourth terms are called the extremes. The second and third terms are called the means.

Means $\longrightarrow \dfrac{a}{b} = \dfrac{c}{d} \longleftarrow$ Extremes

Fundamental Property of Proportions [6.3]

In any proportion, the product of the extremes is equal to the product of the means. In symbols,

$$\text{If} \quad \frac{a}{b} = \frac{c}{d} \quad \text{then} \quad ad = bc$$

Finding an Unknown Term in a Proportion [6.3]

5. Find x: $\dfrac{2}{5} = \dfrac{8}{x}$.

$2 \cdot x = 5 \cdot 8$

$2 \cdot x = 40$

$x = 20$

To find the unknown term in a proportion, we apply the fundamental property of proportions and solve the equation that results by dividing both sides by the number that is multiplied by the unknown. For instance, if we want to find the unknown in the proportion

$$\frac{2}{5} = \frac{8}{x}$$

we use the fundamental property of proportions to set the product of the extremes equal to the product of the means.

Using Proportions to Find Unknown Length in Similar Figures [6.5]

6. Find x.

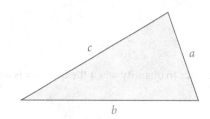

$\dfrac{4}{6} = \dfrac{6}{x}$

$4x = 36$

$x = 9$

Two triangles that have the same shape are similar when their corresponding sides are proportional, or have the same ratio. The triangles below are similar.

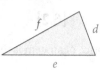

Corresponding Sides	**Ratio**
side a corresponds with side d	$\dfrac{a}{d}$
side b corresponds with side e	$\dfrac{b}{e}$
side c corresponds with side f	$\dfrac{c}{f}$

Because their corresponding sides are proportional, we write

$$\frac{a}{d} = \frac{b}{e} = \frac{c}{f}$$

Mean [6.6]

7. Find the mean for test scores of 74, 63, 74, 80, 83, 88. We add the numbers and divide by 6:

$$\frac{74 + 63 + 74 + 80 + 83 + 88}{6}$$

$$= \frac{462}{6} = 77$$

To find the mean for a set of numbers, we add all the numbers and then divide the sum by the number of values in the set. The mean is sometimes called the arithmetic mean.

Median [6.6]

8. The median for the test scores in Example 7 will be halfway between 74 and 80.

$$\text{Median} = \frac{74 + 80}{2} = 77$$

To find the median for a set of numbers, we write the numbers in order from smallest to largest. If there is an odd number of values, the median is the middle number. If there is an even number of values, then the median is the mean of the two numbers in the middle.

Mode [6.6]

The mode for a set of numbers is the value that occurs most frequently. If more than one number occurs most often, there will be more than one mode. If all the numbers in the set occur the same number of times, there is no mode.

9. The mode for the test scores in Example 7 will be the most frequently occurring score, which is 74.

Range [6.6]

The range for a set of numbers is the difference between the largest number and the smallest number in the sample.

10. The range for the test scores in Example 7 will be the difference between 88 and 63. Range $= 88 - 63 = 25$

Write each ratio as a fraction in lowest terms. [6.1]

1. 36 to 16

2. 12 to 64

3. 81 to 27

4. 7 to 49

5. $\frac{4}{9}$ to $\frac{1}{3}$

6. $\frac{9}{5}$ to $\frac{11}{5}$

7. $\frac{5}{4}$ to $\frac{7}{8}$

8. $\frac{7}{19}$ to $\frac{38}{76}$

9. 5 to $3\frac{3}{4}$

10. $\frac{1}{2}$ to $3\frac{1}{2}$

11. 4 to $8\frac{7}{8}$

12. $2\frac{1}{2}$ to $5\frac{1}{2}$

13. 0.24 to 0.14

14. 6.4 to 0.8

15. 5.1 to 0.17

16. 0.1875 to 6.125

17. $\frac{7}{12}$ to $\frac{5}{12}$

18. $\frac{5}{3}$ to $\frac{5}{8}$

A family of three budgeted the following amounts for some of its monthly bills. Use the pie chart to solve problems 19-23.

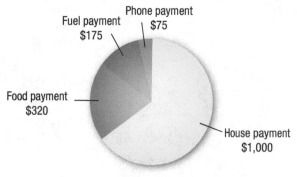

Family Budget

19. Ratio Find the ratio of phone payment to food payment. [6.1]

20. Ratio Find the ratio of house payment to fuel payment. [6.1]

21. Ratio Find the ratio of house payment to food payment. [6.1]

22. Ratio Find the ratio of fuel payment to phone payment. [6.1]

23. Ratio Find the ratio of house payment to the entire family budget. [6.1]

24. Gas Mileage A car travels 348 miles on 12 gallons of gas. What is the gas mileage in miles per gallon? [6.2]

25. Gas Mileage A car travels 412 miles on 16 gallons of gas. What is the gas mileage in miles per gallon? [6.2]

26. Miles/Hour A train travels 432 miles in 6 hours. What is the rate of the train in miles per hour?

27. Kilometers/Hour In 8 hours an airplane travels 5,600 kilometers. What is the rate of the airplane in kilometers per hour?

28. Miles/Hour A car travels 675.4 miles in $12\frac{1}{2}$ hours. Give the rate in miles per hour to the nearest hundredth.

29. Miles/Hour At the beginning of a trip, the odometer on a car read 32,567.2 miles. At the end of the trip, it read 32,741.8 miles. If the trip took $4\frac{1}{4}$ hours, what was the rate of the car in miles per hour to the nearest tenth?

30. Miles/Hour The drive from New York City to Los Angeles is 2,803 miles. If the trip is completed in 40 hours, approximately how many miles per hour would you drive during the trip? Round to the nearest tenth.

31. Unit Price A restaurant sells different sizes of caffe lattes. The prices are shown below. Give the unit price for each coffee drink and indicate which is the better buy. Round to the nearest cent. [6.2]

Solve each of the following equations by dividing both sides by the appropriate number. Be sure to show the division in each case. [6.3]

32. $16n = 48$

33. $10a = 40$

34. $8a = 13$

35. $9 = 11y$

36. $15x = 60$

37. $8b = 64$

38. Name the means, name the extremes, and show that the product of the means is equal to the product of the extremes for:

$$\frac{2}{1} = \frac{4}{1}$$
$$\frac{\ }{4}\ \ \ \frac{\ }{2}$$

Find the unknown term in each proportion. [6.3]

39. $\dfrac{3}{8} = \dfrac{21}{x}$

40. $\dfrac{2.25}{3} = \dfrac{1.5}{x}$

41. $\dfrac{n}{10} = \dfrac{\frac{3}{5}}{\frac{3}{8}}$

42. $\dfrac{321}{1{,}128} = \dfrac{x}{376}$

43. The triangles below are similar figures. Find h. [6.5]

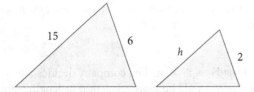

44. The rectangles below are similar figures. Find a. [6.5]

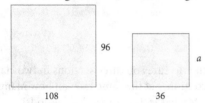

45. Baseball A baseball player gets 9 hits in his first 18 games of the season. If he continues at the same rate, how many hits will he get in 72 games? [6.4]

46. Baseball A baseball player gets 6 hits in 28 plate appearances. If he continues at the same rate, how many hits will he get in his next 42 plate appearances? [6.4]

47. Nutrition If 10 ounces of a certain breakfast cereal contains 3 ounces of sugar, how many ounces of sugar does 25 ounces of the same cereal contain? [6.4]

48. Height of a Building A building casts a shadow 128 feet long, while a 24-foot flagpole casts a shadow 32 feet long. How tall is the building? [6.5]

49. Height of a Person A 7-foot tall basketball player casts a shadow 14 feet long. A gymnast casts a shadow 10 feet long. How tall is the gymnast? [6.5]

50. Nursing Assume 100 mg of a drug is prescribed per 2 kg of the patient's weight. If a child weighs 17 kg, what dosage should be taken? [6.4]

51. Nursing Assume 16 mg of a drug is prescribed per 1 m² of the patient's body surface area. If an adult has a body surface area of 18 m², what dosage should be taken? [6.4]

52. Fuel Economy The table below gives the highway fuel economy for the best selling cars of 2010. [6.6]

Car	Fuel Economy (mpg)
Ford F-150	23
Chevy Silverado	20
Toyota Camry	33
Nissan Altima	32
Honda CR-V	28

a. What is the range in fuel economy?

b. What is the mean fuel economy?

c. What is the median fuel economy?

53. Suspension Bridges The table below shows the 10 longest suspension bridges in the United States. [6.6]

Bridge	Length (feet)
Verrazano-Narrows	4,260
Golden Gate	4,200
Mackinac	3,800
George Washington	3,500
Tacoma Narrows II	2,800
San Francisco-Oakland Bay	2,310
Bronx-Whitestone	2,300
Delaware Memorial	2,150
Seaway Skyway	2,150
Walt Whitman	2,000

a. Find the mean bridge length.

b. Find the median bridge length.

c. What is the mode of the bridge lengths?

d. What is the range of the bridge lengths?

Simplify.

1.   9,341
            296
        + 3,735

2. $2,071 - 1,735$

3. $\dfrac{578}{34}$

4. $(4 \cdot 2) \cdot 6$

5. $24\overline{)12,393}$

6. 4^4

7. $8 \cdot 3^2 - 9$

8. $136 \div 17$

9. $63 + 28$

10. $\dfrac{81}{3}$

11. $(12 - 3) + (509 - 374)$

12. $(4.8)(6.2)$

13. $74.3 - 31.7$

14. $7.3 + 4.27 + 3.09$

15. $29.7 \div 4.5$

16. $\left(\dfrac{1}{2}\right)^4 \left(\dfrac{1}{3}\right)^3$

17. $9 \div \left(\dfrac{3}{4}\right)^2$

18. $\dfrac{3}{8} + \dfrac{5}{12}$

19. $6 \div \left(16 \div 2\dfrac{2}{3}\right)$

20. $16 - 3\dfrac{5}{7}$

Solve.

21. $\dfrac{5}{7} = \dfrac{x}{35}$

22. $\dfrac{3}{8} = \dfrac{9}{x}$

23. Find the perimeter and area of the figure below.

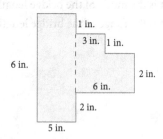

24. Find the perimeter and area of the figure below.

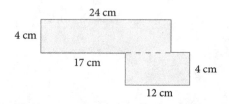

25. Find x if the two rectangles are similar.

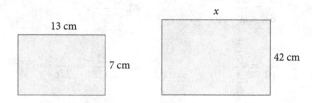

26. Ratio If the ratio of men to women in a self-defense class is 2 to 5, and there are 8 men in the class, how many women are in the class?

27. Surfboard Length A surfing company decides that a surfboard would be more efficient if its length were reduced by $1\frac{5}{8}$ inches. If the original length was 7 feet $\frac{7}{8}$ inches, what will be the new length of the board (in inches)?

28. Teaching A teacher lectures on three sections in two class periods. If she continues at the same rate, on how many sections can the teacher lecture in 46 class periods?

The graph shows the net sales revenue of Amazon over five years. Use the information to answer the following questions.

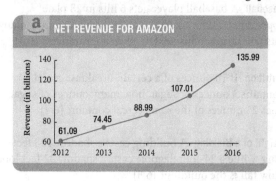

29. What is the ratio of the 2016 net revenue to the 2015 net revenue?

30. What is the mean net revenue from 2012 to 2016, rounded to the nearest tenths place?

Write each ratio as a fraction in lowest terms. [6.1]

1. 48 to 18

2. $\frac{5}{8}$ to $\frac{3}{4}$

3. 6 to $2\frac{4}{7}$

4. 0.14 to 0.4

A family of three budgeted the following amounts for some of its monthly bills. Use the pie chart to solve problems 5 and 6.

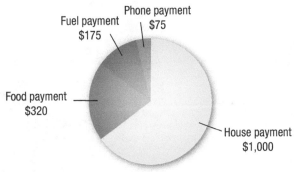

Family Budget

5. Ratio Find the ratio of food payment to phone payment. [6.1]

6. Ratio Find the ratio of food payment to the entire family budget. [6.1]

7. Gas Mileage A car travels 315 miles on 9 gallons of gas. What is the gas mileage in miles per gallon? [6.2]

8. Unit Price A restaurant sells different sizes of caffe lattes. The prices are shown below. Give the unit price for each coffee drink and indicate which is a better buy. Round to the nearest cent. [6.2]

12 oz.   16 oz.

$2.75 $3.45

Find the unknown term in each proportion. [6.3]

9. $\frac{4}{7} = \frac{24}{x}$

10. $\frac{2.5}{5} = \frac{1.5}{x}$

11. Baseball A baseball player gets 13 hits in his first 20 games of the season. If he continues at the same rate, how many hits will he get in 60 games? [6.5]

12. Map Reading The scale on a map indicates that 1 inch on the map corresponds to an actual distance of 15 miles. Two cities are $5\frac{1}{2}$ inches apart on the map. What is the actual distance between the two cities? [6.4]

13. Nursing Assume 90 mg of a drug is prescribed per 3 kg of the patient's weight. If a child weighs 18 kg, what dosage should be taken? [6.4]

14. Nursing Assume 27 mg of a drug is prescribed per 1 m² of the patient's body surface area. If an adult has a body surface area of 1.9 m², what dosage should be taken? [6.4]

15. The triangles below are similar figures. Find h. [6.5]

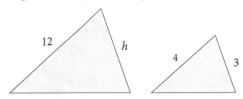

12   h   4   3

The diagram shows the circulation data of daily newspapers in the United States. Use the information to answer the following questions.

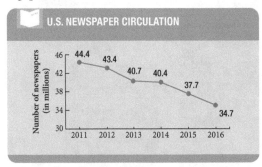

16. What is the ratio of number of newspapers circulated in 2011 to newspapers circulated in 2014?

17. What is the ratio of number of newspapers circulated in 2016 to newspapers circulated in 2015?

18. NBA The table below shows the active NBA players who had the most minutes played in a particular season. [6.6]

Player	Times (Minutes)
LeBron James	3,539
James Harden	3,353
John Wall	3,342
Klay Thompson	3,245
Stephen Curry	3,239

a. What is the range in minutes played?

b. What is the mean number of minutes played?

c. What is the median number of minutes played?

PERCENT

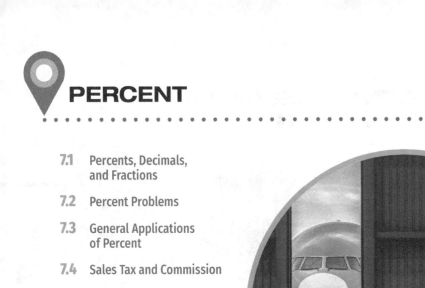

The largest building in the world is so big that it could hold all of the Disney Magic Kingdom theme parks inside it and still have room for twelve acres of covered parking! The Boeing facility adjacent to Paine Field in Everett, Washington has over one million light fixtures with a yearly electric bill of $18 million. The building has the largest floor space in the world and employs 24,000 workers. It was originally opened in 1967 when the company began large-scale manufacturing of commercial aircraft. At that time, Pan American World Airways placed a $525 million order for twenty-five 747 jetliners, requiring the construction of new facilities. Over 300 employees began assembly of the first-ever jumbo jets, and on September 30, 1968, the first 747 rolled out of the factory to worldwide fanfare. Since the inaugural 747, Boeing has expanded its manufacturing programs to include the 767, the 777, and the new 787 Dreamliner.

When the 777 program was launched in 1990, the plant needed to be enlarged to accommodate the increase in production. Suppose you know that the floor space of the Boeing Plant is currently 4.3 million square feet and that the 1990 construction expanded floor space by 50%. What was the floor space of the facility prior to expansion? In order to answer this question, you will need to know how to work problems involving percent, which is one of the topics of this chapter.

YOU ARE HERE

7.1 PERCENTS, DECIMALS, AND FRACTIONS

OBJECTIVES

A Explain the meaning of percents.

B Convert between percents and decimals.

C Convert between percents and fractions.

KEY WORDS

percent

VIDEO EXAMPLES

SECTION 7.1

If you manage your own money, you probably know the importance of a household budget. The following pie chart shows possible percentages for the various categories to which your money may go. The whole pie chart is represented by 100%. In general, 100% of something is the whole thing.

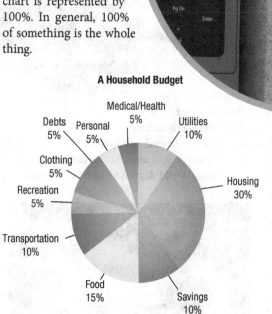

A Household Budget

Medical/Health 5%
Utilities 10%
Debts 5%
Personal 5%
Clothing 5%
Housing 30%
Recreation 5%
Transportation 10%
Food 15%
Savings 10%

In this section, we will look at the meaning of percent. To begin, we learn to change decimals to percents and percents to decimals.

A The Meaning of Percent

Percent means "per hundred." Writing a number as a percent is a way of comparing the number with the number 100. For example, the number 42% (the % symbol is read "percent") is 42 per 100, or

$$42\% = \frac{42}{100}$$

Percents are really fractions (or ratios) with denominator 100.

Example 1 Write each percent as a fraction with a denominator of 100.

a. 33% **b.** 6% **c.** 160%

Solution

a. $33\% = \dfrac{33}{100}$

b. $6\% = \dfrac{6}{100}$

c. $160\% = \dfrac{160}{100}$

If you are wondering if we could reduce some of these fractions further, the answer is yes. We have not done so because the point of this example is that every percent can be written as a fraction with denominator 100.

Practice Problems

1. Write each fraction with a denominator of 100.
   a. 20%
   b. 4%
   c. 230%

B Converting Between Percents and Decimals

To change a percent to a decimal number, we use the meaning of percent.

Example 2 Change 35.2% to a decimal.

Solution We drop the % symbol and write 35.2 over 100.

$$35.2\% = \frac{35.2}{100} \qquad \text{Use the meaning of percent to convert to a fraction with denominator 100.}$$

$$= 0.352 \qquad \text{Divide 35.2 by 100.}$$

2. Change 47.8% to a decimal.

We see from Example 2 that 35.2% is the same as the decimal 0.352. The result is that the % symbol has been dropped and the decimal point has been moved two places to the *left*. Because % always means "per hundred," we will always end up moving the decimal point two places to the left when we change percents to decimals. Because of this, we can write the following rule:

RULE Percent to Decimal

To change a percent to a decimal, drop the % symbol and move the decimal point two places to the *left*.

Example 3 Write each percent as a decimal.

a. 37% **b.** 68% **c.** 120% **d.** 0.8%

Solution We drop the % symbol and move the decimal point to the left two places

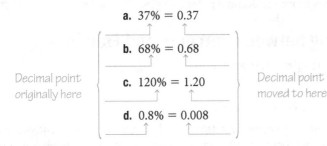

a. 37% = 0.37

b. 68% = 0.68

c. 120% = 1.20

d. 0.8% = 0.008

Decimal point originally here

Decimal point moved to here

3. Write each percent as a decimal.
   a. 23%
   b. 72%
   c. 180%
   d. 0.03%

Answers

1. **a.** $\frac{20}{100}$ **b.** $\frac{4}{100}$ **c.** $\frac{230}{100}$
2. 0.478
3. **a.** 0.23 **b.** 0.72 **c.** 1.80
   d. 0.0003

4. Suppose the cortisone cream in Example 4 was 1% hydrocortisone. Write this number as a decimal.

Example 4   Suppose a cortisone cream is 0.5% hydrocortisone. Writing this number as a decimal, we have

$$0.5\% = 0.005$$

Now we want to do the opposite of what we just did in Examples 2–4. We want to change decimals to percents. We know that 42% written as a decimal is 0.42, which means that in order to change 0.42 back to a percent, we must move the decimal point two places to the *right* and use the % symbol.

$$0.42 = 42\%$$

Notice that we don't show the new decimal point if it is at the end of the number.

RULE   Decimal to Percent

To change a decimal to a percent, we move the decimal point two places to the *right* and use the % symbol.

5. Write each decimal as a percent.
 a. 0.42
 b. 3.86
 c. 0.2
 d. 0.005

Example 5   Write each decimal as a percent.

a. 0.27   **b.** 4.89   **c.** 0.5   **d.** 0.09   **e.** 3

Solution

a. 0.27 = 27%

b. 4.89 = 489%

c. 0.5 = 0.50 = 50%   *Notice here that we put a 0 after the 5 so we can move the decimal point two places to the right.*

d. 0.09 = 09% = 9%   *Notice that we can drop the 0 at the left without changing the value of the number.*

e. 3 = 3.00 = 300%   *Notice here that we have added the decimal point and two zeros so that we can move the decimal point two places to the right.*

6. Suppose the player in Example 6 has a batting average of 0.360. Write that number as a percent.

Example 6   A softball player has a batting average of 0.650. Convert this decimal to a percent.

Solution   Moving the decimal two places to the right, we have 65.0%.

As you can see from these examples, percent is just a way of comparing numbers to 100. To multiply decimals by 100, we move the decimal point two places to the right. To divide by 100, we move the decimal point two places to the left.

C Converting between Percents and Fractions

We will now convert a percent to a fraction.

RULE   Percent to Fraction

To change a percent to a fraction, drop the % symbol and write the original number over 100. Then, if possible, write the fraction in lowest terms with integers in the numerator and denominator.

Example 7   The pie chart shows who pays for college expenses. Change each percent to a fraction in lowest terms.

Solution   In each case, we drop the percent symbol and write the number over 100. Then we reduce to lowest terms if possible.

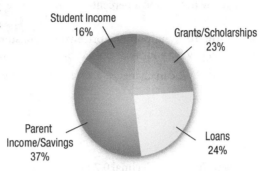

Who Pays College Expenses

Student Income 16%

Grants/Scholarships 23%

Loans 24%

Parent Income/Savings 37%

$$16\% = \frac{16}{100} = \frac{4}{25} \qquad 23\% = \frac{23}{100} \qquad 24\% = \frac{24}{100} = \frac{6}{25} \qquad 37\% = \frac{37}{100}$$

7. Write each percent as a fraction in lowest terms.
   a. 13%
   b. 20%
   c. 54%

Example 8   Change 4.5% to a fraction in lowest terms.

Solution   We begin by writing 4.5 over 100.

$$4.5\% = \frac{4.5}{100}$$

We now multiply the numerator and the denominator by 10 so the numerator will be a whole number.

$$\frac{4.5}{100} = \frac{4.5 \times 10}{100 \times 10} \qquad \text{\textit{Multiply the numerator and the denominator by 10.}}$$

$$= \frac{45}{1,000}$$

$$= \frac{9}{200} \qquad \text{\textit{Reduce to lowest terms.}}$$

8. Change 3.2% to a fraction in lowest terms.

Example 9   Change $32\frac{1}{2}\%$ to a fraction in lowest terms.

Solution   Writing $32\frac{1}{2}$ over 100 produces a complex fraction. We change $32\frac{1}{2}$ to an improper fraction and simplify.

$$32\frac{1}{2}\% = \frac{32\frac{1}{2}}{100}$$

$$= \frac{\frac{65}{2}}{100} \qquad \text{\textit{Change } } 32\frac{1}{2} \text{\textit{ to the improper fraction }} \frac{65}{2}.$$

$$= \frac{65}{2} \div 100 \qquad \text{\textit{Rewrite as division.}}$$

$$= \frac{65}{2} \cdot \frac{1}{100} \qquad \text{\textit{Dividing by 100 is the same as multiplying by }} \frac{1}{100}.$$

$$= \frac{5 \cdot 13 \cdot 1}{2 \cdot 5 \cdot 20} \qquad \text{\textit{Cancel common factors and multiply.}}$$

$$= \frac{13}{40} \qquad \text{\textit{Reduce to lowest terms.}}$$

Note that we could have changed our original mixed number to a decimal first and then changed to a fraction:

$$32\frac{1}{2}\% = 32.5\% = \frac{32.5}{100} = \frac{32.5 \times 10}{100 \times 10} = \frac{325}{1000} = \frac{5 \cdot 5 \cdot 13}{5 \cdot 5 \cdot 40} = \frac{13}{40}$$

The result is the same in both cases.

9. Change $53\frac{1}{4}\%$ to a fraction in lowest terms.

Answers

7. a. $\frac{13}{100}$ **b.** $\frac{1}{5}$ **c.** $\frac{27}{50}$

8. $\frac{4}{125}$

9. $\frac{213}{400}$

To change a fraction to a percent, we can change the fraction to a decimal and then change the decimal to a percent.

10. Write $\frac{3}{5}$ as a percent.

Example 10   Suppose the price your bookstore pays for your textbook is $\frac{7}{10}$ of the price you pay for your textbook. Write $\frac{7}{10}$ as a percent.

Solution   We can change $\frac{7}{10}$ to a decimal by dividing 7 by 10.

$$
\begin{array}{r}
0.7 \\
10\overline{)7.0} \\
-7\,0 \\
\hline
0
\end{array}
$$

We then change the decimal 0.7 to a percent by moving the decimal point two places to the *right* and using the % symbol.

$$0.7 = 70\%$$

You may have noticed that we could have saved some time by simply writing $\frac{7}{10}$ as an equivalent fraction with denominator 100; that is,

$$\frac{7}{10} = \frac{7 \cdot 10}{10 \cdot 10} = \frac{70}{100} = 70\%$$

This is a good way to convert fractions like $\frac{7}{10}$ to percents. It works well for fractions with denominators of 2, 4, 5, 10, 20, 25, and 50, because these numbers are compatible with 100.

11. Change $\frac{5}{8}$ to a percent.

Example 11   Change $\frac{3}{8}$ to a percent.

Solution   We begin by dividing 3 by 8.

$$
\begin{array}{r}
.375 \\
8\overline{)3.000} \\
-2\,4 \\
\hline
60 \\
-5\,6 \\
\hline
40 \\
-40 \\
\hline
0
\end{array}
$$

We then change the decimal to a percent by moving the decimal point two places to the right and using the % symbol.

$$\frac{3}{8} = 0.375 = 37.5\%$$

Example 12   Change $\frac{5}{12}$ to a percent.

Solution   We begin by dividing 5 by 12.

$$
\begin{array}{r}
.4166 \\
12\overline{)5.0000} \\
-48\downarrow \\
\overline{20} \\
-12\downarrow \\
\overline{80} \\
-72\downarrow \\
\overline{80} \\
-72 \\
\overline{8}
\end{array}
$$

Because the 6s repeat indefinitely, we can use mixed number notation to write

$$\frac{5}{12} = 0.41\overline{6}$$

We will now round to the thousandths place and convert to a percent.

$$\frac{5}{12} = 0.417 = 41.7\%$$

12. Change $\frac{7}{9}$ to a percent.

Note   When rounding off, let's agree to round off to the nearest thousandth and then move the decimal point. Our answers in percent form will then be accurate to the nearest tenth of a percent, as in Example 12.

- ●

Example 13   Change $2\frac{1}{2}$ to a percent.

Solution   We first change to a decimal and then to a percent.

$$2\frac{1}{2} = 2.5 = 250\%$$

13. Change $3\frac{1}{4}$ to a percent.

- ●

RULE   Fraction to Percent

To change a fraction to a percent, either write the fraction as a decimal and then change the decimal to a percent, or write the fraction as an equivalent fraction with denominator 100, drop the 100, and use the % symbol.

Table 1 lists some of the most commonly used fractions and decimals and their equivalent percents.

Table 1

Fraction	Decimal	Percent		Fraction	Decimal	Percent
$\frac{1}{2}$	0.5	50%		$\frac{1}{5}$	0.2	20%
$\frac{1}{4}$	0.25	25%		$\frac{2}{5}$	0.4	40%
$\frac{3}{4}$	0.75	75%		$\frac{3}{5}$	0.6	60%
$\frac{1}{3}$	$0.\overline{3}$	$33\frac{1}{3}\%$		$\frac{4}{5}$	0.8	80%
$\frac{2}{3}$	$0.\overline{6}$	$66\frac{2}{3}\%$		$\frac{1}{1}$	1.0	100%

Answers
12. 77.8%
13. 325%

KEY CONCEPT REVIEW

After reading through the preceding section, respond in your own words and in complete sentences.

A. What is the relationship between the word *percent* and the number 100?

B. Explain in words how you would change 25% to a decimal.

C. Explain in words how you would change 25% to a fraction.

D. After reading this section you know that $\frac{1}{2}$, 0.5, and 50% are equivalent. Show mathematically why this is true.

Spotlight on Success

NATHAN, student instructor

Keep steadily before you the fact that all true success depends at last upon yourself. ~ Theodore T. Hunger

Math has always come fairly easily for me and is the academic subject I have enjoyed most. I knew I wanted to attend Cal Poly San Luis Obispo for its high job placement and prestige, but I had no idea what I wanted to study. I decided to major in Mathematics because it is so universal but not so specialized or concentrated that I would get stuck in a field that I did not enjoy. I felt that if I kept studying math and its related fields, I would set myself up to be successful later in life, as math is the foundation for engineering, physics, and other science-related fields. I have not looked back on my decision. I know it will be a degree that I am proud to have achieved.

I appreciate the consistency that math offers in its problems and in its solutions. I like that math can be simplified into smaller easier-to-understand parts, and its answers are almost always definite. It provides challenges that I enjoy solving, like completing a puzzle piece by piece. In the end, I am able to enjoy the success I have put together for myself.

Choose the correct words to fill in the blanks below.

ratio	% symbol	percent
left	decimal	right

1. The word _____ means "per hundred."

2. A percent is a _____ with a denominator of 100.

3. To change a percent to a decimal, drop the % symbol and move the decimal point two places to the _____ .

4. To change a decimal to a percent, move the decimal point two places to the _____ and use the % symbol.

5. To change a percent to a fraction, drop the _____ and write the original number over 100.

6. To change a fraction to a percent, we can change the fraction to a _____ and then change the decimal to a percent.

Problems

A Write each percent as a fraction with denominator 100.

1. 20%   **2.** 40%   **3.** 60%   **4.** 80%

5. 24%   **6.** 48%   **7.** 65%   **8.** 35%

Change each percent to a decimal.

9. 23%   **10.** 34%   **11.** 192%   **12.** 387%

13. 9%   **14.** 7%   **15.** 3.4%   **16.** 5.8%

17. 0.087%   **18.** 0.09%   **19.** 0.9%   **20.** 0.6%

B Change each decimal to a percent.

21. 0.23   **22.** 0.34   **23.** 0.923   **24.** 0.874

25. 0.45   **26.** 0.54   **27.** 0.03   **28.** 0.04

29. 0.6   **30.** 0.9   **31.** 0.008   **32.** 0.005

33. 27   **34.** 6   **35.** 1.23   **36.** 2.34

C Change each percent to a fraction in lowest terms.

37. 60%   **38.** 40%   **39.** 75%   **40.** 25%

41. 4%   **42.** 2%   **43.** 265%   **44.** 342%

45. 71.87%   **46.** 63.6%   **47.** 0.75%   **48.** 0.45%

49. $6\frac{1}{4}$%   **50.** $5\frac{1}{4}$%   **51.** $33\frac{1}{3}$%   **52.** $66\frac{2}{3}$%

D Change each fraction or mixed number to a percent.

53. $\frac{1}{2}$ **54.** $\frac{1}{4}$ **55.** $\frac{3}{4}$ **56.** $\frac{2}{3}$

57. $\frac{1}{3}$ **58.** $\frac{1}{5}$ **59.** $\frac{4}{5}$ **60.** $\frac{1}{6}$

61. $\frac{7}{8}$ **62.** $\frac{1}{8}$ **63.** $\frac{7}{50}$ **64.** $\frac{9}{25}$

65. $3\frac{1}{4}$ **66.** $2\frac{1}{8}$ **67.** $\frac{3}{2}$ **68.** $\frac{7}{4}$

69. Change $\frac{21}{43}$ to a percent. Round to the nearest tenth of a percent

70. Change $\frac{36}{49}$ to a percent. Round to the nearest tenth of a percent

Applying the Concepts

71. Physiology The human body is between 50% and 75% water. Write each of these percents as a decimal.

72. Alcohol Consumption In the United States, 2.7% of those over 15 years of age drink more than 6.3 ounces of alcohol per day. In France, the same figure is 9%. Write each of these percents as a decimal.

73. iPhone The snapshot below shows what users had before their new iPhone. Use the information to answer the following questions.

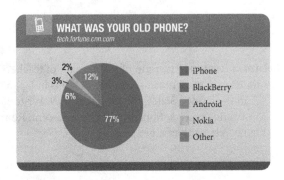

a. Convert each percent to a fraction.

b. Convert each percent to a decimal.

c. About how many times more likely are the respondents to have owned a Blackberry than an Android phone?

74. Foreign Language The chart shows the extent to which Americans say they know a foreign language. Change each percent to a fraction in lowest terms.

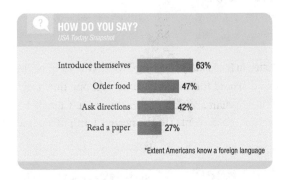

75. Nutrition Although, nutritionally, breakfast is the most important meal of the day, only about $\frac{1}{5}$ of the people in the United States consistently eat breakfast. What percent of the population is this?

76. Children in School In Belgium, 96% of all children between 3 and 6 years of age go to school. In Sweden, the number is only 25%. In the United States, it is 60%. Write each of these percents as a fraction in lowest terms.

77. Student Enrollment The pie chart shows enrollment by college for a university. Change each fraction to a percent. Round to the nearest hundredth.

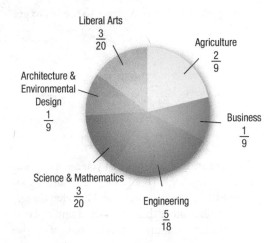

78. Video Games The chart shows the percentage of total Nintendo revenue by region in 2017. Use the information to convert from the percentage to a decimal for the following regions.

a. Europe   **b.** The Americas   **c.** Japan

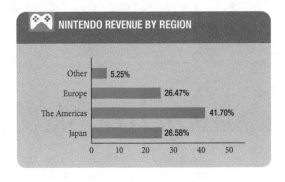

Calculator Problems

Use a calculator to write each fraction as a decimal, and then change the decimal to a percent. Round all answers to the nearest tenth of a percent.

79. $\dfrac{29}{37}$ **80.** $\dfrac{18}{83}$ **81.** $\dfrac{6}{51}$ **82.** $\dfrac{8}{95}$ **83.** $\dfrac{236}{327}$ **84.** $\dfrac{568}{732}$

85. Women in the Military During World War II, $\frac{1}{12}$ of the Soviet armed forces were women. At one time only $\frac{1}{450}$ of the Russian armed forces are women. Change both fractions to percents (to the nearest tenth of a percent).

86. Number of Teachers The ratio of the number of teachers to the number of students in secondary schools in Japan is 1 to 17. In the United States, the ratio is 1 to 19. Write each of these ratios as a fraction and then as a percent. Round to the nearest tenth of a percent.

Getting Ready for the Next Section

Multiply.

87. 0.25(74)   **88.** 0.15(63)   **89.** 0.435(25)   **90.** 0.635(45)

Divide. Round the answers to the nearest thousandth, if necessary.

91. $\dfrac{21}{42}$ **92.** $\dfrac{21}{84}$ **93.** $\dfrac{25}{0.4}$ **94.** $\dfrac{31.9}{78}$

Solve for n. Write the solution using a decimal.

95. $42n = 21$ **96.** $945 = 100n$ **97.** $25 = 0.40n$ **98.** $78n = 31.9$

FIND THE MISTAKE

Each sentence below contains a mistake. Circle the mistake and write the correct word(s) or numbers(s) on the line provided.

1. Writing 0.4% as a decimal gives us 0.4. _____

2. To write 3.21 as a percent, divide the number by 100; that is, move the decimal two places to the left.
   _____

3. Writing 25% as a fraction in lowest terms gives us $\frac{25}{100}$. _____

4. To change $\frac{5}{8}$ to a percent, we change $\frac{5}{8}$ to 0.625 and then move the decimal two places to the left to get 0.00625%. _____

Navigation Skills

Think about your current study routine. Has it been successful? There are many things that you must consider when creating a routine. One important aspect is the environment in which you choose to study. Think about the location where you typically study. Are you able to focus there without distraction? Consider what things may distract you (e.g., cell phones, television, noise, friends who socialize rather than study) and find a place to study where these things are absent. Other important aspects of a productive study routine are time of day you choose to study, and sights and sounds around you during your study time. A study environment that is not distracting will help you focus and foster further success in this course.

PERCENT PROBLEMS

7.2

Scientists have discovered a toxin in the spit of a sea snail that works as a painkiller with greater effectiveness but in smaller dosages and without the addictive risk of the painkiller morphine. The marine cone snail dwells on the ocean floor. The snail shoots its harpoon-like teeth coated in toxic saliva into its prey to poison it. Researchers have discovered how to isolate the saliva's toxin and put it into a pill for humans in pain to ingest. A patient will feel the same pain-reducing effects with 1% of a dose of a popular neuropathic painkiller prescribed in hospitals. If the prescription for an adult of the popular painkiller is 300 milligrams, how many milligrams of the sea snail drug would be dosed as an alternative? In this section, we will work some other percent problems, similar to this one.

OBJECTIVES

A Solve percent problems using equations.

B Solve percent problems using proportions.

KEY WORDS

is

of

A Solving Percent Problems Using Equations

This section is concerned with three kinds of word problems that are associated with percents. Here is an example of each type:

Type A: What number is 15% of 63?

Type B: What percent of 42 is 21?

Type C: 25 is 40% of what number?

The first method we use to solve all three types of problems involves translating the sentences into equations and then solving the equations. The following translations are used to write the sentences as equations:

English	Mathematics
is	=
of	· (multiply)
a number	n
what number	n
what percent	n

The word *is* always translates to an = sign, the word *of* almost always means multiply, and *the number we are looking for* can be represented with a variable, such as n or x.

Practice Problems

1. What number is 20% of 70?

Example 1   What number is 15% of 63?

Solution   Using the translations above and converting 15% to a decimal, we have

What number is 15% of 63?

$$n = 0.15 \cdot 63$$

To perform arithmetic with percents, we have to change to decimals. Solving the equation, we have

$$n = 0.15 \cdot 63$$

$$n = 9.45 \qquad\qquad \text{Multiply.}$$

Therefore, 15% of 63 is 9.45.

2. What percent of 148 is 37?

Example 2   What percent of 42 is 21?

Solution   We translate the sentence as follows:

What percent of 42 is 21?

$$n \cdot 42 = 21$$

We solve for n by dividing both sides by 42.

$$\frac{n \cdot 42}{42} = \frac{21}{42} \qquad\qquad \text{Divide 21 by 42.}$$

$$n = \frac{21}{42}$$

$$n = 0.50$$

Because the original problem asked for a percent, we change 0.50 to a percent.

$$n = 50\%$$

Therefore, 21 is 50% of 42.

3. 55 is 30% of what number?

Example 3   25 is 40% of what number?

Solution   Following the procedure from the first two examples, we have

25 is 40% of what number?

$$25 = 0.40 \cdot n$$

We will now solve the remaining equation.

$$\frac{25}{0.40} = \frac{0.40 \cdot n}{0.40} \qquad\qquad \text{Divide both sides by 0.40.}$$

$$\frac{25}{0.40} = n$$

$$62.5 = n \qquad\qquad \text{Simplify: } 25 \div 0.40 = 62.5$$

Therefore, 25 is 40% of 62.5.

Answers

1. 14
2. 25%
3. 183.33

As you can see, all three types of percent problems are solved in a similar manner. We write *is* as $=$, *of* as $\cdot$, and *what number* as n. The resulting equation is then solved to obtain the answer to the original question. Here are some more examples:

Example 4   What number is 43.5% of 25?

Solution   We translate to an equation and solve for n.

$n = 0.435 \cdot 25$

$n = 10.9$ *Multiply and round to the nearest tenth.*

Therefore, 10.9 is 43.5% of 25.

4. What number is 38.2% of 45?

- ●

Example 5   What percent of 78 is 31.9?

Solution   We will convert to an equation and solve for n.

$n \cdot 78 = 31.9$

$\dfrac{n \cdot 78}{78} = \dfrac{31.9}{78}$ *Divide both sides by 78.*

$n = \dfrac{31.9}{78}$

$n = 0.409$ *Divide and round to the nearest thousandth.*

$n = 40.9\%$ *Convert to a percent.*

Therefore, 40.9% of 78 is 31.9.

5. What percent of 87 is 14.8?

- ●

Example 6   34 is 29% of what number?

Solution $34 = 0.29 \cdot n$

$\dfrac{34}{0.29} = \dfrac{0.29 \cdot n}{0.29}$ *Divide both sides by 0.29.*

$\dfrac{34}{0.29} = n$

$117.2 = n$ *Divide and round to the nearest tenth.*

Therefore, 34 is 29% of 117.2.

6. 23 is 14% of what number?

- ●

Now we will look at one application of percent problems before exploring an alternative method for solving these types of problems. As you will see, these methods use different approaches but result in the same solution.

7. Suppose the item in Example 7 had 62 calories from fat. What percentage of the total calories would be from fat calories?

Example 7 The American Dietetic Association recommends eating foods in which the number of calories from fat is less than 30% of the total number of calories. According to the nutrition label, what percent of the total number of calories are fat calories?

Solution   To solve this problem, we must write the question in the form of one of the three basic percent problems shown in Examples 1–6. Because there are 93 calories from fat and a total of 155 calories, we can write the question this way: 93 is what percent of 155?

Now that we have written the question in the form of one of the basic percent problems, we simply translate it into an equation. Then we solve the equation.

Nutrition Facts	
Serving Size 1 oz	
Servings Per Container About 4	
Amount Per Serving	
Calories 155	Calories from fat 93
	% Daily Value*
Total Fat 11g	**16%**
Saturated Fat 3g	**15%**
Trans Fat 0g	**0%**
Cholesterol 0mg	**0%**
Sodium 148mg	**6%**
Total Carbohydrate 14g	**5%**
Dietary Fiber 1g	**5%**
Sugars 1g	
Protein 2g	
Vitamin A 0% • Vitamin C 9%	
Calcium 1% • Iron 3%	
*Percent Daily Values are based on a 2,000 calorie diet	

FIGURE 1

93 is what percent of 155?

$$93 = n \cdot 155$$

$$\frac{93}{155} = n$$

$$n = 0.60 = 60\%$$

The number of calories from fat in this food is 60% of the total number of calories. Thus the ADA would not consider this to be a healthy food.

B Solving Percent Problems Using Proportions

We can look at percent problems in terms of proportions also. For example, we know that 24% is the same as $\frac{24}{100}$, which reduces to $\frac{6}{25}$. That is,

$$\frac{24}{100} = \frac{6}{25}$$

24 is to 100   as   6 is to 25

We can illustrate this visually with boxes of proportional lengths.

24		6
100		25

In general, we say

$$\frac{\text{Percent}}{100} = \frac{\text{Amount}}{\text{Base}}$$

Percent is to 100   as   amount is to base.

Example 8   What number is 15% of 63?

Solution   This is the same problem we worked in Example 1. We let n be the number in question. We reason that n will be smaller than 63 because it is only 15% of 63. The base is 63 and the amount is n. We compare n to 63 as we compare 15 to 100. Our proportion sets up as follows:

$$\underbrace{15 \text{ is to } 100}_{\downarrow} \quad as \quad \underbrace{n \text{ is to } 63}_{\downarrow}$$

$$\frac{15}{100} = \frac{n}{63}$$

Solving the proportion, we have

$15 \cdot 63 = 100n$ Fundamental property of proportions

$945 = 100n$ Simplify the left side.

$9.45 = n$ Divide each side by 100.

This gives us the same result we obtained in Example 1.

8. What number is 30% of 80?

Example 9   What percent of 42 is 21?

Solution   This is the same problem we worked in Example 2. We let n be the percent in question. The amount is 21 and the base is 42. Here is our reasoning and proportion:

$$\underbrace{n \text{ is to } 100}_{\downarrow} \quad as \quad \underbrace{21 \text{ is to } 42}_{\downarrow}$$

$$\frac{n}{100} = \frac{21}{42}$$

Solving the proportion, we have

$42n = 21 \cdot 100$ Fundamental property of proportions

$42n = 2{,}100$ Simplify the right side.

$n = 50$ Divide each side by 42.

Since n is a percent, our answer is 50%, giving us the same result we obtained in Example 2.

9. What percent of 160 is 56?

Example 10   25 is 40% of what number?

Solution   This is the same problem we worked in Example 3. We let n be the number in question. The base is n and the amount is 25. We compare 25 to n as we compare 40 to 100. Our proportion sets up as follows:

$$\underbrace{40 \text{ is to } 100}_{\downarrow} \quad as \quad \underbrace{25 \text{ is to } n}_{\downarrow}$$

$$\frac{40}{100} = \frac{25}{n}$$

Solving the proportion, we have

$40 \cdot n = 25 \cdot 100$ Fundamental property of proportions

$40n = 2{,}500$ Simplify the right side.

$n = 62.5$ Divide each side by 40.

So 25 is 40% of 62.5, which is the same result we obtained in Example 3.

10. 65 is 60% of what number? Round to the nearest tenth.

Note   When you work the problems in the problem set, use whichever method you like, unless your instructor indicates that you are to use one method instead of the other.

Answers

8. 24

9. 35%

10. 108.3

KEY CONCEPT REVIEW

After reading through the preceding section, respond in your own words and in complete sentences.

A. When we translate a sentence such as "What number is 15% of 63?" into symbols, what does each of the following translate to?

   a. is   **b.** of   **c.** what number

B. Using Example 1 in your text as a guide, answer the question below.

   The number 9.45 is what percent of 63?

C. Show that the answer to the question below is the same as the answer to the question in Example 2 of your text.

   The number 21 is what percent of 42?

D. If 21 is 50% of 42, then 21 is what percent of 84?

Choose the correct words to fill in the blanks below.

multiply   fraction   decimal   variable   equals sign

1. In a mathematical sentence, the word *is* translates to an _____.

2. In a mathematical sentence, the word *of* almost always means _____.

3. When translating a sentence to an equation, the number we are looking for can be represented with a _____.

4. When performing arithmetic with a percent, change the percent to a _____.

5. Change a percent to a _____ to help solve a percent problem using a proportion.

Problems

A, B Solve each of the following problems.

1. What number is 25% of 32?

2. What number is 15% of 75?

3. What number is 20% of 120?

4. What number is 10% of 80?

5. What number is 54% of 38?

6. What number is 72% of 200?

7. What number is 11% of 67?

8. What number is 2% of 49?

9. What percent of 24 is 12?

10. What percent of 80 is 20?

11. What percent of 50 is 5?

12. What percent of 20 is 4?

13. What percent of 36 is 9?

14. What percent of 70 is 14?

15. What percent of 8 is 6?

16. What percent of 15 is 9?

17. 32 is 50% of what number?

18. 16 is 20% of what number?

19. 10 is 20% of what number?

20. 11 is 25% of what number?

21. 37 is 4% of what number?

22. 46 is 8% of what number?

23. 8 is 2% of what number?

24. 6 is 3% of what number?

The following problems can be solved by the same method you used in Problems 1–24.

25. What is 20% of 87?

26. What is 10% of 102?

27. 25% of what number is 30?

28. 10% of what number is 22?

29. 28% of 49 is what number?

30. 97% of 28 is what number?

31. 27 is 120% of what number?

32. 24 is 150% of what number?

33. 65 is what percent of 130?

34. 26 is what percent of 104?

35. What is 0.4% of 235,671?

36. What is 0.8% of 721,423?

37. 4.89% of 2,000 is what number?

38. 3.75% of 4,000 is what number?

39. Write a basic percent problem, the solution to which can be found by solving the equation $n = 0.25(350)$.

40. Write a basic percent problem, the solution to which can be found by solving the equation $n = 0.35(250)$.

41. Write a basic percent problem, the solution to which can be found by solving the equation $n \cdot 24 = 16$.

42. Write a basic percent problem, the solution to which can be found by solving the equation $n \cdot 16 = 24$.

43. Write a basic percent problem, the solution to which can be found by solving the equation $46 = 0.75 \cdot n$.

44. Write a basic percent problem, the solution to which can be found by solving the equation $75 = 0.46 \cdot n$.

Applying the Concepts

Nutrition For each nutrition label in Problems 45–48, find what percent of the total number of calories comes from fat calories. Then refer to Example 7 and indicate whether the label is from a food considered healthy by the American Dietetic Association. Round to the nearest tenth of a percent if necessary.

45. Pizza Dough

Nutrition Facts

Serving Size 1/6 of package (65g)
Servings Per Container: 6

Amount Per Serving

Calories 160	Calories from fat 18

	% Daily Value*
Total Fat 2g	3%
Saturated Fat 0.5g	3%
Poly unsaturated Fat 0g	
Monounsaturated Fat 0g	
Cholesterol 0mg	0%
Sodium 470mg	20%
Total Carbohydrate 31g	10%
Dietary Fiber 1g	4%
Sugars 4g	
Protein 5g	

Vitamin A 0%	●	Vitamin C 0%
Calcium 0%	●	Iron 10%

*Percent Daily Values are based on a 2,000 calorie diet

46. Crackers

Nutrition Facts

Serving Size 30 g. (About 27 crackers)
Servings Per Container: 9

Amount Per Serving

Calories 150	Calories from fat 70

	% Daily Value*
Total Fat 8g	12%
Saturated Fat 2g	10%

47. Shredded Mozzarella Cheese

Nutrition Facts

Serving Size 1 oz (28.3g)
Servings Per Container: 12

Amount Per Serving

Calories 72	Calories from fat 41

	% Daily Value*
Total Fat 4.5g	7%
Saturated Fat 2.9g	14%
Cholesterol 18mg	6%
Sodium 175mg	7%
Total Carbohydrate 0.8g	0%
Fiber 0g	0%
Sugars 0.3g	
Protein 6.9g	

Vitamin A 3%	●	Vitamin C 0%
Calcium 22%	●	Iron 0%

*Percent Daily Values (DV) are based on a 2,000 calorie diet

48. Canned Corn

Nutrition Facts

Serving Size 1 cup
Servings Per Container About 2 ½

Amount Per Serving

Calories 133	Calories from fat 15

	% Daily Value*
Total Fat 3g	3%
Saturated Fat 1g	1%
Cholesterol 0mg	0%
Sodium 530mg	22%
Total Carbohydrate 30g	10%
Dietary Fiber 3g	13%
Sugars 4g	
Protein 4g	

Vitamin A 0%	●	Vitamin C 23%
Calcium 1%	●	Iron 8%

*Percent Daily Values are based on a 2,000 calorie diet

Getting Ready for the Next Section

Solve each equation.

49. $96 = n \cdot 120$

50. $2,400 = 0.48 \cdot n$

51. $114 = 150n$

52. $3,360 = 0.42n$

53. What number is 80% of 60?

54. What number is 25% of 300?

Improving Your Quantitative Literacy

55. Survival Rates for Sea Gulls Here is part of a report concerning the survival rates of Western Gulls that appeared on the website of Cornell University:

> Survival of eggs to hatching is 70%–80%; of hatched chicks to fledgling 50%–70%; of fledglings to age of first breeding <50%.

Based on this information, give an estimate of the number of gulls of breeding age that would be produced by 1,000 Western Gull eggs.

FIND THE MISTAKE • • • • • • • • • • • • • • • •

Each sentence below contains a mistake. Circle the mistake and write the correct word(s) or numbers(s) on the line provided.

1. The question, "What number is 28.5% of 30?" translates to $n \cdot 0.285 = 30$. _____

2. Asking "75 is 30% of what number?" gives us 0.004. _____

3. To answer the question, "What number is 45% of 90?", we can solve the proportion $\frac{90}{x} = \frac{40}{100}$. _____

4. Using a proportion to answer the question, "What percent of 65 is 26?" will give us $n = 250\%$. _____

LANDMARK REVIEW: CHECKING YOUR PROGRESS • • • • • • • • • • • • • • •

Write each percent as a fraction with denominator 100.

1. 15%

2. 27%

3. 14%

4. 89%

Change each percent to a decimal.

5. 17%

6. 28%

7. 5%

8. 6.37%

Change each decimal to a percent.

9. 0.38

10. 0.98

11. 0.09

12. 4.87

Change each fraction or mixed number to a percent. Round to the nearest tenth of a percent if necessary

13. $\frac{1}{10}$

14. $\frac{1}{3}$

15. $\frac{1}{7}$

16. $3\frac{1}{5}$

Solve each of the following problems. Round to the nearest hundredth if necessary.

17. What number is 35% of 15?

18. What percent of 85 is 53?

19. 88 is 37% of what number?

GENERAL APPLICATIONS OF PERCENT

In the 1920s the Woolly Adelgid, a female bug about one millimeter long with a two-month lifespan, was first discovered in the United States. When the Adelgid infests a hemlock tree between Georgia and Maine, the tree overreacts, weakens, and then dies within approximately four years. As these stands of hemlock die, animals lose their habitat, carbon cycles are impacted, and the soil composition is altered. The effects of the Adelgid are apparent when visiting the Great Smoky Mountain National Park, often the most visited national park with over 11 million visitors each year. Visitors to the highest point in the park, Clingman's Dome, see dead hemlocks in the wake of an Adelgid infestation. The national park is taking steps to rid the area of the tiny bug. Natural pesticides are sprayed in accessible areas and injected directly into infected trees. More recently, the park has released a predator beetle. Because this is a non-native species that they are introducing, this approach has been criticized. The predator beetle is expected to reduce the Woolly Adelgid population by 47 to 87%, a considerable amount considering that 1 in 5 trees in the national park are hemlocks.

In this section, we continue our study of percent, allowing us to better understand data like that on the Woolly Adelgid infestation and its impact on the Great Smoky Mountains National Park.

OBJECTIVES

A Solve application problems involving percents.

VIDEO EXAMPLES

SECTION 7.3

A Applications of Percent

Practice Problems

Example 1 On a 120-question test, a student answered 96 correctly. What percent of the problems did the student work correctly?

Solution We have 96 correct answers out of a possible 120. The problem can be restated as

96 is what percent of 120?

$$96 = n \cdot 120$$

$$\frac{96}{120} = \frac{n \cdot 120}{120} \qquad \textit{Divide both sides by 120.}$$

$$\frac{96}{120} = n$$

$$0.80 = n \qquad \textit{Divide 96 by 120.}$$

1. Suppose the test in Example 1 had 130 questions. What percentage of the problems did the student work correctly?

Answer

1. 73.85%

Converting 0.80 to a percent, we see that the student answered 80% of the problems correctly. As a percent, we are comparing the original score to an equivalent score on a 100-question test. That is, 96 correct out of 120 is the same as 80 correct out of 100.

2. How much HCl is in a 60-milliliter bottle that is marked 60% HCl?

Example 2   How much hydrochloric acid, HCl, is in a 60-milliliter bottle that is marked 80% HCl?

Solution   If the bottle is marked 80% HCl, that means 80% of the solution is HCl and the rest is water. Because the bottle contains 60 milliliters, we can restate the question as

What is 80% of 60?

$$n = 0.80 \cdot 60 \qquad \text{Convert to an equation.}$$
$$n = 48 \qquad \text{Multiply.}$$

There are 48 milliliters of HCl in 60 milliliters of 80% HCl solution.

3. If the college in Example 3 has 1,500 female students, what is the total number of students in that college?

Example 3   If 48% of the students in a certain college are female and there are 2,400 female students, what is the total number of students in the college?

Solution   We restate the problem as

2,400 is 48% of what number?

$$2{,}400 = 0.48 \cdot n \qquad \text{Convert to an equation.}$$
$$\frac{2{,}400}{0.48} = \frac{0.48 \cdot n}{0.48} \qquad \text{Divide both sides by 0.48.}$$
$$5{,}000 = n \qquad \text{Divide.}$$

There are 5,000 students.

4. If 35% of the students in Example 4 got a B, how many students received a B?

Example 4   If 25% of the students in elementary algebra courses receive a grade of A, and there are 300 students enrolled in elementary algebra this year, how many students will receive A's?

Solution   We can see that this problem is asking us to find:

What number is 25% of 300?

$$n = 0.25 \cdot 300 \qquad \text{Convert to an equation.}$$
$$n = 75 \qquad \text{Multiply.}$$

Thus, 75 students will receive A's in elementary algebra.

 KEY CONCEPT REVIEW

After reading through the preceding section, respond in your own words and in complete sentences.

A. On the test mentioned in Example 1, how many questions would the student have answered correctly if she had earned a grade of 40%?

B. If the bottle in Example 2 contained 30 milliliters instead of 60, what would the answer be?

C. In Example 3, how many of the students were male?

D. How many of the students mentioned in Example 4 received a grade lower than an A?

Answers

2. 36 ml
3. 3,125 students
4. 105 students

EXERCISE SET 7.3 · · · · · · · · · · · · · · · · · · ·

VOCABULARY REVIEW ·

On the lines below, write the three types of problems found in applications that involve percents. (Hint: We first learned of the three types in the previous section, and then put them to use in this section.)

1. Type A: _____

2. Type B: _____

3. Type C: _____

Problems

A Solve each of the following problems by first restating it as one of the three basic percent problems from the previous section. In each case, be sure to show the equation.

1. Test Scores On a 120-question test a student answered 84 correctly. What percent of the problems did the student work correctly?

2. Test Scores An engineering student answered 81 questions correctly on a 90-question trigonometry test. What percent of the questions did she answer correctly? What percent were answered incorrectly?

3. Mixture Problem A solution of alcohol and water is 80% alcohol. The solution is found to contain 32 milliliters of alcohol. How many milliliters total (both alcohol and water) are in the solution?

4. Family Budget A family spends $720 every month on food. If the family's income each month is $6,000, what percent of the family's income is spent on food?

5. Chemistry How much HCl (hydrochloric acid) is in a 60-milliliter bottle that is marked 75% HCl?

6. Chemistry How much acetic acid is in a 5-liter container of acetic acid and water that is marked 80% acetic acid? How much is water?

7. **Farming** A farmer owns 28 acres of land. Of the 28 acres, only 65% can be farmed. How many acres are available for farming? How many are not available for farming?

8. **Number of Students** Of the 420 students enrolled in a basic math class, only 30% are first-year students. How many are first-year students? How many are not?

9. **Number of Students** If 48% of the students in a certain college are female and there are 1,440 female students, what is the total number of students in the college?

10. **Basketball** A basketball player made 63 out of 75 free throws. What percent is this?

11. **Number of Graduates** Suppose 60% of the graduating class in a certain high school goes on to college. If 240 students from this graduating class are going on to college, how many students are there in the graduating class?

12. **Defective Parts** In a shipment of airplane parts, 3% are known to be defective. If 15 parts are found to be defective, how many parts are in the shipment?

13. **Number of Students** Suppose there are 3,200 students at our school. If 52% of them are female, how many female students are there at our school?

14. **Number of Students** In a certain school, 75% of the students in first-year chemistry have had algebra. If there are 300 students in first-year chemistry, how many of them have had algebra?

15. **Population** In a city of 32,000 people, there are 10,000 people under 25 years of age. What percent of the population is under 25 years of age?

16. **Number of Students** If 45 people enrolled in a psychology course but only 35 completed it, what percent of the students completed the course? (Round to the nearest tenth of a percent.)

Calculator Problems

The following problems are similar to Problems 1–16. They should be set up the same way. Then the actual calculations should be done on a calculator.

17. Number of People Of 7,892 people attending an outdoor concert in Los Angeles, 3,972 are over 18 years of age. What percent is this? (Round to the nearest whole number percent.)

18. Manufacturing A car manufacturer estimates that 25% of the new cars sold in one city have defective engine mounts. If 2,136 new cars are sold in that city, how many will have defective engine mounts?

19. Laptops The chart shows the most popular laptops among college students surveyed. If 5,280 students were surveyed, how many preferred a Dell?

20. Video Games The chart shows the results of a survey of popular video games. If 12,257 people were surveyed, how many people listed Until Dawn as their favorite?

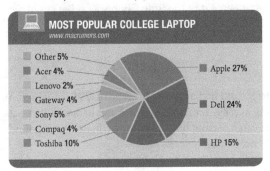

MOST POPULAR VIDEO GAMES	
The Witcher 3: Wild Hunt	97.44%
Uncharted 4: A Thief's End	94.88%
Until Dawn	87.83%
The Last of Us: Remastered	86.92%
DOOM	85.33%

Getting Ready for the Next Section

Multiply.

21. 0.06(550)

22. 0.06(625)

23. 0.03 · 289,500

24. 0.03 · 115,900

Divide. Write your answers as decimals.

25. 5.44 ÷ 0.04

26. 4.35 ÷ 0.03

27. 19.80 ÷ 396

28. 11.82 ÷ 197

29. $\dfrac{1,836}{0.12}$

30. $\dfrac{115}{0.1}$

31. $\dfrac{90}{600}$

32. $\dfrac{105}{750}$

One Step Further: Batting Averages

Batting averages in baseball are given as decimal numbers, rounded to the nearest thousandth. For example, a player had 197 hits in 572 times at bat, for a batting average of .344. This average is found by dividing the number of hits by the number of times he was at bat and then rounding to the nearest thousandth.

$$\text{Batting average} = \frac{\text{Number of hits}}{\text{Number of times at bat}} = \frac{197}{572} = 0.344$$

Because we can write any decimal number as a percent, we can convert batting averages to percents and use our knowledge of percent to solve problems. Looking at the batting average as a percent, we can say that the player will get a hit 34.4% of the times he is at bat.

Each of the following problems can be solved by converting batting averages to percents and translating the problem into one of our three basic percent problems.

33. Ty Cobb has one of the best batting averages of all time. If he has 4,191 career hits in 11,429 times at bat, what percent of the time Cobb was at bat could we expect him to get a hit?

34. Ted Williams has one of the best batting averages of all time. If he has 2,654 career hits in 7,706 times at bat, what percent of the time Cobb was at bat could we expect him to get a hit?

35. Miguel Cabrera had a batting average of .316 in 2016. If his batting average remains the same and he has 500 at-bats in the 2017 season, how many hits will he have?

36. Ichiro Suzuki had a batting average of .291 in 2016. If his batting average remains the same and he has 500 at-bats in the 2017 season, how many hits will he have? Round to the nearest hit.

37. How many hits must Miguel Cabrera have in his first 60 at-bats in 2017 to maintain his average of .316? Round to the nearest hit.

38. How many hits must Ichiro Suzuki have in his first 65 at-bats in 2017 to maintain his average of .291? Round to the nearest hit.

FIND THE MISTAKE •

Each sentence below contains a mistake. Circle the mistake and write the correct word(s) or numbers(s) on the line provided.

1. On a test with 110 questions, a student answered 98 questions correctly. The percentage of questions the student answered correctly is 112.2%. _____

2. A school track team consists of 12 boys and 10 girls. The total number of girls makes up 54.5% percent of the whole team. _____

3. Suppose 39 students in a college class of 130 students received a B on their tests. To find what percent of students earned a B, solve the proportion $\frac{x}{130} = \frac{39}{100}$. _____

4. Suppose a basketball player made 120 out of 150 free throws attempted. To find what percent of free throws the player made, solve the proportion $\frac{30}{150} = \frac{x}{100}$.

_____

SALES TAX AND COMMISSION

7.4

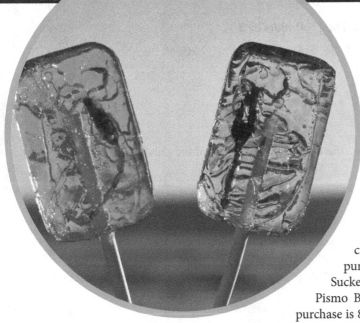

Have an appetite for bugs? A candy company in Pismo Beach, California produces and sells lollipops and other sugary treats with real insects trapped inside! Choose from a wide selection of worms, crickets, scorpions, ants, or butterflies to satisfy that creepy-crawly craving. Suppose you purchase a box of 36 Scorpion Suckers for $81. If sales tax in Pismo Beach at the time of your purchase is 8.75%, how much sales tax will you have to pay in addition to the $81? To solve problems similar to this one, we will first restate them in terms of the problems we have already learned how to solve.

A Application Problems with Sales Tax

Example 1 Suppose the sales tax rate in Mississippi is 6% of the purchase price. If the price of a used refrigerator is $550, how much sales tax must be paid?

Solution Because the sales tax is 6% of the purchase price, and the purchase price is $550, the problem can be restated as

> What is 6% of $550?

We solve this problem, as we did previously, by translating it into an equation.

$$n = 0.06 \cdot 550$$

$$n = 33 \qquad \text{Multiply.}$$

The sales tax is $33. The total price of the refrigerator would be

Purchase price		Sales tax		Total price
↓		↓		↓
$550	+	$33	=	$583

OBJECTIVES · · · · · · · ·

A Solve application problems involving sales tax.

B Solve application problems involving commission.

KEY WORDS · · · · · · · ·

sales tax

tax rate

commission

commission rate

VIDEO EXAMPLES

SECTION 7.4

Practice Problems

1. Suppose the refrigerator in Example 1 cost $700, how much sales tax must be paid?

Note In Example 1, the sales tax rate is 6%, and the sales tax is $33. In most everyday communications, people say "The sales tax is 6%," which is incorrect. The 6% is the tax rate, and the $33 is the actual tax.

Answers

1. $42

495

2. If the sales tax rate is 6% and the tax on a printer is $73.50, what is the total price of the printer?

Example 2   Suppose the sales tax rate is 4%. If the sales tax on a 10-speed bicycle is $5.44, what is the purchase price, and what is the total price of the bicycle?

Solution   We know that 4% of the purchase price is $5.44. We find the purchase price first by restating the problem as

$5.44 is 4% of what number?

$$5.44 = 0.04 \cdot n \qquad \text{Convert to an equation.}$$

We solve the equation by dividing both sides by 0.04.

$$\frac{5.44}{0.04} = \frac{0.04 \cdot n}{0.04} \qquad \text{Divide both sides by 0.04.}$$

$$\frac{5.44}{0.04} = n$$

$$n = 136 \qquad \text{Divide.}$$

The purchase price is $136. The total price is the sum of the purchase price and the sales tax.

$$\begin{aligned}
\text{Purchase price} &= \$136.00 \\
\text{Sales tax} &= + \ 5.44 \\
\hline
\text{Total price} &= \$141.44
\end{aligned}$$

3. Suppose the purchase price of a gaming system is $250 and the sales tax is $17.50. What is the sales tax rate?

Example 3   Suppose the purchase price of a stereo system is $396 and the sales tax is $19.80. What is the sales tax rate?

Solution   We restate the problem as

$19.80 is what percent of $396?

$$19.80 = n \cdot 396 \qquad \text{Convert to an equation.}$$

To solve this equation, we divide both sides by 396.

$$\frac{19.80}{396} = \frac{n \cdot 396}{396} \qquad \text{Divide both sides by 396.}$$

$$\frac{19.80}{396} = n$$

$$n = 0.05 \qquad \text{Divide.}$$

$$n = 5\% \qquad \text{Convert to a percent.}$$

The sales tax rate is 5%.

B Application Problems Involving Commission

Many salespeople work on a **commission** basis. That is, their earnings are a percentage of the amount they sell. The **commission rate** is a percent, and the actual commission they receive is a dollar amount.

Answers

2. $1,298.50

3. 7%

Example 4   A real estate agent gets 3% of the price of each house she sells. If she sells a house for $289,500, how much money does she earn?

Solution   The commission is 3% of the price of the house, which is $289,500. We restate the problem as

What is 3% of $289,500?

$$n = 0.03 \cdot 289{,}500 \qquad \text{Convert to an equation.}$$
$$n = 8{,}685 \qquad \text{Multiply.}$$

The commission is $8,685.

4. A car salesman gets 5% of each car he sells as commission. If he sells a car for $30,000, how much money does he earn?

Example 5   Suppose a car salesperson's commission rate is 12%. If the commission on one of the cars is $1,836, what is the purchase price of the car?

Solution   12% of the sales price is $1,836. The problem can be restated as

12% of what number is $1,836?

$$0.12 \cdot n = 1{,}836 \qquad \text{Convert to an equation.}$$
$$\frac{0.12 \cdot n}{0.12} = \frac{1{,}836}{0.12} \qquad \text{Divide both sides by 0.12.}$$
$$n = 15{,}300$$

The car sells for $15,300.

5. If a real estate agent's comission rate is 6% and the commission on a property is $15,000, what is the purchase price of the property?

Example 6   If the commission on a $600 dining room set is $90, what is the commission rate?

Solution   The commission rate is a percentage of the selling price. That is,

$90 is what percent of $600?

$$90 = n \cdot 600 \qquad \text{Convert to an equation.}$$
$$\frac{90}{600} = \frac{n \cdot 600}{600} \qquad \text{Divide both sides by 600.}$$
$$n = 0.15 \qquad \text{Divide.}$$
$$n = 15\% \qquad \text{Change to a percent.}$$

The commission rate is 15%.

6. If the commission on a $500 sofa is $75, what is the commission rate?

 KEY CONCEPT REVIEW

After reading through the preceding section, respond in your own words and in complete sentences.

A. Explain the difference between the sales tax and the sales tax rate.

B. Rework Example 1 using a sales tax rate of 7% instead of 6%.

C. Suppose the bicycle in Example 2 was purchased in California, where the sales tax rate at the time was 8.25%. How much more would the bicycle have cost?

D. Explain the difference between commission and the commission rate.

Answers

4. $1,500
5. $250,000
6. 15%

EXERCISE SET 7.4 ·

VOCABULARY REVIEW ·

Label the following vocabulary terms below as a dollar amount paid/received (D) or a percent (P).

1. Sales tax _____

2. Sales tax rate _____

3. Commission rate _____

4. Commission _____

Problems

A These problems should be solved by the methods shown in this section. In each case, show the equation needed to solve the problem. Write neatly, and show your work.

1. Sales Tax Suppose the sales tax rate in Mississippi is 7% of the purchase price. If a new food processor sells for $750, how much is the sales tax?

2. Sales Tax If the sales tax rate is 5% of the purchase price, how much sales tax is paid on a television that sells for $980?

3. Sales Tax and Purchase Price Suppose the sales tax rate in Michigan is 6%. How much is the sales tax on a $45 concert ticket? What is the total price?

4. Sales Tax and Purchase Price Suppose the sales tax rate in Hawaii is 4%. How much sales tax is charged on a new car if the purchase price is $16,400? What is the total price?

5. Total Price The sales tax rate is 4%. If the sales tax on a 10-speed bicycle is $6, what is the purchase price? What is the total price?

6. Total Price The sales tax on a new microwave oven is $30. If the sales tax rate is 5%, what is the purchase price? What is the total price?

7. Tax Rate Suppose the purchase price of a dining room set is $450. If the sales tax is $22.50, what is the sales tax rate?

8. Tax Rate If the purchase price of a bottle of California wine is $24 and the sales tax is $1.50, what is the sales tax rate?

B Solve the following problems involving commission.

9. Commission A real estate agent has a commission rate of 3%. If a piece of property sells for $94,000, what is her commission?

10. Commission A tire salesperson has a 12% commission rate. If he sells a set of radial tires for $400, what is his commission?

11. Commission and Purchase Price Suppose a salesperson gets a commission rate of 12% on the lawnmowers she sells. If the commission on one of the mowers is $24, what is the purchase price of the lawnmower?

12. Commission and Purchase Price If an appliance salesperson gets 9% commission on all the appliances she sells, what is the price of a refrigerator if her commission is $67.50?

13. Commission Rate If the commission on an $800 washing machine is $112, what is the commission rate?

14. Commission Rate A realtor makes a commission of $3,600 on a $90,000 house he sells. What is his commission rate?

Calculator Problems

The following problems are similar to Problems 1–14. Set them up in the same way, but use a calculator for the calculations.

15. Sales Tax The sales tax rate on a certain item is 5.5%. If the purchase price is $216.95, how much is the sales tax? (Round to the nearest cent.)

16. Purchase Price If the sales tax rate is 4.75% and the sales tax is $18.95, what is the purchase price? What is the total price? (Both answers should be rounded to the nearest cent.)

17. Tax Rate The purchase price for a new suit is $229.50. If the sales tax is $10.33, what is the sales tax rate? (Round to the nearest tenth of a percent.)

18. Commission If the commission rate for a mobile home salesperson is 11%, what is the commission on the sale of a $15,794 mobile home?

19. Selling Price Suppose the commission rate on the sale of used cars is 13%. If the commission on one of the cars is $519.35, what did the car sell for?

20. Commission Rate If the commission on the sale of $79.40 worth of clothes is $14.29, what is the commission rate? (Round to the nearest percent.)

Getting Ready for the Next Section

Perform the indicated operation.

21. 0.05(22,000)

22. 0.176(1,793,000)

23. 0.25 · 300

24. 0.12 · 450

25. 4 ÷ 25

26. 7 ÷ 35

27. 25 − 21

28. 1,793,000 − 315,568

29. 450 − 54

30. 300 − 75

31. 396 + 19.8

32. 22,000 + 1,100

One Step Further: Luxury Taxes

Suppose a luxury tax requires an additional tax of 10% on a portion of the purchase price of certain luxury items. For expensive cars, it must be paid on the part of the purchase price that exceeded $30,000. For example, if you purchased a Jaguar XJ-S for $53,000, you would pay sales tax on $53,000 and a luxury tax of 10% of $23,000, because the purchase price, $53,000, is $23,000 above $30,000.

33. If you purchased a Jaguar XJ-S for $53,000 in California, where the sales tax rate was 6%, how much would you pay in luxury tax and how much would you pay in sales tax?

34. If you purchased a Mercedes 300E for $43,500 in California, where the sales tax rate was 6%, how much more would you pay in sales tax than luxury tax?

35. How much would you have saved if you had purchased the Jaguar mentioned in Problem 33 in Alaska, which has no sales tax?

36. How much would you have saved if you bought a car in California with a purchase price of $45,000 without the luxury tax?

37. How much would you save in California on taxes (sales and luxury) and the sticker price on a car with a price of $31,500, if you persuaded the car dealer to reduce the price to $29,900?

38. Suppose one of the cars you were interested in had a sticker price of $35,500, while another had a sticker price of $28,500. If you expected to pay full price in California for either car, how much did you save on the sticker price and taxes (sales and luxury) if you bought the less expensive car?

FIND THE MISTAKE •

Each sentence below contains a mistake. Circle the mistake and write the correct word(s) or numbers(s) on the line provided.

1. Suppose the sales tax rate on a new computer is 8%. If the computer cost $650, then the total price of purchase would be $52. _____

2. If a new shirt that costs $32 has sales tax equal to $1.92, then the sales tax rate is 8%. _____

3. A car salesman's commission rate is 7%. To find his commission on a $15,000 sale of a Ford truck, we would solve $15,000 = 7n$. _____

4. A saleswoman makes a commission of $6.80 on a sale of $85 worth of clothing. To find the woman's commission rate, solve the equation $6.80n = 85$ _____

PERCENT INCREASE OR DECREASE, AND DISCOUNT

Many colleges have programs for students with common interests. For example, your college might have certificates or designators that you can earn in addition to your degree. Assume you are enrolled at a college with two campuses. Recently an honors program was formed, allowing highly motivated students the opportunity to take courses that provide alternative approaches to learning. Faculty and advisors have been actively recruiting students for this program. Below are the enrollment trends for each campus over the last two years.

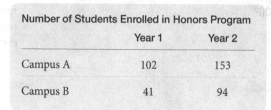

Number of Students Enrolled in Honors Program		
	Year 1	Year 2
Campus A	102	153
Campus B	41	94

Each campus recruited approximately 50 students in the last year. Which campus was more successful in recruiting students? Campus B was arguably more successful because they were able to double the enrollment of honors students on their campus. Percent increase and decrease, the topic of this section, are helpful concepts in understanding problems like this.

A Percent Increases and Decreases

Many times it is more effective to state increases or decreases in terms of percents, rather than the actual number, because with percent we are comparing everything to 100. We saw one example of this in the introduction to this section. By using a percent instead of the number of students recruited, Campus B's recruitment initiatives appear to be more successful. In this section, we will look at several other scenarios in which using a percent is more effective than stating the number.

Example 1 If a person earns $22,000 a year and gets a 5% increase in salary, what is the new salary?

Solution We can find the dollar amount of the salary increase by finding 5% of $22,000.

$$0.05 \cdot 22,000 = 1,100$$

The increase in salary is $1,100. The new salary is the old salary plus the raise.

$22,000	Old salary
+ 1,100	Raise (5% of $22,000)
$23,100	New salary

Practice Problems

1. If a person earns $30,000 per year and gets and 8% raise, what is the new salary?

Example 2 In 1997, there were approximately 1,477,000 arrests for driving under the influence of alcohol or drugs (DUI) in the United States. By 2007, the number of arrests for DUI had decreased 3.4% from the 1997 number. How many people were arrested for DUI in 2007? Round the answer to the nearest thousand.

Solution The decrease in the number of arrests is 3.4% of 1,477,000, or

$$0.034 \cdot 1,477,000 = 50,218$$

Subtracting this number from 1,477,000, we have the number of DUI arrests in 2007.

1,477,000	Number of arrests in 1997
− 50,218	Decrease of 3.4%
1,426,782	Number of arrests in 2007

To the nearest thousand, there were approximately 1,427,000 arrests for DUI in 2007.

2. If a $30,000 car decreased in value by 12.4%, what is it worth?

Example 3 Shoes that usually sell for $25 are on sale for $21. What is the percent decrease in price?

Solution We must first find the decrease in price. Subtracting the sale price from the original price, we have

$$\$25 - \$21 = \$4$$

The decrease is $4. To find the percent decrease (from the original price), we have

$4 is what percent of $25?

$4 = n \cdot 25$	Convert to an equation.
$\dfrac{4}{25} = \dfrac{n \cdot 25}{25}$	Divide both sides by 25.
$n = 0.16$	Divide.
$n = 16\%$	Change to a percent.

The shoes that sold for $25 have been reduced by 16% to $21. In a problem like this, $25 is the *original* (or *marked*) price, $21 is the *sale price*, $4 is the *discount*, and 16% is the *rate of discount*.

3. A jacket that usually sells for $120 is on sale for $108. What is the percent decrease in price?

B Discount

In Example 3, $4 was the discount amount for the shoes on sale. Now we will work some examples that deal directly with **discount**.

Answers

1. $32,400
2. $26,280
3. 10%

4. A pair of shoes that usually sells for $150 is on clearance for 30% off. What is the discount? What is the sale price?

Example 4   During a clearance sale, a suit that usually sells for $300 is marked "25% off." What is the discount? What is the sale price?

Solution   To find the discount, we restate the problem as

What is 25% of 300?

$$n = 0.25 \cdot 300 \qquad \text{Convert to an equation.}$$

$$n = 75 \qquad \text{Multiply.}$$

The discount is $75. The sale price is the original price less the discount.

$300	Original price
− 75	Less the discount (25% of $300)
$225	Sale price

5. A refrigerator that normally sells for $800 is on sale at 15% off. If the sales tax rate is 7%, what is the total bill for the refrigerator?

Example 5   A man buys a washing machine on sale. The machine usually sells for $450, but it is on sale at 12% off. If the sales tax rate is 5%, how much is the total bill for the washer?

Solution   First, we have to find the sale price of the washing machine, and we begin by finding the discount.

What is 12% of $450?

$$n = 0.12 \cdot 450$$

$$n = 54$$

The washing machine is marked down $54. The sale price is

$450	Original price
− 54	Discount (12% of $450)
$396	Sale price

Note It is customary to find the discounted price and then find the sales tax for that amount.

Because the sales tax rate is 5%, we find the sales tax as follows:

What is 5% of 396?

$$n = 0.05 \cdot 396$$

$$n = 19.80$$

The sales tax is $19.80. The total price the man pays for the washing machine is

$396.00	Sale price
+ 19.80	Sales tax
$415.80	Total price

KEY CONCEPT REVIEW

After reading through the preceding section, respond in your own words and in complete sentences.

A. Suppose the person mentioned in Example 1 was earning $32,000 per year and received the same percent increase in salary. How much more would the raise have been?

B. Suppose the shoes mentioned in Example 3 were on sale for $20, instead of $21. Calculate the new percent decrease in price.

C. Suppose a store owner pays $225 for a suit, and then marks it up $75, to $300. Find the percent increase in price.

D. What is discount?

Answers

4. $45, $105

5. $727.60

EXERCISE SET 7.5 ....

VOCABULARY REVIEW •

Read the following description of a television on sale.

An LCD HD television that usually sells for $400 is on sale for $340. The television's price has been reduced $60, which is a 15% percent decrease.

Now match the following quantities mentioned in the above description with their correct labels.

1. $400   **a.** Discount

2. $340   **b.** Original price

3. $60   **c.** Rate of discount

4. 15%   **d.** Sale price

Problems

A, B Solve each of these problems using the method developed in this section.

1. **Salary Increase** If a person earns $23,000 a year and gets a 7% increase in salary, what is the new salary?

2. **Salary Increase** A computer programmer's yearly income of $57,000 is increased by 8%. What is the dollar amount of the increase, and what is her new salary?

3. **Tuition Increase** The yearly tuition at a college is presently $3,000. Next year it is expected to increase by 17%. What will the tuition at this school be next year?

4. **Price Increase** A supermarket increased the price of cheese that sold for $1.98 per pound by 3%. What is the new price for a pound of this cheese? (Round to the nearest cent.)

5. **Car Value** In one year, a new car decreased in value by 20%. If it sold for $16,500 when it was new, what was it worth after 1 year?

6. **Calorie Content** A certain light beer has 20% fewer calories than the regular beer. If the regular beer has 120 calories per bottle, how many calories are in the same-sized bottle of the light beer?

7. **Salary Increase** A person earning $3,500 a month gets a raise of $350 per month. What is the percent increase in salary?

8. **Rate Increase** A student reader is making $6.50 per hour and gets a $0.70 raise. What is the percent increase? (Round to the nearest tenth of a percent.)

9. **Shoe Sale** Shoes that usually sell for $25 are on sale for $20. What is the percent decrease in price?

10. **Enrollment Decrease** The enrollment in a certain elementary school was 410. The next year, the enrollment in the same school was 328. Find the percent decrease in enrollment from one year to the next.

11. **Soda Consumption** The chart shows the consumption of soda in gallons per person per year in different countries. What is the increase in percent of consumption in the United States as compared to Norway? Round to the nearest percent.

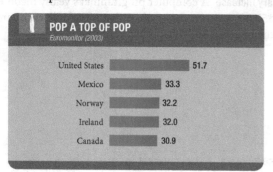

12. **Farmers' Markets** The chart shows the rise in farmers' markets throughout the country. What is the percent increase in farmers' markets from Year 1 to Year 10? Round to the nearest tenth of a percent.

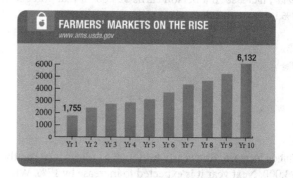

13. **Discount** During a clearance sale, a three-piece suit that usually sells for $300 is marked "15% off." What is the discount? What is the sale price?

14. **Sale Price** On opening day, a new music store offers a 12% discount on all electric guitars. If the regular price on a guitar is $550, what is the sale price?

15. **Total Price** A man buys a washing machine that is on sale. The washing machine usually sells for $450 but is on sale at 20% off. If the sales tax rate in his state is 6%, how much is the total bill for the washer?

16. **Total Price** A bedroom set that normally sells for $1,450 is on sale for 10% off. If the sales tax rate is 5%, what is the total price of the bedroom set if it is bought while on sale?

Calculator Problems

Set up the following problems the same way you set up Problems 1–16. Then use a calculator to do the calculations.

17. Salary Increase A teacher making $43,752 per year gets a 6.5% raise. What is the new salary?

18. Utility Increase A homeowner had a $15.90 electric bill in December. In January, the bill was $17.81. Find the percent increase in the electric bill from December to January. (Round to the nearest whole number.)

19. Soccer The rules for soccer state that the playing field must be from 100 to 120 yards long and 55 to 75 yards wide. The 1999 Women's World Cup was played at the Rose Bowl on a playing field 116 yards long and 72 yards wide. The diagram below shows the smallest possible soccer field, the largest possible soccer field, and the soccer field at the Rose Bowl.

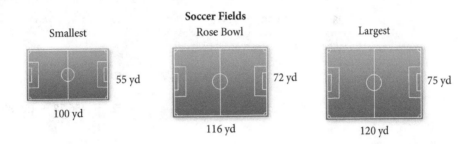

Soccer Fields

Smallest — 55 yd — 100 yd

Rose Bowl — 72 yd — 116 yd

Largest — 75 yd — 120 yd

a. Percent Increase A team plays on the smallest field, then plays in the Rose Bowl. What is the percent increase in the area of the playing field from the smallest field to the Rose Bowl? Round to the nearest tenth of a percent.

b. Percent Increase A team plays a soccer game in the Rose Bowl. The next game is on a field with the largest dimensions. What is the percent increase in the area of the playing field from the Rose Bowl to the largest field? Round to the nearest tenth of a percent.

20. Football The diagrams below show the dimensions of playing fields for the National Football League (NFL), the Canadian Football League (CFL), and Arena Football.

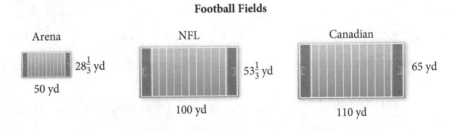

Football Fields

Arena — $28\frac{1}{3}$ yd — 50 yd

NFL — $53\frac{1}{3}$ yd — 100 yd

Canadian — 65 yd — 110 yd

a. Percent Increase Kurt Warner made a successful transition from Arena Football to the NFL, winning the Most Valuable Player award. What was the percent increase in the area of the fields he played on in moving from Arena Football to the NFL? Round to the nearest percent.

b. Percent Decrease Doug Flutie played in the Canadian Football League before moving to the NFL. What was the percent decrease in the area of the fields he played on in moving from the CFL to the NFL? Round to the nearest tenth of a percent.

Getting Ready for the Next Section

Multiply. Round to nearest hundredth if necessary.

21. 0.07(2,000)

22. 0.12(8,000)

23. $600(0.04)\left(\dfrac{1}{6}\right)$

24. $900(0.06)\left(\dfrac{1}{4}\right)$

25. $10,150(0.06)\left(\dfrac{1}{4}\right)$

26. $10,302.25(0.06)\left(\dfrac{1}{4}\right)$

Add.

27. 3,210 + 224.7

28. 900 + 13.50

29. 10,000 + 150

30. 10,150 + 152.25

31. 10,302.25 + 154.53

32. 10,456.78 + 156.85

Simplify.

33. 2,000 + 0.07(2,000)

34. 8,000 + 0.12(8,000)

35. 3,000 + 0.07(3,000)

36. 9,000 + 0.12(9,000)

FIND THE MISTAKE •

Each sentence below contains a mistake. Circle the mistake and write the correct word(s) or numbers(s) on the line provided.

1. If a new model of a car increases 12% from and old model's price of $24,000, then the new selling price is $2,880. _____

2. A lawnmower goes on sale from $98 to $63.70. The percent decrease of the lawnmower's price is 65%. _____

3. A backpack that normally sells for $75 is on sale. The new price of $45 shows a percent increase of 40% _____

4. A designer pair of sunglasses is on sale from $125 for 20% off. If the sales tax is 6% of the sale price, then the total bill for the glasses would be $107.50. _____

INTEREST

7.6

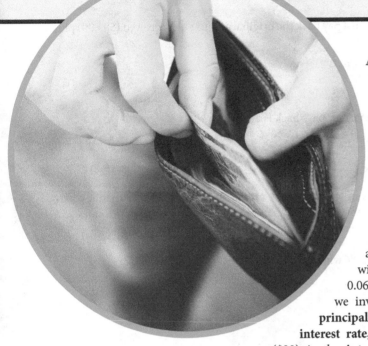

Anyone who has borrowed money from a bank or other lending institution, or who has invested money in a savings account, is probably aware of interest. Interest is the amount of money paid for the use of money. If we put $500 in a savings account that pays 6% annually, the interest will be 6% of $500, or 0.06(500) = $30. The amount we invest ($500) is called the **principal,** the percent (6%) is the **interest rate,** and the money earned ($30) is the **interest.** Depending on the terms of the account, interest is paid at different times during the year. Let's begin by working some examples that involve annual interest.

OBJECTIVES

A Solve application problems involving annual interest.

B Solve application problems involving simple interest.

C Solve application problems involving compound interest.

KEY WORDS

interest

principal

interest rate

simple interest

compound interest

A Interest

Example 1   A man invests $2,000 in a savings plan that pays 7% per year. How much money will be in the account at the end of 1 year?

Solution   In this problem, $2,000 is the principal and 7% is the interest rate. To find the amount of interest he earns in one year, we will multiply the interest rate by the principal. That is, we multiply 7%, converted to a decimal, by $2,000.

$$\text{Interest} = 0.07(\$2{,}000)$$

$$= \$140$$

Thus the interest earned in 1 year is $140. The total amount of money in the account at the end of a year is the original amount plus the $140 interest.

$2,000	Original investment (principal)
+ 140	Interest (7% of $2,000)
$2,140	Amount after 1 year

The amount in the account after 1 year is $2,140.

VIDEO EXAMPLES

SECTION 7.6

Practice Problems

1. A woman invests $3,000 in an account that pays 8% per year in interest. How much is in the account after 1 year?

Answers

1. $3,240

509

2. Ryan finances a $23,000 car at 8% interest for 1 year. What is the total amount he will pay back at the end of the loan?

Example 2   A farmer borrows $8,000 from his local bank at 12%. How much does he pay back to the bank at the end of the year to pay off the loan?

Solution   The interest he pays on the $8,000 is

$$\text{Interest} = 0.12(\$8,000)$$

$$= \$960$$

At the end of the year, he must pay back the original amount he borrowed ($8,000) plus the interest at a rate of 12%.

$$
\begin{array}{ll}
\$8,000 & \text{Amount borrowed (principal)} \\
+\ \ 960 & \text{Interest at 12\%} \\
\hline
\$8,960 & \text{Total amount to pay back}
\end{array}
$$

The total amount that the farmer pays back is $8,960.

B Simple Interest

There are many situations in which interest on a loan is accrued other than a yearly basis. Many short-term loans are for only 30 or 60 days. In these cases, we can use a formula to calculate the interest that has accumulated. This type of interest is called **simple interest.**

The formula is $I = P \cdot R \cdot T$ where

$$I = \text{Interest}$$

$$P = \text{Principal}$$

$$R = \text{Interest rate}$$

$$T = \text{Time (in years, 1 year} = 360 \text{ days)}$$

We could have used this formula to find the interest in Examples 1 and 2. In those two cases, T is 1. When the length of time is in days rather than years, it is common practice in banking to use 360 days for 1 year, and we write T as a fraction. Examples 3 and 4 illustrate this procedure.

3. Suppose the loan in Example 3 is at an interest rate of 6%. How much interest will be paid if the loan is paid back in 90 days?

Example 3   A student takes out an emergency loan for tuition, books, and supplies. The loan is for $600 at an interest rate of 4%. How much interest does the student pay if the loan is paid back in 60 days?

Solution   The principal P is $600, the rate R is 4% = 0.04, and the time T is $\frac{60}{360}$. Notice that T must be given in years, and 60 days = $\frac{60}{360}$ year. Applying the formula, we have

$$I = P \cdot R \cdot T$$

$$I = 600 \cdot 0.04 \cdot \frac{60}{360}$$

$$I = 600 \cdot 0.04 \cdot \frac{1}{6} \qquad \frac{60}{360} = \frac{1}{6}$$

$$I = 4 \qquad \text{Multiply.}$$

The interest is $4. Notice we don't need to add this amount to the principal because the question is only asking for us to find the interest.

Example 4   A woman deposits $900 in an account that pays 6% annually. If she withdraws all the money in the account after 90 days, how much does she withdraw?

Solution   We have $P = \$900$, $R = 0.06$, and $T = 90$ days $= \frac{90}{360}$ year. Using these numbers in the formula, we have

$$I = P \cdot R \cdot T$$

$$I = 900 \cdot 0.06 \cdot \frac{90}{360}$$

$$I = 900 \cdot 0.06 \cdot \frac{1}{4} \qquad \frac{90}{360} = \frac{1}{4}$$

$$I = 13.5 \qquad\qquad \text{Multiply.}$$

The interest earned in 90 days is $13.50. If the woman withdraws all the money in her account, she will withdraw

$900.00	Principal (original amount)
+ 13.50	Interest for 90 days
$913.50	Total amount withdrawn

The woman will withdraw $913.50.

4. If the woman in Example 4 withdrew the money after 180 days, how much did she withdraw?

C Compound Interest

A second common type of interest is **compound interest.** Compound interest includes interest paid on interest. For example, savings accounts often have compound interest. After you are paid interest, the bank will pay you interest next time based on the principal and interest that was added to your account. This is compound interest. We can use what we know about simple interest to help us solve problems involving compound interest.

Example 5   A woman puts $3,000 into a savings account that pays 7% compounded annually. How much money is in the account at the end of 2 years?

Solution   Because the account pays 7% annually, the simple interest at the end of 1 year is 7% of $3,000.

$$\text{Interest after 1 year} = 0.07(\$3,000)$$

$$= \$210$$

Because the interest is paid annually, at the end of 1 year the total amount of money in the account is

$3,000	Principal
+ 210	Interest for 1 year
$3,210	Total in account after 1 year

The interest paid for the second year is 7% of this new total, or

$$\text{Interest paid the second year} = 0.07(\$3,210)$$

$$= \$224.70$$

At the end of 2 years, the total in the account is

$3,210.00	Amount at the beginning of second year
+ 224.70	Interest paid for second year
$3,434.70	Account after 2 years

At the end of 2 years, the account totals $3,434.70. The total interest earned during this 2-year period is

First year		Second year		Total
$210	+	$224.70	=	$434.70.

5. Suppose the woman in Example 5 put $5,000 in the savings account. How much is there at the end of 4 years?

Note   If the interest earned in Example 5 were calculated using the formula for simple interest, $I = P \cdot R \cdot T$, the amount of money in the account at the end of two years would be $3,420.00.

Answers
4. $927
5. $6,553.98

You may have heard of savings and loan companies that offer interest rates that are compounded quarterly. If the interest rate is, say, 6% and it is compounded quarterly, then 4 times per year, or every 90 days, the interest is added to the account. If it is compounded semiannually, then the interest is added to the account every 6 months. Most accounts have interest rates that are compounded daily, which means the simple interest is computed daily and added to the account.

The simple interest formula can be used to solve problems involving compound interest, but often it is more efficient to use a formula specifically for compound interest. The formula is $A = P(1 + \frac{r}{n})^{nt}$ where

A = Amount in the account after t years

P = Principal

r = Interest rate as a decimal

n = Number of times interest is compounded per year

t = Number of years

6. Repeat Example 6 if $600 is borrowed from an account that charges 6% annual interest, compounded monthly.

Example 6   Suppose you borrow $500 from an account with an annual interest rate of 8% compounded quarterly. Find the amount of money owed after 5 years.

Solution   First, we note that $P = 500$, $t = 5$, and $r = 0.08$. Interest that is compounded quarterly is compounded four times a year, giving us $n = 4$. Substituting these numbers into the preceding formula, we have

$$A = 500(1 + \frac{0.08}{4})^{4 \cdot 5}$$

$$= 500(1.02)^{4 \cdot 5} \qquad \text{} \, 1 + \frac{0.08}{4} = 1.02$$

$$= 500(1.02)^{20} \qquad \text{Multiply.}$$

$$= 742.97 \qquad \text{Round to the nearest cent.}$$

Our answer is found on a calculator, and then rounded to the nearest cent.

Note   Because these problems involve money, we are rounding to the hundredths place.

KEY CONCEPT REVIEW

After reading through the preceding section, respond in your own words and in complete sentences.

A. What is the difference between the interest rate and the interest?

B. What is simple interest and how is it different than compound interest?

C. How much does the student in Example 3 pay back if the loan is paid off after a year, instead of after 60 days?

D. In Example 6, how much money would the account contain at the end of 1 year if it were compounded annually, instead of quarterly?

Answers

6. $809.31

VOCABULARY REVIEW •

Choose the correct words to fill in the blanks below.

interest rate   principal   simple   compound

1. For an investment, the amount we invest is called the _____, the percent is called the interest rate, and the money earned is called the interest.

2. In the formula $I = P \cdot R \cdot T$, I = interest, P = principal, R = _____, and T = time.

3. _____ interest is a percent of money earned on the principal investment only.

4. _____ interest is interest earned on interest added to the principal.

Problems

A, B These problems are similar to the examples found in this section. They should be set up and solved in the same way. (Problems 1–12 involve simple interest.)

1. **Savings Account** A man invests $2,000 in a savings plan that pays 8% per year. How much money will be in the account at the end of 1 year?

2. **Savings Account** How much simple interest is earned on $5,000 if it is invested for 1 year at 5%?

3. **Savings Account** A savings account pays 7% per year. How much interest will $9,500 invested in such an account earn in a year?

4. **Savings Account** A local bank pays 5.5% annual interest on all savings accounts. If $600 is invested in this type of account, how much will be in the account at the end of a year?

5. **Bank Loan** A farmer borrows $8,000 from his local bank at 7%. How much does he pay back to the bank at the end of the year when he pays off the loan?

6. **Bank Loan** If $400 is borrowed at a rate of 12% for 1 year, how much is the interest?

7. **Bank Loan** A bank lends one of its customers $2,000 at 8% for 1 year. If the customer pays the loan back at the end of the year, how much does he pay the bank?

8. **Bank Loan** If a loan of $2,000 at 20% for 1 year is to be paid back in one payment at the end of the year, how much does the borrower pay the bank?

9. **Student Loan** A student takes out an emergency loan for tuition, books, and supplies. The loan is for $600 with an interest rate of 5%. How much interest does the student pay if the loan is paid back in 60 days?

10. **Short-Term Loan** If a loan of $1,200 at 9% is paid off in 90 days, what is the interest?

11. **Savings Account** A woman deposits $800 in a savings account that pays 5%. If she withdraws all the money in the account after 120 days, how much does she withdraw?

12. **Savings Account** $1,800 is deposited in a savings account that pays 6%. If the money is withdrawn at the end of 30 days, how much interest is earned?

C The problems that follow involve compound interest.

13. Compound Interest A woman puts $5,000 into a savings account that pays 6% compounded annually. How much money is in the account at the end of 2 years?

14. Compound Interest A savings account pays 5% compounded annually. If $10,000 is deposited in the account, how much is in the account at the end of 2 years?

15. Compound Interest If $8,000 is invested in a savings account that pays 5% compounded quarterly, how much is in the account at the end of a year?

16. Compound Interest Suppose $1,200 is invested in a savings account that pays 6% compounded semiannually. How much is in the account at the end of $1\frac{1}{2}$ years?

Calculator Problems

The following problems should be set up in the same way in which Problems 1–16 have been set up. Then the calculations should be done on a calculator.

17. Savings Account A woman invests $917.26 in a savings account that pays 6.25% annually. How much is in the account at the end of a year?

18. Business Loan The owner of a clothing store borrows $6,210 for 1 year at 11.5% interest. If he pays the loan back at the end of the year, how much does he pay back?

19. Compound Interest Suppose $10,000 is invested in each account below. In each case, find the amount of money in the account at the end of 5 years.

a. Annual interest rate = 6%, compounded quarterly

b. Annual interest rate = 6%, compounded monthly

c. Annual interest rate = 5%, compounded quarterly

d. Annual interest rate = 5%, compounded monthly

20. Compound Interest Suppose $5,000 is invested in each account below. In each case, find the amount of money in the account at the end of 10 years.

a. Annual interest rate = 5%, compounded quarterly

b. Annual interest rate = 6%, compounded quarterly

c. Annual interest rate = 7%, compounded quarterly

d. Annual interest rate = 8%, compounded quarterly

Getting Ready for the Next Section

21. Add: $30 + 3 + 10 + 7$

22. Reduce $\frac{30}{50}$ to lowest terms.

23. What is 61% of 800?

24. What is 12% of 800?

25. Write $\frac{6}{24}$ as a percent.

26. Multiply: $(0.25)(360)$

One Step Further

The following problems are percent problems. Use any of the methods developed in this chapter to solve them.

27. **Movie Making** The bar chart shows the production budget for some of the most expensive movies to win an Academy Award for Best Picture. Find the percent increase from each Best Picture to the next. Round to the nearest percent.

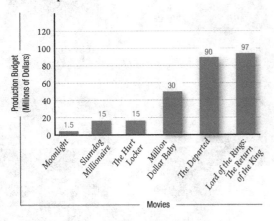

28. **Movie Making** The table below shows how much money each of the Academy Award winners shown at the left has grossed worldwide. Using the information from the previous problem, find the ratio of gross revenue to cost. Write your answer rounded to the nearest percent.

Grossed Revenue	
Moonlight	$65,000,000
Slumdog Millionaire	$378,000,000
The Hurt Locker	$49,000,000
Million Dollar Baby	$217,000,000
The Departed	$290,000,000
Lord of the Rings: The Return of the King	$1,120,000,000

FIND THE MISTAKE ·

Each sentence below contains a mistake. Circle the mistake and write the correct word(s) or numbers(s) on the line provided.

1. A woman invests $1,500 into an account with a 6% annual interest rate. She will have $90 in her account by the end of one year. _____

2. A business man invests $2,750 into an account that has an 8% interest rate per year. To find out how much money will be in the man's account after 72 days, you must multiply the product of 2,750 and 0.08 by 72. _____

3. If a person invests $10,000 into an account that is compounded annually at 6%, then after two years, the account will contain $11,200. _____

4. A woman deposits $4,000 into a savings account that pays 7% compounded quarterly. At the end of the year, the account contains $4,280. _____

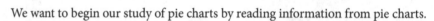

• OBJECTIVES •

A Interpret a pie chart.

B Construct a pie chart.

• • • KEY WORDS • • •

pie chart

VIDEO EXAMPLES

SECTION 7.7

Practice Problems

1. Work Example 1 again if five more students are surveyed, all living in off-campus apartments.

In this section, we will review how to read a **pie chart** and learn how to construct a chart using given data. Pie charts are another way in which to visualize numerical information. They lend themselves well to information that adds up to 100% and are common in the world around us. In fact, it is hard to pick up a newspaper or magazine without seeing a pie chart.

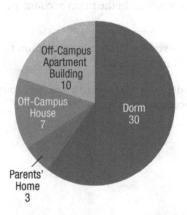

A Interpreting a Pie Chart

We want to begin our study of pie charts by reading information from pie charts.

Example 1 The pie chart shows where a group of freshmen students live. Use the pie chart to answer the following questions.

a. Find the total number of students surveyed.

b. Find the ratio of those living in the dorms to the total surveyed.

c. Find the ratio of those living in their parents' homes to those living in apartments.

Off-Campus Apartment Building 10

Off-Campus House 7

Dorm 30

Parents' Home 3

Answers

1. a. 55 **b.** $\frac{30}{55} = \frac{6}{11}$ **c.** $\frac{1}{5}$

Solution

a. To find the total number of students surveyed we add the numbers in all sections of the pie chart.

$$30 + 3 + 10 + 7 = 50 \text{ students surveyed}$$

b. The ratio of those living in dorms to the total surveyed is

$$\frac{\text{Number living in dorms}}{\text{Total number of students surveyed}} = \frac{30}{50} = \frac{3}{5}$$

This means that out of every 5 students surveyed, we can expect 3 of them to live in dorms.

c. The ratio of those living at home to those living in apartments is

$$\frac{\text{Number living at home}}{\text{Number living in apartments}} = \frac{3}{10}$$

This means that for every 3 students who live at home, 10 live in an apartment.

Example 2   The pie chart shows the market share for different digital movie companies.

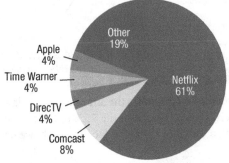

Suppose 800 people were surveyed and their answers matched the results shown above.

a. How many people in the survey stream their digital movies from Netflix?

b. How many people stream their digital movies from Apple and Comcast combined?

Solution

a. To find out how many people in the survey stream from Netflix, we need to find 61% of the 800 that were surveyed.

$$0.61(800) = 488 \text{ of the people surveyed stream their movies from Netflix.}$$

b. The number of people streaming from Apple and Comcast account for 4% + 8% = 12%. To find out how many of the 800 people are in this category, we must find 12% of 800.

$$0.12(800) = 96 \text{ of the people surveyed stream their movies from Apple and Comcast combined.}$$

2. Work Example 2 again if 1,200 people responded to the survey.

3. Construct a pie chart that shows the amount of time spent working an eight-hour day.

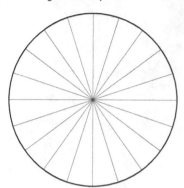

PIE CHART TEMPLATE   *Each slice is 5% of the area of the circle.*

B Constructing Pie Charts

Example 3   A recent study found that Americans spend just over six hours per day on social media sites. Construct a pie chart that shows the amount of time in a day spent on social media.

Solution 1   **Using a Template**   As mentioned previously, pie charts are constructed with percents. Therefore we must first convert data to percents. To find the percent of hours from a day are spent on social media sites, we divide the number of hours spent by the total number of hours in a day. We have

$$\frac{6}{24} = 0.25 \text{ which is } 25\%$$

The area of each section of the template on the lower left is 5% of the area of the whole circle. If we shade 5 sections of the template, we will have shaded 25% of the area of the whole circle.

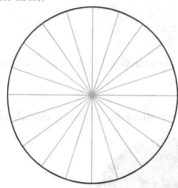

PIE CHART TEMPLATE   *Each slice is 5% of the area of the circle.*

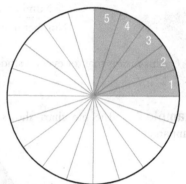

CREATING A PIE CHART   *To shade 25% of the circle, we shade 5 sections of the template.*

The shaded area represents 25%, which is the amount of each day spent on social media sites. The rest of the circle must represent the 75% of the rest of the hours in the day. Shading each area with a different color and labeling each, we have our pie chart.

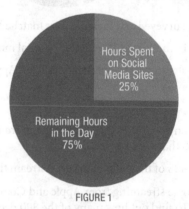

Hours Spent on Social Media Sites 25%

Remaining Hours in the Day 75%

FIGURE 1

HOW TO   **Construct a Pie Chart Using a Template**

Step 1:   Using ratios of each value to the total, convert the data to percentages.

Step 2:   Divide the template based on the percentages found in the previous step.

Step 3:   Shade each area with a different color and label each one.

Solution 2 **Using a Protractor** Since a pie chart is a circle, and a circle contains 360°, we must now convert our data to degrees. We do this by multiplying our percents in decimal form by 360. We have

$$(0.25)360° = 90°$$

Now we place a protractor on top of a circle. First we draw a line from the center of the circle to 0° as shown in Figure 2. Now we measure and mark 90° from our starting point, as shown in Figure 3.

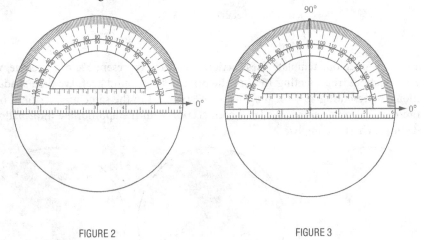

FIGURE 2   FIGURE 3

Finally we draw a line from the center of the circle to this mark, as shown in Figure 4. Then we shade and label the two regions as shown in Figure 5.

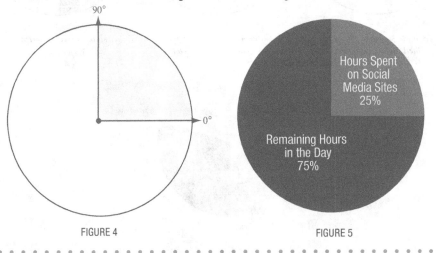

FIGURE 4   FIGURE 5

· ·

HOW TO **Construct a Pie Chart Using a Protractor**

Step 1: Convert data to decimals using ratios of each value to the total.

Step 2: Multiply each decimal by 360 to determine the number of degrees for each area.

Step 3: Use the protractor to divide the circle based on the number of degrees found in the previous step.

Step 4: Shade each area with a different color and label each one.

4. The table below shows the breakdown of the price for the different kinds of cheese in our lasagna. Use the information in the table to construct a pie chart.

Cheese	Percent of Price
Ricotta	15%
Mozzarella	50%
Parmesan	35%

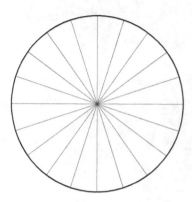

PIE CHART TEMPLATE   *Each slice is 5% of the area of the circle.*

Example 4   Construct a pie chart from the information in the following table.

	How much does it cost to make Lasagna?
Expense	**Percent of Price**
Ground Beef	15%
Cheese	45%
Pasta	5%
Tomato and Vegetables	30%
Other	5%

Solution   Since our template uses sections that each represent 5% of the circle, we shade 3 sections, representing 15% for the price of the ground beef. We then shade 9 sections, representing 45% for the cheese. We proceed in the same manner until our entire recipe is represented. We label each section with the appropriate information, and our pie chart is complete.

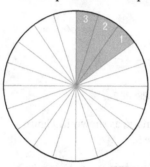

We shade 3 sections to represent the 15% for ground beef

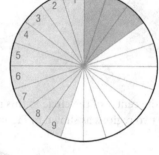

To shade 45% of the circle, we shade 9 sections of the template.

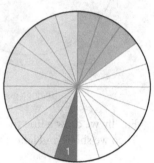

We shade 1 section to represent the 5% for the pasta.

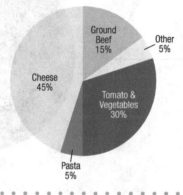

Ground Beef 15%
Other 5%
Cheese 45%
Tomato & Vegetables 30%
Pasta 5%

KEY CONCEPT REVIEW

After reading through the preceding section, respond in your own words and in complete sentences.

A. If a circle is divided into 20 equal slices, then each of the slices is what percent of the total area enclosed by the circle?

B. If a 250 MB computer drive contains 75 MB of data, then how much of the drive is free space?

C. If a 250 MB computer drive contains 75 MB of data, then what percent of the drive contains data?

D. Explain how you would construct a pie chart of monthly expenses for a person who spends $700 on rent, $200 on food, and $100 on entertainment.

Choose the correct words to fill in the blanks below.

template   degrees   percents   protractor

When creating a pie chart, we must first convert the data to _____ . We then convert to _____ by multiplying the percent in decimal form by 360. We can then use either the _____ or a _____ to draw each section of the pie chart.

Problems

A Use the pie charts to solve the following problems.

1. **Students with Jobs** The pie chart shows the results of surveying 200 college students to find out how many hours they worked per week at a job.

    a. Find the ratio of students who work more than 15 hours a week to total students.

    b. Find the ratio of students who don't have a job to students who work more than 15 hours a week.

    c. Find the ratio of students with jobs to total students.

    d. Find the ratio of students with jobs to students without jobs.

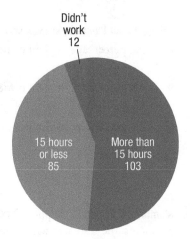

2. **Favorite Salad Dressing** The pie chart shows the results of a survey on favorite salad dressing.

    a. What is the most preferred salad dressing?

    b. Which salad dressing is preferred second most?

    c. Which salad dressing is least preferred?

    d. What percentage of people preferred ranch?

    e. What percentage of people preferred Italian or Thousand Island?

    f. If 50 people responded to the survey, how many people preferred ranch? (Round to the nearest whole number.)

    g. If 50 people responded to the survey, how many people preferred Thousand Island? (Round to the nearest whole number.)

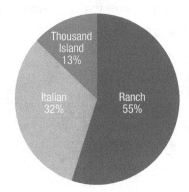

3. Food Dropped on the Floor The pie chart shows the results of a survey about eating food that has been dropped on the floor. Participants were asked whether they eat food that has been on the floor for 3, 5, or 10 seconds.

a. What percentage of people say it is not safe to eat food dropped on the floor?

b. What percentage of people believe the "three-second rule"?

c. What percentage of people will eat foot that stays on the floor for ten seconds or less?

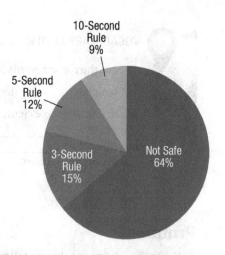

4. Talking to Our Plants A survey showed that most plant owners talk to their plants.

a. What percentage of plant owners say they never talk to their plants?

b. What percentage of plant owners say they talk to their plants all the time?

c. What percentage of plant owners say they talk to their plants sometimes or not often?

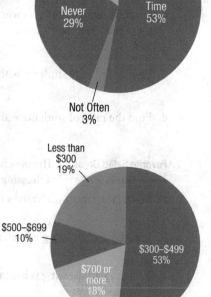

5. Monthly Car Payments Suppose 3,000 people responded to a survey on car loan payments, the results of which are shown in the pie chart. Find the number of people whose monthly payments would be the following:

a. $700 or more

b. Less than $300

c. $500 or more

d. $300 to $699

6. Where Workers Say Germs Lurk A survey asked workers where they thought the most germ-contaminated spot in the workplace was. Suppose the survey took place at a large company with 4,200 employees. Use the pie chart to determine the number of employees who would vote for each of the following as the most germ-contaminated areas.

a. Keyboards

b. Doorknobs

c. Restrooms or other

d. Telephones or doorknobs

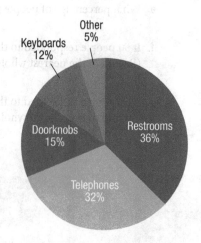

B Construct a pie chart for each of the following problems.

7. Grade Distribution Scores on a recent math test are shown in the table below for a class of 20 students. Construct a pie chart that shows the number of A's, B's, and C's earned on the test. Use the template provided here or use a protractor.

Grade Distribution	
Grade	Number
A	5
B	8
C	7
Total	20

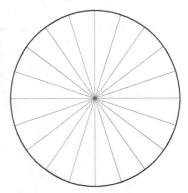

PIE CHART TEMPLATE   *Each slice is 5% of the area of the circle.*

8. Building Sizes The Lean and Mean Gym Company recently ran a promotion for their four locations in the county. The table shows the locations along with the amount of square feet at each location. Use the information in the table to construct a pie chart, using the template provided here or using a protractor. Round to the nearest percent if necessary.

Gym Locker and Size	
Location	Square Feet
Downtown	35,000
Uptown	85,000
Lakeside	25,000
Mall	75,000
Total	220,000

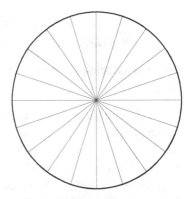

PIE CHART TEMPLATE   *Each slice is 5% of the area of the circle.*

9. Room Sizes Scott and Amy are building their dream house. The size of the house will be 2,400 square feet. The table below shows the size of each room. Use the information in the table to construct a pie chart, using the template provided here or using a protractor. Round to the nearest percent if necessary.

Room Sizes	
Room	Square Feet
Kitchen	400
Dining Room	310
Bedrooms	890
Living Room	600
Bathrooms	200
Total	2,400

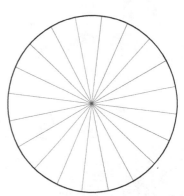

PIE CHART TEMPLATE   *Each slice is 5% of the area of the circle.*

10. **Passenger Train Seating** The table below gives the number of seats sold in the four classes of seating on a passenger train. Create a pie chart from the information in the table. Round to the nearest percent if necessary.

Passenger Train Seating

Seating Class	Number of Seats
Coach	114
Business	85
First Class	32
Sleeper Class	25
Total	256

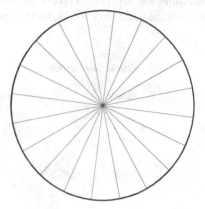

PIE CHART TEMPLATE *Each slice is 5% of the area of the circle.*

FIND THE MISTAKE ·

Each sentence below contains a mistake. Circle the mistake and write the correct word(s) or numbers(s) on the line provided.

1. The percentage of people who live in their parents' home or on campus is 3%. _____

2. The percentage of people who live in a single bedroom apartment or studio, or in an apartment with friends can be found by adding 10% and 35%. _____

3. The number of people who live in a house with friends is 500. _____

4. To find the number of people who decided not to live off campus, multiply 2500 by 84%. _____

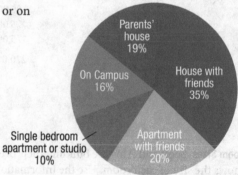

Survey Size: 2,500 Students

access to research
information, such as a
library or the internet

Trail Guide Project

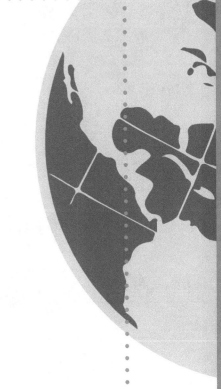

Everyday Math

Most people don't realize how often we use math skills in our daily lives. The obvious skills are used doing things such as paying for groceries, calculating supplies for a home project, or cooking from a recipe. This project will help shed light on some lesser known ways of using math. Choose an occupation from the list below. Research what and how math skills are used in the chosen occupation. Present your findings to the class.

Accountant

Agriculturist

Biologist

Carpenter

Chemist

Computer Programmer

Engineer

Geologist

Graphic Designer

Lawyer

Manager

Marketer

Nurse and Doctor

Meteorologist

Politician

Repair Technician (plumber, electrician, mechanic, etc.)

Teacher

The Meaning of Percent [7.1]

1. 42% means 42 per hundred
or $\frac{42}{100}$.

Percent means "per hundred." It is a way of comparing numbers to the number 100.

Changing Percents to Decimals [7.1]

2. 75% = 0.75

To change a percent to a decimal, drop the % symbol and move the decimal point two places to the *left*.

Changing Decimals to Percents [7.1]

3. 0.25 = 25%

To change a decimal to a percent, move the decimal point two places to the *right*, and use the % symbol.

Changing Percents to Fractions [7.1]

4. $6\% = \frac{6}{100} = \frac{3}{50}$

To change a percent to a fraction, drop the % symbol, and use a denominator of 100. Reduce the resulting fraction to lowest terms, if necessary.

Changing Fractions to Percents [7.1]

5. $\frac{3}{4} = 0.75 = 75\%$
or
$\frac{9}{10} = \frac{90}{100} = 90\%$

To change a fraction to a percent, either write the fraction as a decimal and then change the decimal to a percent, or write the fraction as an equivalent fraction with denominator 100, drop the 100, and use the % symbol.

Basic Word Problems Involving Percents [7.2]

6. Translating to equations, we have:

Type *A*: $n = 0.14 \cdot 68$; $n = 9.52$
Type *B*: $75 \cdot n = 25$; $n = 0.33$
Type *C*: $25 = 0.40 \cdot n$; $n = 62.5$

There are three basic types of word problems:

Type A: What number is 14% of 68?

Type B: What percent of 75 is 25?

Type C: 25 is 40% of what number?

Applications of Percent [7.3, 7.4, 7.5, 7.6]

To solve application problems, we write *is* as =, *of* as · (multiply), and *what number* or *what percent* as *n*. We then solve the resulting equation to find the answer to the original question.

There are many different kinds of application problems involving percent. They include problems on income tax, sales tax, commission, discount, percent increase and decrease, and interest. Generally, to solve these problems, we restate them as an equivalent problem of Type A, B, or C above. Problems involving simple interest can be solved using the formula

$$I = P \cdot R \cdot T$$

where *I* is the interest, *P* is the principal, *R* is the interest rate, and *T* is the time in years. It is standard procedure with simple interest problems to use 360 days = 1 year.

COMMON MISTAKES ·

1. A common mistake is forgetting to change a percent to a decimal when working problems that involve percents in the calculations. We always change percents to decimals before doing any calculations.

2. Moving the decimal point in the wrong direction when converting percents to decimals or decimals to percents is another common mistake. Remember, *percent* means "per hundred." Rewriting a number expressed as a percent as a decimal will make the numerical part smaller.

$$25\% = 0.2$$

Pie Charts [7.7]

A pie chart is another way to give a visual representation of the information in a table.

Seating Class	Number of Sears
First	18
Business	42
Coach	163

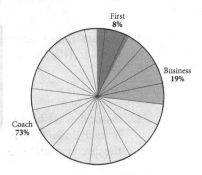

Write each percent as a decimal. [7.1]

1. 56%   **2.** 3%   **3.** 0.4%

4. 137%   **5.** 2004%   **6.** 0.06%

7. 0.008%   **8.** 406%   **9.** 20%

Write each decimal as a percent. [7.1]

10. 0.32   **11.** 0.7   **12.** 1.64

13. 0.04   **14.** 0.008   **15.** 10.57

16. 5   **17.** 137   **18.** 0.102

Write each percent as a fraction or a mixed number in lowest terms. [7.1]

19. 85%   **20.** 128%   **21.** 8.4%

22. 8%   **23.** 51%   **24.** 0.6%

25. 18.75%   **26.** 2.05%   **27.** 173%

Write each number as a percent. [7.1]

28. $\frac{13}{25}$ **29.** $\frac{5}{8}$ **30.** $1\frac{9}{20}$

31. $\frac{7}{4}$ **32.** $\frac{17}{51}$ **33.** $\frac{1}{16}$

34. $\frac{3}{32}$ **35.** $1\frac{5}{8}$ **36.** $\frac{7}{10000}$

Solve each of the following problems.

37. What number is 20% of 64? [7.2]

38. What number is 4% of 49? [7.2]

39. What percent of 50 is 30? [7.2]

40. What percent of 80 is 16? [7.2]

41. 64 is 80% of what number? [7.2]

42. 12 is 3% of what number? [7.2]

43. What is 10% of 207? [7.2]

44. 36 is 150% of what number? [7.2]

45. What is 0.8% of 63,589? [7.2]

46. **Children in School** In Belgium, 96% of all children between 3 and 6 years of age go to school. In Sweden, the number is only 25%. In the United States, it is 60%. Write each of these percents as a fraction in lowest terms. [7.1]

47. Write a basic percent problem, the solution to which can be found by solving the equation $56 = 0.85 \cdot n$. [7.2]

48. **Driver's Test** On a 25-question driver's test, a student answered 21 questions correctly. What percent of the questions did the student answer correctly? [7.3]

49. **Number of Students** In a certain school, 75% of the students in first-year chemistry have had algebra. If there are 500 students in first-year chemistry, how many of them have had algebra? [7.3]

50. **Commission** A salesperson gets a 4% commission rate on all computers she sells. If she sells $25,000 in computers in one day, what is her commission? [7.4]

51. **Tax Rate** If the purchase price of a bottle of California wine is $24 and the sales tax is $1.50, what is the sales tax rate? [7.4]

52. **Discount** A washing machine that usually sells for $830 is marked down to $539.50. What is the discount? What is the discount rate? [7.5]

53. **Total Price** A tennis racket that normally sells for $95 is on sale for 25% off. If the sales tax rate is 8.5%, what is the total price of the tennis racket if it is purchased during the sale? Round to the nearest cent. [7.5]

54. **Commission and Purchase Price** If an appliance salesperson gets 9% commission on all the appliances she sells, what is the price of a refrigerator if her commission is $67.50? [7.4]

55. **Percent Increase** A driver gets into a car accident and his insurance increases by 17%. If he paid $860 before the accident, how much is he paying now? [7.5]

56. **Simple Interest** If $9,600 is invested at 5% simple interest for 8 months, how much interest is earned? [7.6]

57. **Bank Loan** If $400 is borrowed at a rate of 12% for 1 year, how much is the interest?

58. **Compound Interest** How much interest will be earned on a savings account that pays 9% compounded annually, if $18,000 is invested for 3 years? [7.6]

59. **Compound Interest** Suppose $1,200 is invested in a savings account that pays 6% compounded semiannually. How much is in the account at the end of $1\frac{1}{2}$ years? [7.6]

The chart shows the percentage of total Nintendo revenue by region in 2017. If the total revenue for 2017 was approximately $490 million, use the information to answer the following questions.

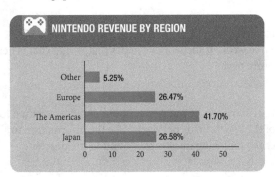

NINTENDO REVENUE BY REGION

60. What was the revenue for Japan?

61. What was the revenue for the Americas?

The diagram shows the trend in number of male athletes in an Ironman Triathlon over five years. Use the information to answer the following questions.

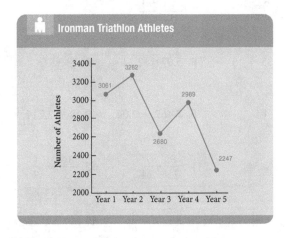

62. What is the percent decrease in athletes from Year 4 to Year 5? Round to the nearest hundredth.

63. If the percent decrease from Year 4 to Year 5 continues, how many athletes will there be in Year 6? Round to the nearest person.

64. **Car Mileage** The table shows how many miles are on most Americans' cars. Use the illustration to create a pie chart. [7.7]

Miles	Percentage
Less than 100,000	52%
100,000-200,000	36%
200,000 +	8%
Don't Know	4%

Solve.

1.   4,381
          623
       + 407

2.   3,062
       − 1,971

3. 13(613)

4. 1,335 ÷ 25

5. $5.07\overline{)162.24}$

6. $\dfrac{6}{5} - \dfrac{2}{5}$

7. $\left(\dfrac{3}{5}\right)^{3}$

8. 7.462 + 2.04

9. 3 − 2.714

10. 3.5(0.34)

11. $\dfrac{8}{21} \cdot \dfrac{7}{24}$

12. $\dfrac{16}{3} \div \dfrac{4}{9}$

13. $\dfrac{5}{6} + \dfrac{3}{8}$

14. $7\dfrac{2}{3} - 3\dfrac{5}{6}$

15. $4 \cdot 3\dfrac{5}{8}$

16. Subtract $2\dfrac{3}{5}$ from 8.6.

17. Find the quotient of $2\dfrac{1}{3}$ and $\dfrac{1}{6}$.

18. Translate into symbols, and then simplify: Three times the sum of 6 and 8.

19. Write the ratio of 4 to 24 as a fraction in lowest terms.

20. If 1 mile is 5,280 feet, how many feet are there in 3.6 miles?

21. If 1 square yard is 1,296 square inches, how many square inches are in $\dfrac{7}{8}$ square yard?

22. Write $\dfrac{5}{8}$ as a percent.

23. Convert 32% to a fraction.

24. Solve the equation $\dfrac{3}{x} = \dfrac{6}{7}$.

25. Simplify: $2 \cdot 4^{2} + 2 \cdot 3^{3} - 6 \cdot 2^{3}$

26. What number is 13% of 30?

27. 217 is what percent of 620?

28. 26.6 is 28% of what number?

29. **Unit Pricing** If a six-pack of Coke costs $7.95, what is the price per can to the nearest cent?

30. **Unit Pricing** A quart of 2% reduced-fat milk contains four 1-cup servings. If the quart costs $3.65, find the price per serving to the nearest cent.

31. **Temperature** Use the formula $C = \dfrac{5(F - 32)}{9}$ to find the temperature in degrees Celsius when the Fahrenheit temperature is 95°F.

32. **Percent Increase** Kendra is earning $2,800 a month when she receives a raise to $3,066 a month. What is the percent increase in her monthly salary?

33. **Driving Distance** If Ethan drives his car 225 miles in 3 hours, how far will he drive in 5 hours if he drives at the same rate?

34. **Movie Tickets** A movie theater has a total of 375 seats. If they have a sellout crowd for a matinee and each ticket costs $8.50, how much money will ticket sales bring in that afternoon?

35. **Geometry** Find the perimeter and area of a square with side 6.2 inches.

36. **Hourly Pay** Jean tutors in the math lab and earns $76.50 in one week. If she works 9 hours that week, what is her hourly pay?

The chart shows the minimum amount of space required for each of the sports fields or courts. Use the information to answer the following questions. Round to the nearest hundredth if necessary.

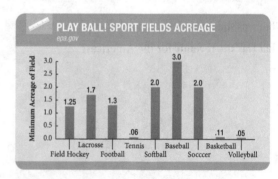

37. If a school will be building 4 baseball diamonds and 7 basketball courts, what is the minimum acreage it will need?

38. If a city will be adding a field hockey facility, two soccer fields, and five volleyball courts, what is the minimum acreage necessary?

Write each percent as a decimal. [7.1]

1. 27%   **2.** 6%   **3.** 0.9%

Write each decimal as a percent. [7.1]

4. 0.64   **5.** 0.3   **6.** 1.49

Write each percent as a fraction or a mixed number in lowest terms. [7.1]

7. 45%   **8.** 136%   **9.** 7.2%

Write each number as a percent. [7.1]

10. $\frac{13}{20}$ **11.** $\frac{7}{8}$ **12.** $2\frac{1}{4}$

Solve each of the following problems.

13. What number is 25% of 48? [7.2]

14. What percent of 80 is 28? [7.2]

15. 30 is 40% of what number? [7.2]

16. Driver's Test On a 25-question driver's test, a student answered 24 questions correctly. What percent of the questions did the student answer correctly? [7.3]

17. Commission A salesperson gets a 6% commission rate on all computers she sells. If she sells $15,000 in computers in one day, what is her commission? [7.4]

18. Discount A dishwasher that usually sells for $725 is marked down to $580. What is the discount? What is the discount rate? [7.5]

19. Total Price A tennis racket that normally sells for $179 is on sale for 30% off. If the sales tax rate is 8%, what is the total price of the tennis racket if it is purchased during the sale? Round to the nearest cent. [7.5]

20. Percent Increase A driver gets into a car accident and his insurance increases by 14%. If he paid $760 before the accident, how much is he paying now? [7.5]

21. Simple Interest If $6,000 is invested at 7% simple interest for 4 months, how much interest is earned? [7.6]

22. Compound Interest How much interest will be earned on a savings account that pays 8% compounded annually, if $16,000 is invested for 2 years? [7.6]

The diagram shows the number of female participants in the Disney's Princess Half Marathon over three years. Use the information to answer the following questions.

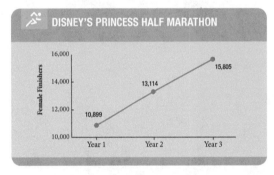

DISNEY'S PRINCESS HALF MARATHON

23. What is the percent increase in female participants from Year 2 to Year 3? Round to the nearest hundredth.

24. If the percent increase from Year 2 to Year 3 holds, how many female participants will there be in Year 4? Round to the nearest person.

25. Computers The chart shows the results of a survey in which individuals were asked which operating system they use. Use the illustration to create a pie chart. [7.7]

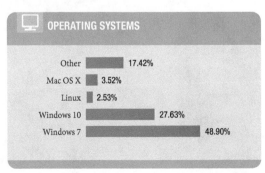

OPERATING SYSTEMS

Other	17.42%
Mac OS X	3.52%
Linux	2.53%
Windows 10	27.63%
Windows 7	48.90%

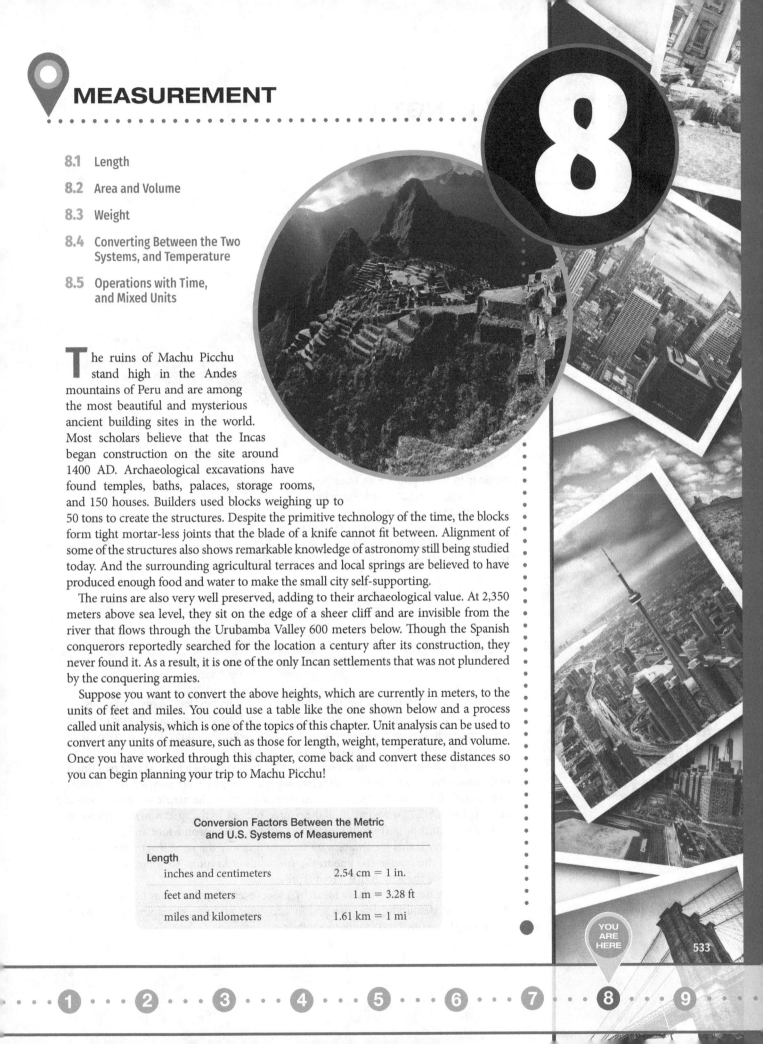

MEASUREMENT

8.1 Length

8.2 Area and Volume

8.3 Weight

8.4 Converting Between the Two Systems, and Temperature

8.5 Operations with Time, and Mixed Units

The ruins of Machu Picchu stand high in the Andes mountains of Peru and are among the most beautiful and mysterious ancient building sites in the world. Most scholars believe that the Incas began construction on the site around 1400 AD. Archaeological excavations have found temples, baths, palaces, storage rooms, and 150 houses. Builders used blocks weighing up to 50 tons to create the structures. Despite the primitive technology of the time, the blocks form tight mortar-less joints that the blade of a knife cannot fit between. Alignment of some of the structures also shows remarkable knowledge of astronomy still being studied today. And the surrounding agricultural terraces and local springs are believed to have produced enough food and water to make the small city self-supporting.

The ruins are also very well preserved, adding to their archaeological value. At 2,350 meters above sea level, they sit on the edge of a sheer cliff and are invisible from the river that flows through the Urubamba Valley 600 meters below. Though the Spanish conquerors reportedly searched for the location a century after its construction, they never found it. As a result, it is one of the only Incan settlements that was not plundered by the conquering armies.

Suppose you want to convert the above heights, which are currently in meters, to the units of feet and miles. You could use a table like the one shown below and a process called unit analysis, which is one of the topics of this chapter. Unit analysis can be used to convert any units of measure, such as those for length, weight, temperature, and volume. Once you have worked through this chapter, come back and convert these distances so you can begin planning your trip to Machu Picchu!

Conversion Factors Between the Metric and U.S. Systems of Measurement	
Length	
inches and centimeters	2.54 cm = 1 in.
feet and meters	1 m = 3.28 ft
miles and kilometers	1.61 km = 1 mi

1   2   3   4   5   6   7   8   9

8.1 LENGTH

OBJECTIVES

A Convert units of length using the U. S. system of measurement.

B Convert units of length using the metric system.

C Solve problems using unit analysis.

KEY WORDS

U. S. system of measurement

length

conversion factor

metric system of measurement

unit analysis

VIDEO EXAMPLES

SECTION 8.1

In this section, we will become more familiar with the units used to measure length. We will look at the U.S. system and the metric system of measurement.

A U.S. System of Measurement

Measuring the length of an object is done by assigning a number to its length. To let other people know what that number represents, we include with it a unit of measure. The most common units used to represent **length** in the U.S. system are inches, feet, yards, and miles. The basic unit of length is the foot. The other units are defined in terms of feet, as Table 1 shows.

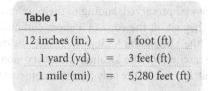

Table 1		
12 inches (in.)	=	1 foot (ft)
1 yard (yd)	=	3 feet (ft)
1 mile (mi)	=	5,280 feet (ft)

As you can see from the table, the abbreviations for inches, feet, yards, and miles are in., ft, yd, and mi, respectively. What we haven't indicated, even though you may not have realized it, is what 1 foot represents. We have defined all our units associated with length in terms of feet, but we haven't said what a foot is.

There is a long history of the evolution of what is now called a foot. At different times in the past, a foot has represented different arbitrary lengths. Currently, a foot is defined to be exactly 0.3048 meter (the basic measure of length in the metric system), where a meter is 1,650,763.73 wavelengths of the orange-red line in the spectrum of krypton-86 in a vacuum (this doesn't mean much to us either). The reason a foot and a meter are defined this way is that we always want them to measure the same length. Because the wavelength of the orange-red line in the spectrum of krypton-86 will always remain the same, so will the length that a foot represents.

Now that we have said what we mean by 1 foot (even though we may not understand the technical definition), we can go on and look at some examples that involve converting from one kind of unit to another.

Example 1   Convert 5 feet to inches.

Solution   Because 1 foot = 12 inches, we can multiply 5 by 12 inches to get

$$5 \text{ feet} = 5 \cdot 12 \text{ inches}$$
$$= 60 \text{ inches}$$

Practice Problems

1. Convert 3 feet to inches.

This method of converting from feet to inches probably seems fairly simple. But as we go further in this chapter, the conversions from one kind of unit to another will become more complicated. For these more complicated problems, we need another way to show conversions so that we can be certain to end them with the correct unit of measure. For example, since 1 ft = 12 in., we can say that there are 12 in. per 1 ft or 1 ft per 12 in.; that is,

$$\frac{12 \text{ in.}}{1 \text{ ft}} \longleftarrow \text{Per} \quad \text{or} \quad \frac{1 \text{ ft}}{12 \text{ in.}} \longleftarrow \text{Per}$$

We call the expressions $\frac{12 \text{ in.}}{1 \text{ ft}}$ and $\frac{1 \text{ ft}}{12 \text{ in.}}$ **conversion factors.** The fraction bar is read as "per." Both these conversion factors are really just the number 1. That is,

$$\frac{12 \text{ in.}}{1 \text{ ft}} = \frac{12 \text{ in.}}{12 \text{ in.}} = 1$$

We already know that multiplying a number by 1 leaves the number unchanged. So, to convert from one unit to the other, we can multiply by one of the conversion factors without changing value. Both the conversion factors above say the same thing about the units feet and inches. They both indicate that there are 12 inches in every foot. The one we choose to multiply by depends on what units we are starting with and what units we want to end up with. If we start with feet and we want to end up with inches, we multiply by the conversion factor

$$\frac{12 \text{ in.}}{1 \text{ ft}}$$

This is because units of feet will divide out and leave us with inches.

$$5 \text{ feet} = 5 \text{ ft} \cdot \frac{12 \text{ in.}}{1 \text{ ft}}$$
$$= 5 \cdot 12 \text{ in.}$$
$$= 60 \text{ in.}$$

The key to this method of conversion lies in setting the problem up so that the correct units divide out to simplify the expression. We are treating units such as feet in the same way we treated factors when reducing fractions. If a factor is common to the numerator and the denominator, we can divide it out and simplify the fraction. The same idea holds for units such as feet.

We can rewrite Table 1 so that it shows the conversion factors associated with units of length, as shown in Table 2.

Note We will use this method of converting from one kind of unit to another throughout the rest of this chapter. However, it is not the only method of converting units. You may see shortcuts that will allow you to get results more quickly. Use shortcuts if you wish, so long as you can consistently get correct answers and are not using your shortcuts because you don't understand our method of conversion. Use the method of conversion as given here until you are good at it, and then use shortcuts if you want to.

Table 2		
Units of Length in the U.S. System		
The relationship between	is	To convert one to the other, multiply by
feet (ft) and inches (in.)	12 in. = 1 ft	$\frac{12 \text{ in.}}{1 \text{ ft}}$ or $\frac{1 \text{ ft}}{12 \text{ in.}}$
feet (ft) and yards (yd)	1 yd = 3 ft	$\frac{3 \text{ ft}}{1 \text{ yd}}$ or $\frac{1 \text{ yd}}{3 \text{ ft}}$
feet (ft) and miles (mi)	1 mi = 5,280 ft	$\frac{5280 \text{ ft}}{1 \text{ mi}}$ or $\frac{1 \text{ mi}}{5280 \text{ ft}}$

Answer

1. 36 inches

2. Suppose a house has high ceilings. Convert 12 feet to yards.

Example 2   The most common ceiling height in houses is 8 feet. What is this height in yards?

Solution   To convert 8 feet to yards, we multiply by the conversion factor $\frac{1\,\text{yd}}{3\,\text{ft}}$ so that feet will divide out and we will be left with yards.

$$8\ \text{ft} = 8\ \cancel{\text{ft}} \cdot \frac{1\ \text{yd}}{3\ \cancel{\text{ft}}} \qquad \textit{Multiply by correct conversion factor.}$$

$$= \frac{8}{3}\ \text{yd} \qquad 8 \cdot \frac{1}{3} = \frac{8}{3}$$

$$= 2\frac{2}{3}\ \text{yd} \qquad \textit{Or 2.67 yd rounded to the nearest hundredth.}$$

3. A football field is 53.33 yards wide. How many inches wide is a football field? Round your answer to the nearest inch.

Example 3   A football field is 100 yards long. How many inches long is a football field?

Solution   In this example, we must convert yards to feet and then feet to inches. We choose the conversion factors that will allow all the units except inches to divide out.

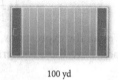

100 yd

$$100\ \text{yd} = 100\ \cancel{\text{yd}} \cdot \frac{3\ \cancel{\text{ft}}}{1\ \cancel{\text{yd}}} \cdot \frac{12\ \text{in.}}{1\ \cancel{\text{ft}}}$$

$$= 100 \cdot 3 \cdot 12\ \text{in.}$$

$$= 3{,}600\ \text{in.}$$

B Metric Units of Length

In the metric system, the standard unit of length is a meter. A meter is a little longer than a yard (about 3.4 inches longer). All units of length in the metric system are written in terms of a meter. The metric system uses prefixes that are based on units of 10 to indicate what part of the basic unit of measure is being used. For example, in *milli*meter the prefix *milli* means "one thousandth" of a meter. Table 3 gives the meanings of the most common metric prefixes.

Table 3
The Meaning of Metric Prefixes

Prefix	Meaning
milli	$\frac{1}{1000}$
centi	$\frac{1}{100}$
deci	$\frac{1}{10}$
deka	10
hecto	100
kilo	1,000

We can use these prefixes to write the other units of length and conversion factors for the metric system, as given in Table 4.

Table 4

Metric Units of Length

The relationship between	is	To convert from one to the other, multiply by	
millimeters (mm) and meters (m)	1,000 mm = 1 m	$\frac{1000 \text{ mm}}{1 \text{ m}}$ or	$\frac{1 \text{ m}}{1000 \text{ mm}}$
centimeters (cm) and meters (m)	100 cm = 1 m	$\frac{100 \text{ cm}}{1 \text{ m}}$ or	$\frac{1 \text{ m}}{100 \text{ cm}}$
decimeters (dm) and meters (m)	10 dm = 1 m	$\frac{10 \text{ dm}}{1 \text{ m}}$ or	$\frac{1 \text{ m}}{10 \text{ dm}}$
dekameters (dam) and meters (m)	1 dam = 10 m	$\frac{10 \text{ m}}{1 \text{ dam}}$ or	$\frac{1 \text{ dam}}{10 \text{ m}}$
hectometers (hm) and meters (m)	1 hm = 100 m	$\frac{100 \text{ m}}{1 \text{ hm}}$ or	$\frac{1 \text{ hm}}{100 \text{ m}}$
kilometers (km) and meters (m)	1 km = 1,000 m	$\frac{1000 \text{ m}}{1 \text{ km}}$ or	$\frac{1 \text{ km}}{1000 \text{ m}}$

We use the same method to convert between units in the metric system as we did with the U.S. system. We choose the conversion factor that will allow the units we start with to divide out, leaving the units we want to end up with.

Example 4   Convert 25 millimeters to meters.

Solution   To convert from millimeters to meters, we multiply by the conversion factor $\frac{1 \text{ m}}{1000 \text{ mm}}$.

$$25 \text{ mm} = 25 \text{ mm} \cdot \frac{1 \text{ m}}{1000 \text{ mm}}$$

$$= \frac{25}{1000} \text{ m}$$

$$= 0.025 \text{ m}$$

4. Convert 35 millimeters to meters.

Example 5   Convert 36.5 centimeters to decimeters.

Solution   We convert centimeters to meters and then meters to decimeters.

$$36.5 \text{ cm} = 36.5 \text{ cm} \cdot \frac{1 \text{ m}}{100 \text{ cm}} \cdot \frac{10 \text{ dm}}{1 \text{ m}}$$

$$= \frac{36.5 \cdot 10}{100} \text{ dm}$$

$$= \frac{365}{100} \text{ dm}$$

$$= 3.65 \text{ dm}$$

5. Convert 50.5 centimeters to decimeters.

C Unit Analysis

The most common units of length in the metric system are millimeters, centimeters, meters, and kilometers. The other units of length we have listed in our table of metric lengths are not as widely used. The method we have used to convert from one unit of length to another in Examples 1–5 is called **unit analysis** or dimensional analysis. If you take a science class, you will see it used many times.

Answers
4. 0.035 meters
5. 5.05 dm

We can summarize the procedure used in unit analysis with the following steps:

HOW TO   Steps Used in Unit Analysis

Step 1: Identify the units you are starting with.

Step 2: Identify the units you want to end with.

Step 3: Find conversion factors that will bridge the starting units and the ending units.

Step 4: Set up the multiplication problem so that all units except the units you want to end with will divide out.

We can use unit analysis to solve other problems that involve conversions.

6. Suppose the rancher in Example 6 is building 7 pens. How much will he spend?

Example 6   A sheep rancher is making new pens for the upcoming lambing season. Each pen is a rectangle 6 feet wide and 8 feet long. The fencing material he wants to use sells for $1.36 per foot. If he is planning to build five separate pens (they are separate because he wants a walkway between them), how much will he have to spend for fencing material?

Solution   To find the amount of fencing material he needs for one pen, we find the perimeter of a pen.

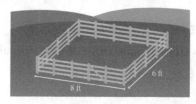

$$P = 2l + 2w$$
$$= 2(8 \text{ ft}) + 2(6 \text{ ft})$$
$$= 16 \text{ ft} + 12 \text{ ft}$$
$$= 28 \text{ ft}$$

We set up the solution to the problem using unit analysis. Our starting unit is *pens* and our ending unit is *dollars*. Here are the conversion factors that will form a bridge between pens and dollars:

$$1 \text{ pen} = 28 \text{ feet of fencing}$$

$$1 \text{ foot of fencing} = 1.36 \text{ dollars}$$

Next we write the multiplication problem, using the conversion factors, that will allow all the units except dollars to divide out.

$$5 \text{ pens} = 5 \text{ pens} \cdot \frac{28 \text{ feet of fencing}}{1 \text{ pen}} \cdot \frac{1.36 \text{ dollars}}{1 \text{ foot of fencing}}$$
$$= 5 \cdot 28 \cdot 1.36 \text{ dollars}$$
$$= \$190.40$$

Answer

6. $266.56

KEY CONCEPT REVIEW

After reading through the preceding section, respond in your own words and in complete sentences.

A. What is a conversion factor?

B. Write the relationship between feet and miles. That is, write an equality that shows how many feet are in every mile.

C. Explain how the metric system uses prefixes to indicate units of measure.

D. Briefly explain how you would use unit analysis to solve a problem.

Spotlight on Success

BUDDY, instructor

What does math mean to me? Well, from a young age, I always knew math was my favorite subject in school. I never knew that math was something of which you could make a career. I like math because it is beautiful and mechanical, as well as confusing, thought-provoking, and hard to understand. Math made me comfortable asking my teachers the simple questions, "Why?" or "Why is that true?", which I think are very important questions with most things in life. Math became very philosophical to me and changed a lot of my world-views.

Math made me a critical thinker. Every statement in math requires a very detailed and rigorous proof, but in the end, there is always a moment of immense coherence where hard evidence and logic made a difficult idea become clear. That moment is a tremendous experience. In math, you can make arguments about whether something is true or false and prove to someone it is one way or the other. I liked the idea of critically analyzing the truth value of any mathematical statement. A lot of things in math were hard to accept as true, and some seemingly obvious things were hard to accept as being not true. This is where the beauty lies in math. It helped me make sense of the world. I found some objective truths, which seemed rare in such a scary and chaotic world, and that was very satisfying for me.

I love being a part of math education. I want to share these wonderful moments and experiences that math has brought into my life. When I see one of my students have that moment of clarity, where an idea finally sticks, and the student begins to see the big picture and truly start to understand an abstract idea, it is an incredibly rewarding feeling. Math means the world to me, and I want to share its wealth of endless knowledge that it can provide with as many students as I can.

EXERCISE SET 8.1 ······································

Problems

A Make the following conversions in the U.S. system by multiplying by the appropriate conversion factor. Write your answers as whole numbers or mixed numbers.

1. 5 ft to inches

2. 9 ft to inches

3. 10 ft to inches

4. 20 ft to inches

5. 2 yd to feet

6. 8 yd to feet

7. 4.5 yd to inches

8. 9.5 yd to inches

9. 27 in. to feet

10. 36 in. to feet

11. 2.5 mi to feet

12. 6.75 mi to feet

13. 48 in. to yards

14. 56 in. to yards

B Make the following conversions in the metric system by multiplying by the appropriate conversion factor. Write your answers as whole numbers or decimals.

15. 18 m to centimeters

16. 18 m to millimeters

17. 4.8 km to meters

18. 8.9 km to meters

19. 5 dm to centimeters

20. 12 dm to millimeters

21. 248 m to kilometers

22. 969 m to kilometers

23. 67 cm to millimeters

24. 67 mm to centimeters

25. 3,498 cm to meters

26. 4,388 dm to meters

27. 63.4 cm to decimeters

28. 89.5 cm to decimeters

Applying the Concepts

29. Softball If the distance between first and second base in softball is 60 feet, how many yards is it from first to second base?

30. Tower Height A transmitting tower is 100 feet tall. How many inches is that?

31. High Jump If a person high jumps 6 feet 8 inches, how many inches is the jump?

6 ft 8 in

32. Desk Width A desk is 48 inches wide. What is the width in yards?

33. Ceiling Height Suppose the ceiling of a home is 2.44 meters above the floor. Express the height of the ceiling in centimeters.

34. Notebook Width Standard-sized notebook paper is 21.6 centimeters wide. Express this width in millimeters.

35. Dollar Width A dollar bill is about 6.5 centimeters wide. Express this width in millimeters.

36. Pencil Length Most new pencils are 19 centimeters long. Express this length in meters.

37. Surveying A unit of measure sometimes used in surveying is the *chain*. There are 80 chains in 1 mile. How many chains are in 37 miles?

38. Surveying Another unit of measure used in surveying is a *link*; 1 link is about 8 inches. About how many links are there in 5 feet?

39. Metric System A very small unit of measure in the metric system is the *micron* (abbreviated *μm*). There are 1,000 *μm* in 1 millimeter. How many microns are in 12 centimeters?

40. Metric System Another very small unit of measure in the metric system is the *angstrom* (abbreviated Å). There are 10,000,000 Å in 1 millimeter. How many angstroms are in 15 decimeters?

41. Horse Racing In horse racing, 1 *furlong* is 220 yards. How many feet are in 12 furlongs?

42. Sailing A *fathom* is a measurement of the depth of water and is equivalent to 6 feet. How many yards are in 19 fathoms?

43. Cell Phones The typical wavelength used by most cell phones today is between 12 and 35 centimeters. Convert these numbers to meters.

44. Credit Card A typical credit card is 85.6 millimeters long. Convert this to meters.

45. Definition of a Foot One foot is 0.3048 meters. Convert this number to centimeters.

46. DNA The length of a DNA strand in the human genome is about 70.9 inches long. Convert this number to feet. Round to the nearest tenth.

47. Farming A farmer is fencing a pasture that is $\frac{1}{2}$ mile wide and 1 mile long. If the fencing material sells for $1.15 per foot, how much will it cost him to fence all four sides of the pasture?

48. Cost of Fencing A family with a swimming pool puts up a chain-link fence around the pool. The fence forms a rectangle 12 yards wide and 24 yards long. If the chain-link fence sells for $2.50 per foot, how much will it cost to fence all four sides of the pool?

49. Farming A 4-H Club group is raising lambs to show at the County Fair. Each lamb eats $\frac{1}{8}$ of a bale of alfalfa a day. If the alfalfa costs $10.50 per bale, how much will it cost to feed one lamb for 120 days?

50. Farming A 4-H Club group is raising pigs to show at the County Fair. Each pig eats 2.4 pounds of grain a day. If the grain costs $5.25 per pound, how much will it cost to feed one pig for 60 days?

Calculator Problems

Perform each of the following conversions with the use of a calculator.

51. Change 751 miles to feet.

52. Change 639.87 centimeters to meters.

53. Change 4,982 yards to inches.

54. Change 379 millimeters to kilometers.

55. Mount Whitney is the highest point in California. It is 14,494 feet above sea level. Give its height in miles to the nearest tenth.

56. The tallest mountain in the United States is Denali (also known as Mount McKinley) in Alaska. It is 20,320 feet tall. Give its height in miles to the nearest tenth.

57. California has 3,427 miles of shoreline. How many feet is this?

58. The tip of the television tower at the top of the Empire State Building in New York City is 1,472 feet above the ground. Express this height in miles to the nearest hundredth.

Getting Ready for the Next Section

Perform the indicated operations.

59. $12 \cdot 12$ **60.** $75 \cdot 43{,}560$ **61.** $864 \div 144$ **62.** $1{,}728 \div 144$

63. $256 \div 640$ **64.** $960 \div 240$ **65.** $45 \cdot \dfrac{9}{1}$ **66.** $1{,}800 \cdot \dfrac{1}{4}$

67. $2.2 \cdot 1{,}000$ **68.** $3.5 \cdot 1{,}000$ **69.** $67.5 \cdot 9$ **70.** $43.5 \cdot 9$

FIND THE MISTAKE •

Each sentence below contains a mistake. Circle the mistake and write the correct word(s) or numbers(s) on the line provided.

1. The average length for a house cat is roughly 18 inches. To show how many feet this is, multiply by the conversion factor $\dfrac{12 \text{ inches}}{1 \text{ foot}}$. _____

2. The length of a parking space is based on the average car length, which measures approximately 15 feet. This length converted to yards is 45 yards. _____

3. A cell phone measures 100 mm in length. To show how many meters this is, multiply 100 mm by the conversion factor $\dfrac{1 \text{ mm}}{1000 \text{ m}}$. _____

4. To complete a unit analysis problem, make sure the units you want to end with will divide out.
   _____

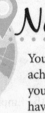

Navigation Skills

Your academic self-image is how you see yourself as a student and the level of success you see yourself achieving. Do you believe you are capable of learning any subject and succeeding in any class you take? If you believe in yourself and work hard by applying the appropriate study methods, you will succeed. If you have a poor outlook for a class, most likely your performance in that class will match that outlook. Self-doubt or questioning the purpose of this course will negatively affect your focus. Furthermore, an inner dialogue of negative statements, such as "I'll never be able to learn this material" or "I'm never going to use this stuff," distract you from achieving success. Consider replacing those thoughts with three positive statements you can say when you notice your mind participating in a negative inner dialogue. Make a commitment to change your attitude for the better. Begin by thinking positively, having confidence in your abilities, and utilizing your resources if you are having difficulty. Asking for help is a sign of a successful student.

AREA AND VOLUME

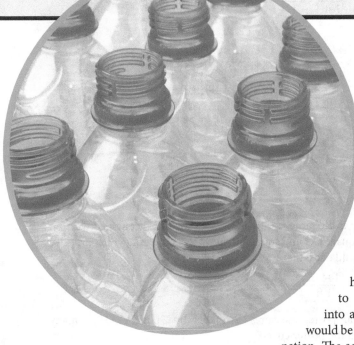

A Area

Currents in the Pacific Ocean have helped to form the Great Pacific Garbage Patch. The patch is an area in the ocean at least the size of Texas where a high concentration of trash and pollutants have accumulated. Dutch scientists and engineers have come up with a plan to turn the garbage patch into a self-sustaining island that would be recognized as an individual nation. The scientists' goal for the island is to recycle plastic waste on the spot, therefore removing the pollutants from the water.

Known as Recycled Island, the proposed size for the island is 4,000 square miles. This measurement is one we've worked with previously to represent the area of an object. Let's review some other formulas for finding the area of a square, a rectangle, and a triangle. Then we'll use unit analysis to solve problems involving such areas.

OBJECTIVES

A Solve problems involving area using unit analysis.

B Solve problems involving volume using unit analysis.

KEY WORDS

area

volume

VIDEO EXAMPLES

SECTION 8.2

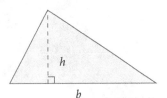

Area = (side)(side)
    = (side)²
$A = s^2$

Area = (length)(width)
    $A = lw$

FIGURE 1

Area = ½(base)(height)

$A = \frac{1}{2}bh$

545

1. Find the number of square feet in 1 square yard.

Example 1   Find the number of square inches in 1 square foot.

Solution   We can think of 1 square foot as $1 \text{ ft}^2 = 1 \text{ ft} \cdot \text{ft}$. To convert from feet to inches, we use the conversion factor 1 foot = 12 inches. Because the unit foot appears twice in 1 ft^2, we multiply by our conversion factor twice.

$$1 \text{ ft}^2 = 1 \text{ ft} \cdot \text{ft} \cdot \frac{12 \text{ in.}}{1 \text{ ft}} \cdot \frac{12 \text{ in.}}{1 \text{ ft}} = 1 \cdot 12 \cdot 12 \text{ in.} = 144 \text{ in}^2$$

This means $1 \text{ ft}^2 = 144 \text{ in}^2$

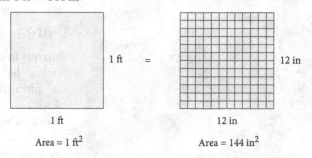

1 ft = 12 in

1 ft   12 in

Area = 1 ft^2 Area = 144 in^2

Now that we know that 1 ft^2 is the same as 144 in^2, we can use this fact as a conversion factor to convert between square feet and square inches. Depending on which units we are converting from, we would use either

$$\frac{144 \text{ in}^2}{1 \text{ ft}^2} \qquad \text{or} \qquad \frac{1 \text{ ft}^2}{144 \text{ in}^2}$$

2. Suppose there is a 2-inch frame around the poster in Example 2. This would increase the length to 40 in. and the width to 28 in. How many square feet of wall space will be covered?

Example 2   A rectangular poster measures 36 inches by 24 inches. How many square feet of wall space will the poster cover?

Solution   One way to work this problem is to find the number of square inches the poster covers, and then convert square inches to square feet.

$$\text{Area of poster} = \text{length} \cdot \text{width} = 36 \text{ in.} \cdot 24 \text{ in.} = 864 \text{ in}^2$$

To finish the problem, we convert square inches to square feet using the conversion fact we found in Example 1.

$$864 \text{ in}^2 = 864 \text{ in}^2 \cdot \frac{1 \text{ ft}^2}{144 \text{ in}^2}$$

$$= \frac{864}{144} \text{ ft}^2$$

$$= 6 \text{ ft}^2$$

Table 1 gives the most common units of area in the U.S. system of measurement, along with the corresponding conversion factors.

Table 1		
U.S. Units of Area		
The relationship between	is	To convert from one to the other, multiply by
square inches (in²) and square feet (ft²)	$144 \text{ in}^2 = 1 \text{ ft}^2$	$\frac{144 \text{ in}^2}{1 \text{ ft}^2}$ or $\frac{1 \text{ ft}^2}{144 \text{ in}^2}$
square yards (yd²) and square feet (ft²)	$9 \text{ ft}^2 = 1 \text{ yd}^2$	$\frac{9 \text{ ft}^2}{1 \text{ yd}^2}$ or $\frac{1 \text{ yd}^2}{9 \text{ ft}^2}$
acres (a) and square feet (ft²)	$1 \text{ acre} = 43{,}560 \text{ ft}^2$	$\frac{43560 \text{ ft}^2}{1 \text{ acre}}$ or $\frac{1 \text{ acre}}{43560 \text{ ft}^2}$
acres (a) and square miles (mi²)	$640 \text{ acres} = 1 \text{ mi}^2$	$\frac{640 \text{ acres}}{1 \text{ mi}^2}$ or $\frac{1 \text{ mi}^2}{640 \text{ acres}}$

Example 3   A dressmaker orders a bolt of material that is 1.5 yards wide and 30 yards long. How many square feet of material were ordered?

Solution   The area of the material in square yards is

$$A = 1.5 \text{ yd} \cdot 30 \text{ yd}$$
$$= 45 \text{ yd}^2$$

Converting this to square feet, we have

$$45 \text{ yd}^2 = 45 \text{ yd}^2 \cdot \frac{9 \text{ ft}^2}{1 \text{ yd}^2}$$

$$= 405 \text{ ft}^2$$

3. Suppose the dressmaker in Example 3 ordered 50 yards of fabric. How many square feet would he have ordered?

Example 4   A farmer has 75 acres of land. How many square feet of land does the farmer have?

Solution   Changing acres to square feet, we have

$$75 \text{ acres} = 75 \text{ acres} \cdot \frac{43560 \text{ ft}^2}{1 \text{ acre}}$$

$$= 75 \cdot 43{,}560 \text{ ft}^2$$

$$= 3{,}267{,}000 \text{ ft}^2$$

4. Suppose the farmer in Example 4 has 125 acres. How many square feet does he have?

Example 5   A new shopping center is to be constructed on 256 acres of land. How many square miles is this?

Solution   Multiplying by the conversion factor that will allow acres to divide out, we have

$$256 \text{ acres} = 256 \text{ acres} \cdot \frac{1 \text{ mi}^2}{640 \text{ acres}}$$

$$= \frac{256}{640} \text{ mi}^2$$

$$= 0.4 \text{ mi}^2$$

5. How many square miles is 348 acres?

Units of area in the metric system can be considered simpler than those in the U.S. system because metric units are given in terms of powers of 10. Table 2 lists the conversion factors that are most commonly used.

Table 2

Metric Units of Area

The relationship between	is	To convert from one to the other, multiply by	
square millimeters and square centimeters	$1 \text{ cm}^2 = 100 \text{ mm}^2$	$\frac{100 \text{ mm}^2}{1 \text{ cm}^2}$ or	$\frac{1 \text{ cm}^2}{100 \text{ mm}^2}$
square centimeters and square decimeters	$1 \text{ dm}^2 = 100 \text{ cm}^2$	$\frac{100 \text{ cm}^2}{1 \text{ dm}^2}$ or	$\frac{1 \text{ dm}^2}{100 \text{ cm}^2}$
square decimeters and square meters	$1 \text{ m}^2 = 100 \text{ dm}^2$	$\frac{100 \text{ dm}^2}{1 \text{ m}^2}$ or	$\frac{1 \text{ m}^2}{100 \text{ dm}^2}$
square meters and ares	$1 \text{ a} = 100 \text{ m}^2$	$\frac{100 \text{ m}^2}{1 \text{ a}}$ or	$\frac{1 \text{ a}}{100 \text{ m}^2}$
ares and hectares	$1 \text{ ha} = 100 \text{ a}$	$\frac{100 \text{ a}}{1 \text{ ha}}$ or	$\frac{1 \text{ ha}}{100 \text{ a}}$
square kilometers and hectares	$1 \text{ km}^2 = 100 \text{ ha}$	$\frac{1 \text{ km}^2}{100 \text{ ha}}$ or	$\frac{100 \text{ ha}}{1 \text{ km}^2}$

Answers
3. 675 ft^2
4. $5{,}445{,}000 \text{ ft}^2$
5. 0.54 mi^2

6. How many square centimeters are in 1 square meter?

Example 6   How many square millimeters are in 1 square meter?

Solution   We start with 1 m² and end up with square millimeters.

$$1 \text{ m}^2 = 1 \text{ m}^2 \cdot \frac{100 \text{ dm}^2}{1 \text{ m}^2} \cdot \frac{100 \text{ cm}^2}{1 \text{ dm}^2} \cdot \frac{100 \text{ mm}^2}{1 \text{ cm}^2}$$

$$= 100 \cdot 100 \cdot 100 \text{ mm}^2$$

$$= 1,000,000 \text{ mm}^2$$

B Volume

Volume is the amount of space an object takes up. Table 3 lists the units of volume in the U.S. system and their conversion factors.

Table 3

Units of Volume in the U.S. System		
The relationship between	is	To convert from one to the other, multiply by
cubic inches (in³) and cubic feet (ft³)	1 ft³ = 1,728 in³	$\frac{1728 \text{ in}^3}{1 \text{ ft}^3}$ or $\frac{1 \text{ ft}^3}{1728 \text{ in}^3}$
cubic feet (ft³) and cubic yards (yd³)	1 yd³ = 27 ft³	$\frac{27 \text{ ft}^3}{1 \text{ yd}^3}$ or $\frac{1 \text{ yd}^3}{27 \text{ ft}^3}$
fluid ounces (fl oz) and pints (pt)	1 pt = 16 fl oz	$\frac{16 \text{ fl oz}}{1 \text{ pt}}$ or $\frac{1 \text{ pt}}{16 \text{ fl oz}}$
pints (pt) and quarts (qt)	1 qt = 2 pt	$\frac{2 \text{ pt}}{1 \text{ qt}}$ or $\frac{1 \text{ qt}}{2 \text{ pt}}$
quarts (qt) and gallons (gal)	1 gal = 4 qt	$\frac{4 \text{ qt}}{1 \text{ gal}}$ or $\frac{1 \text{ gal}}{4 \text{ qt}}$

7. How many fluid ounces are in a 1 gallon container?

Example 7   What is the capacity (volume) in pints of a 1-gallon container of milk?

Solution   We change from gallons to quarts and then quarts to pints by multiplying by the appropriate conversion factors as given in Table 3.

$$1 \text{ gal} = 1 \text{ gal} \cdot \frac{4 \text{ qt}}{1 \text{ gal}} \cdot \frac{2 \text{ pt}}{1 \text{ qt}}$$

$$= 1 \cdot 4 \cdot 2 \text{ pt}$$

$$= 8 \text{ pt}$$

A 1-gallon container has the same capacity as 8 1-pint containers.

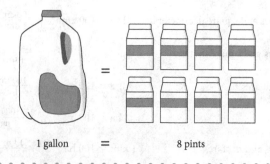

1 gallon   =   8 pints

Answers

6. 10,000 cm²

7. 128 fl oz

Example 8   A dairy herd produces 1,800 quarts of milk each day. How many gallons is this equivalent to?

Solution   Converting 1,800 quarts to gallons, we have

$$1{,}800 \text{ qt} = 1{,}800 \text{ qt} \cdot \frac{1 \text{ gal}}{4 \text{ qt}}$$

$$= \frac{1{,}800}{4} \text{ gal}$$

$$= 450 \text{ gal}$$

We see that 1,800 quarts is equivalent to 450 gallons.

8. How many pints are produced by the dairy herd in Example 8 each day?

In the metric system, the basic unit of measure for volume is the liter. A liter is the volume enclosed by a cube that is 10 cm on each edge, as shown in Figure 2. Using the formula for the volume of a cube, $V = S^3$, we can see that a liter is equivalent to 1,000 cm³.

The other units of volume in the metric system use the same prefixes we encountered previously. The units with prefixes centi, deci, and deka are not as common as the others, so in Table 4 we include only liters, milliliters, hectoliters, and kiloliters.

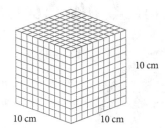

10 cm

10 cm   10 cm

1 liter = 10 cm · 10 cm · 10 cm = 1,000 cm³

FIGURE 2

Here is an example of conversion from one unit of volume to another in the metric system.

Note   As you can see from the table and the discussion here, a cubic centimeter (cm³) and a milliliter (mL) are equal. Both are one thousandth of a liter. It is also common in some fields (like medicine) to abbreviate the term cubic centimeter as cc. Although we will use the notation mL when discussing volume in the metric system, you should be aware that 1 mL = 1 cm³ = 1 cc.

Table 4	Metric Units of Volume		
The relationship between	is	To convert from one to the other, multiply by	
milliliters (mL) and liters (L)	1 L = 1,000 mL	$\frac{1000 \text{ mL}}{1 \text{ liter}}$ or	$\frac{1 \text{ liter}}{1000 \text{ mL}}$
hectoliters (hL) and liters (L)	100 L = 1 hL	$\frac{100 \text{ liters}}{1 \text{ hL}}$ or	$\frac{1 \text{ hL}}{100 \text{ liters}}$
kiloliters (kL) and liters (L)	1,000 L = 1 kL	$\frac{1000 \text{ liters}}{1 \text{ kL}}$ or	$\frac{1 \text{ kL}}{1000 \text{ liters}}$

Example 9   A sports car has a 2.2-liter engine. What is the volume of the engine in milliliters?

Solution   Using the appropriate conversion factor from Table 4, we have

$$2.2 \text{ liters} = 2.2 \text{ liters} \cdot \frac{1000 \text{ mL}}{1 \text{ liter}}$$

$$= 2.2 \cdot 1{,}000 \text{ mL}$$

$$= 2{,}200 \text{ mL}$$

9. A truck has a 4.9 liter engine. What is the volume of the engine in mL?

Answer

8. 3,600 pints

9. 4,900 mL

KEY CONCEPT REVIEW · · · · · · · · · · · · ·

After reading through the preceding section, respond in your own words and in complete sentences.

A. Write the formula for the area of each of the following:

      a. A square of side s

      b. A rectangle with length l and width w

B. What is the relationship between square feet and square inches?

C. Fill in the numerators below so that each conversion factor is equal to 1.

  a. $\dfrac{\boxed{}\ \text{qt}}{1\ \text{gal}}$ **b.** $\dfrac{\boxed{}\ \text{mL}}{1\ \text{liter}}$ **c.** $\dfrac{\boxed{}\ \text{acres}}{1\ \text{mi}^2}$

D. List two examples of units of volume in the U.S. system and two examples of units of volume in the metric system.

 # Spotlight on Success

STEPHANIE, student instructor

For success, attitude is equally as important as ability. ~ Harry F. Banks

Math has always fascinated me. From addition to calculus, I've taken great interest in the material and great pride in my work. Whenever I struggled with concepts, I asked questions and worked problems over and over until they became second nature. I used to assume this was how everyone dealt with concepts they didn't understand. However, in high school, I noticed how easily students got discouraged with mathematics. In my senior year calculus and statistics classes, I was surrounded by bright students who simply gave up on trying to fully understand the material because it seemed confusing or difficult. Even if we shared a similar level of academic ability, the difference between these students' grades and my own reflected a difference in attitude. I noticed many students giving up without really trying to understand the concepts because they lacked confidence and didn't feel they were capable. They began coming to me for help. Though I was glad to help them with the math, I had a greater goal to help them believe they could succeed on their own. Soon the students I tutored gained more understanding and achieved success by simply paying more attention in class and working extra problems outside of class. It was amazing how much improvement I saw in both their confidence levels and their grades. It goes to show that a little extra effort and a positive attitude can truly make a difference.

EXERCISE SET 8.2 ....

VOCABULARY REVIEW •

Choose the correct words to fill in the blanks below.

multiply	U.S. system	volume
metric system	square inches	area

1. In the U.S. system of measurement, the basic unit of measure for _____ is a square foot.

2. The relationship between _____ and square feet is 144 in² = 1 ft².

3. To convert from acres to square feet, _____ by the conversion factor $\frac{43560 \text{ ft}^2}{1 \text{ acre}}$.

4. Cubic inches, pints, and gallons are units of volume in the _____.

5. The units of area in the _____ are given in terms of powers of 10.

6. In the metric system, the basic unit of measure for _____ is the liter.

Problems

A Use the tables given in this section to make the following conversions. Be sure to show the conversion factor used in each case.

1. 3 ft² to square inches   **2.** 5 ft² to square inches   **3.** 288 in² to square feet

4. 720 in² to square feet   **5.** 30 acres to square feet   **6.** 92 acres to square feet

7. 2 mi² to acres   **8.** 7 mi² to acres   **9.** 1,920 acres to square miles

10. 3,200 acres to square miles   **11.** 12 yd² to square feet   **12.** 20 yd² to square feet

13. 17 cm² to square millimeters   **14.** 150 mm² to square centimeters   **15.** 2.8 m² to square centimeters

16. 10 dm² to square millimeters   **17.** 1,200 mm² to square meters   **18.** 19.79 cm² to square meters

19. 5 ares to square meters   **20.** 12 ares to square centimeters   **21.** 7 ha to ares

22. 3.6 ha to ares   **23.** 342 ares to hectares   **24.** 986 ares to hectares

B Make the following conversions using the conversion factors given in Tables 3 and 4.

25. 3.8 yd^3 to cubic feet   **26.** 3 pt to fluid ounces   **27.** 8 pt to fluid ounces   **28.** 2 gal to quarts

29. 12 gal to quarts   **30.** 2.5 gal to pints   **31.** 7 gal to pints   **32.** 15 qt to fluid ounces

33. 5.9 qt to fluid ounces   **34.** 64 pt to gallons   **35.** 256 pt to gallons   **36.** 12 pt to quarts

37. 18 pt to quarts   **38.** 243 ft^3 to cubic yards   **39.** 864 ft^3 to cubic yards   **40.** 5 L to milliliters

41. 9.6 L to milliliters   **42.** 127 mL to liters   **43.** 93.8 mL to liters   **44.** 4 kL to milliliters

45. 3 kL to milliliters   **46.** 14.92 kL to liters   **47.** 4.71 kL to liters

Applying the Concepts

48. Sports The diagrams below show the dimensions of playing fields for the National Football League (NFL), the Canadian Football League, and Arena Football. Find the area of each field and then convert each area to acres. Round answers to the nearest hundredth.

Football Fields

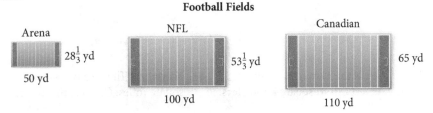

Arena
$28\frac{1}{3}$ yd
50 yd

NFL
$53\frac{1}{3}$ yd
100 yd

Canadian
65 yd
110 yd

49. Soccer The rules for soccer state that the playing field must be from 100 to 120 yards long and 55 to 75 yards wide. The 1999 Women's World Cup was played at the Rose Bowl on a playing field 116 yards long and 72 yards wide. The diagram below shows the smallest possible soccer field, the largest possible soccer field, and the soccer field at the Rose Bowl. Find the area of each one and then convert the area of each to acres. Round to the nearest tenth, if necessary.

Soccer Fields

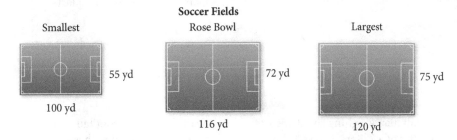

Smallest
55 yd
100 yd

Rose Bowl
72 yd
116 yd

Largest
75 yd
120 yd

50. Swimming Pool A public swimming pool measures 100 meters by 30 meters and is rectangular. What is the area of the pool in ares?

51. Construction A family decides to put tiles in the entryway of their home. The entryway has an area of 6 square meters. If each tile is 5 centimeters by 5 centimeters, how many tiles will it take to cover the entryway?

52. Landscaping A landscaper is putting in a brick patio. The area of the patio is 110 square meters. If the bricks measure 10 centimeters by 20 centimeters, how many bricks will it take to make the patio? Assume no space between bricks.

53. Sewing A dressmaker is using a pattern that requires 2 square yards of material. If the material is on a bolt that is 54 inches wide, how long must a piece of material from the bolt be to ensure sure there is enough material for the pattern?

54. **Passport** A typical passport has an area of 17.1 square inches. Convert this to square feet. Round to the nearest thousandth.

55. **Volleyball** A volleyball court has an area of about 162 square meters. Convert this to square decimeters.

56. **Pentagon** The total floor area of the Pentagon is about 620,000 square meters. Convert this to square kilometers.

57. **Manhattan** The area of Manhattan Island is about 33.8 square miles. Convert this to acres.

58. **Walt Disney World** Walt Disney World covers an area of 122 square kilometers. Convert this to hectares.

59. **Blood Plasma** A 6-foot tall man weighing about 175 pounds has about 7.1 pints of blood plasma in his body. Convert this volume to quarts.

60. **Lung Capacity** A 6-foot tall man weighing about 150 pounds has a lung capacity of 4.2 liters. Convert this volume to milliliters.

61. **Heart Volume** A 6-foot tall man weighing about 181 pounds has a heart with a volume of 0.2 gallons. Convert this volume to pints.

62. **Red Blood Cells** A 5.5-foot tall woman weighing about 130 pounds has about 1.5 liters of red blood cells. Convert this volume to milliliters.

63. **Red Blood Cells** A 5'3" woman weighing 124 pounds has about 214 cubic inches of blood. Convert this volume to cubic feet. Round to the nearest thousandth.

64. **Filling Coffee Cups** If a regular-size coffee cup holds about $\frac{1}{2}$ pint, about how many cups can be filled from a 1-gallon coffee maker?

65. **Filling Glasses** If a regular-size drinking glass holds about 0.25 liter of liquid, how many glasses can be filled from a 750-milliliter container?

66. Capacity of a Refrigerator A refrigerator has a capacity of 20 cubic feet. What is the capacity of the refrigerator in cubic inches?

67. Volume of a Tank The gasoline tank in a car holds 18 gallons of gas. What is the volume of the tank in quarts?

68. Filling Glasses How many 8-fluid-ounce glasses of water will it take to fill a 3-gallon aquarium?

69. Filling a Container How many 5-milliliter test tubes filled with water will it take to fill a 1-liter container?

Calculator Problems

Set up the following problems as you have been doing. Use a calculator to perform each conversion. Round all answers to two decimal places where appropriate.

70. Convert 93.4 qt to gallons.

71. Convert 7,362 fl oz to gallons.

72. Geography Lake Superior is the largest of the Great Lakes. It covers 31,700 square miles of area. What is the area of Lake Superior in acres?

73. Geography The state of California consists of 156,360 square miles of land and 2,330 square miles of water. Write the total area (both land and water) in acres.

74. Geography Death Valley National Monument contains 2,067,795 acres of land. How many square miles is this?

75. Geography The Badlands National Monument in South Dakota was established in 1929. It covers 243,302 acres of land. What is the area in square miles?

76. How many cubic feet are contained in 796 cubic yards?

77. The engine of a car has a volume of 440 cubic inches. What is the volume in cubic feet?

78. Volume of Water The Grand Coulee Dam holds 10,585,000 cubic yards of water. What is the volume of water in cubic feet?

79. Volume of Water Hoover Dam was built in 1936 on the Colorado River in Nevada. It holds a volume of 4,400,000 cubic yards of water. What is this volume in cubic feet?

Getting Ready for the Next Section

Perform the indicated operations.

80. $12 \cdot 16$

81. $15 \cdot 16$

82. $3 \cdot 2,000$

83. $5 \cdot 2,000$

84. $3 \cdot 1,000 \cdot 100$

85. $5 \cdot 1,000 \cdot 100$

86. $50 \cdot 250$

87. $75 \cdot 200$

88. $12,500 \cdot \dfrac{1}{1,000}$

89. $15,000 \cdot \dfrac{1}{1,000}$

FIND THE MISTAKE •

Each sentence below contains a mistake. Circle the mistake and write the correct word(s) or numbers(s) on the line provided.

1. A rectangular computer monitor is 24 inches by 30 inches. To find the area of the computer monitor in square feet, divide the product of 24 and 30 by 12. _____

2. A family bought 320 acres of land. The area of this land in square miles is 204,800 mi². _____

3. A 3-quart container of ice cream can hold 1.5 pints of ice cream. _____

4. To find how many milliliters four 2-liter soda bottles can hold, you must find the product of 8 L and $\frac{1 \text{ mL}}{1000 \text{ L}}$.

_____

WEIGHT

The indigenous Polynesian people of New Zealand, called the Māori, revered the longfin eel. The Māori believed the eel was a guardian of sacred places, and representations of the eel appeared frequently in the culture's mythology. They often maintained special ponds in a river where they kept the eels and fed them daily. The eels lived for decades, growing to 6 feet in length and 80 pounds in weight!

OBJECTIVES

A Solve problems involving weight using unit analysis.

KEY WORDS

weight

VIDEO EXAMPLES

SECTION 8.3

A Weight

Pounds are a common unit of measure for weight in the U.S. system. In this section, we'll use unit analysis to work problems involving **weight**. The most common units of weight in the U.S. system are ounces, pounds, and tons. The relationships among these units are given in Table 1.

Table 1

Units of Weight in the U.S. System		
The relationship between	is	To convert from one to the other, multiply by
ounces (oz) and pounds (lb)	1 lb = 16 oz	$\frac{16 \text{ oz}}{1 \text{ lb}}$ or $\frac{1 \text{ lb}}{16 \text{ oz}}$
pounds (lb) and tons (T)	1 T = 2,000 lb	$\frac{2000 \text{ lb}}{1 \text{ T}}$ or $\frac{1 \text{ T}}{2000 \text{ lb}}$

Example 1 Convert 12 pounds to ounces.

Solution Using the conversion factor from the table, and applying the method we have been using, we have

$$12 \text{ lb} = 12 \text{ lb} \cdot \frac{16 \text{ oz}}{1 \text{ lb}}$$

$$= 12 \cdot 16 \text{ oz}$$

$$= 192 \text{ oz}$$

Thus, 12 pounds is equivalent to 192 ounces.

Practice Problems

1. Convert 20 pounds to ounces.

Answers

1. 320 oz

557

2. Convert 5 tons to pounds.

Example 2   Convert 3 tons to pounds.

Solution   We use the conversion factor from the table. We have

$$3\text{ T} = 3\text{ T} \cdot \frac{2000\text{ lb}}{1\text{ T}}$$

$$= 6{,}000\text{ lb}$$

Therefore, 6,000 pounds is the equivalent of 3 tons.

In the metric system, the basic unit of weight is a gram. We use the same prefixes we have already used to write the other units of weight in terms of grams. Table 2 lists the most common metric units of weight and their conversion factors.

Note   In this chapter we've discussed both metric tons and tons in the U. S. system. We use a lower case t to denote metric tons and a capital T to denote tons in the U. S. system.

Table 2

Metric Units of Weight

The relationship between	is	To convert from one to the other, multiply by
milligrams (mg) and grams (g)	1 g = 1,000 mg	$\frac{1000\text{ mg}}{1\text{ g}}$ or $\frac{1\text{ g}}{1000\text{ mg}}$
centigrams (cg) and grams (g)	1 g = 100 cg	$\frac{100\text{ cg}}{1\text{ g}}$ or $\frac{1\text{ g}}{100\text{ cg}}$
kilograms (kg) and grams (g)	1,000 g = 1 kg	$\frac{1000\text{ g}}{1\text{ kg}}$ or $\frac{1\text{ kg}}{1000\text{ g}}$
metric tons (t) and kilograms (kg)	1,000 kg = 1 t	$\frac{1000\text{ kg}}{1\text{ t}}$ or $\frac{1\text{ t}}{1000\text{ kg}}$

3. Convert 4 metric tons to kilograms.

Example 3   Convert 3 kilograms to centigrams.

Solution   We convert kilograms to grams and then grams to centigrams.

$$3\text{ kg} = 3\text{ kg} \cdot \frac{1000\text{ g}}{1\text{ kg}} \cdot \frac{100\text{ cg}}{1\text{ g}}$$

$$= 3 \cdot 1{,}000 \cdot 100\text{ cg}$$

$$= 300{,}000\text{ cg}$$

Therefore, 3 kilograms is equivalent to 300,000 centigrams.

4. Suppose the bottle in Example 4 contained 75 tablets. How many grams of vitamin C are in the bottle?

Example 4   A bottle of vitamin C contains 50 tablets. Each tablet contains 250 milligrams of vitamin C. What is the total number of grams of vitamin C in the bottle?

Solution   We begin by finding the total number of milligrams of vitamin C in the bottle. Since there are 50 tablets, and each contains 250 mg of vitamin C, we can multiply 50 by 250 to get the total number of milligrams of vitamin C in one bottle.

$$50 \cdot 250\text{ mg} = 12{,}500\text{ mg}$$

Next, we convert 12,500 mg to grams using the conversion factor from the table.

$$12{,}500\text{ mg} = 12{,}500\text{ mg} \cdot \frac{1\text{ g}}{1000\text{ mg}}$$

$$= \frac{12500}{1000}\text{ g}$$

$$= 12.5\text{ g}$$

The bottle contains 12.5 grams of vitamin C.

Answers

2. 10,000 lb
3. 4,000 kg
4. 18.75 g

● **KEY CONCEPT REVIEW** ·

After reading through the preceding section, respond in your own words and in complete sentences.

A. What is the relationship between pounds and ounces?

B. Write the conversion factor used to convert from pounds to ounces.

C. Write the conversion factor used to convert from milligrams to grams.

D. What is the relationship between grams and kilograms?

EXERCISE SET 8.3 ··························

Problems

A Use the conversion factors in Tables 1 and 2 to make the following conversions.

1. 8 lb to ounces

2. 5 lb to ounces

3. 2 T to pounds

4. 5 T to pounds

5. 192 oz to pounds

6. 176 oz to pounds

7. 1,800 lb to tons

8. 10,200 lb to tons

9. 1 T to ounces

10. 3 T to ounces

11. $3\frac{1}{2}$ lb to ounces

12. $5\frac{1}{4}$ lb to ounces

13. $6\frac{1}{2}$ T to pounds

14. $4\frac{1}{5}$ T to pounds

15. 2 kg to grams

16. 5 kg to grams

17. 4 cg to milligrams

18. 3 cg to milligrams

19. 2 kg to centigrams

20. 5 kg to centigrams

21. 5.08 g to centigrams

22. 7.14 g to centigrams

23. 450 cg to grams

24. 979 cg to grams

25. 478.95 mg to centigrams

26. 659.43 mg to centigrams

27. 1,578 mg to grams

28. 1,979 mg to grams

29. 42,000 cg to kilograms

30. 97,000 cg to kilograms

Applying the Concepts

31. Fish Oil A bottle of fish oil contains 60 soft gels, each containing 800 mg of the omega-3 fatty acid. How many total grams of the omega-3 fatty acid are in this bottle?

32. Fish Oil A bottle of fish oil contains 50 soft gels, each containing 300 mg of the omega-6 fatty acid. How many total grams of the omega-6 fatty acid are in this bottle?

33. B-Complex A certain B-complex vitamin supplement contains 50 mg of riboflavin, or vitamin B_2. A bottle contains 80 vitamins. How many total grams of riboflavin are in this bottle?

34. B-Complex A certain B-complex vitamin supplement contains 30 mg of thiamine, or vitamin B_1. A bottle contains 80 vitamins. How many total grams of thiamine are in this bottle?

35. Aspirin A bottle of low-strength aspirin contains 120 tablets. Each tablet contains 81 mg of aspirin. How many total grams of aspirin are in this bottle?

36. Aspirin A bottle of maximum-strength aspirin contains 90 tablets. Each tablet contains 500 mg of aspirin. How many total grams of aspirin are in this bottle?

37. Dairy Cow A typical dairy cow has a mass of 0.77 tons. Convert this to pounds.

38. Snowflake The mass of a typical snowflake is 0.000003 kilograms. Convert this to milligrams.

39. Brain Mass A man who is 6 feet, 2 inches tall has a brain mass of about 1.4 kilograms. Convert this to grams.

40. Brain Mass A child who is 4 feet, 2 inches tall has a brain mass of about 48 ounces. Convert this to pounds.

41. Penny A United States penny has a mass of 2.5 grams. Convert this to centigrams.

42. Quarter A United States quarter has a mass of 0.0125 pounds. Convert this to ounces.

Coca Cola Bottles The soft drink Coke™ is sold throughout the world. Although the size of the bottle varies between different countries, a "six-pack" is sold everywhere. For each of the problems, find the number of liters in a "six-pack" from the given bottle size. Write each fraction or mixed number as a decimal.

Country	Bottle size	Liters in a 6-pack
43. Estonia	500 mL	
44. Israel	350 mL	
45. Jordan	250 mL	
46. Kenya	300 mL	

Getting Ready for the Next Section

Perform the indicated operations. Round to the nearest hundredth if necessary.

47. $8 \cdot 2.54$

48. $9 \cdot 3.28$

49. $3 \cdot 1.06 \cdot 2$

50. $3 \cdot 5 \cdot 3.79$

51. $80.5 \div 1.61$

52. $96.6 \div 1.61$

53. $125 \div 2.20$

54. $165 \div 2.20$

55. $2,000 \div 16.39$ (Round your answer to the nearest whole number.)

56. $2,200 \div 16.39$ (Round your answer to the nearest whole number.)

57. $\dfrac{9}{5}(120) + 32$

58. $\dfrac{9}{5}(40) + 32$

59. $\dfrac{5(102 - 32)}{9}$

60. $\dfrac{5(101.6 - 32)}{9}$

One Step Further

61. Ethanol Ethanol has a density of 0.789 grams per cubic centimeter. Convert this to kilograms per cubic centimeter.

62. Gold Gold has a density of 0.697 pounds per cubic inch. Convert this to ounces per cubic inch.

FIND THE MISTAKE

Determine if each statement uses the correct conversion factor. If it does not, give the correct conversion factor. Circle the mistake and write the correct word(s) or numbers(s) on the line provided.

1. To convert 48 ounces to pounds, multiply by $\frac{1\,lb}{16\,oz}$. _____

2. To convert a car's weight of 2.5 tons to pounds, multiply by $\frac{2.5\,T}{2000\,lbs}$. _____

3. Converting 6,000 g to kg gives us 6 kg after multiplying by $\frac{1000\,kg}{1\,g}$. _____

4. A piece of chocolate candy weighs 150 cg. To find the weight in grams of a package that contains 32 candies, multiply the product of 150 and 32 by $\frac{1\,g}{100\,cg}$. _____

LANDMARK REVIEW: CHECKING YOUR PROGRESS

Make the following conversions.

1. 7 ft to inches

2. 27 in to yards

3. 7 mi to inches

4. 15 ft to miles

5. 38 m to centimeters

6. 14.3 centimeters to decimeters

7. 43 decimeters to meters

8. 115 cm to meters

9. 8 ft² to square inches

10. 2,487 acres to square miles

11. 14 mi² to acres

12. 5 yd² to square feet

13. 7 ares to square meters

14. 14.3 cm² to square meters

15. 350 mm² to square centimeters

16. 4.2 ha to ares

17. 7 lb to ounces

18. 15 oz to pounds

19. 2 T to ounces

20. 1,500 lb to tons

21. 6.5 kg to grams

22. 5 cg to milligrams

23. 1,759 mg to grams

24. 859 cg to grams

8.4

 CONVERTING BETWEEN THE TWO SYSTEMS, AND TEMPERATURE

 OBJECTIVES

A Convert units of measurement between the metric system and the U. S. system.

B Solve problems involving temperature on both the Fahrenheit and Celsius scales.

KEY WORDS

temperature

degree

VIDEO EXAMPLES

SECTION 8.4

Because many of us have always used the U.S. system of measurement in our everyday lives, we are much more familiar with it on an intuitive level than we are with the metric system. We probably have an intuitive idea of how long feet and inches are, how much a pound weighs, and what a square yard of material looks like. Because of this, solving problems that involve the metric system can be challenging at first. We have trouble visualizing how long a meter is or how much a gram weighs. The following list is intended to give you something to associate with each basic unit of measurement in the metric system.

- A meter is just a little longer than a yard.

- The length of the edge of a sugar cube is about 1 centimeter.

- A liter is just a little larger than a quart.

- A sugar cube has a volume of approximately 1 milliliter.

- A paper clip weighs about 1 gram.

- A 2-pound can of coffee weighs about 1 kilogram.

A Convert Between Systems

The following table presents the conversion factors that allow us to convert between these two systems.

Table 1		
Conversion Factors Between the Metric and U.S. Systems of Measurement		
The relationship between	is	To convert from one to the other, multiply by
Length		
inches and centimeters	2.54 cm = 1 in.	$\frac{2.54\ cm}{1\ in.}$ or $\frac{1\ in.}{2.54\ cm}$
feet and meters	1 m = 3.28 ft	$\frac{3.28\ ft}{1\ m}$ or $\frac{1\ m}{3.28\ ft}$
miles and kilometers	1.61 km = 1 mi	$\frac{1.61\ km}{1\ mi}$ or $\frac{1\ mi}{1.61\ km}$

Area

square inches and square centimeters	$6.45 \text{ cm}^2 = 1 \text{ in}^2$	$\dfrac{6.45 \text{ cm}^2}{1 \text{ in}^2}$ or $\dfrac{1 \text{ in}^2}{6.45 \text{ cm}^2}$
square meters and square yards	$1.196 \text{ yd}^2 = 1 \text{ m}^2$	$\dfrac{1.196 \text{ yd}^2}{1 \text{ m}^2}$ or $\dfrac{1 \text{ m}^2}{1.196 \text{ yd}^2}$
acres and hectares	$1 \text{ ha} = 2.47 \text{ acres}$	$\dfrac{2.47 \text{ acres}}{1 \text{ ha}}$ or $\dfrac{1 \text{ ha}}{2.47 \text{ acres}}$

Volume

cubic inches and milliliters	$16.39 \text{ mL} = 1 \text{ in}^3$	$\dfrac{16.39 \text{ mL}}{1 \text{ in}^3}$ or $\dfrac{1 \text{ in}^3}{16.39 \text{ mL}}$
liters and quarts	$1.06 \text{ qt} = 1 \text{ liter}$	$\dfrac{1.06 \text{ qt}}{1 \text{ liter}}$ or $\dfrac{1 \text{ liter}}{1.06 \text{ qt}}$
gallons and liters	$3.79 \text{ liters} = 1 \text{ gal}$	$\dfrac{3.79 \text{ liters}}{1 \text{ gal}}$ or $\dfrac{1 \text{ gal}}{3.79 \text{ liters}}$

Weight

ounces and grams	$28.3 \text{ g} = 1 \text{ oz}$	$\dfrac{28.3 \text{ g}}{1 \text{ oz}}$ or $\dfrac{1 \text{ oz}}{28.3 \text{ g}}$
kilograms and pounds	$2.20 \text{ lb} = 1 \text{ kg}$	$\dfrac{2.20 \text{ lb}}{1 \text{ kg}}$ or $\dfrac{1 \text{ kg}}{2.20 \text{ lb}}$

There are many other conversion factors that we could have included in Table 1. We have listed only the most common ones. Almost all of them are approximations. That is, most of the conversion factors are decimals that have been rounded to an appropriate place. If we want more accuracy, we could obtain a table that has more digits in the conversion factors.

Practice Problems

Example 1 Convert 8 inches to centimeters.

1. Convert 4 feet to meters.

Solution Choosing the appropriate conversion factor from Table 1, we have

$$8 \text{ in.} = 8 \text{ in.} \cdot \frac{2.54 \text{ cm}}{1 \text{ in.}}$$

$$= 8 \cdot 2.54 \text{ cm}$$

$$= 20.32 \text{ cm}$$

Therefore, 8 inches is approximately 20.32 centimeters.

Example 2 Convert 80.5 kilometers to miles.

2. Convert 400 inches to kilometers.

Solution Using the conversion factor that takes us from kilometers to miles, we have

$$80.5 \text{ km} = 80.5 \text{ km} \cdot \frac{1 \text{ mi}}{1.61 \text{ km}}$$

$$= \frac{80.5}{1.61} \text{ mi}$$

$$= 50 \text{ mi}$$

So 50 miles is equivalent to 80.5 kilometers. If we travel at 50 miles per hour in a car, we are moving at the rate of 80.5 kilometers per hour.

Answers

1. 1.22 meters
2. 0.01 km

3. Convert 5 liters to gallons.

Example 3   Convert 3 liters to pints.

Solution   Because Table 1 doesn't list a conversion factor that will take us directly from liters to pints, we first convert liters to quarts, and then convert quarts to pints.

$$3 \text{ liters} = 3 \text{ liters} \cdot \frac{1.06 \text{ qt}}{1 \text{ liter}} \cdot \frac{2 \text{ pt}}{1 \text{ qt}}$$

$$= 3 \cdot 1.06 \cdot 2 \text{ pt}$$

$$= 6.36 \text{ pt}$$

Thus, 3 liters is approximately 6.36 pints.

4. A truck engine has a volume of 3 liters. What is the volume in cubic inches?

Example 4   The engine in a car has a volume of 2 liters. What is the volume in cubic inches, rounding to the nearest cubic inch?

Solution   We convert liters to milliliters and then milliliters to cubic inches.

$$2 \text{ liters} = 2 \text{ liters} \cdot \frac{1000 \text{ mL}}{1 \text{ liter}} \cdot \frac{1 \text{ in}^3}{16.39 \text{ mL}}$$

$$= \frac{2 \cdot 1000}{16.39} \text{ in}^3 \qquad \textit{This calculation can be done on a calculator.}$$

$$= 122 \text{ in}^3 \qquad \textit{Round to the nearest cubic inch.}$$

We have found that the car's engine has a volume of 122 in³.

5. If a person weighs 180 pounds, what is his weight in kilograms?

Example 5   If a person weighs 125 pounds, what is her weight in kilograms?

Solution   Converting from pounds to kilograms, we have

$$125 \text{ lb} = 125 \text{ lb} \cdot \frac{1 \text{ kg}}{2.20 \text{ lb}}$$

$$= \frac{125}{2.20} \text{ kg}$$

$$= 56.8 \text{ kg} \qquad \textit{Round to the nearest tenth.}$$

Therefore, she weighs approximately 56.8 kilograms.

B Temperature

We end this section with a discussion of temperature in both systems of measurement.

In the U.S. system, we typically measure temperature on the Fahrenheit scale. On this scale, water boils at 212 degrees and freezes at 32 degrees. When we write 32 degrees measured on the Fahrenheit scale, we use the notation

32°F (read, "32 degrees Fahrenheit")

In the metric system, the scale we use to measure temperature is the Celsius scale (formerly called the centigrade scale). On this scale, water boils at 100 degrees and freezes at 0 degrees. When we write 100 degrees measured on the Celsius scale, we use the notation

100°C (read, "100 degrees Celsius")

Answers

3. 1.33 gallons
4. 183 in³
5. 81.8 kg

Table 2 is intended to give you a sense of the relationship between the two temperature scales. Table 3 gives the formulas, in both symbols and words, that are used to convert between the two scales.

Table 2

Situation	Temperature Fahrenheit	Temperature Celsius
Water freezes	32°F	0°C
Room temperature	68°F	20°C
Normal body temperature	98.6°F	37°C
Water boils	212°F	100°C
Bake cookies	350°F	176.7°C
Broil meat	554°F	290°C

Table 3

To convert from	Formula In symbols
Fahrenheit to Celsius	$C = \dfrac{5(F - 32)}{9}$
Celsius to Fahrenheit	$F = \dfrac{9}{5}C + 32$

Note When using these formulas to convert between Fahrenheit and Celsius, we follow the order of operations.

The following examples show how we use the formulas given in Table 3.

Example 6 Convert 120°C to degrees Fahrenheit.

Solution We use the formula

$$F = \frac{9}{5}C + 32$$

and replace C with 120.

$$F = \frac{9}{5}(120) + 32$$

$$F = 216 + 32 \qquad \text{Multiply.}$$

$$F = 248 \qquad \text{Add.}$$

We see that 120°C is equivalent to 248°F; they both mean the same temperature.

6. Convert 102°C to Fahrenheit.

Example 7 A man with the flu has a temperature of 102°F. What is his temperature on the Celsius scale?

Solution We use the formula $C = \dfrac{5(F-32)}{9}$ and replace F with 102.

$$C = \frac{5(102 - 32)}{9} \qquad \text{Subtract.}$$

$$C = \frac{5(70)}{9} \qquad \text{Simplify.}$$

$$C = 38.9 \qquad \text{Round to the nearest tenth.}$$

The man's temperature, rounded to the nearest tenth, is 38.9°C on the Celsius scale.

7. Convert 120°F to Celsius.

Answers
6. 215.6°F
7. 48.9°C

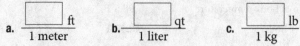

KEY CONCEPT REVIEW •

After reading through the preceding section, respond in your own words and in complete sentences.

A. Write the equality that gives the relationship between centimeters and inches.

B. Write the equality that gives the relationship between grams and ounces.

C. Fill in the numerators below so that each conversion factor is equal to 1.

a. $\dfrac{\boxed{}\ \text{ft}}{1\ \text{meter}}$ b. $\dfrac{\boxed{}\ \text{qt}}{1\ \text{liter}}$ c. $\dfrac{\boxed{}\ \text{lb}}{1\ \text{kg}}$

D. Is it a hot day if the temperature outside is 37°C?

VOCABULARY REVIEW ·

Choose the correct words to fill in the blanks below.

quarts   Celsius   Fahrenheit   centimeters

1. The relationship between _____ and inches is 2.54 cm = 1 in.

2. The relationship between _____ and liters is 1.06 qt = 1 liter.

3. Use the formula $F = \dfrac{9}{5}C + 32$ to convert a _____ temperature to a _____ temperature.

Problems

A, B   Use Tables 1 and 3 to make the following conversions.

1. 6 in. to centimeters

2. 1 ft to centimeters

3. 4 m to feet

4. 2 km to feet

5. 6 m to yards

6. 15 mi to kilometers

7. 20 mi to meters

8. 600 m to yards

9. 5 m² to square yards

10. 2 in² to square centimeters

11. 10 ha to acres

12. 50 ares to acres

13. 500 in³ to milliliters

14. 400 in³ to liters

15. 2 L to quarts

16. 15 L to quarts

17. 20 gal to liters

18. 15 gal to liters

19. 12 oz to grams

20. 1 lb to grams (round to the nearest 10 grams)

21. 15 kg to pounds

22. 10 kg to ounces (round to the nearest ounce)

23. 185°C to degrees Fahrenheit

24. 20°C to degrees Fahrenheit

25. 86°F to degrees Celsius

26. 122°F to degrees Celsius

Calculator Problems

Perform each of the following conversions with the use of a calculator. Round to the nearest hundredth.

27. 10 cm to inches

28. 100 mi to kilometers

29. 25 ft to meters

30. 400 mL to cubic inches

31. 49 qt to liters

32. 65 L to gallons

33. 500 g to ounces

34. 100 lb to kilograms

35. Weight Give your weight in kilograms.

36. Height Give your height in meters and centimeters.

37. Sports The 100-yard dash is a popular race in track. How far is 100 yards in meters?

38. Engine Displacement A 351-cubic-inch engine has a volume of how many liters?

39. Sewing 25 square yards of material is how many square meters?

40. Weight How many grams does a 5 lb 4 oz roast weigh?

41. Speed 55 miles per hour is equivalent to how many kilometers per hour?

42. Capacity A 1-quart container holds how many liters?

43. Sports A high jumper jumps 6 ft 8 in. How many meters is this?

44. Farming A farmer owns 57 acres of land. How many hectares is that?

45. Body Temperature A person has a temperature of 101°F. What is the person's temperature, to the nearest tenth, on the Celsius scale?

46. Air Temperature If the temperature outside is 30°C, is it a better day for water skiing or for snow skiing?

Getting Ready for the Next Section

Perform the indicated operations.

47. $15 + 60$

48. $25 + 60$

49.
$$\begin{array}{r} 37 \\ + 45 \\ \hline \end{array}$$

50.
$$\begin{array}{r} 37 \\ + 46 \\ \hline \end{array}$$

51. $3 + 0.25$

52. $2 + 0.75$

53. $82 - 60$

54. $73 - 60$

55.
$$\begin{array}{r} 75 \\ - 34 \\ \hline \end{array}$$

56.
$$\begin{array}{r} 85 \\ - 42 \\ \hline \end{array}$$

57. $12 \cdot 4$

58. $8 \cdot 4$

59. $3 \cdot 60 + 15$

60. $2 \cdot 65 + 45$

61. $3 + 16 \cdot \dfrac{1}{60}$

62. $2 + 45 \cdot \dfrac{1}{60}$

63. If fish costs \$6.00 per pound, find the cost of 15 pounds of fish.

64. If fish costs \$5.00 per pound, find the cost of 14 pounds of fish.

One Step Further

65. Caffeine Caffeine has a density of 1.23 grams per cubic centimeter. Convert this to ounces per cubic inch.

66. Caffeine A lethal dosage of caffeine is 192 milligrams per kilogram. This means a person would have to consume 192 milligrams of caffeine for every kilogram they weigh for them to get a lethal dose of caffeine. If a person weighs 150 pounds, how many grams of caffeine would they have to take for it to be lethal?

67. Ibuprofen Ibuprofen is considered toxic if a person exceeds 1,255 milligrams per kilogram. If a person weights 120 pounds, how many grams is considered a toxic dose?

68. Molasses Molasses has a density of 1.42 grams per cubic centimeter. Convert this to pounds per cubic foot. Round to the nearest hundredth.

FIND THE MISTAKE •

Each sentence below contains a mistake. Circle the mistake and write the correct word(s) or numbers(s) on the line provided.

1. To convert 6 miles to km, divide 6 miles by $\dfrac{1.61 \text{ km}}{1 \text{ mi}}$. _____

2. Suppose a pasta recipe requires a half gallon of water, but your measuring cup only measures milliliters. To find how many milliliters are equal to a half gallon of water, multiply $\frac{1}{2}$ gal by $\dfrac{3.79 \text{ ml}}{1 \text{ gal}}$.

_____

3. To convert 25° Celsius to Fahrenheit, use the formula $C = \dfrac{5(F-32)}{9}$ to get 77° F. _____

4. A cookie recipe requires you to bake them at 325° F. This temperature in Celsius is 33° C (rounded to the nearest degree). _____

8.5 OPERATIONS WITH TIME, AND MIXED UNITS

OBJECTIVES

A Convert units of time using unit analysis.

B Add and subtract units of time.

KEY WORDS

time

mixed units

VIDEO EXAMPLES

SECTION 8.5

Before computers were prevalent in the workplace, many occupations required the use of a time card. A time card records the number of hours and minutes an employee spends at work. At the end of a work week, the hours and minutes are totaled separately, and then the minutes are converted to hours so each employee could be paid for the number of hours he or she worked that week.

A Time

In this section, we will perform operations with mixed units of measure. For instance, mixed units are used when we use 2 hours 30 minutes, rather than 2 and a half hours, or 5 feet 9 inches, rather than five and three-quarter feet. As you will see, many of these types of problems arise in everyday life.

The relationship between	is	To convert from one to the other, multiply by
minutes and seconds	1 min = 60 sec	$\frac{1 \text{ min}}{60 \text{ sec}}$ or $\frac{60 \text{ sec}}{1 \text{ min}}$
hours and minutes	1 hr = 60 min	$\frac{1 \text{ hr}}{60 \text{ min}}$ or $\frac{60 \text{ min}}{1 \text{ hr}}$

Practice Problems

1. Convert 5 hours 12 minutes to
   a. minutes.
   b. hours.

Example 1 Convert 3 hours 15 minutes to

a. minutes. **b.** hours.

Solution

a. To convert to minutes, we multiply the hours by the conversion factor then add minutes.

$$3 \text{ hr } 15 \text{ min} = 3 \text{ hr} \cdot \frac{60 \text{ min}}{1 \text{ hr}} + 15 \text{ min} = 180 \text{ min} + 15 \text{ min} = 195 \text{ min}$$

b. To convert to hours, we multiply the minutes by the conversion factor then add hours.

$$3 \text{ hr } 15 \text{ min} = 3 \text{ hr} + 15 \text{ min} \cdot \frac{1 \text{ hr}}{60 \text{ min}} = 3 \text{ hr} + 0.25 \text{ hr} = 3.25 \text{ hr}$$

Answers

1. a. 312 minutes **b.** 5.2 hours

572

Example 2   Add 5 minutes 37 seconds and 7 minutes 45 seconds.

Solution   First, we align the units properly.

$$
\begin{array}{r}
5\ \text{min}\quad 37\ \text{sec} \\
+\ 7\ \text{min}\quad 45\ \text{sec} \\
\hline
12\ \text{min}\quad 82\ \text{sec}
\end{array}
$$

Since there are 60 seconds in every minute, we write 82 seconds as 1 minute 22 seconds. We have

$$
\begin{aligned}
12\ \text{min } 82\ \text{sec} &= 12\ \text{min} + 1\ \text{min } 22\ \text{sec} \\
&= 13\ \text{min } 22\ \text{sec}
\end{aligned}
$$

2. Add 3 hours 45 minutes and 4 hours 20 minutes.

The idea of adding the units separately is similar to adding mixed numbers. That is, we align the whole numbers with the whole numbers and the fractions with the fractions.

Similarly, when we subtract units of time, we "borrow" 60 seconds from the minutes column, or 60 minutes from the hours column.

Example 3   Subtract 34 minutes from 8 hours 15 minutes.

Solution   Again, we first line up the numbers in the hours column, and then the numbers in the minutes column.

$$
\begin{array}{r}
8\ \text{hr}\quad 15\ \text{min} \\
-\qquad\ 34\ \text{min} \\
\hline
\end{array}
$$

Since there are 60 minutes in an hour, we borrow 1 hour from the hours column and add 60 minutes to the minutes column. Then we subtract.

$$
\begin{array}{r}
7\ \text{hr}\quad 75\ \text{min} \\
-\qquad\ 34\ \text{min} \\
\hline
7\ \text{hr}\quad 41\ \text{min}
\end{array}
$$

3. Subtract 43 minutes from 4 hours 10 minutes.

B Mixed Units

Next we will solve problems involving mixed units.

Example 4   Jake purchases 4 halibut. The fish cost $6.00 per pound, and each weighs 3 lb 12 oz. What is the cost of the fish?

Solution   First, we multiply each unit by 4.

$$
\begin{array}{r}
3\ \text{lb}\quad 12\ \text{oz} \\
\times\qquad\qquad 4 \\
\hline
12\ \text{lb}\quad 48\ \text{oz}
\end{array}
$$

To convert the 48 ounces to pounds, we multiply the ounces by the conversion factor

$$
\begin{aligned}
12\ \text{lb } 48\ \text{oz} &= 12\ \text{lb} + 48\ \text{oz} \cdot \frac{1\ \text{lb}}{16\ \text{oz}} \\
&= 12\ \text{lb} + 3\ \text{lb} \\
&= 15\ \text{lb}
\end{aligned}
$$

Finally, we multiply the 15 lb and $6.00/lb for a total price of $90.00.

4. Suppose Jake purchased 6 of the halibut in Example 4. What is the cost?

Answers
2. 8 hours 5 minutes
3. 3 hours 27 minutes
4. $135.00

5. Convert the advertised speed in Example 7 to yards per minute.

Example 5   A ski resort in Vermont advertised their new high-speed chair lift as "the world's fastest chair lift, with a speed of 1,100 feet per second." Show why the speed cannot be correct.

Solution   To solve this problem, we can convert feet per second into miles per hour, a unit of measure we are more familiar with on an intuitive level. Here are the conversion factors we will use:

$$1 \text{ mile} = 5{,}280 \text{ feet}$$

$$1 \text{ hour} = 60 \text{ minutes}$$

$$1 \text{ minute} = 60 \text{ seconds}$$

$$1{,}100 \text{ ft/second} = \frac{1100 \text{ feet}}{1 \text{ second}} \cdot \frac{1 \text{ mile}}{5280 \text{ feet}} \cdot \frac{60 \text{ seconds}}{1 \text{ minute}} \cdot \frac{60 \text{ minutes}}{1 \text{ hour}}$$

$$= \frac{1100 \cdot 60 \cdot 60 \text{ miles}}{5280 \text{ hours}}$$

$$= 750 \text{ miles/hour}$$

Because this is an extremely high speed, we can conclude that the speed cannot be correct.

KEY CONCEPT REVIEW

After reading through the preceding section, respond in your own words and in complete sentences.

A. Explain the difference between saying *2 and a half hours* and saying *2 hours and 30 minutes*.

B. How are operations with mixed units of measure similar to operations with mixed numbers?

C. Why do we borrow a 1 from the hours column and add 60 to the minutes column when subtracting in Example 3?

D. Give an example of when you may have to use multiplication with mixed units of measure.

Answer

5. 22,000 yd/min

Choose the correct words to fill in the blanks below.

columns   seconds   borrow   minutes

1. To convert from _____ to _____, multiply by the conversion factor $\frac{60 \text{ sec}}{1 \text{ min}}$.

2. Adding mixed units is similar to adding mixed numbers, such that we align the units separately in _____ and add.

3. To subtract units of time, we may need to _____ 60 seconds from the minutes column, or 60 minutes from the hours column.

Problems

A Use the tables of conversion factors given in this section and other sections in this chapter to make the following conversions. (Round your answers to the nearest hundredth if necessary.)

1. Convert 4 hours 30 minutes to
   a. minutes.

   b. hours.

2. Convert 2 hours 45 minutes to
   a. minutes.

   b. hours.

3. Convert 5 hours 20 minutes to
   a. minutes.

   b. hours.

4. Convert 4 hours 40 minutes to
   a. minutes.

   b. hours.

5. Convert 6 minutes 30 seconds to
   a. seconds.

   b. minutes.

6. Convert 8 minutes 45 seconds to
   a. seconds.

   b. minutes.

7. Convert 5 minutes 20 seconds to
   a. seconds.

   b. minutes.

8. Convert 4 minutes 40 seconds to
   a. seconds.

   b. minutes.

9. Convert 2 pounds 8 ounces to
   a. ounces.

   b. pounds.

10. Convert 3 pounds 4 ounces to
   a. ounces.

   b. pounds.

11. Convert 4 pounds 12 ounces to
   a. ounces.

   b. pounds.

12. Convert 5 pounds 16 ounces to
   a. ounces.

   b. pounds.

13. Convert 4 feet 6 inches to
   a. inches.

   b. feet.

14. Convert 3 feet 3 inches to
   a. inches.

   b. feet.

15. Convert 5 feet 9 inches to
   a. inches.

   b. feet.

16. Convert 3 feet 4 inches to
   a. inches.

   b. feet.

17. Convert 2 gallons 1 quart to
   a. quarts.

   b. gallons.

18. Convert 3 gallons 2 quarts to
   a. quarts.

   b. gallons.

Perform the indicated operation. Again, remember to use the appropriate conversion factor.

19. Add 4 hours 47 minutes and 6 hours 13 minutes.

20. Add 5 hours 39 minutes and 2 hours 21 minutes.

21. Add 8 feet 10 inches and 13 feet 6 inches.

22. Add 16 feet 7 inches and 7 feet 9 inches.

23. Add 4 pounds 12 ounces and 6 pounds 4 ounces.

24. Add 11 pounds 9 ounces and 3 pounds 7 ounces.

25. Subtract 2 hours 35 minutes from 8 hours 15 minutes.

26. Subtract 3 hours 47 minutes from 5 hours 33 minutes.

27. Subtract 3 hours 43 minutes from 7 hours 30 minutes.

28. Subtract 1 hour 44 minutes from 6 hours 22 minutes.

29. Subtract 4 hours 17 minutes from 5 hours 9 minutes.

30. Subtract 2 hours 54 minutes from 3 hours 7 minutes.

31. Speed Limit The maximum speed limit on part of Highway 101 in California is 55 miles/hour. Convert 55 miles/hour to feet/second. (Round to the nearest tenth.)

32. Speed Limit The maximum speed limit on part of I-4 in Florida is 65 miles/hour. Convert 65 miles/hour to feet/second. (Round to the nearest tenth.)

33. Track and Field A person who runs the 100-yard dash in 10.5 seconds has an average speed of 9.52 yards/second. Convert 9.52 yards/second to miles/hour. (Round to the nearest tenth.)

34. Track and Field A person who runs a mile in 8 minutes has an average speed of 0.125 miles/minute. Convert 0.125 miles/minute to miles/hour.

35. Speed of a Bullet The bullet from a rifle leaves the barrel traveling 1,500 feet/second. Convert 1,500 feet/second to miles/hour. (Round to the nearest whole number.)

36. Speed of a Bullet A bullet from a machine gun on a B-17 Flying Fortress in World War II had a muzzle speed of 1,750 feet/second. Convert 1,750 feet/second to miles/hour. (Round to the nearest whole number.)

Applying the Concepts

Triathlon The Ironman Triathlon World Championship, held each October in Kona on the island of Hawaii, consists of three parts: a 2.4-mile ocean swim, a 112-mile bike race, and a 26.2-mile marathon. The table shows the results from the 2016 event. Use the table to answer Problems 31–34.

Triathlete	Swim Time (Hr:Min:Sec)	Bike Time (Hr:Min:Sec)	Run Time (Hr:Min:Sec)	Total Time (Hr:Min:Sec)
Jan Frodeno	0:48:02	4:29:00	2:45:34	
Sebastian Kienle	0:52:27	4:23:55	2:49:03	

37. Fill in the total time column.

38. How much faster was Jan's total time than Sebastian's?

39. How much faster was Sebastian's bike time than Jan's?

40. How much faster was Jan than Sebastian in the run?

41. Cost of Fish Fredrick is purchasing four whole salmon. The fish cost $4.00 per pound, and each weighs 6 lb 8 oz. What is the cost of the fish?

42. Cost of Steak Mike is purchasing eight top sirloin steaks. The meat costs $4.00 per pound, and each steak weighs 1 lb 4 oz. What is the total cost of the steaks?

43. Stationary Bike Maggie rides a stationary bike for 1 hour and 15 minutes, 4 days a week. After 2 weeks, how many hours has she spent riding the stationary bike?

44. Gardening Scott works in his garden for 1 hour and 5 minutes, 3 days a week. After 4 weeks, how many hours has Scott spent gardening?

45. Cost of Fabric Allison is making a quilt. She buys 3 yards and 1 foot each of six different fabrics. The fabrics cost $7.50 a yard. How much will Allison spend?

46. Cost of Lumber Trish is building a fence. She buys six fence posts at the lumberyard, each measuring 5 ft 4 in. The lumber costs $3 per foot. How much will Trish spend?

47. Molecular Weight Silver nitrate has a molecular weight of 169.9 grams per mole. If you have a solution containing 2.1 moles, how many grams of silver nitrate do you have?

48. Molecular Weight Potassium chloride has a molecular weight of 74.6 grams per mole. How many moles do you have if you have 52.3 grams of potassium chloride? Round to the nearest tenth.

49. Cost of Wheat Wheat is being sold for 560 cents per bushel. If a farmer sells 5,231 bushels, how many dollars will he make?

50. Cost of Corn Corn is being sold for 403 cents per bushel. If a farmer sells 3,503 bushels, how many dollars will he make?

One Step Further

51. In 2017, the horse Always Dreaming won the Kentucky Derby with a time of 2:03:59, or two minutes and 3.59 seconds. The record time for the Kentucky Derby is still held by Secretariat, who won the race with a time of 1:59.40 in 1973. How much faster did Secretariat run in 1973 than Always Dreaming?

52. In 2017, the horse Tapwrit won the Belmont Stakes with a time of 2:30:02, or two minutes and 30.02 seconds. The record time for the Belmont Stakes is still held by Secretariat, who won the race with a time of 2:24.00 in 1973. How much faster did Secretariat run in 1973 than Tapwrit?

FIND THE MISTAKE

Each sentence below contains a mistake. Circle the mistake and write the correct word(s) or numbers(s) on the line provided.

1. Converting 6 feet 6 inches to inches gives us 72 inches. _____

2. The correct way to write the sum of 2 hours, 55 min and 4 hours, 10 min is 6 hours and 65 minutes.
_____

3. The correct way to subtract 27 minutes from 6 hours and 12 minutes is to add 60 minutes to the 6 hours. _____

4. Jane is buying two cups of frozen yogurt. One cup contains 3 ounces and the other contains 11.9 grams. If each ounce cost $1.50, then the total purchase price will be $4.50. _____

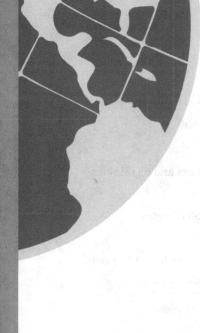

 # Trail Guide Project

SUPPLIES NEEDED · · · · ·

an object to hide

a piece of paper

a pen or pencil

a metric ruler

a large measuring device such as a measuring tape or a yardstick

Hunting for Treasure

Geocaching is a modern-day treasure hunt. For this popular outdoor activity, people hunt for hidden containers called geocaches using a GPS receiver or mobile device. According to the official geocaching website, there are over 1.5 million geocaches hidden around the world and over 5 million participants. These participants use GPS coordinates to find a geocache. Each geocache includes a logbook that the participant signs upon discovery. Then the geocacher returns the container to its original location.

For this project, you are going to create your own treasure hunt. However, instead of GPS, you will rely on the tried and true treasure map. Break into an even number of groups. Each group should decide what to hide as its hidden treasure. It can be as simple as a pencil or a folded piece of paper. Then draw a map that leads your treasure hunter from your classroom's door to the hidden item. Your map should be drawn using centimeters for distance. Provide a key that states 1 cm on the map equals a unit of measurement from the U.S. System (e.g., inch, foot, or yard), which will be needed to find the treasure. For instance, 1 cm on the map could equal 3 feet on land. Once your map is complete and your treasure is hidden, exchange maps with another group. Convert your metric measurements to the indicated U.S. System unit of measure and use a ruler to find the treasure. Happy hunting!

CHAPTER 8 SUMMARY......................................

Conversion Factors [8.1, 8.2, 8.3, 8.4, 8.5]

To convert from one kind of unit to another, we choose an appropriate conversion factor from one of the tables given in this chapter. For example, if we want to convert 5 feet to inches, we look for conversion factors that give the relationship between feet and inches. There are two conversion factors for feet and inches:

$$\frac{12 \text{ in.}}{1 \text{ ft}} \quad \text{and} \quad \frac{1 \text{ ft}}{12 \text{ in.}}$$

1. Convert 5 feet to inches.

$5 \text{ ft} = 5 \text{ ft} \cdot \dfrac{12 \text{ in.}}{1 \text{ ft}}$

$\quad = 5 \cdot 12 \text{ in.}$

$\quad = 60 \text{ in.}$

Length [8.1]

2. Convert 8 feet to yards.

$8 \text{ ft} = 8 \text{ ft} \cdot \dfrac{1 \text{ yd}}{3 \text{ ft}}$

$\quad = \dfrac{8}{3} \text{ yd}$

$\quad = 2\dfrac{2}{3} \text{ yd}$

U.S. System

The relationship between	is	To convert from one to the other, multiply by
feet and inches	12 in. = 1 ft	$\frac{12 \text{ in.}}{1 \text{ ft}}$ or $\frac{1 \text{ ft}}{12 \text{ in.}}$
feet and yards	1 yd = 3 ft	$\frac{3 \text{ ft}}{1 \text{ yd}}$ or $\frac{1 \text{ yd}}{3 \text{ ft}}$
feet and miles	1 mi = 5,280 ft	$\frac{5280 \text{ ft}}{1 \text{ mi}}$ or $\frac{1 \text{ mi}}{5280 \text{ ft}}$

3. Convert 25 millimeters to meters.

$25 \text{ mm} = 25 \text{ mm} \cdot \dfrac{1 \text{ m}}{1000 \text{ mm}}$

$\quad = \dfrac{25}{1000} \text{ m}$

$\quad = 0.025 \text{ m}$

Metric System

The relationship between	is	To convert from one to the other, multiply by
millimeters (mm) and meters (m)	1,000 mm = 1 m	$\frac{1000 \text{ mm}}{1 \text{ m}}$ or $\frac{1 \text{ m}}{1000 \text{ mm}}$
centimeters (cm) and meters (m)	100 cm = 1 m	$\frac{100 \text{ cm}}{1 \text{ m}}$ or $\frac{1 \text{ m}}{100 \text{ cm}}$
decimeters (dm) and meters (m)	10 dm = 1 m	$\frac{10 \text{ dm}}{1 \text{ m}}$ or $\frac{1 \text{ m}}{10 \text{ dm}}$
dekameters (dam) and meters (m)	1 dam = 10 m	$\frac{10 \text{ m}}{1 \text{ dam}}$ or $\frac{1 \text{ dam}}{10 \text{ m}}$
hectometers (hm) and meters (m)	1 hm = 100 m	$\frac{100 \text{ m}}{1 \text{ hm}}$ or $\frac{1 \text{ hm}}{100 \text{ m}}$
kilometers (km) and meters (m)	1 km = 1,000 m	$\frac{1000 \text{ m}}{1 \text{ km}}$ or $\frac{1 \text{ km}}{1000 \text{ m}}$

Area [8.2]

4. Convert 256 acres to square miles.

$256 \text{ acres} = 256 \text{ acres} \cdot \dfrac{1 \text{ mi}^2}{640 \text{ acres}}$

$\quad = \dfrac{256}{640} \text{ mi}^2$

$\quad = 0.4 \text{ mi}^2$

U.S. System

The relationship between	is	To convert from one to the other, multiply by
square inches and square feet	$144 \text{ in}^2 = 1 \text{ ft}^2$	$\frac{144 \text{ in}^2}{1 \text{ ft}^2}$ or $\frac{1 \text{ ft}^2}{144 \text{ in}^2}$
square yards and square feet	$9 \text{ ft}^2 = 1 \text{ yd}^2$	$\frac{9 \text{ ft}^2}{1 \text{ yd}^2}$ or $\frac{1 \text{ yd}^2}{9 \text{ ft}^2}$
acres and square feet	$1 \text{ acre} = 43,560 \text{ ft}^2$	$\frac{43560 \text{ ft}^2}{1 \text{ acre}}$ or $\frac{1 \text{ acre}}{43560 \text{ ft}^2}$
acres and square miles	$640 \text{ acres} = 1 \text{ mi}^2$	$\frac{640 \text{ acres}}{1 \text{ mi}^2}$ or $\frac{1 \text{ mi}^2}{640 \text{ acres}}$

Metric System

The relationship between	is	To convert from one to the other, multiply by
square millimeters and square centimeters	$1 \text{ cm}^2 = 100 \text{ mm}^2$	$\dfrac{100 \text{ mm}^2}{1 \text{ cm}^2}$ or $\dfrac{1 \text{ cm}^2}{100 \text{ mm}^2}$
square centimeters and square decimeters	$1 \text{ dm}^2 = 100 \text{ cm}^2$	$\dfrac{100 \text{ cm}^2}{1 \text{ dm}^2}$ or $\dfrac{1 \text{ dm}^2}{100 \text{ cm}^2}$
square decimeters and square meters	$1 \text{ m}^2 = 100 \text{ dm}^2$	$\dfrac{100 \text{ dm}^2}{1 \text{ m}^2}$ or $\dfrac{1 \text{ m}^2}{100 \text{ dm}^2}$
square meters and ares	$1 \text{ a} = 100 \text{ m}^2$	$\dfrac{100 \text{ m}^2}{1 \text{ a}}$ or $\dfrac{1 \text{ a}}{100 \text{ m}^2}$
ares and hectares	$1 \text{ ha} = 100 \text{ a}$	$\dfrac{100 \text{ a}}{1 \text{ ha}}$ or $\dfrac{1 \text{ ha}}{100 \text{ a}}$
square kilometers and hectares	$1 \text{ km}^2 = 100 \text{ ha}$	$\dfrac{1 \text{ km}^2}{100 \text{ ha}}$ or $\dfrac{100 \text{ ha}}{1 \text{ km}^2}$

Volume [8.2]

5. Convert 452 hectoliters to liters.

$$452 \text{ hL} = 452 \text{ hL} \cdot \frac{100 \text{ L}}{1 \text{ hL}}$$

$$= 45{,}200 \text{ L}$$

U.S. System

The relationship between	is	To convert from one to the other, multiply by
cubic inches (in³) and cubic feet (ft³)	$1 \text{ ft}^3 = 1{,}728 \text{ in}^3$	$\dfrac{1728 \text{ in}^3}{1 \text{ ft}^3}$ or $\dfrac{1 \text{ ft}^3}{1728 \text{ in}^3}$
cubic feet (ft³) and cubic yards (yd³)	$1 \text{ yd}^3 = 27 \text{ ft}^3$	$\dfrac{27 \text{ ft}^3}{1 \text{ yd}^3}$ or $\dfrac{1 \text{ yd}^3}{27 \text{ ft}^3}$
fluid ounces (fl oz) and pints (pt)	$1 \text{ pt} = 16 \text{ fl oz}$	$\dfrac{16 \text{ fl oz}}{1 \text{ pt}}$ or $\dfrac{1 \text{ pt}}{16 \text{ fl oz}}$
pints (p) and quarts (qt)	$1 \text{ qt} = 2 \text{ pt}$	$\dfrac{2 \text{ pt}}{1 \text{ qt}}$ or $\dfrac{1 \text{ qt}}{2 \text{ pt}}$
quarts (qt) and gallons (gal)	$1 \text{ gal} = 4 \text{ qt}$	$\dfrac{4 \text{ qt}}{1 \text{ gal}}$ or $\dfrac{1 \text{ gal}}{4 \text{ qt}}$

Metric System

The relationship between	is	To convert from one to the other, multiply by
milliliters (mL) and liters (L)	$1 \text{ liter (L)} = 1{,}000 \text{ mL}$	$\dfrac{1000 \text{ mL}}{1 \text{ liter}}$ or $\dfrac{1 \text{ liter}}{1000 \text{ mL}}$
hectoliters (hL) and liters (L)	$100 \text{ liters} = 1 \text{ hL}$	$\dfrac{100 \text{ liters}}{1 \text{ hL}}$ or $\dfrac{1 \text{ hL}}{100 \text{ liters}}$
kiloliters (kL) and liters (L)	$1{,}000 \text{ liters (L)} = 1 \text{ kL}$	$\dfrac{1000 \text{ liters}}{1 \text{ kL}}$ or $\dfrac{1 \text{ kL}}{1000 \text{ liters}}$

Weight [8.3]

6. Convert 12 pounds to ounces.

$$12 \text{ lb} = 12 \text{ lb} \cdot \frac{16 \text{ oz}}{1 \text{ lb}}$$

$$= 12 \cdot 16 \text{ oz}$$

$$= 192 \text{ oz}$$

U.S. System

The relationship between	is	To convert from one to the other, multiply by
ounces (oz) and pounds (lb)	$1 \text{ lb} = 16 \text{ oz}$	$\dfrac{16 \text{ oz}}{1 \text{ lb}}$ or $\dfrac{1 \text{ lb}}{16 \text{ oz}}$
pounds (lb) and tons (T)	$1 \text{ T} = 2{,}000 \text{ lb}$	$\dfrac{2000 \text{ lb}}{1 \text{ T}}$ or $\dfrac{1 \text{ T}}{2000 \text{ lb}}$

Metric System

The relationship between	is	To convert from one to the other, multiply by
milligrams (mg) and grams (g)	1 g = 1,000 mg	$\dfrac{1000 \text{ mg}}{1 \text{ g}}$ or $\dfrac{1 \text{ g}}{1000 \text{ mg}}$
centigrams (cg) and grams (g)	1 g = 100 cg	$\dfrac{100 \text{ cg}}{1 \text{ g}}$ or $\dfrac{1 \text{ g}}{100 \text{ cg}}$
kilograms (kg) and grams (g)	1,000 g = 1 kg	$\dfrac{1000 \text{ g}}{1 \text{ kg}}$ or $\dfrac{1 \text{ kg}}{1000 \text{ g}}$
metric tons (t) and kilograms (kg)	1,000 kg = 1 t	$\dfrac{1000 \text{ kg}}{1 \text{ t}}$ or $\dfrac{1 \text{ t}}{1000 \text{ kg}}$

Converting Between the Systems [8.4]

Conversion Factors

The relationship between	is	To convert from one to the other, multiply by
Length		
inches and centimeters	2.54 cm = 1 in.	$\dfrac{2.54 \text{ cm}}{1 \text{ in.}}$ or $\dfrac{1 \text{ in.}}{2.54 \text{ cm}}$
feet and meters	1 m = 3.28 ft	$\dfrac{3.28 \text{ ft}}{1 \text{ m}}$ or $\dfrac{1 \text{ m}}{3.28 \text{ ft}}$
miles and kilometers	1.61 km = 1 mi	$\dfrac{1.61 \text{ km}}{1 \text{ mi.}}$ or $\dfrac{1 \text{ mi}}{1.61 \text{ km}}$
Area		
square inches and square centimeters	6.45 cm² = 1 in²	$\dfrac{6.45 \text{ cm}^2}{1 \text{ in}^2}$ or $\dfrac{1 \text{ in}^2}{6.45 \text{ cm}^2}$
square meters and square yards	1.196 yd² = 1 m²	$\dfrac{1.196 \text{ yd}^2}{1 \text{ m}^2}$ or $\dfrac{1 \text{ m}^2}{1.196 \text{ yd}^2}$
acres and hectares	1 ha = 2.47 acres	$\dfrac{2.47 \text{ acres}}{1 \text{ ha}}$ or $\dfrac{1 \text{ ha}}{2.47 \text{ acres}}$
Volume		
cubic inches and milliliters	16.39 mL = 1 in³	$\dfrac{16.39 \text{ mL}}{1 \text{ in}^3}$ or $\dfrac{1 \text{ in}^3}{16.39 \text{ mL}}$
liters and quarts	1.06 qt = 1 liter	$\dfrac{1.06 \text{ qt}}{1 \text{ liter}}$ or $\dfrac{1 \text{ liter}}{1.06 \text{ qt}}$
gallons and liters	3.79 liters = 1 gal	$\dfrac{3.79 \text{ liters}}{1 \text{ gal}}$ or $\dfrac{1 \text{ gal}}{3.79 \text{ liters}}$
Weight		
ounces and grams	28.3 g = 1 oz	$\dfrac{28.3 \text{ g}}{1 \text{ oz}}$ or $\dfrac{1 \text{ oz}}{28.3 \text{ g}}$
kilograms and pounds	2.20 lb = 1 kg	$\dfrac{2.20 \text{ lb}}{1 \text{ kg}}$ or $\dfrac{1 \text{ kg}}{2.20 \text{ lb}}$

7. Convert 8 inches to centimeters.

$$8 \text{ in.} = 8 \text{ in.} \cdot \frac{2.54 \text{ cm}}{1 \text{ in.}}$$
$$= 8 \cdot 2.54 \text{ cm}$$
$$= 20.32 \text{ cm}$$

Temperature [8.4]

Temperature Conversions

To convert from	Formula In symbols
Fahrenheit to Celsius	$C = \dfrac{5(F - 32)}{9}$
Celsius to Fahrenheit	$F = \dfrac{9}{5}C + 32$

8. Convert 120°C to degrees Fahrenheit.

$$F = \frac{9}{5}C + 32$$
$$F = \frac{9}{5}(120) + 32$$
$$F = 216 + 32$$
$$F = 248$$

Time [8.5]

The relationship between	is	To convert from one to the other, multiply by
minutes and seconds	1 min = 60 sec	$\dfrac{1 \text{ min}}{60 \text{ sec}}$ or $\dfrac{60 \text{ sec}}{1 \text{ min}}$
hours and minutes	1 hr = 60 min	$\dfrac{1 \text{ hr}}{60 \text{ min}}$ or $\dfrac{60 \text{ min}}{1 \text{ hr}}$

Use the tables in the chapter to make the following conversions. [8.1, 8.2, 8.3, 8.4]

1. 9 yd to feet

2. 570 m to kilometers

3. 84 inches to feet

4. 10 yards to inches

5. 5.5 yd to inches

6. 6.75 mi to feet

7. 6.2 kilometers to meters

8. 4.7 m to decimeters

9. 2.5 acres to square feet

10. 792 in² to square feet

11. 16.4 L to milliliters

12. 969 m to kilometers

13. 77°F to degrees Celsius

14. 45°C to degrees Fahrenheit

15. 46 T to pounds

16. 136 oz to pounds

17. $5\frac{1}{4}$ lb to ounces

18. 5 kg to grams

19. 990 in² to square feet

20. 7.3 a to square meters

21. 20 yd² to square feet

22. 150 mm² to square centimeters

23. 7 gal to pints

24. 18 pt to quarts

25. 167.4 ft³ to cubic yards

26. 65°C to degrees Fahrenheit

27. 46 mg to g

28. 53 mg to oz

Work the following problems. When necessary, round answers to the nearest hundredth. [8.1, 8.2, 8.3, 8.4]

29. How many gallons are there in a 1.5-liter bottle of cola?

30. Change 15 L to quarts.

31. Change 627 yd to inches.

32. Change 600 m to yards.

33. 5 pints to liters

34. 5 mi to kilometers

35. 10 km to miles

36. 13 L to quarts

37. 50,000 in² to acres

38. 1,000 acres to mi²

39. 2 square miles to acres

40. Change 94 qt to liters.

41. Change 498 ft to meters.

42. How many liters are contained in an 15-quart container?

43. 37 cm to inches

44. 42 mi to kilometers

45. 47 in² to square centimeters

46. 23 ha to acres

47. 57 qt to liters

48. 47 lb to kilograms

49. Change 7 hours 15 minutes to [8.5]
   a. minutes.
   b. hours.

50. Convert 3 gallons 2 quarts to
   a. quarts.
   b. gallons.

51. Add 5 pounds 11 ounces and 10 pounds 7 ounces. [8.5]

52. Add 16 feet 7 inches and 7 feet 9 inches. [8.5]

53. Subtract 5 feet 2 inches from 22 feet 1 inch. [8.5]

54. Subtract 3 hours 47 minutes from 5 hours 33 minutes. [8.5]

55. **Engine Displacement** A motorcycle engine has a volume of 650 mL. What is the volume in cubic feet?

56. **Sewing** 25 square yards of material is how many square meters?

57. **Sewing** 50 square inches of material is how many square yards?

58. **Construction** A 6-square-foot pantry floor is to be tiled using tiles that measure 4 inches by 4 inches. How many tiles will be needed to cover the pantry floor?

59. **Construction** A concert hall measuring 200 feet by 400 feet is to be covered with carpet. How many square yards of carpet will be needed to cover the floor?

60. **Filling an Aquarium** How many 16-fluid ounce glasses of water will it take to fill a 9-gallon aquarium?

61. **Track and Field** A person who runs a mile in 8 minutes has an average speed of 0.125 miles/minute. Convert 0.125 miles/minute to miles/hour. [8.5]

62. **Speed of a Bullet** A bullet from a M1911 handgun used during in World War II had a muzzle velocity of 980 feet/second. Convert 980 feet/second to km/hour. (Round to the nearest whole number.) [8.5]

63. **Speed of a Bullet** A bullet from a machine gun on a B-17 Flying Fortress in World War II had a muzzle speed of 1,750 feet/second. Convert 1,750 feet/second to miles/hour. (Round to the nearest whole number.) [8.5]

64. **Manhattan** The area of Manhattan Island is about 33.8 square miles. Convert this to acres. [8.2]

65. **Santa Cruz** The area of Santa Cruz Island off the California coast is about 61,776 acres. Convert this to square miles. [8.2]

66. **Red Blood Cells** A 5'3" woman weighing 124 pounds has about 214 cubic inches of blood. Convert this volume to cubic feet. Round to the nearest thousandth. [8.2]

67. **Brain Mass** A 4'2" child has a brain mass of about 48 ounces. Convert this to pounds. [8.3]

68. **Cost of Steak** Mike is purchasing eight top sirloin steaks. The meat costs $4.00 per pound, and each steak weighs 1 lb 4 oz. What is the total cost of the steaks? [8.5]

The chart shows the annual sales for the top frozen pizza retailers in the United States. Use the information to answer the following questions.

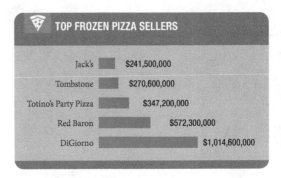

TOP FROZEN PIZZA SELLERS	
Jack's	$241,500,000
Tombstone	$270,600,000
Totino's Party Pizza	$347,200,000
Red Baron	$572,300,000
DiGiorno	$1,014,600,000

69. If there are 12.07 Mexican pesos to 1 U.S. dollar, convert the sales of DiGiorno and Red Baron to pesos.

70. If there are 0.88 euros to the dollar, convert the sales of Jack's and Tombstone to euros.

Simplify.

1.
$$\begin{array}{r} 3,420 \\ 679 \\ + 7,524 \end{array}$$

2.
$$\begin{array}{r} 7,000 \\ - 5,999 \end{array}$$

3. $378 \div 14$

4. $6(3 \cdot 9)$

5. $24\overline{)8,565}$

6. 3^5

7. $16 + 72 \div 2^2$

8. $\dfrac{468}{52}$

9. $17 + 39$

10. $(12 + 6) + (84 - 36)$

11. $\dfrac{60}{4}$

12. $11.5(3.9)$

13. $6.2 + 11.36 + 4.09$

14. $52.6 - 3.82$

15. $3.2\overline{)43.2}$

16. $\left(\dfrac{1}{3}\right)^2 \left(\dfrac{1}{4}\right)^3$

17. $12 \div \left(\dfrac{2}{3}\right)^2$

18. $\dfrac{7}{48} + \dfrac{5}{12}$

19. $\left(15 \div 1\dfrac{2}{3}\right) \div 4$

20. $13 - 4\dfrac{3}{4}$

21. $\dfrac{5}{8}(3.6) - \dfrac{1}{2}(0.3)$

22. $\dfrac{3}{8}(4.8) - \dfrac{1}{4}(2.9)$

23. $14 + \dfrac{7}{13} \div \dfrac{21}{26}$

Solve.

24. $4x = 17$

25. $36 = 8y$

26. $\dfrac{6}{7} = \dfrac{18}{x}$

27. Find the perimeter and area of the figure below.

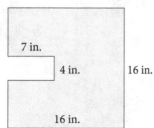

28. Find the perimeter of the figure below.

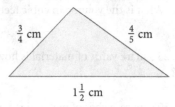

29. Find the difference between 35 and 17.

30. If a car travels 288 miles in $4\dfrac{1}{2}$ hours, what is its rate in miles per hour?

31. What number is 32% of 6,450?

32. Factor 630 into a product of prime factors.

33. Find $\dfrac{3}{5}$ of the product of 15 and 6.

34. If 5,280 feet = 1 mile, convert 8,484 feet to miles. Round to the nearest tenth.

The diagram shows the number of viewers who watched different prime time shows during one week. Use the information to answer the following questions. Round to the nearest hundredth if necessary.

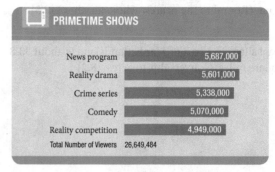

PRIMETIME SHOWS	
News program	5,687,000
Reality drama	5,601,000
Crime series	5,338,000
Comedy	5,070,000
Reality competition	4,949,000
Total Number of Viewers	26,649,484

35. Of the viewers who watched these shows, what percentage watched a news program?

36. Of the viewers who watched these shows, what percentage watched the two reality shows?

Use the tables in the chapter to make the following conversions. [8.1, 8.2, 8.3, 8.4]

1. 3 yd to feet

2. 640 m to kilometers

3. 4 acres to square feet

4. 864 in² to square feet

5. 12 L to milliliters

6. 3 mi to kilometers

7. 8 L to quarts

8. 90°F to degrees Celsius (round to the nearest tenth.)

9. 2.6 T to pounds

10. 112 oz to pounds

11. 648 in² to square feet

12. 6.3 a to square meters

13. 116.1 ft³ to cubic yards

14. 20°C to degrees Fahrenheit

Work the following problems. Round answers to the nearest hundredth. [8.1, 8.2, 8.3, 8.4]

15. How many gallons are there in a 2-liter bottle of cola?

16. Change 362 yd to inches.

17. A car engine has a volume of 376 in³. What is the volume in cubic feet?

18. Change 65 qt to liters.

19. Change 375 ft to meters.

20. How many liters are contained in an 11-quart container?

21. 27 cm to inches

22. 9 mi to kilometers

23. 29 in² to square centimeters

24. 17 ha to acres

25. 36 qt to liters

26. 23 lb to kilograms

27. Construction A 30-square-foot pantry floor is to be tiled using tiles that measure 6 inches by 6 inches. How many tiles will be needed to cover the pantry floor?

28. Filling an Aquarium How many 8-fluid ounce glasses of water will it take to fill a 12-gallon aquarium?

29. Change 2 hours 45 minutes to [8.5]
  a. minutes.
  b. hours.

30. Add 4 pounds 9 ounces and 2 pounds 7 ounces. [8.5]

The chart shows the amount of caffeine in different kinds of soda, measured in milligrams. Use the information to make the following conversions.

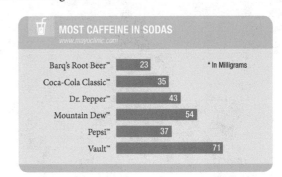

MOST CAFFEINE IN SODAS
www.mayoclinic.com

	* In Milligrams
Barq's Root Beer™	23
Coca-Cola Classic™	35
Dr. Pepper™	43
Mountain Dew™	54
Pepsi™	37
Vault™	71

31. Convert the amount of caffeine found in all the sodas to grams.

32. Convert the amount of caffeine found in all the sodas to ounces.

EXPONENTS AND POLYNOMIALS

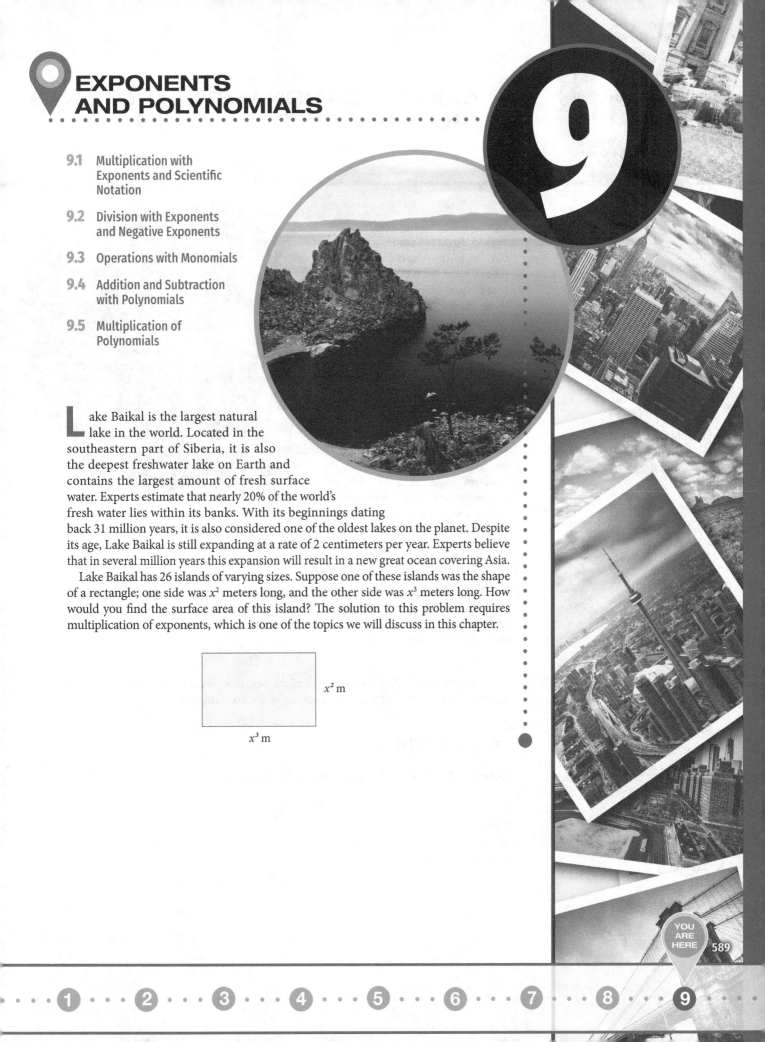

L ake Baikal is the largest natural lake in the world. Located in the southeastern part of Siberia, it is also the deepest freshwater lake on Earth and contains the largest amount of fresh surface water. Experts estimate that nearly 20% of the world's fresh water lies within its banks. With its beginnings dating back 31 million years, it is also considered one of the oldest lakes on the planet. Despite its age, Lake Baikal is still expanding at a rate of 2 centimeters per year. Experts believe that in several million years this expansion will result in a new great ocean covering Asia.

Lake Baikal has 26 islands of varying sizes. Suppose one of these islands was the shape of a rectangle; one side was x^2 meters long, and the other side was x^3 meters long. How would you find the surface area of this island? The solution to this problem requires multiplication of exponents, which is one of the topics we will discuss in this chapter.

x^2 m

x^3 m

9.1

MULTIPLICATION WITH EXPONENTS AND SCIENTIFIC NOTATION

• • • OBJECTIVES • • •

A Evaluate exponent expressions.

B Simplify exponent expressions using the product property.

C Simplify exponent expressions using the power property.

D Simplify exponent expressions using the distributive property.

E Write numbers greater than 10 in scientific notation and exponaded form.

• • • KEY WORDS • • •

product property of exponents

power property of exponents

distributive property of exponents

volume

rectangular solid

scientific notation

Practice Problems

1. Simplify.

a. 5^3

b. -2^4

c. $(-3)^4$

d. $\left(-\frac{2}{3}\right)^2$

Answers

1. a. 125 **b.** -16 **c.** 81 **d.** $\frac{4}{9}$

During a hike up Bishop's Peak in San Luis Obispo, CA, a thirty-year-old hiker's heart beat 145 times per minute. If he hiked up the mountain and back down again in 4.5 hours, his heart beats approximately 39,150 times. In this section, we will learn how to write this large number in scientific notation. For instance, 39,150 can be written as 3.915×10^4. But first, we must learn to evaluate exponents and work with properties of exponents to further understand their meaning in this notation.

A Evaluating Exponents

Recall that an **exponent** is a number written just above and to the right of another number, which is called the **base.** In the expression 5^2, for example, the exponent is 2 and the base is 5. the expression 5^2 is read "5 to the second power" or "5 squared." The meaning of the expression is

$$5^2 = 5 \cdot 5 = 25$$

In the expression 5^3, the exponent is 3 and the base is 5. The expression 5^3 is read "5 to the third power" or "5 cubed." The meaning of the expression is

$$5^3 = 5 \cdot 5 \cdot 5 = 125$$

Here are some further examples:

Example 1   Write each expression as a single number.

a. 4^3 **b.** -3^4 **c.** $(-2)^5$ **d.** $\left(-\frac{3}{4}\right)^2$

Solution

a. $4^3 = 4 \cdot 4 \cdot 4 = 16 \cdot 4 = 64$ Exponent 3, base 4

b. $-3^4 = -3 \cdot 3 \cdot 3 \cdot 3 = -81$ Exponent 4, base 3

c. $(-2)^5 = (-2)(-2)(-2)(-2)(-2) = -32$ Exponent 5, base -2

d. $\left(-\frac{3}{4}\right)^2 = \left(-\frac{3}{4}\right)\left(-\frac{3}{4}\right) = \frac{9}{16}$ Exponent 2, base $-\frac{3}{4}$

VIDEO EXAMPLES

SECTION 9.1

Earlier in this text we discussed the difference between $(-5)^2$ and -5^2. Recall, $(-5)^2 = -5 \cdot -5 = 25$ because the base, -5, is squared. On the other hand, -5^2 is the opposite of 5^2 or $-(5 \cdot 5)$, which is -25.

We can simplify our work with exponents by developing some properties of exponents. We want to list the things we know are true about exponents and then use these properties to simplify expressions that contain exponents.

B Product Property of Exponents

The first property of exponents applies to products with the same base. We can use the definition of exponents, as indicating repeated multiplication, to simplify expressions like $7^4 \cdot 7^2$.

$$7^4 \cdot 7^2 = (7 \cdot 7 \cdot 7 \cdot 7)(7 \cdot 7)$$
$$= (7 \cdot 7 \cdot 7 \cdot 7 \cdot 7 \cdot 7)$$
$$= 7^6 \qquad \text{Note: } 4 + 2 = 6$$

As you can see, multiplication with the same base resulted in addition of exponents. This is true for every base. We can summarize this result with the following property.

PROPERTY **Product Property of Exponents**

If a is any real number and r and s are integers, then

$$a^r \cdot a^s = a^{r+s}$$

In words: To multiply two expressions with the same base, add exponents and use the common base.

Here is an example using the product property.

Example 2 Use the product property to simplify the following expressions. Leave your answers in terms of exponents.

a. $5^3 \cdot 5^6$ **b.** $x^7 \cdot x^8$ **c.** $3^4 \cdot 3^8 \cdot 3^5$

Solution

a. $5^3 \cdot 5^6 = 5^{3+6} = 5^9$

b. $x^7 \cdot x^8 = x^{7+8} = x^{15}$

c. $3^4 \cdot 3^8 \cdot 3^5 = 3^{4+8+5} = 3^{17}$

2. Simplify, leaving your answers in terms of exponents.
   a. $5^4 \cdot 5^5$
   b. $x^3 \cdot x^7$
   c. $4^5 \cdot 4^2 \cdot 4^6$

Note In Example 2, notice that each base in the original problem is the same base that appears in the answer and that it is written only once in the answer. A very common mistake when using the product property is to write a 2 in front of the base in the answer. For example, people making this mistake would get $2x^{15}$ or $(2x)^{15}$ as the result in Example 2b. To avoid this mistake, it's important to understand the meaning of the product property exactly as it is written.

C Power Property of Exponents

Another common type of expression involving exponents is one in which an expression containing an exponent is raised to another power. The expression $(5^3)^2$ is an example.

$$(5^3)^2 = (5^3)(5^3)$$
$$= 5^{3+3}$$
$$= 5^6 \qquad \text{Note: } 3 \cdot 2 = 6$$

As you can see, the resulting exponent is the product of the original powers, as summarized in the following property.

Answers
2. **a.** 5^9 **b.** x^{10} **c.** 4^{13}

3. Simplify.
  a. $(3^4)^5$
  b. $(x^7)^2$

PROPERTY   Power Property of Exponents

If a is any real number and r and s are integers, then

$$(a^r)^s = a^{r \cdot s}$$

In words: A power raised to another power is the base raised to the product of the powers.

Example 3   Simplify the following expressions:

a. $(4^5)^6$ **b.** $(x^3)^5$

Solution

a. $(4^5)^6 = 4^{5 \cdot 6} = 4^{30}$

b. $(x^3)^5 = x^{3 \cdot 5} = x^{15}$

D Distributive Property of Exponents

The third property of exponents applies to expressions in which the product of two or more numbers or variables is raised to a power. Let's look at how the expression $(2x)^3$ can be simplified:

$$(2x)^3 = (2x)(2x)(2x)$$

$$= (2 \cdot 2 \cdot 2)(x \cdot x \cdot x)$$

$$= 2^3 \cdot x^3$$

$$= 8x^3$$

From this example, we can see the exponent 3 distributes over the product $2x$. We can generalize this result into a third property of exponents.

Note   A common mistake when using this property is to not distribute the exponent to both parts of the base as in

$$(2x)^3 \neq 2x^3$$

Be careful to follow the property correctly, as we have shown here.

PROPERTY   Distributive Property of Exponents

If a and b are any two real numbers and r is an integer, then

$$(ab)^r = a^r b^r$$

In words: The power of a product is the product of each factor to the power.

Here are some examples using the distributive property of exponents to simplify expressions.

4. Simplify.

  a. $\left(-\dfrac{1}{3}x^3y^5\right)^2$

  b. $(x^5)^2(x^4)^3$

  c. $(3y)^2(2y^3)$

  d. $(3x^3y^2)^2(2xy^4)^3$

Example 4   Simplify the following expressions:

a. $\left(-\dfrac{1}{4}x^4y^3\right)^2$ **b.** $(x^4)^3(x^2)^5$ **c.** $(2y)^3(3y^2)$ **d.** $(2x^2y^5)^3(3x^4y)^2$

Solution

a. $\left(-\dfrac{1}{4}x^4y^3\right)^2 = \left(-\dfrac{1}{4}\right)^2(x^4)^2(y^3)^2$ Distributive property of exponents

$$= \dfrac{1}{16}x^8y^6$$ Power property of exponents

b. $(x^4)^3(x^2)^5 = x^{12} \cdot x^{10}$ Power property of exponents

$$= x^{22}$$ Product property of exponents

c. $(2y)^3(3y^2) = 2^3y^3(3y^2)$ *Distributive property of exponents*

              $= 8 \cdot 3(y^3 \cdot y^2)$ *Commutative and associative properties*

              $= 24y^5$ *Product property of exponents*

d. $(2x^2y^5)^3(3x^4y)^2 = 2^3(x^2)^3(\,y^5)^3 \cdot 3^2(x^4)^2y^2$ *Distributive property of exponents*

              $= 8x^6y^{15} \cdot 9x^8y^2$ *Power property of exponents*

              $= 8 \cdot 9(x^6x^8)(\,y^{15}y^2)$ *Commutative and associative properties*

              $= 72x^{14}y^{17}$ *Product property of exponents*

⬤ FACTS FROM GEOMETRY

Volume of a Rectangular Solid

By looking at the figure below, we can see why "five squared" is associated with 5^2. This is because of its relation to finding the area of a square with side length 5 units.

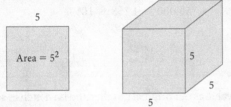

FIGURE 1   FIGURE 2

To see why the phrase "five cubed" is associated with the expression 5^3, we have to find the **volume** of a cube for which all three dimensions are 5 units long. The volume of a cube is a measure of the space occupied by the cube. To calculate the volume of the cube shown in Figure 2, we multiply the three dimensions together to get $5 \cdot 5 \cdot 5 = 5^3$.

    The cube shown in Figure 2 is a special case of a general category of three dimensional geometric figures called **rectangular solids.** Rectangular solids have rectangles for sides, and all connecting sides meet at right angles. The three dimensions are length, width, and height. To find the volume of a rectangular solid, we find the product of the three dimensions, as shown in Figure 2.

> *Note*   If we include units with the dimensions of the diagrams, then the units for the area will be square units and the units for volume will be cubic units.
>
> If a square has a side 5 inches long, then its area will be
>
> $A = (5 \text{ inches})^2 = 25 \text{ inches}^2$
>
> where the unit inches^2 stands for square inches.
>
> If a cube has a single side 5 inches long, then its volume will be $V = (5 \text{ inches})^3 = 125 \text{ inches}^3$ where the unit inches^3 stands for cubic inches.
>
> The volume of a rectangular solid is found by multiplying the length, width, and height. If a rectangular solid has a length of 5 inches, a width of 4 inches, and a height of 3 inches, then its volume is
>
> $V = (5 \text{ in})(4 \text{ in})(3 \text{ in})$
> $= 60 \text{ inches}^3$

E Scientific Notation for Large Numbers

Many branches of science require working with very large numbers. In astronomy, for example, distances commonly are given in light-years. A light-year is the distance light travels in a year. It is approximately 5,880,000,000,000 miles. This number is difficult to use in calculations because of the number of zeros it contains. Scientific notation provides a way of writing very large numbers in a more manageable form.

DEFINITION   scientific notation

A number is in **scientific notation** when it is written as the product of a number and an integer power of 10. A number written in scientific notation has the form

$$n \times 10^r$$

where $1 \le |n| < 10$ and r is an integer.

> *Note*   When we say
>
> $1 \le |n| < 10$
>
> this means that n must be between -1 and -10 or between 1 and 10. The number can be 1 or -1 but cannot be 10 or -10. In symbols,
>
> $-10 < n \le -1$
>
> or
>
> $1 \le n < 10$

5. Write 4,810,000 in scientific notation.

Example 5   Write 376,000 in scientific notation.

Solution We must rewrite 376,000 as the product of a number n and a power of 10 where $1 \le |n| < 10$. To do so, we move the decimal point 5 places to the left so that it appears between the 3 and the 7, giving us 3.76. Then we multiply this number by 10^5. The number that results has the same value as our original number and is written in scientific notation.

$$376,000 = 3.76 \times 10^5$$

Moved 5 places.
Decimal point was originally here.
Keeps track of the 5 places we moved the decimal point.

6. Write 5,473,000 in scientific notation.

Example 6   Write 4,758,000 in scientific notation.

Solution As with the previous example, we must move the decimal to the left but in this case, we move it 6 places. It now appears between the 4 and the 7, giving us 4.758. We multiply our result by 10^6.

$$4,758,000 = 4.758 \times 10^6$$

Moved 6 places.
Decimal point was originally here.
Keeps track of the 6 places we moved the decimal point.

Our answer has the same value as our original number and is written in scientific notation.

7. Write 3.05×10^5 in expanded form.

Example 7   Write 4.52×10^3 in expanded form.

Solution Since 10^3 is 1,000, we can think of this as simply a multiplication problem; that is,

$$4.52 \times 10^3 = 4.52 \times 1,000 = 4,520$$

On the other hand, we can think of the exponent 3 as indicating the number of places we need to move the decimal point to write our number in expanded form. Since our exponent is positive 3, we move the decimal point three places to the right.

$$4.52 \times 10^3 = 4,520$$

In the next section, we will see how a negative power of 10 affects our answers in scientific notation.

 KEY CONCEPT REVIEW

After reading through the preceding section, respond in your own words and in complete sentences.

A. Explain the difference between -5^2 and $(-5)^2$.

B. How do you multiply two expressions containing exponents when they each have the same base?

C. Explain in words how you would use the product property and the distributive property of exponents to simplify $(2x^3)^2$.

D. How would you write 5,190,000 in scientific notation?

Answers

5. 4.81×10^6

6. 5.473×10^6

7. 305,000

VOCABULARY REVIEW ·

Choose the correct words to fill in the blanks below.

power   distributive   scientific notation
exponent   product   base

1. In the expression 7^3, the 7 is called the _____ and the 3 is called the _____ .

2. The _____ property for exponents states that you should add exponents and use the common base to multiply two expressions with the same base.

3. The _____ property for exponents states that a power raised to another power is the base raised to the product of the powers.

4. The _____ property for exponents states that if a product is raised to a power then the result is the product of each factor raised to that same power.

5. _____ is a way of writing very large numbers that is more manageable and takes the form $n \times 10^r$.

Problems

A Name the base and exponent in each of the following expressions. Then use the definition of exponents as repeated multiplication to simplify.

1. 4^2 **2.** 6^2 **3.** $(0.3)^2$ **4.** $(0.03)^2$ **5.** 4^3

6. 10^3 **7.** $(-5)^2$ **8.** -5^2 **9.** -2^3 **10.** $(-2)^3$

11. 3^4 **12.** $(-3)^4$ **13.** $\left(\dfrac{2}{3}\right)^2$ **14.** $\left(\dfrac{2}{3}\right)^3$ **15.** $\left(\dfrac{1}{2}\right)^4$

16. $\left(\dfrac{4}{5}\right)^2$ **17.** $\left(-\dfrac{3}{4}\right)^2$ **18.** $\left(-\dfrac{2}{3}\right)^4$ **19.** $\left(-\dfrac{1}{6}\right)^2$ **20.** $\left(-\dfrac{1}{9}\right)^2$

21. a. Complete the following table.

Number x	1	2	3	4	5	6	7
Square x^2							

b. Using the results of part a, fill in the blank in the following statement: For numbers larger than 1, the square of the number is _____ than the number.

22. a. Complete the following table.

Number x	$\dfrac{1}{2}$	$\dfrac{1}{3}$	$\dfrac{1}{4}$	$\dfrac{1}{5}$	$\dfrac{1}{6}$	$\dfrac{1}{7}$	$\dfrac{1}{8}$
Square x^2							

b. Using the results of part a, fill in the blank in the following statement: For numbers between 0 and 1, the square of the number is _____ than the number.

B Use the product property of exponents to simplify the following expressions.

23. $x^4 \cdot x^5$

24. $x^7 \cdot x^3$

25. $y^{10} \cdot y^{20}$

26. $y^{30} \cdot y^{30}$

27. $2^5 \cdot 2^4 \cdot 2^3$

28. $4^2 \cdot 4^3 \cdot 4^4$

29. $x^4 \cdot x^6 \cdot x^8 \cdot x^{10}$

30. $x^{20} \cdot x^{18} \cdot x^{16} \cdot x^{14}$

C Use the power property of exponents to write each of the following problems with a single exponent. (Assume all variables are positive numbers.)

31. $(x^2)^5$

32. $(x^5)^2$

33. $(5^4)^3$

34. $(5^3)^4$

35. $(y^3)^3$

36. $(y^7)^2$

37. $(2^5)^{10}$

38. $(10^5)^2$

39. $(a^3)^x$

40. $(a^5)^x$

41. $(b^x)^y$

42. $(b^r)^s$

D Use the distributive property of exponents to simplify each of the following expressions.

43. $(4x)^2$

44. $(2x)^4$

45. $(2y)^5$

46. $(5y)^2$

47. $(-3x)^4$

48. $(-3x)^3$

49. $(0.5ab)^2$

50. $(0.4ab)^2$

51. $(4xyz)^3$

52. $(5xyz)^3$

53. $(-4xy)^3$

54. $(-3xy)^4$

Simplify the following expressions by using the properties of exponents.

55. $(2x^4)^3$

56. $(3x^5)^2$

57. $(4a^3)^2$

58. $(5a^2)^2$

59. $(x^2)^3(x^4)^2$

60. $(x^5)^2(x^3)^5$

61. $(a^3)^1(a^2)^4$

62. $(a^4)^1(a^1)^3$

63. $(2x)^3(2x)^4$

64. $(3x)^2(3x)^3$

65. $(3x^2)^3(2x)^4$

66. $(3x)^3(2x^3)^2$

67. $(4x^2y^3)^2$

68. $(9x^3y^5)^2$

69. $\left(\dfrac{2}{3}a^4b^5\right)^3$

70. $\left(\dfrac{3}{4}ab^7\right)^3$

E Write each number in scientific notation.

71. 43,200

72. 432,000

73. 570

74. 5,700

75. 238,000

76. 2,380,000

77. 10,000,000,000

78. 20

Write each number in expanded form.

79. 2.49×10^3

80. 2.49×10^4

81. 3.52×10^2

82. 3.52×10^5

83. 2.8×10^4

84. 2.8×10^3

85. -3.1×10^5

86. -4.2×10^6

Applying the Concepts

87. Complete the following table, and then construct a graph of the information in the table.

Number x	-3	-2	-1	0	1	2	3
Square x^2							

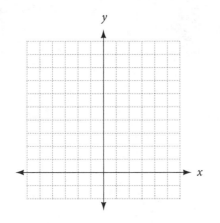

88. Complete the table, and then construct a graph of the information in the table.

Number x	-3	-2	-1	0	1	2	3
Cube x^3							

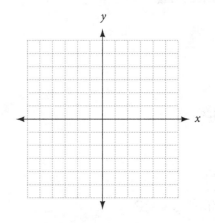

89. Complete the table. When you are finished, notice how the points in this table could be used to refine the graph you created in Problem 87.

Number x	-2.5	-1.5	-0.5	0	0.5	1.5	2.5
Square x^2							

90. Complete the following table. When you are finished, notice that this table contains exactly the same entries as the table from Problem 87. This table uses fractions, whereas the table from Problem 87 uses decimals.

Number x	$-\frac{5}{2}$	$-\frac{3}{2}$	$-\frac{1}{2}$	0	$\frac{1}{2}$	$\frac{3}{2}$	$\frac{5}{2}$
Square x^2							

91. The five largest lakes in the world (by area) are listed below in the table. Complete the table by writing each area in scientific notation. Round your answer to two decimal places.

Name	Location	Area (sq. mi.)	Scientific Notation
Caspian Sea	5 countries	152,239	
Superior	US, Canada	31,820	
Victoria	Tanzania, Uganda	26,828	
Huron	US, Canada	23,010	
Michigan	US	22,400	

92. The table below lists the five outer planets (from Earth), and their average distance to Earth in miles. Write each distance in scientific notation. Round your answer to two decimal places.

Planet	Average Distance	Scientific Notation
Mars	48.60 million	
Jupiter	390.60 million	
Saturn	777.00 million	
Uranus	1.69 billion	
Neptune	2.70 billion	

93. **Volume of a Cube** Find the volume of a cube if each side is 3 inches long.

94. **Volume of a Cube** Find the volume of a cube if each side is 3 feet long.

95. **Volume of a Cube** A bottle of perfume is packaged in a box that is in the shape of a cube. Find the volume of the box if each side is 2.5 inches long. Round to the nearest tenth.

96. **Volume of a Cube** A television set is packaged in a box that is in the shape of a cube. Find the volume of the box if each side is 18 inches long.

In Chapter 5 we said $\sqrt{x^2}$ is x because $x \cdot x = x^2$. Now we can say $\sqrt{x^6} = x^3$ because $x^3 \cdot x^3 = x^6$. Using this concept, simplify each of the following.

97. $\sqrt{x^{20}}$

98. $\sqrt{x^{16}}$

99. $\sqrt{20x^3y^3}$

100. $\sqrt{72x^5y^3}$

101. $7\sqrt{18x^3} - 3\sqrt{50x^3}$

102. $8\sqrt{48x^3} + 2\sqrt{12x^3}$

103. Age in seconds If you are 21 years old, you have been alive for more than 650,000,000 seconds. Write the number of seconds in scientific notation.

104. Distance Around Earth The distance around Earth at the equator is more than 130,000,000 feet. Write the number of feet in scientific notation.

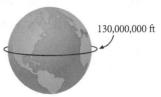

130,000,000 ft

105. Lifetime Earnings If you earn at least $12 an hour and work full-time for 30 years, you will make at least 7.4×10^5 dollars. Write your total earnings in expanded form.

106. Heart Beats per Year If your pulse is 72, then in one year your heart will beat at least 3.78×10^7 times. Write the number of heart beats in expanded form.

107. Investing If you put $1,000 into a savings account every year from the time you are 25 years old until you are 55 years old, you will have more than 1.8×10^5 dollars in the account when you reach 55 years of age (assuming 10% annual interest). Write 1.8×10^5 in expanded form.

108. Investing If you put $20 into a savings account every month from the time you are 20 years old until you are 30 years old, you will have more than 3.27×10^3 dollars in the account when you reach 30 years of age (assuming 6% annual interest compounded monthly). Write 3.27×10^3 in expanded form.

109. Investing The value of an investment of $8,000 growing at 7% per year is given by the formula $V = 8000(1.07)^t$, where t represents the number of years the money is invested. Find the value of the investment after 20 years.

110. Investing The value on an investment of $15,000 growing at 5% per year is given by the formula $V = 15000(1.05)^t$, where t represents the number of years the money is invested. Find the value of this investment after 25 years.

Displacement The displacement, or volume, in cubic inches, of a car engine is given by the formula

$$d = \pi \cdot s \cdot c \cdot \left(\frac{1}{2} \cdot b \right)^2$$

where s is the stroke, b is the bore, and c is the number of cylinders. (Note: The bore is the diameter of a cylinder in a piston engine and the stroke is the distance the cylinder travels.)

Calculate the engine displacement for each of the following cars. Use 3.14 to approximate π and round to the nearest cubic inch.

111. Ferrari Modena 8 cylinders, 3.35 inches of bore, 3.11 inches of stroke

112. Audi A8 8 cylinders, 3.32 inches of bore, 3.66 inches of stroke

113. Mitsubishi Eclipse 6 cylinders, 3.59 inches of bore, 2.99 inches of stroke

114. Porsche 911 GT3 6 cylinders, 3.94 inches of bore, 3.01 inches of stroke

Getting Ready for the Next Section

Subtract.

115. $4 - 7$

116. $-4 - 7$

117. $4 - (-7)$

118. $-4 - (-7)$

119. $15 - 20$

120. $15 - (-20)$

121. $-15 - (-20)$

122. $-15 - 20$

Simplify each expression.

123. $2(3) - 4$

124. $5(3) - 10$

125. $4(3) - 3(2)$

126. $-8 - 2(3)$

127. $2(5 - 3)$

128. $2(3) - 4 - 3(-4)$

129. $5 + 4(-2) - 2(-3)$

130. $2(3) + 4(5) - 5(2)$

FIND THE MISTAKE •

Each sentence below contains a mistake. Circle the mistake and write the correct word(s) or numbers(s) on the line provided.

1. Simplifying the expression $\left(-\frac{12}{32}\right)^3$ will give a positive answer. _____

2. You would use the distributive property for exponents to simplify the expression $x^8 \cdot x^4 \cdot x^{10}$.
_____

3. To simplify the expression $(x^3 \cdot y)^4 (y \cdot z^2)^8$, we must first use the power property of exponents.
_____

4. 5.83×10^5 in an example of a number written in expanded form. _____

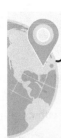

Navigation Skills

It's not uncommon for an instructor to give a final exam at the end of a course. Sometimes this test is cumulative, meaning it covers all of the content in the class, and sometimes it just covers a portion of the material. In either case, preparing for an exam is different from preparing for a unit or chapter test. Here are some suggestions for preparing for this kind of assessment:

- Make a study plan. Decide if you are going to study from your old tests and assignments or if your instructor is going provide a review.
- Start studying early and break your study time up into smaller increments. Because it usually takes longer to study for a final exam, this technique will make studying for this type of exam less challenging. Also, this will allow for time to contact your instructor with any questions that you may have.
- Keep a list of topics that you need to review more than once so that you can come back to them in the days leading up to the exam. You want these topics to be fresh in your mind.
- Make a practice test. In this book, you can use the cumulative reviews in each chapter to review material and create your own practice test.

NEGATIVE EXPONENTS

Imagine you are a sculpture artist specializing in glass blowing. Your most demanded pieces are multicolored glass balls used as Christmas ornaments or sun-catchers hung in windows. Each glass ball fits into a cube-shaped box with a side of x inches long. Suppose you need to figure out how many small cube-shaped boxes will fit into a larger shipping box, also shaped like a cube but with a side of $5x$ inches long. First, you would need to find the volume of each box.

Volume for the smaller box: $x \cdot x \cdot x = x^3$
Volume for the larger box: $5x \cdot 5x \cdot 5x = (5x)^3$

To find how many smaller boxes fit in the larger box, we use division.

$$\frac{(5x)^3}{x^3}$$

In this section, we will learn a property of exponents under division that will help us simplify this problem.

Previously, we found that multiplication with the same base results in addition of exponents; that is, $a^r \cdot a^s = a^{r+s}$. Since division is the inverse operation of multiplication, we can expect division with the same base to result in subtraction of exponents.

A Negative Exponents

To develop the properties for exponents under division, we again apply the definition of exponents.

$$\frac{x^5}{x^3} = \frac{x \cdot x \cdot x \cdot x \cdot x}{x \cdot x \cdot x} \qquad \text{Definition of exponents}$$

$$= \frac{x \cdot x \cdot x \cdot x \cdot x}{x \cdot x \cdot x} \qquad \text{Cancel common factors.}$$

$$= x^2 \qquad \text{Simplify.}$$

Notice, $5 - 3 = 2$.

OBJECTIVES

A Convert from negative to positive exponents.

B Simplify expressions using the quotient property of exponents.

C Simplify expressions using the distributive property of exponents.

D Simplify expressions involving exponents of 0 and 1.

E Simplify expressions using combinations of the properties of exponents.

F Write numbers in scientific notation and expanded form using negative exponents.

KEY WORDS

negative exponent property

quotient property of exponents

expanded distributive property of exponents

VIDEO EXAMPLES

SECTION 9.2

$$\frac{2^4}{2^7} = \frac{2 \cdot 2 \cdot 2 \cdot 2}{2 \cdot 2 \cdot 2 \cdot 2 \cdot 2 \cdot 2 \cdot 2}$$ *Definition of exponents*

$$= \frac{2 \cdot 2 \cdot 2 \cdot 2}{2 \cdot 2 \cdot 2 \cdot 2 \cdot 2 \cdot 2 \cdot 2}$$ *Cancel common factors.*

$$= \frac{1}{2^3}$$ *Simplify.*

Notice, $7 - 4 = 3$.

In both cases, division with the same base resulted in subtraction of the smaller exponent from the larger. The problem is deciding whether the answer is a fraction. The problem is resolved easily by the following property.

PROPERTY Negative Exponent Property

If r is a positive integer, then $a^{-r} = \dfrac{1}{a^r} = \left(\dfrac{1}{a}\right)^r$ where $(a \neq 0)$.

The following examples illustrate how we use this property to simplify expressions that contain negative exponents.

Example 1 Write each expression with a positive exponent and then simplify.

a. 2^{-3} **b.** 5^{-2} **c.** $3x^{-6}$ **d.** $(4x)^{-3}$

Solution

a. $2^{-3} = \dfrac{1}{2^3} = \dfrac{1}{8}$ *Note: Negative exponents do not indicate negative numbers. they indicate reciprocals.*

b. $5^{-2} = \dfrac{1}{5^2} = \dfrac{1}{25}$

c. $3x^{-6} = 3 \cdot \dfrac{1}{x^6} = \dfrac{3}{x^6}$ *Note: Be careful not to apply the negative exponents to the 3.*

d. $(4x)^{-3} = 4^{-3}x^{-3} = \dfrac{1}{4^3x^3} = \dfrac{1}{64x^3}$

B Quotient Property of Exponents

Now let us look back to our original problem and try to work it again with the help of a negative exponent. We know that $\frac{2^4}{2^7} = \frac{1}{2^3}$. Let us decide now that with division of the same base, we will always subtract the exponent in the denominator from the exponent in the numerator and see if this conflicts with what we know is true.

$$\frac{2^4}{2^7} = 2^{4-7}$$ *Subtract the bottom exponent from the top exponent.*

$$= 2^{-3}$$ *Subtract.*

$$= \frac{1}{2^3}$$ *Definition of negative exponents*

Subtracting the exponent in the denominator from the exponent in the numerator and then using the negative exponent property gives us the same result we obtained previously. We can now continue the list of properties of exponents we started in the previous section.

PROPERTY **Quotient Property of Exponents**

If a is any real number and r and s are integers, then

$$\frac{a^r}{a^s} = a^{r-s} \qquad (a \neq 0)$$

In words: To divide with the same base, subtract the exponent in the denominator from the exponent in the numerator and raise the base to the exponent that results.

The following examples show how we use the quotient property of exponents and the negative exponent property to simplify expressions involving division.

Example 2 Simplify the following expressions. Write all answers using positive exponents.

a. $\dfrac{x^9}{x^6}$ **b.** $\dfrac{x^4}{x^{10}}$ **c.** $\dfrac{2^{15}}{2^{20}}$

Solution In each case, we subtract the exponent in the denominator from the exponent in the numerator.

a. $\dfrac{x^9}{x^6} = x^{9-6} = x^3$

b. $\dfrac{x^4}{x^{10}} = x^{4-10} = x^{-6} = \dfrac{1}{x^6}$

c. $\dfrac{2^{15}}{2^{20}} = 2^{15-20} = 2^{-5} = \dfrac{1}{2^5} = \dfrac{1}{32}$

2. Simplify each expression.

a. $\dfrac{x^{10}}{x^4}$

b. $\dfrac{x^5}{x^7}$

c. $\dfrac{2^{21}}{2^{25}}$

C Expanded Distributive Property of Exponents

Our final property of exponents is similar to the distributive property of exponents, but it involves division instead of multiplication. After we have stated the property, we will give a proof of it. The proof shows why this property is true.

PROPERTY **Expanded Distributive Property of Exponents**

If a and b are any two real numbers ($b \neq 0$) and r is an integer, then

$$\left(\frac{a}{b}\right)^r = \frac{a^r}{b^r}$$

In words: A quotient raised to a power is the quotient of each term raised to that power.

> **Note** This property may also lead to division by zero (undefined) if a is zero and r is less than zero.

In mathematics we use proofs to show why properties are valid. Here is the proof of this property.

$$\left(\frac{a}{b}\right)^r = \left(a \cdot \frac{1}{b}\right)^r \qquad \text{Definition of division}$$

$$= a^r \cdot \left(\frac{1}{b}\right)^r \qquad \text{Distributive property of exponents}$$

$$= a^r \cdot b^{-r} \qquad \text{Negative exponent property}$$

$$= a^r \cdot \frac{1}{b^r} \qquad \text{Negative exponent property}$$

$$= \frac{a^r}{b^r} \qquad \text{Multiply.}$$

3. Simplify each expression.

  a. $\left(\dfrac{x}{5}\right)^2$

  b. $\left(\dfrac{2}{a}\right)^3$

  c. $\left(\dfrac{3}{4}\right)^3$

Example 3   Simplify the following expressions:

  a. $\left(\dfrac{x}{2}\right)^3$ **b.** $\left(\dfrac{5}{y}\right)^2$ **c.** $\left(\dfrac{2}{3}\right)^4$

Solution

  a. $\left(\dfrac{x}{2}\right)^3 = \dfrac{x^3}{2^3} = \dfrac{x^3}{8}$

  b. $\left(\dfrac{5}{y}\right)^2 = \dfrac{5^2}{y^2} = \dfrac{25}{y^2}$

  c. $\left(\dfrac{2}{3}\right)^4 = \dfrac{2^4}{3^4} = \dfrac{16}{81}$

D   Zero and One as Exponents

Recall the definition of 0 and 1 as exponents from Chapter 1. We will review the concept here and justify why we use them as defined.

To obtain an expression for x^1, we will solve a problem two different ways:

$$\dfrac{x^3}{x^2} = \dfrac{x \cdot x \cdot x}{x \cdot x} = x$$

$$\dfrac{x^3}{x^2} = x^{3-2} = x^1$$

Hence $x^1 = x$.

Stated generally, this rule says that $a^1 = a$. This seems reasonable and we will use it since it is consistent with our property of division using the same base.

We use the same procedure to obtain an expression for x^0

$$\dfrac{5^2}{5^2} = \dfrac{25}{25} = 1$$

$$\dfrac{5^2}{5^2} = 5^{2-2} = 5^0$$

Hence $5^0 = 1$.

It seems, therefore, that the best definition of x^0 is 1 for all bases x except $x = 0$. In the case of $x = 0$, we have 0^0, which we will not define. This definition will probably seem awkward at first. Most people would like to define x^0 as 0 when they first encounter it. Remember, the zero in this expression is an exponent, so x^0 does not mean to multiply by zero. Thus, we can make the general statement that $a^0 = 1$ for all real numbers except $a = 0$.

Here are some examples involving the exponents 0 and 1.

4. Simplify each expression.

  a. 10^0

  b. 10^1

  c. $6^1 + 6^0$

  d. $(3x^5y^2)^0$

Example 4   Simplify the following expressions.

  a. 8^0 **b.** 8^1 **c.** $4^0 + 4^1$ **d.** $(2x^2y)^0$

Solution

  a. $8^0 = 1$

  b. $8^1 = 8$

  c. $4^0 + 4^1 = 1 + 4 = 5$

  d. $(2x^2y)^0 = 1$

E Combinations of Properties

Here is a summary of the definitions and properties of exponents we have developed so far. For each definition or property in the list, a and b are real numbers, and r and s are integers.

Definitions of Exponents	Properties of Exponents	
$a^1 = a$	**1.** $a^r \cdot a^s = a^{r+s}$	Product Property of Exponents
$a^0 = 1 \qquad a \neq 0$	**2.** $(a^r)^s = a^{rs}$	Power Property of Exponents
	3. $(ab)^r = a^r b^r$	Distributive Property of Exponents
	4. $a^{-r} = \dfrac{1}{a^r} = \left(\dfrac{1}{a}\right)^r \quad a \neq 0$	Negative Exponent Property
	5. $\dfrac{a^r}{a^s} = a^{r-s} \quad a \neq 0$	Quotient Property of Exponents
	6. $\left(\dfrac{a}{b}\right)^r = \dfrac{a^r}{b^r} \quad b \neq 0$	Expanded Distributive Property of Exponents

Here are some additional examples. These examples use a combination of the preceding properties and definitions.

Example 5   Simplify each expression. Write all answers with positive exponents.

a. $\dfrac{(5x^3)^2}{x^4} = \dfrac{25x^6}{x^4}$ *Power and distributive properties of exponents*

$\qquad\qquad = 25x^2$ *Quotient property of exponents*

b. $\dfrac{x^{-8}}{(x^2)^3} = \dfrac{x^{-8}}{x^6}$ *Power property of exponents*

$\qquad\quad = x^{-8-6}$ *Quotient property of exponents*

$\qquad\quad = x^{-14}$ *Subtract.*

$\qquad\quad = \dfrac{1}{x^{14}}$ *Negative exponent property*

c. $\left(\dfrac{y^5}{y^3}\right)^2 = \dfrac{(y^5)^2}{(y^3)^2}$ *Expanded distributive property of exponents*

$\qquad\quad = \dfrac{y^{10}}{y^6}$ *Power property of exponents*

$\qquad\quad = y^4$ *Quotient property of exponents*

Notice in Example 5c that we could have simplified inside the parentheses first and then raised the result to the second power:

$$\left(\dfrac{y^5}{y^3}\right)^2 = (y^{5-3})^2 = (y^2)^2 = y^4$$

5. Simplify, and write your answers with positive exponents only.

a. $\dfrac{x^{-6}}{(x^3)^4}$

b. $\dfrac{(2x^3)^2}{x^4}$

c. $\left(\dfrac{y^8}{y^3}\right)^2$

d. $(2x^4)^{-2}$

e. $x^{-6} \cdot x^2$

f. $\dfrac{a^5(a^{-2})^4}{(a^{-3})^2}$

Answers

5. a. $\dfrac{1}{x^{18}}$ **b.** $4x^2$ **c.** y^{10} **d.** $\dfrac{1}{4x^8}$

e. $\dfrac{1}{x^4}$ **f.** a^3

d. $(3x^5)^{-2} = \dfrac{1}{(3x^5)^2}$ Negative exponent property

$\qquad\quad = \dfrac{1}{9x^{10}}$ Power and distributive properties of exponents

e. $x^{-8} \cdot x^5 = x^{-8+5}$ Product property of exponents

$\qquad\quad = x^{-3}$ Add.

$\qquad\quad = \dfrac{1}{x^3}$ Negative exponent property

f. $\dfrac{(a^3)^2 a^{-4}}{(a^{-4})^3} = \dfrac{a^6 a^{-4}}{a^{-12}}$ Power property of exponents

$\qquad\quad = \dfrac{a^2}{a^{-12}}$ Product property of exponents

$\qquad\quad = a^{14}$ Quotient property of exponents

In the next two examples we use division to compare the area and volume of geometric figures.

6. Suppose the side of the larger square in Example 6 is 4 times as long as the side of the smaller square. How many smaller squares will it take to cover the larger square?

Example 6   Suppose you have two squares, one of which is larger than the other. If the length of a side of the larger square is 3 times as long as the length of a side of the smaller square, how many of the smaller squares will it take to cover up the larger square?

Solution   If we let x represent the length of a side of the smaller square, then the length of a side of the larger square is $3x$. The area of each square, along with a diagram of the situation, is given in Figure 1.

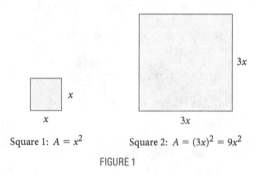

Square 1: $A = x^2$ Square 2: $A = (3x)^2 = 9x^2$

FIGURE 1

To find out how many smaller squares it will take to cover up the larger square, we divide the area of the larger square by the area of the smaller square.

$$\frac{\text{Area of Square 2}}{\text{Area of Square 1}} = \frac{9x^2}{x^2} = 9$$

It will take 9 of the smaller squares to cover the larger square.

Answer

6. It will take 16 smaller squares to cover the larger square.

Example 7 Suppose you have two boxes, each of which is a cube. If the length of a side in the second box is 3 times as long as the length of a side of the first box, how many of the smaller boxes will fit inside the larger box?

Solution If we let x represent the length of a side of the smaller box, then the length of a side of the larger box is $3x$. The volume of each box, along with a diagram of the situation, is given in Figure 2.

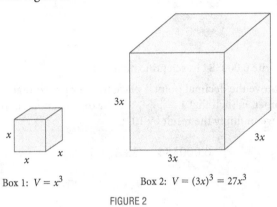

Box 1: $V = x^3$ Box 2: $V = (3x)^3 = 27x^3$

FIGURE 2

To find out how many smaller boxes will fit inside the larger box, we divide the volume of the larger box by the volume of the smaller box.

$$\frac{\text{Volume of Box 2}}{\text{Volume of Box 1}} = \frac{27x^3}{x^3} = 27$$

We can fit 27 of the smaller boxes inside the larger box.

F Scientific Notation for Small Numbers

Now that we have completed our list of definitions and properties of exponents, we can expand the work we did previously with scientific notation. Recall that a number is in scientific notation when it is written in the form

$$n \times 10^r$$

where $1 \le |n| < 10$ and r is an integer.

Since negative exponents give us reciprocals, we can use negative exponents to write very small numbers in scientific notation. For example, the number 0.00057, when written in scientific notation, is equivalent to 5.7×10^{-4}. Here's why:

$$5.7 \times 10^{-4} = 5.7 \times \frac{1}{10^4} = 5.7 \times \frac{1}{10000} = \frac{5.7}{10000} = 0.00057$$

The table below lists some other numbers in both scientific notation and expanded form.

Number written the long way		Same number written in scientific notation
376,000	=	3.76×10^5
−3,200	=	-3.2×10^3
46	=	4.6×10^1
8	=	8×10^0
−0.47	=	-4.7×10^{-1}
0.093	=	9.3×10^{-2}
−0.0002	=	-2×10^{-4}

7. Suppose the side of the larger box in Example 7 is 4 times as long as the side of the smaller box. How many of the smaller boxes can be fit into the larger box?

Note Recall,
$$1 \le |n| < 10$$
means that n must be between −1 and −10 or between 1 and 10. The number can be 1 or −1 but cannot be 10 or −10.

Answer

7. The larger box will hold 64 smaller boxes.

Notice that in each case, when the number is written in scientific notation, the decimal point in the first number is placed so that the absolute value of the number is 1 or larger but less than 10. The exponent on 10 in the second number keeps track of the number of places we moved the decimal point.

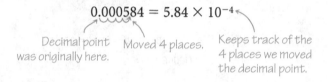

$$376,000 = 3.76 \times 10^5$$

Moved 5 places.

Decimal point was originally here.

Keeps track of the 5 places we moved the decimal point.

$$0.00688 = 6.88 \times 10^{-3}$$

Moved 3 places.

Keeps track of the 3 places we moved the decimal point.

8. Write 0.00273 in scientific notation.

Example 8   Write 0.000584 in scientific notation.

Solution   We move the decimal point 4 place to the right so that 0.000584 will be a product of a number, n, such that $1 \le |n| < 10$. The decimal point appears between the 5 and the 8, and we multiply the result by 10^{-4}.

$$0.000584 = 5.84 \times 10^{-4}$$

Decimal point was originally here.

Moved 4 places.

Keeps track of the 4 places we moved the decimal point.

KEY CONCEPT REVIEW

After reading through the preceding section, respond in your own words and in complete sentences.

A. Explain how to simplify the expression $\dfrac{x^2}{x^6}$

B. Explain the difference between 3^2 and 3^{-2}.

C. Explain what happens when you use 0 as an exponent.

D. What does a negative exponent mean in scientific notation?

Choose the correct words to fill in the blanks below.

exponents   quotient   expanded   negative

1. The _____ exponent property states that $a^{-r} = \frac{1}{a^r} = \left(\frac{1}{a}\right)^r$ if r is a positive integer and a does not equal zero.

2. The _____ property for exponents allows you to divide with the same base by subtracting the exponent in the denominator from the exponent in the numerator and raise the base to the exponent that results.

3. The _____ distributive property for exponents states that $\left(\frac{a}{b}\right)^r = \frac{a^r}{b^r}$ if a and b are any two real numbers, b does not equal zero, and r is an integer.

4. Negative _____ used in scientific notation represent very small numbers.

Problems

A Write each of the following with positive exponents, and then simplify, when possible.

1. 3^{-2}
2. 3^{-3}
3. 6^{-2}
4. 2^{-6}
5. 8^{-2}

6. 3^{-4}
7. 5^{-3}
8. 9^{-2}
9. -3^{-2}
10. -5^{-3}

11. -8^{-1}
12. -7^{-2}
13. $2x^{-3}$
14. $8x^{-1}$
15. $(2x)^{-3}$

16. $(5x)^{-1}$
17. $(5y)^{-2}$
18. $6y^{-2}$
19. 10^{-2}
20. 10^{-3}

21. Complete the following table.

Number x	Square x^2	Power of 2 2^x
-3		
-2		
-1		
0		
1		
2		
3		

22. Complete the following table.

Number x	Cube x^3	Power of 3 3^x
-3		
-2		
-1		
0		
1		
2		
3		

B Use the quotient property of exponents to simplify each of the following expressions. Write all answers that contain exponents with positive exponents only.

23. $\dfrac{5^1}{5^3}$

24. $\dfrac{7^6}{7^8}$

25. $\dfrac{x^{10}}{x^4}$

26. $\dfrac{x^4}{x^{10}}$

27. $\dfrac{4^3}{4^0}$

28. $\dfrac{4^0}{4^3}$

29. $\dfrac{(2x)^7}{(2x)^4}$

30. $\dfrac{(2x)^4}{(2x)^7}$

31. $\dfrac{6^{11}}{6}$

32. $\dfrac{8^7}{8}$

33. $\dfrac{6}{6^{11}}$

34. $\dfrac{8}{8^7}$

35. $\dfrac{2^{-5}}{2^3}$

36. $\dfrac{2^{-5}}{2^{-3}}$

37. $\dfrac{2^5}{2^{-3}}$

38. $\dfrac{2^{-3}}{2^{-5}}$

39. $\dfrac{(3x)^{-5}}{(3x)^{-8}}$

40. $\dfrac{(2x)^{-10}}{(2x)^{-15}}$

41. $\dfrac{(-4x)^{10}}{(-4x)^8}$

42. $\dfrac{(-3x)^4}{(-3x)^7}$

C Use the expanded distributive property of exponents to simplify each of the following expressions. Write all answers with positive exponents only.

43. $\left(\dfrac{x}{3}\right)^3$

44. $\left(\dfrac{x}{2}\right)^4$

45. $\left(\dfrac{4}{y}\right)^2$

46. $\left(\dfrac{-6}{y}\right)^2$

47. $\left(-\dfrac{5}{x}\right)^3$

48. $\left(\dfrac{-4}{y}\right)^2$

49. $\left(\dfrac{-8}{y}\right)^2$

50. $\left(\dfrac{-3}{a}\right)^4$

D Simplify the following expressions.

51. $(-27x)^0$

52. $(-9y^2)^0$

53. $(-2y)^1$

54. $(-8y^2)^1$

55. $(-3ab^2)^1$

56. $(-4x^2y)^1$

57. $(-2xy^2)^0$

58. $\left(\dfrac{x^3}{y^4}\right)^0$

E Simplify the following expressions. Any answers that contain exponents should contain positive exponents only.

59. $(3xy)^4$

60. $(4xy)^3$

61. 10^0

62. 10^1

63. $(2a^2b)^1$

64. $(2a^2b)^0$

65. $(7y^3)^{-2}$

66. $(5y^4)^{-2}$

67. $x^{-3}x^{-5}$

68. $x^{-6} \cdot x^8$

69. $y^7 \cdot y^{-10}$

70. $y^{-4} \cdot y^{-6}$

71. $\dfrac{(x^2)^3}{x^4}$

72. $\dfrac{(x^5)^3}{x^{10}}$

73. $\dfrac{(a^4)^3}{(a^3)^2}$

74. $\dfrac{(a^5)^3}{(a^5)^2}$

75. $\dfrac{y^7}{(y^2)^8}$

76. $\dfrac{y^2}{(y^3)^4}$

77. $\left(\dfrac{y^7}{y^2}\right)^8$

78. $\left(\dfrac{y^2}{y^3}\right)^4$

79. $\dfrac{(x^{-2})^3}{x^{-5}}$

80. $\dfrac{(x^2)^{-3}}{x^{-5}}$

81. $\left(\dfrac{x^{-2}}{x^{-5}}\right)^3$

82. $\left(\dfrac{x^2}{x^{-5}}\right)^{-3}$

83. $\left(\dfrac{2a^{-3}b^2}{4a^{-5}b^6}\right)^{-2}$

84. $\left(\dfrac{3a^{-4}b^3}{2a^{-3}b^4}\right)^{-3}$

85. $\dfrac{(a^3)^2(a^4)^5}{(a^5)^2}$

86. $\dfrac{(a^4)^8(a^2)^5}{(a^3)^4}$

87. $\dfrac{(a^{-2})^3(a^4)^2}{(a^{-3})^{-2}}$

88. $\dfrac{(a^{-5})^{-3}(a^7)^{-1}}{(a^{-3})^5}$

89. $\dfrac{(3x^{-2}y^{-4})(4x^3y^{-2})^{-2}}{(3x^3y^{-2})^{-2}}$

90. $\dfrac{(4x^{-7}y^{-3})(2x^4y^{-3})^{-1}}{(2x^2y^{-2})^{-2}}$

F Write each of the following numbers in scientific notation.

91. 0.0048   **92.** 0.000048   **93.** 25   **94.** 35

95. −0.000009   **96.** −0.0009   **97.** −0.000087   **98.** −0.00000514

Write each of the following numbers in expanded form.

99. 4.23×10^{-3} **100.** 4.23×10^{3} **101.** 8×10^{-5} **102.** 8×10^{5}

103. -4.2×10^{0} **104.** -4.2×10^{1} **105.** -3.6×10^{-3} **106.** -2.05×10^{-4}

107. Complete the following table.

Expanded Form	Scientific Notation $n \times 10^{r}$
0.000357	3.57×10^{-4}
0.00357	
0.0357	
0.357	
3.57	
35.7	
357	
3,570	
35,700	

108. Complete the following table.

Expanded Form	Scientific Notation $n \times 10^{r}$
0.000123	1.23×10^{-4}
	1.23×10^{-3}
	1.23×10^{-2}
	1.23×10^{-1}
	1.23×10^{0}
	1.23×10^{1}
	1.23×10^{2}
	1.23×10^{3}
	1.23×10^{4}

Applying the Concepts

109. Complete the following table, and then construct a line graph of the information in the table.

Number x	Power of x 2^{x}
−3	
−2	
−1	
0	
1	
2	
3	

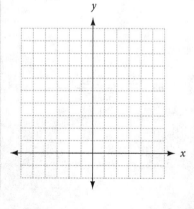

110. Complete the following table, and then construct a line graph of the information in the table.

Number x	Power of x 3^{x}
−3	
−2	
−1	
0	
1	
2	
3	

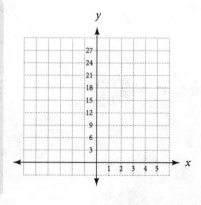

111. Some home computers can do a calculation in 2×10^{-3} seconds. Write this number in expanded form.

112. Some of the cells in the human body have a radius of 3×10^{-5} inches. Write this number in expanded form.

113. Distance from the Sun The table below shows the average distance, in kilometers, from the Sun to some other planets. Write each number in scientific notation.

Planet	Average distance from the Sun (km)
Mercury	57,000,000
Earth	150,000,000
Jupiter	779,000,000
Neptune	4,500,000,000

114. Some cameras used in scientific research can take one picture every 0.000000167 second. Write this number in scientific notation.

115. The number 25×10^3 is not in scientific notation because 25 is larger than 10. Write 25×10^3 in scientific notation.

116. The number 0.25×10^3 is not in scientific notation because 0.25 is less than 1. Write 0.25×10^3 in scientific notation.

117. The number 23.5×10^4 is not in scientific notation because 23.5 is not between 1 and 10. Rewrite 23.5×10^4 in scientific notation.

118. The number 375×10^3 is not in scientific notation because 375 is not between 1 and 10. Rewrite 375×10^3 in scientific notation.

119. The number 0.82×10^{-3} is not in scientific notation because 0.82 is not between 1 and 10. Rewrite 0.82×10^{-3} in scientific notation.

120. The number 0.93×10^{-2} is not in scientific notation because 0.93 is not between 1 and 10. Rewrite 0.93×10^{-2} in scientific notation.

Comparing Areas Suppose you have two squares, one of which is larger than the other. Suppose further that the side of the larger square is twice as long as the side of the smaller square.

121. If the length of the side of the smaller square is 10 inches, give the area of each square. Then find the number of smaller squares it will take to cover the larger square.

122. How many smaller squares will it take to cover the larger square if the length of the side of the smaller square is 1 foot?

123. If the length of the side of the smaller square is x, find the area of each square. Then find the number of smaller squares it will take to cover the larger square.

124. Suppose the length of the side of the larger square is 1 foot. How many smaller squares will it take to cover the larger square?

Comparing Volumes Suppose you have two boxes, each of which is a cube. Suppose further that the length of a side of the second box is twice as long as the length of a side of the first box.

125. If the length of a side of the first box is 6 inches, give the volume of each box. Then find the number of smaller boxes that will fit inside the larger box.

126. How many smaller boxes can be placed inside the larger box if the length of a side of the second box is 1 foot?

127. If the length of a side of the first box is x, find the volume of each box. Then find the number of smaller boxes that will fit inside the larger box.

128. Suppose the length of a side of the larger box is 12 inches. How many smaller boxes will fit inside the larger box?

129. The radius of Earth is 6,378 km, while the radius of Jupiter is 71,472 km. How many Earths would fit inside of Jupiter? Answer this by comparing volume. The volume can be calculated using the formula $\frac{4}{3}\pi r^3$.

130. The radius of Jupiter is 71,472 km, while the radius of the sun is 695,000 km. How many Jupiters would fit inside the sun? Answer this by comparing their volumes. The volume can be calculated using the formula $\frac{4}{3}\pi r^3$.

Getting Ready for the Next Section

Simplify.

131. $3(4.5)$

132. $\dfrac{1}{2} \cdot \dfrac{5}{7}$

133. $\dfrac{4}{5}(10)$

134. $\dfrac{9.6}{3}$

135. $6.8(3.9)$

136. $9 - 20$

137. $-3 + 15$

138. $2x \cdot x \cdot \dfrac{1}{2}x$

139. $x^5 \cdot x^3$

140. $y^2 \cdot y$

141. $\dfrac{x^3}{(x^2)}$

142. $\dfrac{x^2}{x}$

143. $\dfrac{y^3}{y^5}$

144. $\dfrac{x^2}{x^5}$

145. $\dfrac{x^4}{(x^2)^2}$

146. $\dfrac{(y^2)^3}{y^6}$

Write in expanded form.

147. 3.4×10^2

148. 6.0×10^{-4}

149. 3.5×10^{-5}

150. -2.1×10^4

FIND THE MISTAKE •

Each sentence below contains a mistake. Circle the mistake and write the correct word(s) or numbers(s) on the line provided.

1. The negative exponent property says that $x^{-y} = \dfrac{y}{x}$. _____

2. When using the quotient property of exponents to simplify the expression $\dfrac{y^{12}}{y^8}$, we get y^{20}. _____

3. When using the expanded distributive property of exponents to simplify the expression $\left(\dfrac{x}{3}\right)^4$, we get $\dfrac{x^4}{3}$. _____

4. The number 0.00238 written in scientific notation is 2.38×10^{-2}. _____

OBJECTIVES

A Multiply monomials.

B Divide monomials.

C Multiply and divide numbers written in scientific notation.

D Add and subtract monomials.

KEY WORDS

monomial

numerical coefficient

terms

like terms

VIDEO EXAMPLES

SECTION 9.3

A preschool teacher needs to cover the wood floors in two of her classrooms with carpet to provide a softer play surface for her students. She hires a carpet installer who creates a formula to know how much carpet will be needed. The first room is in the shape of a square with a wall the length of x. The second room is the shape of a rectangle, with one wall the same length as the first room but a second wall twice as long. Using our knowledge of area, we can write two monomials that each represent the area of the rooms.

Square room area: $x \cdot x = x^2$

Rectangular room area: $x \cdot 2x = 2x^2$

Later in this section, we can add these monomials to determine how much carpet the installer will need. But first, we will discuss multiplication and division of monomials.

 **DEFINITION** **monomial**

A **monomial** is a one-term expression that is either a constant (number) or the product of a constant and one or more variables raised to whole number exponents.

The following are examples of monomials:

$$-3 \qquad 15x \qquad -23x^2y \qquad 49x^4y^2z^4 \qquad \frac{3}{4}a^2b^3$$

The numerical part of each monomial is called the **numerical coefficient,** or just **coefficient.** Monomials are also called **terms.** The expression x^3 is also a monomial. For x^3, the coefficient is 1 because $x^3 = 1 \cdot x^3$.

A Multiplying Monomials

There are two basic steps involved in the multiplication of monomials. First, we rewrite the products using the commutative and associative properties. Then, we simplify by multiplying coefficients and adding exponents of like bases.

Example 1   Multiply each expression.

a. $(-3x^2)(4x^3)$ **b.** $\left(\dfrac{4}{5}x^5 \cdot y^2\right)(10x^3 \cdot y)$

Solution

a. $(-3x^2)(4x^3) = (-3 \cdot 4)(x^2 \cdot x^3)$ Commutative and associative properties

$\qquad\qquad\qquad = -12x^5$ Simplify.

b. $\left(\dfrac{4}{5}x^5 \cdot y^2\right)(10x^3 \cdot y) = \left(\dfrac{4}{5} \cdot 10\right)(x^5 \cdot x^3)(y^2 \cdot y)$ Commutative and associative properties

$\qquad\qquad\qquad\qquad = 8x^8 y^3$ Simplify.

Practice Problems

1. Multiply.
   a. $(-2x^3)(5x^2)$
   b. $(4x^6 y^3)(2xy^2)$

B Dividing Monomials

We can expect division of monomials to proceed in a similar way. Since our properties are consistent, division of monomials will result in division of coefficients and subtraction of exponents of like bases.

Example 2   Divide each expression.

a. $\dfrac{15x^3}{3x^2}$ **b.** $\dfrac{39x^2 y^3}{3xy^5}$

Solution

a. $\dfrac{15x^3}{3x^2} = \dfrac{15}{3} \cdot \dfrac{x^3}{x^2}$ Write as separate fractions.

$\qquad\quad = 5x$ Divide coefficients, subtract exponents.

b. $\dfrac{39x^2 y^3}{3xy^5} = \dfrac{39}{3} \cdot \dfrac{x^2}{x} \cdot \dfrac{y^3}{y^5}$ Write as separate fractions.

$\qquad\quad = 13x \cdot \dfrac{1}{y^2}$ Divide coefficients, subtract exponents.

$\qquad\quad = \dfrac{13x}{y^2}$ Write answer as a single fraction.

2. Divide.

   a. $\dfrac{27x^4 y^3}{9xy^2}$

   b. $\dfrac{25x^4}{5x}$

In Example 2b, the expression $\dfrac{y^3}{y^5}$ simplifies to $\dfrac{1}{y^2}$ because of the quotient property of exponents and the negative exponent property. If we were to show all the work in this simplification process, it would look like this:

$\dfrac{y^3}{y^5} = y^{3-5}$ Quotient property of exponents

$\qquad = y^{-2}$ Subtract.

$\qquad = \dfrac{1}{y^2}$ Negative exponent property

The point of this explanation is this: Even though we may not show all the steps when simplifying an expression involving exponents, the result we obtain still can be justified using the properties of exponents. We have not introduced any new properties in Example 2; we have just not shown the details of each simplification.

Answers

1. **a.** $-10x^5$ **b.** $8x^7 y^5$

2. **a.** $3x^3 y$ **b.** $5x^3$

3. Divide $\frac{13a^6b^2}{39a^4b^7}$.

Example 3   Divide $25a^5b^3$ by $50a^2b^7$.

Solution   We will write the division using a fraction and simplify.

$$\frac{25a^5b^3}{50a^2b^7} = \frac{25}{50} \cdot \frac{a^5}{a^2} \cdot \frac{b^3}{b^7} \quad \text{Write as separate fractions.}$$

$$= \frac{1}{2} \cdot a^3 \cdot \frac{1}{b^4} \quad \text{Divide coefficients, subtract exponents.}$$

$$= \frac{a^3}{2b^4} \quad \text{Write answer as a single fraction.}$$

Notice in Example 3 that dividing 25 by 50 results in $\frac{1}{2}$. This is the same result we would obtain if we reduced the fraction $\frac{25}{50}$ to lowest terms, and there is no harm in thinking of it that way. Also, notice that the expression $\frac{b^3}{b^7}$ simplifies to $\frac{1}{b^4}$ by the quotient property of exponents and the negative exponent property, even though we have not shown the steps involved in doing so.

C Multiplication and Division of Numbers Written in Scientific Notation

We multiply and divide numbers written in scientific notation using the same steps we used to multiply and divide monomials.

4. Multiply $(3 \times 10^6)(3 \times 10^{-8})$.

Example 4   Multiply $(4 \times 10^7)(2 \times 10^{-4})$.

Solution   Since multiplication is commutative and associative, we can rearrange the order of these numbers and group them as follows:

$$(4 \times 10^7)(2 \times 10^{-4}) = (4 \times 2)(10^7 \times 10^{-4})$$
$$= 8 \times 10^3$$

Notice that we add exponents, $7 + (-4) = 3$, when we multiply with the same base.

5. Divide $\frac{4.8 \times 10^{20}}{2 \times 10^{12}}$.

Example 5   Divide $\frac{9.6 \times 10^{12}}{3 \times 10^4}$.

Solution   We group the numbers between 1 and 10 separately from the powers of 10 and proceed as we did in Example 4:

$$\frac{9.6 \times 10^{12}}{3 \times 10^4} = \frac{9.6}{3} \times \frac{10^{12}}{10^4}$$
$$= 3.2 \times 10^8$$

Notice that the procedure we used in both of these examples is very similar to multiplication and division of monomials, for which we multiplied or divided coefficients and added or subtracted exponents.

D Addition and Subtraction of Monomials

Addition and subtraction of monomials will be almost identical since subtraction is defined as addition of the opposite. With multiplication and division of monomials, the key was rearranging the numbers and variables using the commutative and associative properties. With addition, the key is application of the distributive property. We sometimes use the phrase *combine monomials* to describe addition and subtraction of monomials.

Answers
3. $\frac{a^2}{3b^5}$
4. 9×10^{-2}
5. 2.4×10^8

DEFINITION like terms
Two monomials with the same variable part (same variables raised to the same powers) are called **like terms**.

You can add only like terms. This is because the distributive property (which is the key to addition of monomials) can only be applied to like terms.

Example 6 Combine the following monomials.

a. $-3x^2 + 15x^2$ **b.** $9x^2y - 20x^2y$ **c.** $5x^2 + 8y^2$

solution

a. $-3x^2 + 15x^2 = (-3 + 15)x^2$ Distributive property
           $= 12x^2$ Add coefficients.

b. $9x^2y - 20x^2y = (9 - 20)x^2y$ Distributive property
           $= -11x^2y$ Add coefficients.

c. $5x^2 + 8y^2$ In this case, we cannot apply the distributive property, so we cannot add the monomials.

The next examples show how we simplify expressions containing monomials when more than one operation is involved.

Example 7 Apply the distributive property to simplify.

a. $x^2\left(1 - \dfrac{6}{x}\right)$ **b.** $ab\left(\dfrac{1}{b} - \dfrac{1}{a}\right)$

Solution

a. $x^2\left(1 - \dfrac{6}{x}\right) = x^2 \cdot 1 - x^2 \cdot \dfrac{6}{x} = x^2 - \dfrac{6x^2}{x} = x^2 - 6x$

b. $ab\left(\dfrac{1}{b} - \dfrac{1}{a}\right) = ab \cdot \dfrac{1}{b} - ab \cdot \dfrac{1}{a} = \dfrac{ab}{b} - \dfrac{ab}{a} = a - b$

Example 8 Simplify $\dfrac{(6x^4y)(3x^7y^5)}{9x^5y^2}$.

Solution We begin by multiplying the two monomials in the numerator.

$$\dfrac{(6x^4y)(3x^7y^5)}{9x^5y^2} = \dfrac{18x^{11}y^6}{9x^5y^2}$$ Simplify numerator.

$$= 2x^6y^4$$ Divide.

Example 9 Simplify $\dfrac{(6.8 \times 10^5)(3.9 \times 10^{-7})}{7.8 \times 10^{-4}}$.

Solution We group the numbers between 1 and 10 separately from the powers of 10.

$$\dfrac{(6.8)(3.9)}{7.8} \times \dfrac{(10^5)(10^{-7})}{10^{-4}} = 3.4 \times 10^{5+(-7)-(-4)}$$

$$= 3.4 \times 10^2$$

6. Combine if possible.

  a. $-4x^2 + 9x^2$

  b. $12x^2y - 15x^2y$

  c. $6x^2 + 9x^3$

7. Apply the distributive property.

  a. $a^2\left(2 - \dfrac{4}{a}\right)$

  b. $xy\left(\dfrac{3}{x} + \dfrac{2}{y}\right)$

8. Simplify $\dfrac{(10x^3y^2)(6xy^4)}{12x^2y^3}$.

9. Simplify $\dfrac{(1.2 \times 10^6)(6.3 \times 10^{-5})}{6 \times 10^{-10}}$.

Answers
6. a. $5x^2$ **b.** $-3x^2y$
  c. Cannot be combined
7. a. $2a^2 - 4a$ **b.** $3y + 2x$
8. $5x^2y^3$
9. 1.26×10^{11}

10. Simplify $\frac{24x^7}{3x^2} + \frac{14x^9}{7x^4}$.

Example 10 Simplify $\frac{14x^5}{2x^2} + \frac{15x^8}{3x^5}$.

Solution Simplifying each expression separately and then combining like terms gives

$$\frac{14x^5}{2x^2} + \frac{15x^8}{3x^5} = 7x^3 + 5x^3 \qquad \text{Divide.}$$

$$= 12x^3 \qquad \text{Add.}$$

KEY CONCEPT REVIEW

After reading through the preceding section, respond in your own words and in complete sentences.

A. What is a monomial?

B. Describe how you would multiply $3x^2$ and $5x^2$.

C. Describe how you would add $3x^2$ and $5x^2$.

D. Describe how you would multiply two numbers written in scientific notation.

Answer

10. $10x^5$

VOCABULARY REVIEW •

Choose the correct words to fill in the blanks below.

terms   coefficient   subtraction   variable   monomial

1. A _____ is a one-term expression that is either a constant or the product of a constant and one or more variables raised to whole number exponents.

2. Monomials are also called _____.

3. The numerical _____ of $7xy^2$ is 7.

4. Two monomials with the same _____ part are called like terms.

5. Division of monomials will result in division of coefficients and _____ of exponents of like bases.

Problems

A Multiply each expression and simplify.

1. $(3x^4)(4x^3)$

2. $(6x^5)(-2x^2)$

3. $(-2y^4)(8y^7)$

4. $(5y^{10})(2y^5)$

5. $(8x)(4x)$

6. $(7x)(5x)$

7. $(10a^3)(10a)(2a^2)$

8. $(5a^4)(10a)(10a^4)$

9. $(6ab^2)(-4a^2b)$

10. $(-5a^3b)(4ab^4)$

11. $(4x^2y)(3x^3y^3)(2xy^4)$

12. $(5x^6)(-10xy^4)(-2x^2y^6)$

B Divide each expression and simplify. Write all answers with positive exponents only.

13. $\dfrac{15x^3}{5x^2}$

14. $\dfrac{25x^5}{5x^4}$

15. $\dfrac{18y^9}{3y^{12}}$

16. $\dfrac{24y^4}{8y^7}$

17. $\dfrac{32a^3}{64a^4}$

18. $\dfrac{25a^5}{75a^6}$

19. $\dfrac{21a^2b^3}{-7ab^5}$

20. $\dfrac{32a^5b^6}{8ab^5}$

21. $\dfrac{3x^3y^2z}{27xy^2z^3}$

22. $\dfrac{5x^5y^4z}{30x^3yz^2}$

23. $\dfrac{-4x^2y^3z}{16x^5yz^2}$

24. $\dfrac{-16x^3yz^2}{24xy^7z}$

25. Fill in the table.

a	b	ab	$\dfrac{a}{b}$	$\dfrac{b}{a}$
10	$5x$			
$20x^3$	$6x^2$			
$25x^5$	$5x^4$			
$3x^{-2}$	$3x^2$			
$-2y^4$	$8y^7$			

26. Fill in the table.

a	b	ab	$\dfrac{a}{b}$	$\dfrac{b}{a}$
$10y$	$2y^2$			
$10y^2$	$2y$			
$5y^3$	15			
5	$15y^3$			
$4y^{-3}$	$4y^3$			

Simplify. Write all answers with positive exponents only.

27. $\dfrac{(3x^2)(8x^5)}{6x^4}$

28. $\dfrac{(7x^3)(6x^8)}{14x^5}$

29. $\dfrac{(9a^2b)(2a^3b^4)}{18a^5b^7}$

30. $\dfrac{(21a^5b)(2a^8b^4)}{14ab}$

31. $\dfrac{(4x^3y^2)(9x^4y^{10})}{(3x^5y)(2x^6y)}$

32. $\dfrac{(5x^4y^4)(10x^3y^3)}{(25xy^5)(2xy^7)}$

33. $\dfrac{(-2xy^2)(-4x^3y)}{(-6xy^3)(xy)}$

34. $\dfrac{(-12a^3b^2)(3ab^3)}{(-6a^2b^2)(ab)}$

C Find each product. Write all answers in scientific notation.

35. $(3 \times 10^3)(2 \times 10^5)$

36. $(4 \times 10^8)(1 \times 10^6)$

37. $(3.5 \times 10^4)(5 \times 10^{-6})$

38. $(7.1 \times 10^5)(2 \times 10^{-8})$

39. $(5.5 \times 10^{-3})(2.2 \times 10^{-4})$

40. $(3.4 \times 10^{-2})(4.5 \times 10^{-6})$

Find each quotient. Write all answers in scientific notation.

41. $\dfrac{8.4 \times 10^5}{2 \times 10^2}$

42. $\dfrac{9.6 \times 10^{20}}{3 \times 10^6}$

43. $\dfrac{6 \times 10^8}{2 \times 10^{-2}}$

44. $\dfrac{8 \times 10^{12}}{4 \times 10^{-3}}$

45. $\dfrac{2.5 \times 10^{-6}}{5 \times 10^{-4}}$

46. $\dfrac{4.5 \times 10^{-8}}{9 \times 10^{-4}}$

47. $\dfrac{-4.0 \times 10^{-6}}{8.0 \times 10^{-3}}$

48. $\dfrac{-1.5 \times 10^{-3}}{-6.0 \times 10^2}$

Simplify each expression, and write all answers in scientific notation.

49. $\dfrac{(6 \times 10^8)(3 \times 10^5)}{9 \times 10^7}$

50. $\dfrac{(8 \times 10^4)(5 \times 10^{10})}{2 \times 10^7}$

51. $\dfrac{(5 \times 10^3)(4 \times 10^{-5})}{2 \times 10^{-2}}$

52. $\dfrac{(7 \times 10^6)(4 \times 10^{-4})}{1.4 \times 10^{-3}}$

53. $\dfrac{(2.8 \times 10^{-7})(3.6 \times 10^4)}{2.4 \times 10^3}$

54. $\dfrac{(5.4 \times 10^2)(3.5 \times 10^{-9})}{4.5 \times 10^6}$

D Combine by adding or subtracting like terms as indicated.

55. $3x^2 + 5x^2$

56. $4x^3 + 8x^3$

57. $8x^5 - 19x^5$

58. $75x^6 - 50x^6$

59. $2a + a - 3a$

60. $5a + a - 6a$

61. $10x^3 - 8x^3 + 2x^3$

62. $7x^5 + 8x^5 - 12x^5$

63. $20ab^2 - 19ab^2 + 30ab^2$

64. $18a^3b^2 - 20a^3b^2 + 10a^3b^2$

65. $-3x^2y - 7x^2y - x^2y$

66. $-2a^3b + a^3b - 12a^3b$

67. Fill in the table.

a	b	ab	a + b
$5x$	$3x$		
$4x^2$	$2x^2$		
$3x^3$	$6x^3$		
$2x^4$	$-3x^4$		
x^5	$7x^5$		

68. Fill in the table.

a	b	ab	a − b
$2y$	$3y$		
$-2y$	$3y$		
$4y^2$	$5y^2$		
y^3	$-3y^3$		
$5y^4$	$7y^4$		

Apply the distributive property to simplify each expression.

69. $xy\left(x + \dfrac{1}{y}\right)$

70. $xy\left(y + \dfrac{1}{x}\right)$

71. $xy\left(\dfrac{1}{y} + \dfrac{1}{x}\right)$

72. $xy\left(\dfrac{1}{x} - \dfrac{1}{y}\right)$

73. $x^2\left(1 - \dfrac{4}{x^2}\right)$

74. $x^2\left(1 - \dfrac{9}{x^2}\right)$

75. $x^2\left(1 - \dfrac{1}{x} - \dfrac{6}{x^2}\right)$

76. $x^2\left(1 - \dfrac{5}{x} + \dfrac{6}{x^2}\right)$

77. $x^2\left(1 - \dfrac{5}{x}\right)$

78. $x^2\left(1 - \dfrac{3}{x}\right)$

79. $x^2\left(1 - \dfrac{8}{x}\right)$

80. $x^2\left(1 - \dfrac{6}{x}\right)$

Simplify.

81. $\dfrac{18x^4}{3x} + \dfrac{21x^7}{7x^4}$

82. $\dfrac{24x^{10}}{6x^4} + \dfrac{32x^7}{8x}$

83. $\dfrac{45a^6}{9a^4} - \dfrac{50a^8}{2a^6}$

84. $\dfrac{16a^9}{4a} - \dfrac{28a^{12}}{4a^4}$

85. $\dfrac{6x^7y^4}{3x^2y^2} + \dfrac{8x^5y^8}{2y^6}$

86. $\dfrac{40x^{10}y^{10}}{8x^2y^5} + \dfrac{10x^8y^8}{5y^3}$

Getting Ready for the Next Section

Simplify.

87. $3 - 8$

88. $-5 + 7$

89. $-1 + 7$

90. $1 - 8$

91. $3(5)^2 + 1$

92. $3(-2)^2 - 5(-2) + 4$

93. $2x^2 + 4x^2$

94. $3x^2 - x^2$

95. $-5x + 7x$

96. $x - 2x$

97. $-(2x + 9)$

98. $-(4x^2 - 2x - 6)$

99. Find the value of $2x + 3$ when $x = 4$.

100. Find the value of $(3x)^2$ when $x = 3$.

101. Find the value of $(-2x)^2$ when $x = -3$.

102. Find the value of $(-5y)^3$ when $y = -1$.

FIND THE MISTAKE •

Each sentence below contains a mistake. Circle the mistake and write the correct word(s) or numbers(s) on the line provided.

1. The coefficient of the monomial $12x^4y^2z$ is 4. _____

2. Multiplying the monomials $-15x^3y$ and $2x^2$ gives us $30x^6y$. _____

3. When dividing $28x^6y^2$ by $4x^2y$, write the problem as the separate fractions $\frac{28x^6}{4x^2} \cdot \frac{y^2}{y}$. _____

4. Monomials with like terms have the same coefficients but different variable parts.

_____

LANDMARK REVIEW: CHECKING YOUR PROGRESS • • • • • • • • • • • • • • •

Simplify the following expressions. Assume all variables are positive numbers and any answers containing exponents should contain positive exponents only.

1. -7^2

2. $x^5 \cdot x^3$

3. $(x^3)^2$

4. $(3a)^3$

5. $(2y)^2(4y)^3$

6. $\frac{5^4}{5^2}$

7. $\frac{(3x)^5}{(3x)^2}$

8. $3x^{-7}$

9. $\frac{2^{-4}}{2^{-2}}$

10. $\frac{(a^2)^3}{(a^4)^2}$

11. $(4xy)^1$

12. $(14x^ny^m)^0$

13. $\frac{9 \times 10^5}{3 \times 10^3}$

14. $\frac{(3 \times 10^5)(6 \times 10^4)}{9 \times 10^6}$

15. $(6x^2y)(3x^3y^3)$

16. $\frac{3a^3b^2c}{6abc^4}$

17. $9x^2 - 4x^2$

18. $10y^2 - 3y^2 + 2y^2$

19. $x^2\left(2 - \frac{10}{x}\right)$

20. $\frac{36y^8}{4y^2} - \frac{40y^{10}}{2y^4}$

ADDITION AND SUBTRACTION OF POLYNOMIALS

9.4

Suppose we left the television and the ceiling fan on when we left the house for the day. The amount of energy wasted by the ceiling fan was 5 less watts per hour than the television that wasted x watts per hour. The next day, we left on the television, the ceiling fan, and the stereo, which wasted three times the amount of the television. How much total energy did we waste over the two days? To help us solve this problem, we will arrange all our given information into a table.

OBJECTIVES · · · · · · ·

A Add and subtract polynomials.

B Evaluate polynomial expressions for a given value.

KEY WORDS · · · · · ·

polynomial
binomial
trinomial
degree

Energy Use (Watts/Hour)

	Television	Ceiling fan	Stereo
Day 1	x	$x - 5$	
Day 2	x	$x - 5$	$3x$

VIDEO EXAMPLES

SECTION 9.4

Next we need to learn how to add these two polynomials together to get our answer. Once you have read through this section, return to this problem and try to solve it.

In this section we will extend what we learned in Section 9.3 to expressions called polynomials. We begin this section with the definition of a polynomial.

DEFINITION polynomial

A **polynomial** is a finite sum of monomials.

Here are some examples of polynomials:

$$3x^2 + 2x + 1 \qquad 15x^2y + 21xy^2 - y^2 \qquad 3a - 2b + 4c - 5d$$

Polynomials can be further classified by the number of terms they contain. A polynomial with two terms is called a **binomial**. If it has three terms, it is a **trinomial**. As stated before, a **monomial** has only one term.

DEFINITION   degree

The degree of a monomial is the sum of the exponents of the variables; whereas the degree of a polynomial in one variable is the highest power to which the variable is raised.

Various degrees of polynomials:

$3x^5 + 2x^3 + 1$	A trinomial of degree 5
$2x + 1$	A binomial of degree 1
$3x^2 + 2x + 1$	A trinomial of degree 2
$3x^5$	A monomial of degree 5
-9	A monomial of degree 0

A Adding and Subtracting Polynomials

There are no new rules for adding one or more polynomials. We rely only on our previous knowledge. Here are some examples.

Example 1   Add $(2x^2 - 5x + 3) + (4x^2 + 7x - 8)$.

Solution   We use the commutative and associative properties to group like terms together and then apply the distributive property to add.

$$(2x^2 - 5x + 3) + (4x^2 + 7x - 8)$$

$$= (2x^2 + 4x^2) + (-5x + 7x) + (3 - 8) \qquad \text{Commutative and associative properties}$$

$$= (2 + 4)x^2 + (-5 + 7)x + (3 - 8) \qquad \text{Distributive property}$$

$$= 6x^2 + 2x - 5 \qquad \text{Add.}$$

The results here indicate that to add two polynomials, we add coefficients of like terms.

• •

Example 2   Add $x^2 + 3x + 2x + 6$.

Solution   The only like terms here are the two middle terms. We combine them as usual to get

$$x^2 + 3x + 2x + 6 = x^2 + 5x + 6$$

• •

The opposite of a polynomial is the opposite of each of its terms. When you subtract one polynomial from another you subtract each of its terms.

Example 3   Subtract $(3x^2 + x + 4) - (x^2 + 2x + 3)$.

Solution   To subtract $x^2 + 2x + 3$, we change the sign of each of its terms and add. If you are having trouble remembering why we do this, remember that we can think of $-(x^2 + 2x + 3)$ as $-1(x^2 + 2x + 3)$. If we distribute the -1 across $x^2 + 2x + 3$, we get $-x^2 - 2x - 3$.

$$(3x^2 + x + 4) - (x^2 + 2x + 3)$$

$$= 3x^2 + x + 4 - x^2 - 2x - 3 \qquad \text{Take the opposite of each term in the second polynomial.}$$

$$= (3x^2 - x^2) + (x - 2x) + (4 - 3) \qquad \text{Group like terms.}$$

$$= 2x^2 - x + 1 \qquad \text{Add.}$$

• •

Practice Problems

1. Add
   $(2x^2 + 3x + 4) + (5x^2 - 6x - 3)$.

2. Add $x^2 + 7x + 4x + 28$.

3. Subtract
   $(5x^2 + x + 2) - (x^2 + 3x + 7)$.

Answers

1. $7x^2 - 3x + 1$
2. $x^2 + 11x + 28$
3. $4x^2 - 2x - 5$

Example 4 Subtract $-4x^2 + 5x - 7$ from $x^2 - x - 1$.

Solution The polynomial $x^2 - x - 1$ comes first, then the subtraction sign, and finally the polynomial $-4x^2 + 5x - 7$ in parentheses.

$$(x^2 - x - 1) - (-4x^2 + 5x - 7)$$

$$= x^2 - x - 1 + 4x^2 - 5x + 7 \qquad \text{Take the opposite of each term in the second polynomial.}$$

$$= (x^2 + 4x^2) + (-x - 5x) + (-1 + 7) \qquad \text{Group like terms.}$$

$$= 5x^2 - 6x + 6 \qquad \text{Add.}$$

4. Subtract $-4x^2 - 3x + 8$ from $x^2 + x + 1$.

B Finding the Value of a Polynomial

The last topic we want to consider in this section is finding the value of a polynomial for a given value of the variable.

To find the value of the polynomial $3x^2 + 1$ when x is 5, we replace x with 5 and simplify the result.

When $\rightarrow$ $\qquad x = 5$

the polynomial $\rightarrow$ $\qquad 3x^2 + 1$

becomes $\rightarrow$ $\qquad 3(5)^2 + 1 = 3(25) + 1$

$$= 75 + 1$$

$$= 76$$

Example 5 Find the value of $3x^2 - 5x + 4$ when $x = -2$.

Solution We replace x with -2 and simplify:

$$3(-2)^2 - 5(-2) + 4 = 3(4) + 10 + 4$$

$$= 12 + 10 + 4$$

$$= 26$$

5. Find the value of $2x^2 - x + 3$ when $x = -3$.

Example 6 Find the value of $2x^2 + 3x + 5$ when $x = 3$.

Solution We replace x with 3 and simplify:

$$2(3)^2 + 3(3) + 5 = 2(9) + 9 + 5$$

$$= 18 + 9 + 5$$

$$= 32$$

6. Find the value of $4x^2 + 2x - 3$ when $x = 5$.

 KEY CONCEPT REVIEW

After reading through the preceding section, respond in your own words and in complete sentences.

A. What is the difference between a binomial and a trinomial?

B. What is the degree of a polynomial?

C. Describe how you would subtract one polynomial from another.

D. How you would find the value of $3x^2 - 5x + 4$ when x is -2?

Answers

4. $5x^2 + 4x - 7$

5. 24

6. 107

VOCABULARY REVIEW ·

Choose the correct words to fill in the blanks below.

degree   like   polynomial   opposite

1. A _____ is a finite sum of monomials.

2. The _____ of a polynomial in one variable is the highest power to which the variable is raised.

3. To add and subtract polynomials, first group _____ terms.

4. The _____ of a polynomial is the opposite of each of its terms.

Problems

Identify each of the following polynomials as a trinomial, binomial, or monomial, and give the degree in each case.

1. $2x^3 - 3x^2 + 1$

2. $4x^2 - 4x + 1$

3. $5 + 8a - 9a^3$

4. $6 + 12x^3 + x^4$

5. $2x - 1$

6. $4 + 7x$

7. $45x^2 - 1$

8. $3a^3 + 8$

9. $7a^2$

10. $90x$

11. -4

12. 56

A Perform the following additions and subtractions.

13. $(2x^2 + 3x + 4) + (3x^2 + 2x + 5)$

14. $(x^2 + 5x + 6) + (x^2 + 3x + 4)$

15. $(3a^2 - 4a + 1) + (2a^2 - 5a + 6)$

16. $(5a^2 - 2a + 7) + (4a^2 - 3a + 2)$

17. $x^2 + 4x + 2x + 8$

18. $x^2 + 5x - 3x - 15$

19. $6x^2 - 3x - 10x + 5$

20. $10x^2 + 30x - 2x - 6$

21. $x^2 - 3x + 3x - 9$

22. $x^2 - 5x + 5x - 25$

23. $3y^2 - 5y - 6y + 10$

24. $y^2 - 18y + 2y - 12$

25. $(6x^3 - 4x^2 + 2x) + (9x^2 - 6x + 3)$

26. $(5x^3 + 2x^2 + 3x) + (2x^2 + 5x + 1)$

27. $\left(\dfrac{2}{3}x^2 - \dfrac{1}{5}x - \dfrac{3}{4}\right) + \left(\dfrac{4}{3}x^2 - \dfrac{4}{5}x + \dfrac{7}{4}\right)$

28. $\left(\dfrac{3}{8}x^3 - \dfrac{5}{7}x^2 - \dfrac{2}{5}\right) + \left(\dfrac{5}{8}x^3 - \dfrac{2}{7}x^2 + \dfrac{7}{5}\right)$

29. $(a^2 - a - 1) - (-a^2 + a + 1)$

30. $(5a^2 - a - 6) - (-3a^2 - 2a + 4)$

31. $\left(\dfrac{5}{9}x^3 + \dfrac{1}{3}x^2 - 2x + 1\right) - \left(\dfrac{2}{3}x^3 + x^2 + \dfrac{1}{2}x - \dfrac{3}{4}\right)$

32. $\left(4x^3 - \dfrac{2}{5}x^2 + \dfrac{3}{8}x - 1\right) - \left(\dfrac{9}{2}x^3 + \dfrac{1}{4}x^2 - x + \dfrac{5}{6}\right)$

33. $(4y^2 - 3y + 2) + (5y^2 + 12y - 4) - (13y^2 - 6y + 20)$

34. $(2y^2 - 7y - 8) - (6y^2 + 6y - 8) + (4y^2 - 2y + 3)$

35. Subtract $10x^2 + 23x - 50$ from $11x^2 - 10x + 13$.

36. Subtract $2x^2 - 3x + 5$ from $4x^2 - 5x + 10$.

37. Subtract $3y^2 + 7y - 15$ from $11y^2 + 11y + 11$.

38. Subtract $15y^2 - 8y - 2$ from $3y^2 - 3y + 2$.

39. Add $50x^2 - 100x - 150$ to $25x^2 - 50x + 75$.

40. Add $7x^2 - 8x + 10$ to $-8x^2 + 2x - 12$.

41. Subtract $2x + 1$ from the sum of $3x - 2$ and $11x + 5$.

42. Subtract $3x - 5$ from the sum of $5x + 2$ and $9x - 1$.

B Find the value of the following polynomials for the given variables.

43. Find the value of the polynomial $x^2 - 2x + 1$ when x is 3.

44. Find the value of the polynomial $x^2 - 4x + 8$ when x is 3.

45. Find the value of the polynomial $x^2 + 3x - 2$ when x is -2.

46. Find the value of the polynomial $x^2 + 5x - 4$ when x is -2.

47. Find the value of the polynomial $3x^2 - 8x + 9$ when x is 4.

48. Find the value of the polynomial $2x^2 - 9x + 6$ when x is 4.

49. Find the value of the polynomial $5x^2 + 7x - 3$ when x is -2.

50. Find the value of the polynomial $4x^2 + 9x - 2$ when x is -3.

Applying the Concepts

51. Packaging A crystal ball with a diameter of 6 inches is being packaged for shipment. If the crystal ball is placed inside a circular cylinder with radius 3 inches and height 6 inches, how much volume will need to be filled with padding? Leave your answer in terms of π. (The volume of a sphere with radius r is $\frac{4}{3}\pi r^3$, and the volume of a right circular cylinder with radius r and height h is $\pi r^2 h$.)

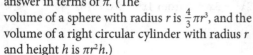

52. Packaging Suppose the circular cylinder of Problem 51 has a radius of 6 inches and a height of 8 inches. How much volume will need to be filled with padding? Leave your answer in terms of π.

Getting Ready for the Next Section

Simplify each expression.

53. $(-5)(-1)$

54. $3(-4)$

55. $(-1)(6)$

56. $(-7) \cdot 8$

57. $(5x)(-4x)$

58. $(3x)(2x)$

59. $3x(-7)$

60. $3x(-1)$

61. $5x + (-3x)$

62. $-3x - 10x$

63. $7x - 15x$

64. $-5x - x$

Multiply.

65. $3(2x - 6)$

66. $5(2xy - 7)$

67. $-3(xy - 4)$

68. $-4(a^2 - 9)$

FIND THE MISTAKE •

Each sentence below contains a mistake. Circle the mistake and write the correct word(s) or numbers(s) on the line provided.

1. The degree of the polynomial $x^2 + 6 + 4x - x^7$ is 2. _____

2. Adding $x^3 + 4x^2 - 8 + x^2$ gives us $6x^5 - 8$. _____

3. Subtracting $2x^2 + 3x - 2$ from $4x^2 + 5x - 9$ gives us $2x^5 + 8x - 11$. _____

4. The value of the polynomial $7a^2 + 5a - 10$ when a is 4 is 794. _____

OBJECTIVES

A Multiply a monomial with a polynomial.

B Multiply two binomials.

C Solve application problems involving multiplying polynomials.

KEY WORDS

FOIL method

column method

VIDEO EXAMPLES

SECTION 9.5

Practice Problems

1. Multiply $2x^3(4x^2 - 5x + 3)$.

Swamp soccer is an exhilarating team sport played just like a standard game of soccer, except the field is a muddy swamp or bog. By the end of the game, most if not all players are soaked and covered head to toe in mud. Suppose you are a coach of your local swamp soccer team. You have coached the team for x years and plan to spend two more years coaching before retiring. If the amount of money you spend on uniforms each year can be given by the binomial $30x + 10$, how much will you have spent by the end of your coaching career?

We can set up this problem as the multiplication of two binomials. Therefore, if $x + 2$ equals the number of total coaching years, then we have

$$(x + 2)(30x + 10)$$

Before we explore the multiplication of two binomials further, let's look at an example of multiplying monomials with polynomials.

A Multiplying Monomials with Polynomials

We begin our discussion of multiplication of polynomials by finding the product of a monomial and a trinomial.

Example 1 Multiply $3x^2(2x^2 + 4x + 5)$.

Solution Applying the distributive property gives us

$$3x^2(2x^2 + 4x + 5) = 3x^2(2x^2) + 3x^2(4x) + 3x^2(5) \qquad \text{Distributive property}$$
$$= 6x^4 + 12x^3 + 15x^2 \qquad \text{Multiply.}$$

B Multiplying Binomials

The distributive property is the key to multiplication of polynomials. We can use it to find the product of any two polynomials. There are some shortcuts we can use in certain situations, however. Let's look at an example that involves the product of two binomials.

Answers

1. $8x^5 - 10x^4 + 6x^3$

Example 2 Multiply $(3x - 5)(2x - 1)$.

Solution
$$(3x - 5)(2x - 1) = 3x(2x - 1) - 5(2x - 1)$$
$$= 3x(2x) + 3x(-1) + (-5)(2x) + (-5)(-1)$$
$$= 6x^2 - 3x - 10x + 5$$
$$= 6x^2 - 13x + 5$$

2. Multiply $(2x - 4)(3x + 2)$.

If we look closely at the second and third lines of work in this example, we can see that the terms in the answer come from all possible products of terms in the first binomial with terms in the second binomial. This result is generalized as follows.

RULE Multiplication of Two Polynomials

To multiply any two polynomials, multiply each term in the first with each term in the second.

There are two ways we can put this rule to work, the first of which is called the FOIL method.

FOIL Method

If we look at the original problem in Example 2 and then at the answer, we see that the first term in the answer came from multiplying the first terms in each binomial.

$$3x \cdot 2x = 6x^2 \qquad \text{First}$$

The middle term in the answer came from adding the products of the two outside terms with the two inside terms in each binomial.

$$3x(-1) = -3x \qquad \text{Outside}$$
$$\underline{-5(2x) = -10x} \qquad \text{Inside}$$
$$= -13x$$

The last term in the answer came from multiplying the two last terms.

$$-5(-1) = 5 \qquad \text{Last}$$

We use the mnemonic device FOIL to summarize these steps. Using the phrase "FOIL method" reminds us to multiply the first terms in each binomial, the outside and inside terms, and then the last terms in each binomial.

Example 3 Multiply $(2x + 3)(5x - 4)$.

Solution
$$(2x + 3)(5x - 4) = \underline{2x(5x)} + \underline{2x(-4)} + \underline{3(5x)} + \underline{3(-4)}$$
$$\qquad\qquad\qquad \uparrow \qquad\quad \uparrow \qquad\quad \uparrow \qquad\quad \uparrow$$
$$\qquad\qquad\quad \text{First} \quad \text{Outside} \quad \text{Inside} \quad \text{Last}$$
$$= 10x^2 - 8x + 15x - 12$$
$$= 10x^2 + 7x - 12$$

3. Multiply $(3x + 5)(2x - 1)$.

Column Method

The FOIL method can be applied only when multiplying two binomials. To find products of polynomials with more than two terms, we use what we refer to as the column method.

The column method of multiplying two polynomials is very similar to long multiplication with whole numbers. It is just another way of finding all possible products of terms in one polynomial with terms in another polynomial.

Answers

2. $6x^2 - 8x - 8$

3. $6x^2 + 7x - 5$

4. Multiply $(3x - 2)(2x^2 - 3x + 4)$.

Example 4 Multiply $(2x + 3)(3x^2 - 2x + 1)$.

Solution

$$
\begin{array}{r}
3x^2 - 2x + 1 \\
2x + 3 \\
\hline
9x^2 - 6x + 3 \\
6x^3 - 4x^2 + 2x \\
\hline
6x^3 + 5x^2 - 4x + 3
\end{array}
$$

$\leftarrow 3(3x^2 - 2x + 1)$
$\leftarrow 2x(3x^2 - 2x + 1)$
Add like terms.

It will be to your advantage to become very fast and accurate at multiplying polynomials. You should be comfortable using either method. The following examples illustrate the three types of multiplication.

5. Multiply.

a. $5a^2(3a^2 - 2a + 4)$

b. $(x + 3)(y - 5)$

c. $(x + 2y)(a + b)$

d. $(4x + 1)(3x + 5)$

Example 5 Multiply.

a. $4a^2(2a^2 - 3a + 5) = 4a^2(2a^2) + 4a^2(-3a) + 4a^2(5)$

$= 8a^4 - 12a^3 + 20a^2$

b. $(x - 2)(y + 3) = x(y) + x(3) + (-2)(y) + (-2)(3)$

$\quad\text{F}\quad\quad\text{O}\quad\quad\text{I}\quad\quad\text{L}$

$= xy + 3x - 2y - 6$

c. $(x + y)(a - b) = x(a) + x(-b) + y(a) + y(-b)$

$\quad\text{F}\quad\quad\text{O}\quad\quad\text{I}\quad\quad\text{L}$

$= xa - xb + ya - yb$

d. $(5x - 1)(2x + 6) = 5x(2x) + 5x(6) + (-1)(2x) + (-1)(6)$

$\quad\text{F}\quad\quad\text{O}\quad\quad\text{I}\quad\quad\text{L}$

$= 10x^2 + 30x + (-2x) + (-6)$

$= 10x^2 + 28x - 6$

6. Find the square of $(4x - 5)$.

Example 6 Multiply $(3x - 2)^2$.

Solution To square $(3x - 2)$, we multiply it by itself.

$(3x - 2)^2 = (3x - 2)(3x - 2)$ Definition of exponents

$= 9x^2 - 6x - 6x + 4$ FOIL method

$= 9x^2 - 12x + 4$ Combine like terms.

7. Multiply using the FOIL method.

a. $(3x - 5)(3x + 5)$

b. $(x - 4)(x + 4)$

c. $(4x - 1)(4x + 1)$

Example 7 Multiply using the FOIL method.

a. $(2x - 3)(2x + 3)$ **b.** $(x - 5)(x + 5)$ **c.** $(3x - 1)(3x + 1)$

Solution

a. $(2x - 3)(2x + 3) = 4x^2 + 6x - 6x - 9$ FOIL method

$= 4x^2 - 9$

b. $(x - 5)(x + 5) = x^2 + 5x - 5x - 25$ FOIL method

$= x^2 - 25$

c. $(3x - 1)(3x + 1) = 9x^2 + 3x - 3x - 1$ FOIL method

$= 9x^2 - 1$

Answers

4. $6x^3 - 13x^2 + 18x - 8$
5. a. $15a^4 - 10a^3 + 20a^2$
b. $xy - 5x + 3y - 15$
c. $ax + bx + 2ay + 2by$
d. $12x^2 + 23x + 5$
6. $16x^2 - 40x + 25$
7. a. $9x^2 - 25$ **b.** $x^2 - 16$
c. $16x^2 - 1$

Notice that in each case the middle term is zero and therefore doesn't appear in the answer. The answers all turn out to be the difference of two squares. This observation allows us to generalize the result to the following:

> **RULE Difference of Two Squares**
>
> When multiplying two binomials that differ only in the sign between their terms, subtract the square of the last term from the square of the first term.
>
> $$(a - b)(a + b) = a^2 - b^2$$

C Applications

Example 8   The length of a rectangle is 3 more than twice the width. Write an expression for the area of the rectangle.

Solution   We begin by drawing a rectangle and labeling the width with x. Since the length is 3 more than twice the width, we label the length with $2x + 3$.

$$2x + 3$$

x

Since the area A of a rectangle is the product of the length and width, we write our formula for the area of this rectangle as

$$A = x(2x + 3)$$
$$A = 2x^2 + 3x \qquad \text{Multiply.}$$

8. The length of a rectangle is 5 more than three times the width. Write an expression for the area.

Suppose that a store sells x items at p dollars per item. The total amount of money obtained by selling the items is called the revenue. It can be found by multiplying the number of items sold, x, by the price per item, p. For example, if 100 items are sold for $6 each, the revenue is $100(6) = \$600$. Similarly, if 500 items are sold for $8 each, the total revenue is $500(8) = \$4,000$. If we denote the revenue with the letter R, then the formula that relates R, x, and p is

$$\text{Revenue} = (\text{number of items sold})(\text{price of each item})$$

In symbols: $R = xp$.

Example 9   A store selling flash drives for home computers knows from past experience that it can sell x flash drives each day at a price of p dollars each, according to the equation $x = 800 - 100p$. Write a formula for the daily revenue that involves only the variables R and p.

Solution   From our previous discussion we know that the revenue R is given by the formula

$$R = xp$$

But, since $x = 800 - 100p$, we can substitute $800 - 100p$ for x in the revenue equation to obtain

$$R = (800 - 100p)p$$
$$R = 800p - 100p^2$$

This last formula gives the revenue R in terms of the price p.

9. Suppose the store in Example 9 can sell x flash drives for p dollars according to the equation $x = 700 - 110p$. Find the revenue.

KEY CONCEPT REVIEW

After reading through the preceding section, respond in your own words and in complete sentences.

A. Describe how you would use the column method to multiply two polynomials.

B. Describe how the distributive property is used to multiply a monomial and a polynomial.

C. Describe how you would use the FOIL method to multiply two binomials.

D. Show how the product of two binomials can be a trinomial.

 Spotlight on Success

RYAN, student instructor

You do not determine a man's greatness by his talent or wealth, as the world does, but rather by what it takes to discourage him. ~ **Dr. Jerry Falwell**

From very early in school, I seemed to have a knack for math, but I also had a knack for laziness and procrastination. In rare times, I would really focus in class and nail all the material, but more often I would spend my time goofing off with friends and coasting on what came easily to me. My parents tried their hardest to motivate me, to do anything they could to help me succeed, but when it came down to it, it was on me to control the outcome.

At one point, my dad voiced his frustrations with having to pay for such a good education when I wasn't taking advantage of it. He told me that if I didn't get above a 3.8 GPA, that I would be attending a different school the following fall. It was the motivation I needed. Finally, I understood the importance of trying my best in school. That semester I achieved the goal my dad had given to me.

But it wasn't that easy. I encountered numerous things in high school that could have derailed my academic journey. I felt abandoned by people I considered family, I suffered multiple injuries requiring surgery, and I experienced the death of a classmate and teammate. There was so much going on that I could have just shut down and gone back to coasting by, but luckily, I had already learned my lesson. I managed to stay positive and work hard through all the challenges. Everything paid off senior year when I was accepted to California Polytechnic State University and managed to pass every AP test I took. This journey has taught me that one of the most important things we can do is to work hard no matter what the circumstances; if we refuse to be discouraged, then we can achieve greatness.

VOCABULARY REVIEW •

Choose the correct words to fill in the blanks below.

term   distributive   products   column   binomials

1. To multiply a monomial with a polynomial, apply the _____ property.

2. To multiply any two polynomials, multiply each _____ in the first with each term in the second.

3. The FOIL method allows us to multiply any two _____ by finding the sum of the products of the first, outside, inside, and last two terms.

4. Use the column method to find the _____ of polynomials with more than two terms.

5. The _____ method of multiplying two polynomials is similar to long multiplication with whole numbers.

Problems

A Multiply the following by applying the distributive property.

1. $2x(3x + 1)$

2. $4x(2x - 3)$

3. $2x^2(3x^2 - 2x + 1)$

4. $5x(4x^3 - 5x^2 + x)$

5. $2ab(a^2 - ab + 1)$

6. $3a^2b(a^3 + a^2b^2 + b^3)$

7. $y^2(3y^2 + 9y + 12)$

8. $5y(2y^2 - 3y + 5)$

9. $4x^2y(2x^3y + 3x^2y^2 + 8y^3)$

10. $6xy^3(2x^2 + 5xy + 12y^2)$

11. $-2xy^2(2x - 3y + 7)$

12. $-3x^2y(4x - 5y + 9)$

B Multiply the following binomials. You should do about half the problems using the FOIL method and the other half using the column method. Remember, you want to be comfortable using both methods

13. $(x + 3)(x + 4)$

14. $(x + 2)(x + 5)$

15. $(x + 6)(x + 1)$

16. $(x + 1)(x + 4)$

17. $(a + 5)(a - 3)$

18. $(a + 2)(2a - 1)$

19. $(a - 6)(3a + 2)$

20. $(a - 8)(a + 2)$

21. $(x - a)(y + b)$

22. $\left(x + \frac{1}{2}\right)\left(x + \frac{3}{2}\right)$

23. $\left(x + \frac{3}{5}\right)\left(x + \frac{2}{5}\right)$

24. $\left(y + \frac{5}{6}\right)\left(y - \frac{5}{6}\right)$

25. $\left(y - \frac{4}{7}\right)\left(y + \frac{4}{7}\right)$

26. $(2x - 3)(x - 4)$

27. $(3x - 5)(x - 2)$

28. $(2x - 5)(3x - 2)$

29. $(3x + 6)(2x - 1)$

30. $(2x + 3)(a + 4)$

31. $(2x - 3)(a - 4)$

32. $(5x - 4)(5x + 4)$

33. $(6x + 5)(6x - 5)$

34. $\left(2x - \frac{1}{2}\right)\left(x + \frac{3}{2}\right)$

35. $\left(4x - \frac{3}{2}\right)\left(x + \frac{1}{2}\right)$

36. $(1 - 2a)(3 - 4a)$

37. $(1 - 3a)(3 + 2a)$

38. $(x + 2)^2$

39. $(a + 3)^2$

40. $(a - 3)^2$

41. $(x - 2)^2$

42. $(x - 5)^2$

43. $(x - 4)^2$

44. $\left(a - \frac{1}{2}\right)^2$

45. $\left(a + \frac{1}{2}\right)^2$

46. $(a + 0.8)^2$

47. $(a - 0.4)^2$

48. $(2x - 1)^2$

49. $(3x + 2)^2$

50. $(4a + 5)^2$

51. $(3x - 2)^2$

52. $(4x - 5y)^2$

53. $(5x + 4y)^2$

54. $(7m + 2n)^2$

55. $(6x - 10y)^2$

56. $(a + 5)(a - 5)$

57. $(a - 6)(a + 6)$

58. $(y - 1)(y + 1)$

59. $(y - 2)(y + 2)$

60. $(9 + x)(9 - x)$

61. $(10 - x)(10 + x)$

62. $(2x + 5)(2x - 5)$

63. $(3x + 5)(3x - 5)$

For each of the following problems, fill in the area of each small rectangle and square, and then add the results together to find the indicated product. Also, show that you get the same answer by multiplying the binomials and simplifying the product.

64. $(x + 2)(x + 3)$

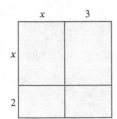

65. $(x + 4)(x + 5)$

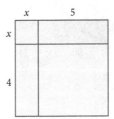

66. $(x + 1)(2x + 2)$

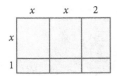

67. $(2x + 1)(2x + 2)$

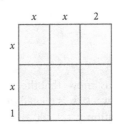

Multiply the following polynomials, and simplify your answer.

68. $(a - 3)(a^2 - 3a + 2)$

69. $(a + 5)(a^2 + 2a + 3)$

70. $(x + 2)(x^2 - 2x + 4)$

71. $(x + 3)(x^2 - 3x + 9)$

72. $(2x + 1)(x^2 + 8x + 9)$

73. $(3x - 2)(x^2 - 7x + 8)$

74. $(5x^2 + 2x + 1)(x^2 - 3x + 5)$

75. $(2x^2 + x + 1)(x^2 - 4x + 3)$

76. $(3a^4 + 2)(2a^2 + 5)$

77. $(7a^4 - 8)(4a^3 - 6)$

78. $(x + 3)(x + 4)(x + 5)$

79. $(x - 3)(x - 4)(x - 5)$

Simplify the following expressions.

80. $(x - 3)(x - 2) + 2$

81. $(2x - 5)(3x + 2) - 4$

82. $(2x - 3)(4x + 3) + 4$

83. $(3x + 8)(5x - 7) + 52$

84. $(x + 4)(x - 5) + (-5)(2)$

85. $(x + 3)(x - 4) + (-4)(2)$

86. $2(x - 3) + x(x + 2)$

87. $5(x + 3) + 1(x + 4)$

88. $3x(x + 1) - 2x(x - 5)$

89. $4x(x - 2) - 3x(x - 4)$

90. $x(x + 2) - 3$

91. $2x(x - 4) + 6$

C Solve.

92. **Area** The length of a rectangle is 5 units more than twice the width. Write an expression for the area of the rectangle.

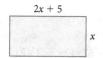

93. **Area** The length of a rectangle is 2 more than three times the width. Write an expression for the area of the rectangle.

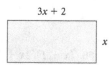

94. **Revenue** A store selling hair ribbons knows that the number of ribbons it can sell each week, x, is related to the price per ribbon, p, by the equation $x = 1,200 - 100p$. Write an expression for the weekly revenue that involves only the variables R and p. (*Remember:* The equation for revenue is $R = xp$.)

95. **Revenue** A store selling headphones knows from past experience that the number of headphones it can sell each week, x, is related to the price per set, p, by the equation $x = 1,300 - 100p$. Write an expression for the weekly revenue that involves only the variables R and p.

Applying the Concepts

96. **Area** The width and length of a rectangle are given by two consecutive integers. Write an expression for the area of the rectangle.

97. **Area** The width and length of a rectangle are given by two consecutive even integers. Write an expression for the area of the rectangle.

98. A rectangular swimming pool has a length which is three times as long as its width. A five foot pathway is built to surround the entire pool.

   a. Write and simplify an expression for the total area of the pool plus the pathway.

   b. Write and simplify an expression for the area of the pathway alone.

99. A circular garden has a radius of r feet. A 2-foot-wide rock border is placed around the entire garden.

2 ft

   a. Write and simplify an expression in terms of π for the total area of the garden plus the rock border.

   b. Write and simplify an expression for the area of the rock border alone.

100. A rectangular piece of cardboard has a length that is 1 inch more than twice the width w. Squares of sides 2 inches are cut from the corners, and the resulting flaps are folded up to create the sides of a box.

a. Write and simplify an expression for the volume of the box.

b. Write and simplify an expression for the surface area of the box. Assume the box is open (with no top).

FIND THE MISTAKE •

Each sentence below contains a mistake. Circle the mistake and write the correct word(s) or numbers(s) on the line provided.

   1. To find the product of two binomials, multiply the first terms and then multiply the second terms.

   _____

   2. When using the FOIL method to multiply the binomials $(9x - 2)$ and $(5x + 3)$, the product of the two outside terms is -6. _____

   3. For the problem $(x^2 - 4)(3x^2 + 6)$, adding the products of the two outside terms with the two inside terms gives us $4x^2 + 2$. _____

   4. For the problem $4x^2(3x^2 + 4x + 9)$, the degree of the answer is 2. _____

Trail Guide Project

Universal Mass

Research the history of mass and common units used to measure it. For example, when the French invented the metric system toward the end of the 18th century, what item did they use as an equivalent for 1 kilogram? Explain how our knowledge of mass has changed over time. Then find the mass in kilograms of the following items. Write the values in expanded form and in scientific notation.

	Mass	
	Expanded Form	Scientific Notation
Mercury		
Venus		
Earth		
Mars		
Jupiter		
Saturn		
Uranus		
Neptune		
Sun		
Earth's Moon		

Use the above masses to answer the following questions.

1. A tonne is a unit of measurement for mass in the metric system that equals 1000 kg. If oxygen takes up 23.1% of Earth's mass, how much is this quantity in tonnes?

2. Find the difference in mass between the following pairings. Write your answer in scientific notation.

   a. Moon vs. Earth _____

   b. Mars vs. Jupiter and Saturn _____

   c. Uranus and Neptune vs. Mercury and Venus _____

   d. Sun vs. all seven planets combined _____

Exponents: Definition and Properties [9.1, 9.2]

Integer exponents indicate repeated multiplications.

$a^r \cdot a^s = a^{r+s}$ *Product property for exponents*

$\dfrac{a^r}{a^s} = a^{r-s}$ *Quotient property for exponents*

$(ab)^r = a^r \cdot b^r$ *Distributive property for exponents*

$\left(\dfrac{a}{b}\right)^r = \dfrac{a^r}{b^r}$ *Expanded distributive property for exponents*

$(a^r)^s = a^{r \cdot s}$ *Power property for exponents*

$a^{-r} = \dfrac{1}{a^r}$ *Negative exponents property*

1. a. $2^3 = 2 \cdot 2 \cdot 2 = 8$

b. $x^5 \cdot x^3 = x^{5+3} = x^8$

c. $\dfrac{x^5}{x^3} = x^{5-3} = x^2$

d. $(3x)^2 = 3^2 \cdot x^2 = 9x^2$

e. $\left(\dfrac{2}{3}\right)^3 = \dfrac{2^3}{3^3} = \dfrac{8}{27}$

f. $(x^5)^3 = x^{5 \cdot 3} = x^{15}$

g. $3^{-2} = \dfrac{1}{3^2} = \dfrac{1}{9}$

h. $4x^{-3} = \dfrac{4}{x^3}$

Multiplication of Monomials [9.3]

To multiply two monomials, multiply coefficients and add exponents.

2. $(5x^2)(3x^4) = 15x^6$

Division of Monomials [9.3]

To divide two monomials, divide coefficients and subtract exponents.

3. $\dfrac{12x^9}{4x^5} = 3x^4$

Scientific Notation [9.1, 9.2, 9.3]

A number is in scientific notation when it is written as the product of a number n, $1 \le |n| < 10$, and an integer power of 10.

4. $768{,}000 = 7.68 \times 10^5$
$0.00039 = 3.9 \times 10^{-4}$

Addition and Subtraction of Polynomials [9.4]

To add two polynomials, add coefficients of like terms. To subtract one polynomial from another, add the opposite of the second to the first.

5. $(3x^2 - 2x + 1) + (2x^2 + 7x - 3)$
$= 5x^2 + 5x - 2$

6. $(3x + 5) - (4x - 3)$
$= 3x + 5 - 4x + 3$
$= -x + 8$

Multiplication of Polynomials [9.5]

To multiply a polynomial by a monomial, we apply the distributive property. To multiply two binomials we use the FOIL method. In other situations we use the Column method. Each method achieves the same result: To multiply any two polynomials, we multiply each term in the first polynomial by each term in the second polynomial.

7. a. $2a^2(5a^2 + 3a - 2)$
$= 10a^4 + 6a^3 - 4a^2$

b. $(x + 2)(3x - 1)$
$= 3x^2 - x + 6x - 2$
$= 3x^2 + 5x - 2$

c.
$$
\begin{array}{r}
2x^2 - 3x + 4 \\
3x - 2 \\
\hline
-4x^2 + 6x - 8 \\
6x^3 - 9x^2 + 12x - 8 \\
\hline
6x^3 - 13x^2 + 18x - 8
\end{array}
$$

d. $(x + 3)(x - 3) = x^2 - 9$

643

Name the base and exponent in each of the following expressions. Then use the definition of exponents as repeated multiplication to simplify. [9.1]

1. -5^2 **2.** $(-2)^4$

Simplify each of the following expressions. [9.1]

3. $(-7)^3$ **4.** $-\left(-\dfrac{1}{2}\right)^2$

5. $\left(\dfrac{2}{3}\right)^3$ **6.** -5^{-2}

7. $y^{30} \cdot y^{30}$ **8.** $(x^5)^2$

9. $(-3x)^3$ **10.** $(0.5xy)^2$

11. $(6b^2)^2$ **12.** $(x^7)^2(x^3)^4$

13. $(9x^3y^5)^2$ **14.** $\left(\dfrac{3}{4}ab^7\right)^3$

15. $(4x^3)^3(2x^5)^2$

Write each number in scientific notation. [9.1, 9.2]

16. 4,780,000   **17.** 30

18. -0.00000718 **19.** 0.03478

20. Write 3.47×10^4 in expanded form. [9.1]

21. Write -2.05×10^{-4} in standard form. [9.2]

22. Write 0.0398×10^3 in scientific notation. [9.2]

Simplify each expression. Write all answers with positive exponents only. [9.2]

23. 7^{-2} **24.** $8x^{-2}$

25. $(-3)^{-3}$ **26.** $(17a^2b^7)^0$

27. $\dfrac{a^{-3}}{a^{-1}}$ **28.** $\dfrac{(2x)^4}{(2x)^7}$

29. $\dfrac{(2x)^{-12}}{(2x)^{-15}}$ **30.** $\left(\dfrac{x}{2}\right)^{-5}$

31. $\left(\dfrac{-7}{y}\right)^2$ **32.** $\left(\dfrac{y^4}{y^6}\right)^2$

33. $\left(\dfrac{2a^{-5}b^4}{3a^{-2}b^5}\right)^{-3}$ **34.** $\dfrac{(x^{-2})^3(x^{-3})^{-5}}{(x^{-4})^{-2}}$

Multiply each expression and simplify. [9.3]

35. $(2a^4)(5a^2)(8a^4)$ **36.** $(-6a^4b^2)(5ab^7)$

Divide each expression and simplify. Write all answers with positive exponents only. [9.3]

37. $\dfrac{27y^4}{9y^7}$ **38.** $\dfrac{24a^5b^6}{6ab^5}$

Simplify. Write all answers with positive exponents only. [9.3]

39. $\dfrac{25x^7y^8z^{-3}}{5x^6y^8z^{-4}}$ **40.** $\dfrac{(6a^2b)^2(9a^3b^3)}{18a^4b^7}$

41. $\dfrac{6x^2}{3x^{-1}} + \dfrac{18x^5}{6x^2}$ **42.** $\dfrac{(2.7 \times 10^3)(3.2 \times 10^{-2})}{7.2 \times 10^5}$

43. $xy\left(y + \dfrac{1}{x}\right)$ **44.** $xy\left(\dfrac{3}{x} - \dfrac{2}{y}\right)$

45. $x^2\left(1 - \dfrac{9}{x^2}\right)$ **46.** $x^2\left(1 - \dfrac{5}{x} + \dfrac{6}{x^2}\right)$

Add or subtract as indicated. [9.4]

47. $8x^2 - 6x + 5x - 2$

48. $(5x^2 - 3x + 4) - (3x^2 + 4x - 7)$

49. Subtract $2x + 8$ from $3x - 6$.

50. Add $7x^2 - 8x + 10$ to $-8x^2 + 2x - 12$.

51. Subtract $6x + 2$ from $x + 3$.

52. Find the value of $2y^2 - 4y + 8$ when y is -2.

53. Find the value of the polynomial $x^2 - 2x + 4$ when x is 3.

Multiply. [9.5]

54. $2a^2(4a^2 + 5a + 7)$ **55.** $(x - 2)(x + 3)$

56. $(3x - 3)(4x - 4)$ **57.** $(x + 3)(x^2 + 3x + 9)$

58. $\left(x + \dfrac{3}{5}\right)\left(x + \dfrac{2}{5}\right)$ **59.** $\left(y + \dfrac{5}{6}\right)\left(y - \dfrac{5}{6}\right)$

60. $(x + 1)^3$ **61.** $(3a - 2)^2$

62. $(x - 4)(x + 4)$ **63.** $(2x - b)(2x + b)$

64. Volume Find the volume of a cube if the length of a side is 1.5 miles. [9.1]

65. Volume Find the volume of a rectangular solid if the length is one third the width, and the height is six times the width. [9.5]

66. The illustration below shows prices for some of the most expensive cars in the world. Write the prices of the cars in scientific notation. Round your answer to the nearest tenth.

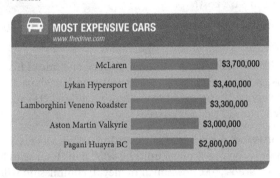

MOST EXPENSIVE CARS
www.thedrive.com

McLaren	$3,700,000
Lykan Hypersport	$3,400,000
Lamborghini Veneno Roadster	$3,300,000
Aston Martin Valkyrie	$3,000,000
Pagani Huayra BC	$2,800,000

67. The illustration below shows some of the close finishes from the 2016 Rio Olympic games. Write the margin of victory for each race in scientific notation.

CLOSE CALLS IN RIO
NBC Olympics

Clement/Mucheru — M 400M Hurdles	0.05 seconds
Ibarguen/Rojas — W Triple Jump	0.19 seconds
Drouin/Barshim — M High Jump	0.02 seconds
Thompson/Bowie — W 100 M	0.12 seconds

Simplify.

1. $4,310 + 734$

2. $\dfrac{4}{7} + \dfrac{1}{4}$

3. $15.15 - 4.631$

4. $5\dfrac{5}{6} - 3\dfrac{1}{3}$

5. $6,314(321)$

6. $0.014(60)$

7. $143\overline{)5,148}$

8. $\dfrac{7}{28} \div \dfrac{14}{36}$

9. Round the number 536,204 to the nearest ten thousand.

10. Write 0.36 as a fraction in lowest terms.

11. Change $\dfrac{61}{8}$ to a mixed number in lowest terms.

12. Find the difference of 0.64 and $\dfrac{3}{8}$.

13. Write the decimal 0.37 as a percent.

Use the tables given in Chapter 8 to make the following conversion.

14. 9 kilograms to pounds

15. Write 136% as a fraction or mixed number in lowest terms.

16. What percent of 74 is 25.9?

Simplify.

17. $\left(\dfrac{1}{2}\right)^4 + \left(\dfrac{1}{8}\right)^2$

18. $7x - 4 + 5x + 7$

19. $-|-9|$

20. $\dfrac{-4(-5) + 3(-7)}{14 - 11}$

21. $21 - 4(6 - 2)$

22. $\sqrt{36} - \sqrt{81}$

Solve.

23. $\dfrac{4}{7}y = 24$

24. $-4(3x + 5) = 3(2x + 9)$

25. Subtract -9 from 4.

26. Solve: $\dfrac{4.8}{4} = \dfrac{7.2}{x}$

Perform the indicated operations.

27. $(-4x^2 - 5x + 3) + (3x^2 - 2x + 1) - (x^2 + 3x + 7)$

28. $(5x + 1)^2$

29. $(x - 2)(x^2 + 2x + 4)$

30. Age Ben is 5 years older than Ryan. In 6 years the sum of their ages will be 69. How old are they now?

31. Gas Mileage A truck travels 690 miles on 30 gallons of gas. What is the gas mileage in miles per gallon.

32. Discount A surfboard that usually sells for $560 is marked down to $420. What is the discount? What is the discount rate?

33. Geometry Find the length of the hypotenuse of a right triangle with sides of 3 and 4 meters.

34. Cost of Coffee If coffee costs $7.36 per pound, how much will 1 lb 8 oz, cost?

35. Interest If $2,400 is invested at 8% simple interest for 60 days, how much interest is earned?

36. Wildflower Seeds C.J. works in a nursery, and one of his tasks is filling packets of wildflower seeds. If each packet is to contain $\frac{1}{5}$ pound of seeds, how many packets can be filled from 12 pounds of seeds?

37. Commission A car stereo salesperson receives a commission of 6% on all units he sells. If his total sales for March are $7,800, how much money in commission will he make?

38. Volume How many 12-fluid ounce glasses of water will it take to fill a 12-gallon aquarium?

The chart shows the number of dogs in the United States over five years. Use the information to answer the following questions.

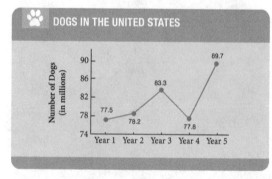

DOGS IN THE UNITED STATES

39. How many more dogs were there in Year 5 than Year 4? What is the percent increase from Year 4 to Year 5? Round to the nearest tenth.

40. Round the number of dogs in Year 1 and Year 5 to the nearest million. Use the rounded numbers to find the ratio of dogs in Year 1 to Year 5.

Simplify each of the following expressions. [9.1]

1. $(-3)^5$

2. $\left(\dfrac{2}{5}\right)^2$

3. $(2x^2)^3(3x^2)^2$

4. Write 2.47×10^5 in expanded form. [9.1]

Simplify each expression. Write all answers with positive exponents only. [9.2]

5. -3^{-2}

6. $(7a^2b^2)^1$

7. $\dfrac{a^{-4}}{a^{-1}}$

8. $\dfrac{(x^{-2})^3(x^{-4})^{-1}}{x}$

9. Write 0.0278×10^3 in scientific notation. [9.2]

Simplify. Write all answers with positive exponents only. [9.3]

10. $\dfrac{35x^3y^3z}{7xyz^3}$

11. $\dfrac{(3a^2b)(12a^2b)}{4ab^2}$

12. $\dfrac{24x^3}{3x^2} - \dfrac{33x^{-1}}{11x^{-2}}$

13. $\dfrac{(3.2 \times 10^{-3})(1.8 \times 10^2)}{3.6 \times 10^{-5}}$

Add or subtract as indicated. [9.4]

14. $8x^2 - 4x + 3x - 12$

15. $(3x^2 - x + 3) - (2x^2 - 8x + 3)$

16. Subtract $5x + 8$ from $-(x + 2)$.

17. Find the value of $2y^2 - y - 4$ when y is 3.

Multiply. [9.5]

18. $2a^2(3a^2 + 5a - 4)$

19. $\left(x - \dfrac{3}{2}\right)\left(x + \dfrac{1}{2}\right)$

20. $(4x + 3)(2x - 2)$

21. $(x + 3)(x - 3)$

The illustration below shows the top grossing classic Disney animated movies of all time.

TOP GROSSING ANIMATED DISNEY MOVIES
www.destican.com

Snow White and the Seven Dwarfs (1937)	$782,620,000
101 Dalmatians (1961)	$717,405,900
Fantasia (1941)	$596,252,200
The Lion King (1994)	$554,524,300
The Jungle Book (1967)	$529,021,800

Write the total revenue for the given movies in scientific notation, rounded to the nearest hundredth.

22. Snow White and the Seven Dwarfs

23. The Lion King

The illustration below shows the number of stars received by the top rated comic strips of all time at an online rating site.

TOP RATED COMIC STRIPS
http://www.rateitall.com/t-141-comic-strips.aspx

Calvin and Hobbes	4.49
Far Side	4.47
Raising Duncan	3.89
Peanuts	3.85
Dilbert	3.66

Write the difference in the number of stars received by the following strips in scientific notation.

24. Calvin and Hobbes compared to Far Side

25. Raising Duncan compared to Peanuts

Chapter 1

Exercise Set 1.1

Vocabulary Review **1.** place value **2.** standard form, expanded form **3.** hyphen **4.** comma **5.** set **6.** counting numbers **7.** whole numbers

Problems **1.** 8 ones, 7 tens **3.** 5 ones, 4 tens
5. 8 ones, 4 tens, 3 hundreds **7.** 8 ones, 0 tens, 6 hundreds
9. 8 ones, 7 tens, 3 hundreds, 2 thousands **11.** 9 ones, 6 tens, 5 hundreds, 3 thousands, 7 ten thousands, 2 hundred thousands
13. Ten thousands **15.** Hundred millions **17.** Ones
19. Hundred thousands **21.** 600 + 50 + 8 **23.** 60 + 8
25. 4,000 + 500 + 80 + 7 **27.** 30,000 + 2,000 + 600 + 70 + 4
29. 3,000,000 + 400,000 + 60,000 + 2,000 + 500 + 70 + 7
31. 400 + 7 **33.** 30,000 + 60 + 8 **35.** 3,000,000 + 4,000 + 8
37. 547 **39.** 6,323 **41.** 27,035 **43.** 70,907
45. 180,643 **47.** 406,008 **49.** Twenty-nine
51. Forty **53.** Five hundred seventy-three
55. Seven hundred seven **57.** Seven hundred seventy
59. Twenty-three thousand, five hundred forty
61. Three thousand, four **63.** Three thousand, forty
65. One hundred four million, sixty-five thousand, seven hundred eighty
67. Five billion, three million, forty thousand, eight **69.** Two million, five hundred forty-six thousand, seven hundred thirty-one
71. Twenty million, four hundred thirty-two thousand **73.** 325
75. 5,432 **77.** 86,762 **79.** 2,000,200 **81.** 2,002,200
83. Thousands **85.** 100,000 + 6,000 + 800 + 60 + 9
87. Three million, fourteen thousand, five hundred seventy-two dollars **89.** 3 inches **91.** 5 inches **93.** 6 **95.** 3
97. 12

Find the Mistake **1.** The place value of the 7 in the number 562,472 is tens. **2.** The number 12,789 written in expanded form is 10,000 + 2,000 + 700 + 80 + 9. **3.** The number 9,023,627,003 written in words is nine billion, twenty-three million, six hundred twenty-seven thousand, three. **4.** Writing forty million, three hundred forty-eight thousand, thirteen in digits gives 40,348,013.

Exercise Set 1.2

Vocabulary Review **1.** carrying **2.** sum **3.** zero **4.** commutative **5.** associative **6.** solution, inspection **7.** perimeter **8.** variable

Problems **1.** 15 **3.** 14 **5.** 24 **7.** 15 **9.** 20 **11.** 68
13. 98 **15.** 7,297 **17.** 6,487 **19.** 96 **21.** 7,449 **23.** 65
25. 102 **27.** 875 **29.** 829 **31.** 10,391 **33.** 16,204
35. 155,554 **37.** 111,110 **39.** 17,391 **41.** 14,892
43. 180 **45.** 2,220 **47.** 18,285 **49.** 774 **51.** 7,195
53.

First Number a	Second Number b	Their Sum $a + b$
61	38	99
63	36	99
65	34	99
67	32	99

55.

First Number a	Second Number b	Their Sum $a + b$
9	16	25
36	64	100
81	144	225
144	256	400

57. 9 + 5 **59.** 8 + 3 **61.** 4 + 6 **63.** 1 + (2 + 3)
65. 2 + (1 + 6) **67.** (1 + 9) + 1 **69.** 4 + (n + 1)
71. n = 4 **73.** n = 5 **75.** n = 8 **77.** n = 8 **79.** n = 9
81. n = 4 **83.** The sum of 4 and 9 **85.** The sum of 8 and 1
87. The sum of 2 and 3 is 5. **89. a.** 5 + 2 **b.** 8 + 3
91. a. m + 1 **b.** m + n **93.** 12 in. **95.** 16 ft
97. 26 yd **99.** 18 in. **101.** 19 yd **103.** 34 gallons
105. $349

Find the Mistake **1.** To find the sum of 786 and 49, add the ones place by writing the 5 and carrying the 1. **2.** The problem (12 + 7) + 3 = 12 + (7 + 3) uses the associative property of addition. **3.** The solution for the equation 47 = x + 29 is x = 18. **4.** The perimeter of a rectangle with a length of 35 inches and a width of 15 inches is 100 inches.

Exercise Set 1.3

Vocabulary Review **1.** difference **2.** columns **3.** borrowing **4.** estimation

Problems **1.** 32 **3.** 22 **5.** 10 **7.** 111
9. The difference of 10 and 2. **11.** The difference of a and 6.
13. The difference of 8 and 2 is 6. **15.** 8 − 3 **17.** $y − 9$
19. 3 − 2 = 1 **21.** 312 **23.** 403 **25.** 1,111 **27.** 4,544
29. 15 **31.** 33 **33.** 5 **35.** 33 **37.** 95 **39.** 152
41. 274 **43.** 488 **45.** 538 **47.** 163 **49.** 1,610 **51.** 46,083
53.

First Number a	Second Number b	The Difference of a and b $a − b$
25	15	10
24	16	8
23	17	6
22	18	4

55.

First Number a	Second Number b	The Difference of a and b $a − b$
400	256	144
400	144	256
225	144	81
225	81	144

57. n = 6 **59.** n = 19 **61.** n = 9 **63.** n = 13 **65.** n = 25
67. n = 11 **69.** n = 9 **71.** n = 1 **73.** $255 **75.** 33 feet
77. 168 students **79.** $574

81. a.

Year	Number of Users (Millions)
2014	171
2015	189
2016	207

b. 36 million

Find the Mistake **1.** Translating "The difference of 22 and 3 is 19" into symbols gives us 22 − 3 = 19. **2.** To subtract 50 from 290, vertically align the digits with the same place value. **3.** To find the difference of 85 and 27, begin by borrowing 1 ten from the tens column and subtracting 7 from 15. **4.** The solution for the equation 108 = 130 − y is y = 22.

Landmark Review

1. 500 + 40 + 9
2. 1,000 + 400 + 90 + 3 **3.** 60,000 + 200 + 40 + 3
4. 30,000,000 + 400,000 + 3,000 + 5 **5.** 18 **6.** 31 **7.** 117
8. 7,650 **9.** 103,701 **10.** 402,162 **11.** 530 **12.** 1,235
13. 17 **14.** 22 **15.** 12 **16.** 102 **17.** x = 5
18. n = 14 **19.** a = 7 **20.** y = 20 **21.** x = 16
22. n = 4 **23.** y = 5 **24.** x = 1

Exercise Set 1.4

Vocabulary Review **1.** round **2.** less **3.** more **4.** horizontal axis, vertical axis **5.** estimate

Problems **1.** 40 **3.** 50 **5.** 50 **7.** 80 **9.** 460 **11.** 470
13. 56,780 **15.** 4,500 **17.** 1,200 **19.** 500 **21.** 800
23. 900 **25.** 1,100 **27.** 5,000 **29.** 39,600
31. 5,000 **33.** 10,000 **35.** 1,000 **37.** 658,000
39. 608,000 **41.** 5,745,000

| | Rounded to the Nearest | | |
Original Number	Ten	Hundred	Thousand
43. 7,821	7,820	7,800	8,000
45. 5,999	6,000	6,000	6,000
47. 10,985	10,990	11,000	11,000
49. 99,999	100,000	100,000	100,000

51. $15,200   **53.** $31,000   **55.** 1,200   **57.** 1,900
59. 58,000   **61.** 11,900   **63.** 5,000   **65.** 96,000
67.

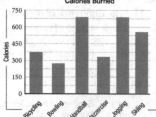

Calories Burned

69. a.

Year	Projected Sales (Millions)
1	9
2	19
3	30

b. 21 million units

71. $3,000,000   **73.** 27,380,000 viewers   **75.** 8,500,000 viewers
77. a.

Venue	Capacity
National Stadium	91,000
Aquatic Center	17,000
Indoor Stadium	18,000
Tennis Courts	17,400
Center Stadium	38,000

b. 74,000 people

Find the Mistake   1. Rounding 12,456 to the nearest hundred gives us 12,500.   **2.** To round 102,673 to the nearest ten, replace the 3 with a zero to get 102,670.   **3.** To estimate the sum of 14,256 and 2,789 by rounding to the nearest hundred, add 14,300 and 2,800.   **4.** Using the bar chart below, Student C's home is 8 more miles from school than Student A's home.

Exercise Set 1.5
Vocabulary Review   1. addition   **2.** factors   **3.** distributive
4. multiplication property of zero   **5.** commutative
6. associative   **7.** area   **8.** identity property of multiplication
Problems   1. 300   **3.** 600   **5.** 3,000   **7.** 5,000   **9.** 21,000
11. 81,000   **13.** The product of 6 and 7   **15.** The product of 2 and n
17. The product of 9 and 7 is 63.   **19.** $7 \cdot n$ **21.** $6 \cdot 7 = 42$
23. $0 \cdot 6 = 0$ **25.** Products: $9 \cdot 7$ and 63   **27.** Products: 4(4) and 16
29. Factors: 2, 3, and 4   **31.** Factors: 2, 2, and 3   **33.** 9(5)
35. $7 \cdot 6$ **37.** $(2 \cdot 7) \cdot 6$ **39.** $(3 \times 9) \times 1$ **41.** $7(2) + 7(3) = 35$
43. $9(4) + 9(7) = 99$ **45.** $3(x) - 3(1) = 3x - 3$
47. $2(x) - 2(5) = 2x - 10$ **49.** 100   **51.** 228   **53.** 36
55. 1,440   **57.** 950   **59.** 1,725   **61.** 121   **63.** 1,552
65. 4,200   **67.** 66,248   **69.** 279,200   **71.** 12,321
73. 106,400   **75.** 198,592   **77.** 612,928   **79.** 333,180
81. 18,053,805   **83.** 263,646,976

85.

First Number a	Second Number b	Their product ab
11	11	121
11	22	242
22	22	484
22	44	968

87.

First Number a	Second Number b	Their product $a \cdot b$
25	10	250
25	100	2,500
25	1,000	25,000
25	10,000	250,000

89.

First Number a	Second Number b	Their product $(a)(b)$
12	20	240
36	20	720
12	40	480
36	40	1,440

91. 25 in.^{2} **93.** 84 m^2 **95.** 192 cm^2 **97.** $n = 3$
99. $n = 9$ **101.** $n = 0$ **103.** $n = 12$ **105.** $n = 11$
107. $n = 9$ **109.** 2,860 miles   **111.** 1,500 square feet without the garage, 2,067 square feet with the garage   **113.** 1,142 calories
115. about 220 crackers   **117.** No   **119.** 180,000
121. 120,000   **123.** 7,000,000   **125.** 1,250   **127.** 96
Find the Mistake   1. Factors are numbers that when multiplied together give a product.   **2.** The distributive property is used to show that $16(5 + 9) = 16(5) + 16(9)$.   **3.** The first step when multiplying 73 and 4 is to multiply 4 and 3 by writing down the 2 and carrying the 1.   **4.** The area of a rectangle with a length of 35 inches and a width of 8 inches is 280 square inches.

Exercise Set 1.6
Vocabulary Review   1. quotient   **2.** dividend, divisor
3. remainder   **4.** undefined
Problems   1. $6 \div 3$ **3.** $45 \div 9$ **5.** $r \div s$ **7.** $20 \div 4 = 5$
9. $2 \cdot 3 = 6$ **11.** $9 \cdot 4 = 36$ **13.** $6 \cdot 8 = 48$ **15.** $7 \cdot 4 = 28$
17. 5   **19.** 8   **21.** Undefined   **23.** Undefined   **25.** 23
27. 1,530   **29.** 1,350   **31.** 18,000   **33.** 16,680
35. 24,000   **37.** 45   **39.** 49   **41.** 432   **43.** 1,438
45. 705   **47.** 3,020   **49.** 61 R 4   **51.** 90 R 1   **53.** 13 R 7
55. 234 R 6   **57.** 402 R 4   **59.** 35 R 35
61.

First Number a	Second Number b	The Quotient of a and b $\dfrac{a}{b}$
100	25	4
100	26	3 R 22
100	27	3 R 19
100	28	3 R 16

63. a   **65.** b   **67.** 1   **69.** 2   **71.** 4   **73.** 6   **75.** $1,850
77. 16¢   **79.** 5 miles   **81.** 6 glasses with 2 oz left over
83. 3 bottles   **85.** 19 miles   **87.** 665 mg   **89.** 437
91. 3,247   **93.** 869   **95.** 5,684   **97.** 169 gal
Find the Mistake   1. The division notation $\frac{10}{5}$ is equivalent to $5\overline{)10}$ **2.** The quotient of 198 and 11 is 18.   **3.** To divide 1,640 by 12, first estimate the number of twelves we can subtract from 16.   **4.** Dividing 2,380 by 13 gives a remainder of 1.

Exercise Set 1.7
Vocabulary Review **1.** multiplication **2.** factor
3. exponent, base **4.** zero **5.** grouping symbols
6. left, right **7.** squared, cubed
Problems **1.** Base 4, Exponent 5 **3.** Base 3, Exponent 6
5. Base 8, Exponent 2 **7.** Base 9, Exponent 1
9. Base 4, Exponent 0 **11.** 36 **13.** 8 **15.** 1 **17.** 1
19. 81 **21.** 10 **23.** 12 **25.** 1 **27.** 12 **29.** 100
31. 4 **33.** 43 **35.** 16 **37.** 84 **39.** 14 **41.** 74
43. 12,768 **45.** 104 **47.** 416 **49.** Undefined **51.** 21
53. 7 **55.** 16 **57.** 84 **59.** 40 **61.** 41 **63.** 18
65. 405 **67.** 124 **69.** 11 **71.** 91 **73.** 7
75. $8(4 + 2) = 48$ **77.** $2(10 + 3) = 26$ **79.** $3(3 + 4) + 4 = 25$
81. $20 \div 2 - 9 = 1$ **83.** $8 \cdot 5 + 5 \cdot 4 = 60$ **85.** 247 calories
87. 407 calories **89.** Big Mac has 263 more calories which is
more than twice the calories.
91. 4 **93.** 16 **95.** Answers will vary
Find the Mistake **1.** The expression 8^4 means that 8 is used as a
factor 4 times. **2.** The number 7 raised to the third power equals
$7^3 = 343$. **3.** Following the order of operations, work all additions
and subtractions after evaluating any exponents. **4.** Simplifying
$(4 + 1)^3 - (9 + 1)^2$ gives 25.

Chapter 1 Review
1. 9 ones, 8 tens, 7 hundreds
2. 1 ones, 8 tens, 4 hundreds, 6 thousands
3. Fifty thousand, six hundred thirty-one **4.** 965
5. 12,072,009 **6.** $50,000 + 900 + 5$
7. $100,000 + 20,000 + 3,000 + 300 + 20 + 1$ **8.** c **9.** f
10. e **11.** a **12.** 35 **13.** 20 **14.** 669 **15.** 3,999
16. 996 **17.** 216 **18.** 1,887 **19.** 16,322 **20.** $n = 2$
21. $n = 8$ **22.** $P = 58m$ **23.** $x - 2$ **24.** $b - a$
25. 18 **26.** 10 **27.** 811 **28.** 2,486 **29.** 7,986
30. $n = 5$ **31.** $n = 1$ **32.** 600 **33.** 57,000
34. 630,000 **35.** 7,000 **36.** 20,000 **37.** $4(5) + 4(8) = 52$
38. $5(x) - 5(8) = 5x - 40$ **39.** 1,096 **40.** 16,898
41. 239,760 **42.** 48,332,256 **43.** 45 cm^2 **44.** $n = 10$
45. $n = 9$ **46.** 65 **47.** 27 **48.** 94 **49.** 608
50. 468 R 12 **51.** 88 R 42 **52.** $3(11 + 4) = 45$
53. $30 \div 5 - 2 = 4$ **54.** $6 \div 2 + 7 = 10$
55. $10 \cdot 5 - 6 \cdot 2 = 38$ **56.** 8 **57.** 1 **58.** 10,566
59. Undefined **60.** 9 **61.** 4 **62.** 205 **63.** $7x - 14$
64. 12 **65.** 0 **66.** $2,650,000; Two million, six hundred
fifty thousand dollars **67.** $1,000,000; One million dollars
68. $123,100 **69.** $11,400 **70.** 23 miles

Chapter 1 Test
1. Thirty thousand, six hundred fifty-two **2.** 6,007,029
3. $200,000 + 80,000 + 5,000 + 600 + 30 + 4$ **4.** d **5.** g
6. c **7.** b **8.** 698 **9.** 24,603 **10.** $P = 62m$
11. 521 **12.** 4,787 **13.** 240,000 **14.** 810 **15.** 19,758
16. 72 **17.** 23 **18.** $2(13 + 4) = 34$ **19.** $18 \div 6 + 12 = 15$
20. 40 **21.** 3 **22.** 80 **23.** $5x - 20$ **24.** Undefined **25.** 0
26. 6,061,265; Six million, sixty-one thousand, two hundred
sixty-five **27.** 26,004,409; Twenty-six million, four thousand,
four hundred nine

Chapter 2

Exercise Set 2.1
Vocabulary Review **1.** origin **2.** positive **3.** less than, greater
than **4.** absolute value **5.** opposites **6.** negative **7.** integers

Problems **1.** 4 is less than 7. **3.** 5 is greater than -2.
5. -10 is less than -3. **7.** 0 is greater than -4 **9.** $30 > -30$
11. $-10 < 0$ **13.** $-3 > -15$ **15.** $3 < 7$ **17.** $7 > -5$
19. $-6 < 0$ **21.** $-12 < -2$ **23.** $-9 < |9|$
25. $-3 < |6|$ **27.** $15 > |-4|$ **29.** $|-2| < |-7|$ **31.** 2
33. 100 **35.** 8 **37.** 231 **39.** 42 **41.** 200 **43.** 8
45. 231 **47.** -3 **49.** 2 **51.** -75 **53.** 0 **55.** 2
57. 8 **59.** -2 **61.** -8 **63.** 0 **65.** Positive
67. -100 **69.** -20 **71.** -360 **73.** $-61°$ F
75. $-5°$ F **77.** $-3°$ F **79.** 10° F and 25-mph wind
81. 25 **83.** 5 **85.** 6 **87.** 19
Find the Mistake **1.** The expression $-4 < 1$ is read "-4 is less
than 1." **2.** The number -3 appears to the right of the number
-24 on the number line. **3.** The opposite of -18 is 18.
4. The absolute value of -36 is 36.

Exercise Set 2.2
Vocabulary Review same, absolute values, different, smaller,
larger, sign
Problems **1.** 5 **3.** 1 **5.** -2 **7.** -6 **9.** 4 **11.** 4
13. -9 **15.** 15 **17.** -3 **19.** -11 **21.** -7 **23.** -3
25. -16 **27.** -8 **29.** -127 **31.** 49 **33.** 34
35.

First Number a	Second Number b	Their Sum a + b
5	-3	2
5	-4	1
5	-5	0
5	-6	-1
5	-7	-2

37.

First Number x	Second Number y	Their Sum x + y
-5	-3	-8
-5	-4	-9
-5	-5	-10
-5	-6	-11
-5	-7	-12

39. -4 **41.** 10 **43.** -445 **45.** 107 **47.** -1
49. -20 **51.** -17 **53.** -50 **55.** -7 **57.** 3
59. 50 **61.** -73 **63.** -11 **65.** 17 **67.** -18
69. -8 **71.** 11 **73.** -3 **75.** $-4 + 17 + (-6) = 7$
77. $10 + x = 4; x = -6$ **79.** $-5 + x = -8; x = -3$
81. $-7 + x = 2; x = 9$ **83.** $(-9) + (-2) + 10 = -1$
85. b **87.** c **89.** b **91.** a **93.** $0
95. $(-\$17) + \$14 + (-\$21) = -\$24$
97. $2 + (-1) + 3 = 4$ **99.** $-5°$ F, $-15°$ F **101.** -3
103. 5 **105.** 15 **107.** 6 **109.** 2
Find the Mistake **1.** The problem $6 + (-10) = -4$ is interpreted
as, "Start at the origin, move 6 units in the positive direction, and
then move 10 units in the negative direction." **2.** Adding two numbers with different signs will give an answer that has the same sign as
the number with the larger absolute value. **3.** Adding -8 and -5
gives us -13. **4.** The sum of -2, 4, -3, and -5 is -6.

Exercise Set 2.3
Vocabulary Review **1.** subtract **2.** opposite **3.** addition
4. negative **5.** positive
Problems **1.** 2 **3.** 2 **5.** -8 **7.** -5 **9.** 7 **11.** 12
13. 3 **15.** -7 **17.** -3 **19.** -13 **21.** -50
23. -100 **25.** 399 **27.** -21

29.

First Number x	Second Number y	Their Difference x − y
8	6	2
8	7	1
8	8	0
8	9	-1
8	10	-2

31.

First Number x	Second Number y	Their Difference x − y
8	-6	14
8	-7	15
8	-8	16
8	-9	17
8	-10	18

33. −7   **35.** −9   **37.** −14   **39.** −11   **41.** −400
43. 4; 7   **45.** 0; −3   **47.** 5; 2   **49.** 11   **51.** −4   **53.** 8
55. 6   **57.** b   **59.** a   **61.** −100   **63.** b   **65.** a
67. 44°   **69.** −11 − (−22) = 11° F   **71.** 3 − (−24) = 27° F
73. 60 − (−26) = 86° F   **75.** −14 − (−26) = 12° F   **77.** 30
79. 36   **81.** 64   **83.** 48   **85.** 41   **87.** 40

Find the Mistake   1. Subtracting 5 from 4 is the same as adding 4 and
−5.   **2.** To subtract −1 from 8, we must move 1 unit in the positive
direction from 8 on the number line.   **3.** The problem 11 − (−7) is
read, "11 subtract negative 7."   **4.** To find the difference of −5 and 6,
change 6 to −6, and add to −5.

Landmark Review   1. 2, −2   **2.** 11, 11   **3.** 25, −25
4. 110, 110   **5.** 7   **6.** −5   **7.** −3   **8.** −15   **9.** 11   **10.** −3
11. 2   **12.** −20   **13.** 4   **14.** −6   **15.** −12   **16.** 15   **17.** −9   **18.** 11

Exercise Set 2.4
Vocabulary Review   1. base, exponent   **2.** positive
3. negative   **4.** zero
Problems   1. −56   **3.** −60   **5.** 56   **7.** 81
9. −24   **11.** 24   **13.** −6   **15. a.** 16 **b.** −16
17. a. −125 **b.** −125   **19. a.** 16 **b.** −16

21.

Number x	Square x^2
−3	9
−2	4
−1	1
0	0
1	1
2	4
3	9

23.

First Number x	Second Number y	Their Product xy
6	2	12
6	1	6
6	0	0
6	−1	−6
6	−2	−12

25.

First Number a	Second Number b	Their Product ab
−5	3	−15
−5	2	−10
−5	1	−5
−5	0	0
−5	−1	5
−5	−2	10
−5	−3	15

27. −4   **29.** 50
31. 1   **33.** −35
35. −22   **37.** −30
39. −25   **41.** 9
43. −13   **45.** 19
47. 6   **49.** −25
51. 26   **53.** −40
55. 97   **57.** −6
59. −4   **61.** −17
63. −16°
65. a gain of $200

67.

Pitcher, Team	Rolaids Points
John Smoltz, Atlanta	164
Trevor Hoffman, San Diego	124
Rafael Soriano, Tampa Bay	131
Jim Johnson, Baltimore	149
Craig Kimbrel, Atlanta	125

69. 70

	Product
Eagle	0
Birdie	−7
Par	0
Bogie	+3
Double Bogie	+2
Total:	−2

71. a   **73.** a
75. b   **77.** 7
79. 5   **81.** −5
83. 9   **85.** 4
87. 7   **89.** 405
91. undefined

Find the Mistake   1. Writing the problem 6(−4) as repeated
addition gives us (−4) + (−4) + (−4) + (−4) + (−4) + (−4).
2. Multiplying a negative by a positive and then by another

negative will give us a positive answer.   **3.** The problem $(-5)^3$ can
also be written as $(-5)(-5)(-5)$.

4. −5(3 − 6) − 2(3 + 1) = −5(−3) − 2(4)
$$= 15 + (-8)$$
$$= 7$$

Exercise Set 2.5
Vocabulary Review   1. same   **2.** different
Problems   1. −3   **3.** −5   **5.** 3   **7.** 2   **9.** −4
11. −2   **13.** 0   **15.** −5

17.

First Number a	Second Number b	The Quotient of a and b $a \div b$
100	−5	−20
100	−10	−10
100	−25	−4
100	−50	−2

19.

First Number a	Second Number b	The Quotient of a and b $\frac{a}{b}$
−100	−5	20
−100	5	−20
100	−5	−20
100	5	20

21. 1   **23.** −6   **25.** −2   **27.** −1   **29.** 0
31. Undefined   **33.** −1   **35.** 2   **37.** −3
39. Undefined   **41.** 4   **43.** −5   **45.** 8   **47.** 3
49. 55   **51.** −68   **53.** −3   **55.** 51   **57.** 5
59. 5   **61.** 30   **63.** 1   **65.** −5   **67.** 35   **69.** 6
71. −1   **73.** c   **75.** a   **77.** d
79.

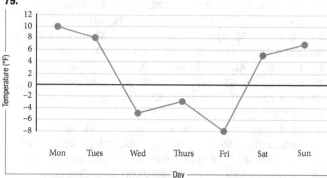

81. 5(3) + 5(7)   **83.** 36   **85.** 7,500   **87.** 350
89. a. 7 **b.** 2 **c.** 7 **d.** −6 **e.** −4
Find the Mistake   1. False: Dividing a negative number by a positive
number will give a negative number for an answer.   **2.** True

3. $\dfrac{-6(-6-2)}{-11-1} = \dfrac{-6(-8)}{-12} = \dfrac{48}{-12} = -4$

4. $[(-5)(5) - 20] \div -3^2 = -45 \div (-9)$
$$= 5$$

Chapter 2 Review
1. −25 is less than −7   **2.** −17 < −2   **3.** 24, 24   **4.** −16, 16
5. <   **6.** <   **7.** >   **8.** >   **9.** 8,500   **10.** 4   **11.** 6
12. −3   **13.** −8   **14.** −11   **15.** 29   **16.** −57
17. −117   **18.** −16   **19.** 84   **20.** −24   **21.** −14
22. 16   **23.** −637   **24.** 16   **25.** 25   **26.** −64
27. −25   **28.** −64   **29.** −9   **30.** −105   **31.** −11
32. 36   **33.** undefined   **34.** −3   **35.** 9   **36.** −60

37. 81   **38.** 27   **39.** undefined   **40.** 84   **41.** -89
42. -56 **43.** 0   **44.** 3   **45.** 2   **46.** -2 **47.** 13
48. -15 **49.** -20 **50.** 6   **51.** -4 **52.** 9   **53.** -7
54. -73 **55.** 18   **56.** 2   **57.** -77 **58.** 4   **59.** -12
60. -48 **61.** 20   **62.** -27 **63.** -12 and 4
64. $250   **65.** $50°$ **66.** 87 degrees
67. $-$175   **68.** $441 - 1{,}299 = -858$ texts
69. $896 - 952 = -56$ minutes

Chapter 2 Cumulative Review
1. 4,307   **2.** 6 hundreds, 8 tens, 4 ones   **3.** 5,700
4. 20   **5.** 3   **6.** 374   **7.** 2,417   **8.** 3   **9.** 7   **10.** 9
11. 5   **12.** 1,770   **13.** 980,826   **14.** 15   **15.** 137
16. $6 \times (10 + 4) = 84$ **17.** $(9 \times 3) + (7 \times 4) = 55$
18. 14   **19.** 1   **20.** -25 **21.** 49   **22.** 395
23. 206   **24.** 2   **25.** 108   **26.** -10 **27.** 144
28. 8   **29.** -17 **30.** 4   **31.** -51 **32.** -45
33. 66   **34.** 25   **35.** 29   **36.** 81   **37.** 63
38. 5   **39.** -3 **40.** 6   **41.** undefined
42. 0   **43.** -2 **44.** -12 **45.** 5   **46.** -17 **47.** 50
48. 243   **49.** -54 **50.** 24 cm; 36 cm^2 **51.** 12 in.
52. $-17, 7$ **53.** 4

Chapter 2 Test
1. $-27, 27$ **2.** 18, 18   **3.** $<$ **4.** $<$ **5.** 4
6. -14 **7.** -3 **8.** -36 **9.** 72   **10.** -21
11. -27 **12.** 4   **13.** 14   **14.** -18 **15.** undefined
16. -4 **17.** -43 **18.** 8   **19.** -34 **20.** 0
21. 37   **22.** -21 **23.** -1 **24.** -19 **25.** -6
26. -41 **27.** 17   **28.** 36   **29.** -8 **30.** -15
31. -6 **32.** $-$59   **33.** $17°$
34. $2{,}000 - 5{,}000 = -3{,}000$ animals
35. $1{,}000 - 4{,}000 = -3{,}000$ animals

Chapter 3

Exercise Set 3.1
Vocabulary Review   **1.** equal   **2.** variable   **3.** right, straight
4. acute, obtuse   **5.** complementary   **6.** supplementary
7. protractor
Problems   **1.** $20a$ **3.** $-18x$ **5.** $-10y$ **7.** $60y$
9. $5 + x$ **11.** $13 + x$ **13.** $12a + 21$ **15.** $7x + 28$
17. $7x + 35$ **19.** $6a - 42$ **21.** $20 + 4x$ **23.** $6x + 15$
25. $-12x + 6y$ **27.** $35 - 20y$ **29.** $10x$ **31.** $4a$ **33.** y
35. $-8x$ **37.** $3a$ **39.** $-5x$ **41.** $6x + 11$ **43.** $2x + 2$
45. $-a + 12$ **47.** $4y - 4$ **49.** $-2x + 4$ **51.** $8x - 6$
53. $-x + 3$ **55.** $a - 3$ **57.** $6x + 16$ **59.** $10x - 11$
61. $19y + 32$ **63.** $-18y + 18$ **65.** $6x + 14$ **67.** $-15a + 19$
69. 14   **71.** 27   **73.** -19 **75.** -23 **77.** 12
79. -25 **81.** 1   **83.** 18   **85.** 12   **87.** 2   **89.** 42
91. 18   **93.** 28   **95.** 40   **97.** 26   **99.** 4   **101.** $75°$
103. $55°$ **105.** $6(x + 4) = 6x + 24$ **107.** $4x + 4$
109. $10x - 4$ **111.** Complement: $65°$; supplement: $155°$; acute
113. a. $32°$F   **b.** $22°$F   **c.** $-18°$F   **115. a.** $27   **b.** $47   **117.** 0
119. -6 **121.** -3 **123.** -5 **125.** x **127.** $y - 2$
Find the Mistake   **1.** Multiplying $-3(4x - 2)$ using the distributive
property gives us $-12x + 6$.   **2.** The first step when simplifying
$2(5y + 1) + 4(5y - 1)$ is to apply the distributive property to get $10y$
$+ 2 + 20y - 4 = 30y - 2$.   **3.** To find the value of $-3y + 2y$ when
$y = 6$, we must plug in the value of y for both y's to get $-3(6) + 2(6)$
$= -6$.   **4.** Suppose x and y are complementary angles. If $x = 25°$,
then y must equal $65°$.

Exercise Set 3.2
Vocabulary Review   **1.** variable   **2.** addition   **3.** solution
4. isolate   **5.** subtraction
Problems   **1.** Yes   **3.** Yes   **5.** No   **7.** Yes   **9.** No
11. No   **13.** $x = 6$ **15.** $x = 11$ **17.** $a = -15$
19. $x = 1$ **21.** $y = -3$ **23.** $b = -13$ **25.** $x = -4$
27. $x = -3$ **29.** $a = 2$ **31.** $a = -6$ **33.** $a = -6$
35. $x = -1$ **37.** $x = -2$ **39.** $x = -16$ **41.** $a = -3$
43. $x = 10$ **45.** $x = 8$ **47.** $x = 13$
49. $x = 24$ **51.** $157°$ **53.** $x + 67° + 67° = 180°$; $46°$
55. $x - 12 = 30$; $x = 42$ **57.** $8 + 5 = x - 7$; $x = 20$
59. 5   **61.** -5 **63.** x **65.** $7x - 11$ **67.** 1   **69.** 1
Find the Mistake   **1.** The solution for an equation is a number
that when used in place of the variable makes the equation a true
statement.   **2.** Adding the same quantity to both sides of an equation will not change the solution to the equation.   **3.** To solve the
problem $x - 2 = 3$, add 2 to each side of the equation.   **4.** Solving
$-3x - 6 + 4x = 9$ gives us $x = 15$.

Exercise Set 3.3
Vocabulary Review   **1.** multiplication   **2.** nonzero   **3.** simplify
Problems   **1.** $x = 8$ **3.** $x = -6$ **5.** $x = -6$ **7.** $x = -6$
9. $y = 48$ **11.** $y = -28$ **13.** $a = 16$ **15.** $x = -7$
17. $y = -8$ **19.** $x = 6$ **21.** $x = -7$ **23.** $y = -4$
25. $x = 2$ **27.** $a = 3$ **29.** $x = 4$ **31.** $a = -24$
33. $a = 12$ **35.** $x = -8$ **37.** $x = 15$ **39.** $a = 3$
41. $y = -1$ **43.** $x = 1$ **45.** $x = 3$ **47.** $x = 1$
49. $a = -1$ **51.** $x = -1$ **53.** $y = -14$ **55.** $x = 9$
57. $x = 8$ **59.** 4 three-pointers   **61.** $2x + 5 = 19$; $x = 7$
63. $5x - 6 = 9$; $x = 3$ **65.** $6x = -24$; $x = -4$ **67.** $6a - 16$
69. $-15x + 3$ **71.** $3y - 9$ **73.** $16x - 6$
Find the Mistake   **1.** The multiplication property of equality says
that multiplying the same nonzero quantity to both sides of an
equation never changes the solution.   **2.** To isolate x on the left side
of the equation $\frac{x}{3} = -9$, we must multiply each side by 3.   **3.** The
first step to finding a solution for the equation $-6 = 12 - 6y$ is to
subtract 12 from both sides.   **4.** The first step to solving $-9x = 45$
is to divide both sides of the equation by -9 to get $x = -5$.

Exercise Set 3.4
Vocabulary Review   **1.** linear   **2.** simplify   **3.** variable
4. constant   **5.** multiplication, division   **6.** solution
Problems   **1.** $x = 3$ **3.** $x = 2$ **5.** $x = -3$ **7.** $y = -4$
9. $x = 0$ **11.** $a = 2$ **13.** $x = -2$ **15.** $x = 3$
17. $y = -1$ **19.** $x = 7$ **21.** $x = -3$ **23.** $a = 1$
25. $x = -2$ **27.** $x = 4$ **29.** $x = 5$ **31.** $x = 10$
33. $x = 5$ **35.** 242 miles   **37.** 502 miles   **39.** 35
41. 65   **43.** 2   **45.** $l = 14$ **47.** $y = -2$
Find the Mistake   **1.** The solution to the linear equation
$6a + 1 = -3a - 8$ is a negative number.   **2.** The last step to finding
the solution to the linear equation $2(3x - 2) = -x + 10$ uses the
division property of equality to isolate the variable on one side of the
equation.   **3.** To solve $4x = 28$, we divide each side by 4.

Landmark Review
1. $12x + 24$ **2.** $12y - 17$
3. $18x + 11$ **4.** $6x - 7$ **5.** -2 **6.** 2   **7.** 1   **8.** -23
9. $x = 6$ **10.** $y = 19$ **11.** $z = 7$ **12.** $a = -10$ **13.** $y = 0$
14. $x = 15$ **15.** $x = 46$ **16.** $a = 13$ **17.** $x = 15$
18. $x = -10$ **19.** $y = -60$ **20.** $x = -36$ **21.** $x = -1$
22. $x = -5$ **23.** $y = 10$ **24.** $a = -7$

Exercise Set 3.5

Vocabulary Review   1. formula   **2.** variable   **3.** rate, time
Problems   1. 108 ft; 704 ft^2 **3.** 12 inches   **5.** 23 yards
7. The length of one side is 8 cm.   **9.** $240   **11.** 12 ft
13. $C = 100°C$; yes   **15.** $F = 32°F$; yes   **17.** 30°C   **19.** 5°F
21. a. 4 hrs **b.** 220 miles   **23. a.** 4 hours **b.** 65 mph
25. 360 in.^{3} **27.** $y = -11$ **29.** $y = -2$ **31.** $x = 3$
33. $x = 7$ **35.** $y = 1$ **37.** $y = 3$ **39.** $y = 0$ **41.** $y = 8$
43. $x = 0$ **45.** $x = 6$
47. Complement: 45°; supplement: 135°
49. Complement: 59°; supplement: 149°
51.

Age (Years)	Maximum Heart Rate (Beats per Minute)
18	202
19	201
20	200
21	199
22	198
23	197

53. a. 45 in.^{2} **b.** 14 mm   **55.** 2,400 lb   **57.** $x + 5$
59. $3x$ **61.** $3(x + 8)$ **63.** $4 - x$ **65.** $3x - 4$
Find the Mistake   1. A formula is an equation with two variables.
2. Using the formula $C = \frac{5(F - 32)}{9}$ to find C when $F = 75°$, we have
$C = \frac{5(75 - 32)}{9}$.   **3.** To find y when $x = 6$ in the equation $5x + 8y$
$= 24$, we must solve $5(6) + 8y = 24$.   **4.** Two angles, x and y, are
supplementary if $x + y = 180°$.

Exercise Set 3.6

Vocabulary Review   1. known   **2.** unknown   **3.** variable
4. equation   **5.** sentence   **6.** reread
Problems   1. $x + 3$ **3.** $2x + 1$ **5.** $5x - 6$ **7.** $3(x + 1)$
9. $5(3x + 4)$ **11.** $4x - 7$ **13.** The number is 2.   **15.** The
number is -2.   **17.** The number is 3.   **19.** The number is
5.   **21.** The number is -2.   **23.** length = 10 m; width = 5 m.
25. 7 ft.   **27.** 20°, 40°, and 120°.   **29.** 108°
31. 45°, 45°, and 90°   **33.** 15° and 165°   **35.** 28° and 62°
37. Patrick is 33; Pat is 53.

	Now	In 2 Years
Patrick	x	$x + 2$
Pat	$x + 20$	$x + 22$

39. Sue is 35; Dale is 39.   **41.** $x = 8, y = 6, z = 9$
43. 39 hours   **45.** $62   **47.** Yes   **49.** 2   **51.** 4
53. 5   **55.** $3x$ **57.** 2   **59.** 8
Find the Mistake   1. $x + 7x = 16$ **2.** $x + x + x = 18$
3. $(x + 16) + (x + 10) = 56$ **4.** $8(3x) + 12x = 180$

Chapter 3 Review

1. $8a$ **2.** $-8x$ **3.** $13x + 8$ **4.** $-2b - 10$
5. $4x + 15$ **6.** $12x + 6$ **7.** $5x + 13$ **8.** $34a + 10$
9. -22 **10.** -3 **11.** -11 **12.** 5   **13.** No   **14.** No
15. Yes   **16.** -18 **17.** -5 **18.** 5   **19.** $x = -7$
20. $x = 2$ **21.** $x = -120$ **22.** $x = 16$ **23.** $x = 3$
24. $x = -11$ **25.** $x = -2$ **26.** $x = -3$ **27.** $x = 9$
28. $x = 5$ **29.** $x = -5$ **30.** $y = -11$ **31.** $a = 3$
32. $x = -6$ **33.** $x = 0$ **34.** $x = 2$ **35.** 15 m
36. 104°F   **37.** $C = 10°C$ **38.** 195 miles   **39.** 474 mph
40. 504 yd^3 **41.** Complement : 18°; supplement: 108°
42. Complement: 30°; supplement: 120°   **43.** The number is -4.

44. The number is 4.   **45.** Molly is 14; Kevin is 8
46. Sarah is 48; Turner is 51   **47.** 20°, 60°, 100°   **48.** 4 ft.
49. 29° and 61°   **50.** length = 17 cm; width = 13 cm

Chapter 3 Cumulative Review

1. 12,052   **2.** 4,892   **3.** 9,000   **4.** 689,000   **5.** 315
6. 48,332,256   **7.** 89   **8.** 20 R 23   **9.** 43   **10.** 76
11. 66   **12.** 403   **13.** >   **14.** >   **15.** 7   **16.** -4
17. -7 **18.** -636 **19.** 4   **20.** -117 **21.** -25
22. 81   **23.** -81 **24.** -23 **25.** 66   **26.** 36   **27.** 2
28. 0   **29.** 2   **30.** 25   **31.** $3y + 15$ **32.** $40x + 32$
33. $6x$ **34.** $-6x$ **35.** -32 **36.** 13   **37.** -17
38. -13 **39.** $x = 26$ **40.** $x = -32$ **41.** $x = -8$
42. $x = 4$ **43.** $x = -2$ **44.** $x = 0$ **45.** -23 **46.** 10
47. The number is -3 **48.** The number is 5

Chapter 3 Test

1. $10x - 5$ **2.** $-2b + 3$ **3.** $11x - 36$ **4.** $5x + 13$
5. -7 **6.** -3 **7.** No   **8.** Yes   **9.** 3   **10.** -3
11. $x = 13$ **12.** $x = -63$ **13.** $x = 18$ **14.** $x = -8$
15. $x = 1$ **16.** $x = 11$ **17.** 12 m   **18.** 15°C
19. 225 miles   **20.** 506 mph   **21.** The number is -9
22. Susan is 27; Karen is 24   **23.** 18°, 36°, 126°   **24.** 18°, 72°
25. length is 13 cm; width is 7 cm

Chapter 4

Exercise Set 4.1

Vocabulary Review   1. fraction   **2.** numerator,
denominator   **3.** proper, improper   **4.** equivalent   **5.** mixed
Problems   1. 1, 3   **3.** $-2, 3$ **5.** 6, 1   **7.** $a, -b$
9.   **11.** $\frac{3}{4}, \frac{1}{2}, \frac{9}{10}$

Numerator a	Denominator b	Fraction $\frac{a}{b}$
3	5	$\frac{3}{5}$
-1	7	$-\frac{1}{7}$
$-x$	$-y$	$\frac{x}{y}$
$x + 1$	x	$\frac{x+1}{x}$

13–21.

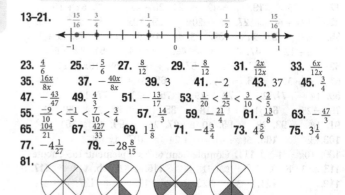

23. $\frac{4}{6}$ **25.** $-\frac{5}{6}$ **27.** $\frac{8}{12}$ **29.** $-\frac{8}{12}$ **31.** $\frac{2x}{12x}$ **33.** $\frac{6x}{12x}$
35. $\frac{16x}{8x}$ **37.** $-\frac{40x}{8x}$ **39.** 3   **41.** -2 **43.** 37   **45.** $\frac{3}{4}$
47. $-\frac{43}{47}$ **49.** $\frac{4}{3}$ **51.** $-\frac{13}{17}$ **53.** $\frac{1}{20} < \frac{4}{25} < \frac{3}{10} < \frac{2}{5}$
55. $\frac{-9}{10} < \frac{-1}{5} < \frac{7}{10} < \frac{3}{4}$ **57.** $\frac{14}{3}$ **59.** $-\frac{21}{4}$ **61.** $\frac{13}{8}$ **63.** $-\frac{47}{3}$
65. $\frac{104}{21}$ **67.** $\frac{427}{33}$ **69.** $1\frac{1}{8}$ **71.** $-4\frac{3}{4}$ **73.** $4\frac{5}{6}$ **75.** $3\frac{1}{4}$
77. $-4\frac{1}{27}$ **79.** $-28\frac{8}{15}$
81.

83. $\frac{1}{2}, \frac{1}{2}, \frac{1}{4}, \frac{1}{4}$ **85.** $\frac{4}{5}$ **87.** $\frac{29}{43}$ **89.** $\frac{71}{12}$ **91.** $\frac{1526}{5}$ ¢   **93.** $\frac{12}{50}$
95. d   **97.** a   **99.** 108   **101.** 60   **103.** 4   **105.** 5
107. 7   **109.** 51
Find the Mistake   1. For the fraction $\frac{21}{7}$, the denominator is 7.
2. The fraction $\frac{90}{15}$ is considered an improper fraction.   **3.** Changing
$6\frac{4}{5}$ to an improper fraction gives us $\frac{34}{5}$.

4. If we divide the numerator and denominator of the fraction $\frac{8}{12}$ by 4, then we get the equivalent fraction $\frac{2}{3}$.

Exercise Set 4.2

Vocabulary Review   1. prime   **2.** divisor   **3.** composite
4. lowest terms
Problems   1. Prime   **3.** Composite; factors: 3, 5, 7
5. Composite; 3 is a factor   **7.** Prime   **9.** $2^2 \cdot 3$ **11.** 3^4
13. $5 \cdot 43$ **15.** $3 \cdot 5$ **17.** $\frac{1}{2}$ **19.** $\frac{2}{3}$ **21.** $\frac{4}{5}$ **23.** $-\frac{9}{5}$
25. $\frac{7}{11}$ **27.** $-\frac{3}{7}$ **29.** $-\frac{1}{7}$ **31.** $\frac{7}{9}$ **33.** $\frac{7}{5}$ **35.** $-\frac{3}{5}$
37. $\frac{5}{3}$ **39.** $\frac{42}{55}$ **41. a.** $\frac{2}{17}$ **b.** $\frac{3}{26}$ **c.** $\frac{1}{9}$ **d.** $\frac{3}{28}$ **e.** $\frac{2}{19}$
43. a. $\frac{1}{45}$ **b.** $\frac{1}{30}$ **c.** $\frac{1}{18}$ **d.** $\frac{1}{15}$ **e.** $\frac{1}{10}$ **45. a.** $\frac{1}{3}$ **b.** $\frac{5}{6}$ **c.** $\frac{1}{5}$
47. $\frac{9}{16}$
49–51.

53. 2   **55.** $\frac{1}{4}$ **57.** $\frac{2}{3}$
59. $\frac{7}{15}$ **61.** $\frac{1}{4}$ **63.** 3   **65.** 45   **67.** $2^2 \cdot 3 \cdot 5$
69. $2^2 \cdot 3 \cdot 5$ **71.** 9   **73.** 25   **75.** 49 in.²   **77.** b
Find the Mistake   1. The number 30 is a composite number because it has 10 as a divisor.   **2.** The number 70 factored into a product of primes is $2 \cdot 5 \cdot 7$.   **3.** When reducing the fraction $\frac{32}{48}$ to lowest terms, divide out the common factor 16 to get $\frac{2}{3}$.   **4.** Reducing the fraction $\frac{112}{14}$ to lowest terms gives us $\frac{8}{1} = 8$.

Landmark Review   1. Numerator 3; denominator 5

2. Numerator 1; denominator 3   **3.** Numerator 7; denominator 15
4. Numerator 4; denominator x **5.** $\frac{4x}{8x}$ **6.** $\frac{6x}{8x}$ **7.** $\frac{x}{8x}$
8. $\frac{20x}{8x}$ **9.** $\frac{1}{2}$ **10.** $\frac{3}{5}$ **11.** $\frac{3}{5}$ **12.** $\frac{5}{8}$ **13.** $\frac{17}{18}$ **14.** $\frac{31}{42}$

Exercise Set 4.3

Vocabulary Review   1. product   **2.** fractions   **3.** of   **4.** triangle
Problems   1. $\frac{8}{15}$ **3.** $\frac{7}{8}$ **5.** 1   **7.** $\frac{27}{4}$
9. $\frac{1}{24}$ **11.** $\frac{24}{125}$ **13.** $-\frac{9}{64}$
15.

First Number x	Second Number y	Their Product xy
$\frac{1}{2}$	$\frac{2}{3}$	$\frac{1}{3}$
$\frac{2}{3}$	$\frac{3}{4}$	$\frac{1}{2}$
$\frac{3}{4}$	$\frac{4}{5}$	$\frac{3}{5}$
$\frac{5}{a}$	$-\frac{a}{6}$	$-\frac{5}{6}$

17.

First Number x	Second Number y	Their Product xy
$\frac{1}{2}$	30	15
$\frac{1}{5}$	30	6
$\frac{1}{6}$	30	5
$\frac{1}{15}$	30	2

19. -1 **21.** $\frac{3}{5}$ **23.** 9   **25.** 1   **27.** -8 **29.** $-\frac{3}{35}$
31. $\frac{4}{9}$ **33.** $\frac{9}{16}$ **35.** $\frac{1}{4}$ **37.** $\frac{8}{27}$ **39.** $\frac{1}{2}$ **41.** $\frac{9}{100}$
43. 3   **45.** 24   **47.** 4   **49.** 9   **51.** $\frac{3}{10}$; numerator should be 3, not 4   **53.** $\frac{1}{4}$; answer should be positive.   **55.** 14
57. -14 **59.** 5   **61.** -6 **63.** 3 yd²   **65.** 133 in.²
67. $\frac{4}{9}$ ft²   **69.** 3,600 students   **71.** 126, 500 ft²
73. About 2,132 children   **75.** $\frac{1}{27}$ **77.** $\frac{8}{27}$ **79.** 2   **81.** 3
83. 2   **85.** 5   **87.** 3   **89.** $\frac{4}{3}$ **91.** 3   **93.** $\frac{1}{7}$
Find the Mistake   1. To find the product of two fractions, multiply the numerators and multiply the denominators.   **2.** To multiply $\frac{6}{7}$ by $\frac{12}{9}$, find the product of the numerators and divide it by the product of the denominators to get $\frac{72}{63}$.   **3.** Simplifying $\left(\frac{5}{6}\right)^2 \cdot \frac{8}{9}$ gives $\frac{50}{81}$.   **4.** The area of a triangle with a height of 14 inches and a base of 32 inches is 224 square inches.

Exercise Set 4.4

Vocabulary Review   1. product   **2.** reciprocal   **3.** divisor
4. fraction
Problems   1. $\frac{15}{4}$ **3.** $\frac{4}{3}$ **5.** 9   **7.** 200   **9.** $\frac{3}{8}$ **11.** -1
13. $-\frac{49}{64}$ **15.** $\frac{3}{4}$ **17.** $\frac{15}{16}$ **19.** $\frac{56}{625}$ **21.** $\frac{5}{18}$ **23.** $-\frac{9}{2}$
25. $-\frac{2}{9}$ **27.** 9   **29.** $\frac{4}{5}$ **31.** $-\frac{15}{2}$ **33.** 40   **35.** $\frac{7}{10}$
37. 13   **39.** 12   **41.** 186   **43.** 646   **45.** $17\frac{1}{2}$ **47.** $\frac{3}{5}$
49. 40   **51.** $3 \cdot 5 = 15$; $3 \div \frac{1}{5} = 3 \cdot \frac{5}{1} = 15$ **53.** 14 blankets
55. 48 bags   **57.** 6   **59.** $\frac{7}{16}$ **61.** 1,778 students
63. 28 cartons   **65.** $0 < \frac{1}{2} < 1 < \frac{3}{2}$ **67.** $\frac{1}{6} < \frac{1}{3} < \frac{1}{2} < \frac{5}{6}$
Find the Mistake   1. Two numbers whose product is 1 are said to be reciprocals.   **2.** Dividing the fraction $\frac{12}{7}$ by $\frac{4}{9}$ is equivalent to $\frac{12}{7} \cdot \frac{9}{4}$.   **3.** To work the problem $\frac{22}{5} \div \frac{10}{3}$, multiply the first fraction by the reciprocal of the second fraction.   **4.** The quotient of $\frac{14}{11}$ and $\frac{32}{6}$ is $\frac{21}{88}$.

Exercise Set 4.5

Vocabulary Review   1. least common denominator
2. equivalent   **3.** numerators   **4.** lowest terms
Problems   1. $\frac{2}{3}$ **3.** $\frac{1}{4}$ **5.** $\frac{1}{2}$ **7.** $-\frac{1}{3}$ **9.** $\frac{3}{2}$ **11.** -1
13. $\frac{4}{5}$ **15.** $\frac{10}{3}$
17.

First Number a	Second Number b	The Sum of a and b $a + b$
$\frac{1}{2}$	$\frac{1}{3}$	$\frac{5}{6}$
$\frac{1}{3}$	$\frac{1}{4}$	$\frac{7}{12}$
$\frac{1}{4}$	$\frac{1}{5}$	$\frac{9}{20}$
$\frac{1}{5}$	$\frac{1}{6}$	$\frac{11}{30}$

19.

First Number a	Second Number b	The Sum of a and b $a + b$
$\frac{1}{12}$	$\frac{1}{2}$	$\frac{7}{12}$
$\frac{1}{12}$	$\frac{1}{3}$	$\frac{5}{12}$
$\frac{1}{12}$	$\frac{1}{4}$	$\frac{1}{3}$
$\frac{1}{12}$	$\frac{1}{6}$	$\frac{1}{4}$

21. $\frac{7}{9}$ **23.** $\frac{7}{3}$ **25.** $\frac{7}{4}$ **27.** $\frac{7}{6}$ **29.** $\frac{1}{20}$ **31.** $\frac{7}{10}$
33. $\frac{19}{24}$ **35.** $\frac{13}{60}$ **37.** $\frac{31}{100}$ **39.** $\frac{67}{144}$ **41.** $\frac{29}{35}$ **43.** $\frac{949}{1260}$
45. $-\frac{88}{9}$ **47.** $\frac{10}{3}$ **49.** -1 **51.** $-\frac{11}{15}$ **53.** $\frac{13}{420}$
55. $\frac{41}{24}$ **57.** $\frac{53}{60}$ **59.** $\frac{5}{4}$ **61.** $\frac{3}{4}$ **63.** $\frac{1}{4}$ **65.** 19
67. 3   **69.** 9   **71.** 4   **73.** $\frac{1}{4} < \frac{3}{8} < \frac{1}{2} < \frac{3}{4}$ **75.** $\frac{160}{63}$
77. $\frac{5}{8}$ **79.** $\frac{7}{3}$ **81.** 3   **83.** $\frac{9}{2}$ pints   **85.** \$1,325   **87.** $\frac{7}{18}$

89.

Grade	Number of Students	Fraction of Students
A	5	$\frac{1}{8}$
B	8	$\frac{1}{5}$
C	20	$\frac{1}{2}$
Below C	7	$\frac{7}{40}$
Total	40	1

91. 10 lots   **93.** $\frac{3}{2}$ in   **95.** $\frac{9}{5}$ ft   **97.** $\frac{11}{4}$ **99.** $\frac{14}{5}$
101. $\frac{44}{5} = 8\frac{4}{5}$ **103.** $-\frac{4}{7}$ **105.** a. $\frac{5}{20}$ b. $\frac{12}{20}$ c. $\frac{18}{20}$ d. $\frac{2}{20}$
107. $\frac{13}{15}$ **109.** $\frac{7}{4} = 1\frac{3}{4}$
Find the Mistake   1. The fractions $\frac{a}{c}$ and $\frac{b}{c}$ can be added to become $\frac{a+b}{c}$ because they have a common denominator.   **2.** Subtracting $\frac{12}{21}$ from $\frac{18}{21}$ gives us $\frac{6}{21} = \frac{2}{7}$.   **3.** The least common denominator for a set of denominators is the smallest number that is exactly divisible by each denominator.   **4.** The LCD for the fractions $\frac{4}{6}, \frac{2}{8}$, and $\frac{3}{4}$ is 24.

Exercise Set 4.6
Vocabulary Review   1. mixed number   **2.** improper fraction
3. addition sign, columns   **4.** borrow
Problems   1. $5\frac{1}{10}$ **3.** $13\frac{2}{3}$ **5.** $6\frac{93}{100}$ **7.** $5\frac{5}{6}$ **9.** $-9\frac{3}{4}$
11. $3\frac{1}{5}$ **13.** $12\frac{1}{2}$ **15.** $-9\frac{9}{20}$ **17.** $\frac{32}{45}$ **19.** $1\frac{2}{3}$ **21.** 4
23. $-4\frac{3}{10}$ **25.** $-\frac{1}{10}$ **27.** $-3\frac{1}{5}$ **29.** $2\frac{1}{8}$ **31.** $5\frac{4}{5}$
33. $12\frac{2}{9}$ **35.** $3\frac{4}{9}$ **37.** 15   **39.** $1\frac{3}{10}$ **41.** $4\frac{1}{8}$ **43.** $4\frac{1}{3}$
45. $11\frac{3}{8}$ **47.** $8\frac{6}{7}$ **49.** $3\frac{3}{8}$ **51.** $10\frac{4}{15}$ **53.** $2\frac{1}{15}$ **55.** 9
57. $18\frac{1}{10}$ **59.** 14   **61.** 17   **63.** $6\frac{1}{4}$ **65.** $9\frac{7}{10}$ **67.** $5\frac{1}{2}$
69. $\frac{2}{3}$ **71.** $1\frac{11}{12}$ **73.** $3\frac{11}{12}$ **75.** $5\frac{19}{20}$ **77.** $5\frac{1}{2}$ **79.** $\frac{13}{24}$
81. $10\frac{5}{12}$ **83.** $7\frac{1}{2}$ **85.** $\frac{11}{13}$ **87.** $3\frac{1}{2}$ **89.** $1\frac{1}{3}$ **91.** $5\frac{29}{40}$
93. $5\frac{1}{2}$ cups   **95.** $\frac{5}{6}$ cup   **97.** $2,441\frac{3}{5}$¢   **99.** $163\frac{3}{4}$ mi
101. $2\frac{1}{4}$ yd²   **103.** $\frac{3}{4} < \frac{5}{4} < 1\frac{1}{2} < 2\frac{1}{8}$ **105.** $12\frac{1}{4}$ in.
107. $31\frac{1}{6}$ in.   **109.** NFL: $P = 306\frac{2}{3}$ yd; Canadian: $P = 350$ yd; Arena: $P = 156\frac{2}{3}$ yd   **111.** 3   **113.** $4\frac{63}{64}$ **115.** $\frac{9}{10}$
117. $3\frac{5}{8}$ **119.** $2\frac{1}{4}$ **121.** $3\frac{1}{16}$ **123.** $2\frac{1}{4}$ ft²   **125.** $3\frac{3}{8}$ ft²
Find the Mistake   1. Multiplying $4\frac{3}{8}$ and $9\frac{2}{7}$ gives us the mixed number $40\frac{5}{8}$.   **2.** The answer to the division problem $3\frac{9}{14} \div 2$ written as a mixed number is $1\frac{23}{28}$.   **3.** To begin adding $3\frac{9}{14}$ and $5\frac{1}{3}$, write each mixed number with the addition sign and then apply the commutative and associative properties, such that $\left(3 + \frac{9}{14}\right) + \left(5 + \frac{1}{3}\right)$.   **4.** The first step when subtracting $8 - 3\frac{2}{7} = 4\frac{5}{7}$ is to borrow 1 from 8 in the form of $\frac{7}{7}$.

Landmark Review   1. 1   **2.** $\frac{1}{5}$ **3.** $\frac{19}{15}$ **4.** $\frac{5}{4}$
5. $\frac{73}{105}$ **6.** $\frac{41}{30} = 1\frac{11}{30}$ **7.** $\frac{1}{10}$ **8.** $\frac{29}{8}$ **9.** $\frac{14}{3}$
10. $\frac{21}{2}$ **11.** $\frac{5}{4}$ **12.** $4\frac{2}{3}$ **13.** $4\frac{3}{5}$ **14.** $3\frac{1}{2}$
15. $2\frac{8}{17}$ **16.** $23\frac{3}{8}$ **17.** $9\frac{4}{9}$ **18.** $1\frac{1}{5}$ **19.** $2\frac{5}{16}$
20. $5\frac{11}{15}$ **21.** $10\frac{7}{40}$ **22.** $6\frac{1}{14}$ **23.** $5\frac{5}{6}$

Exercise Set 4.7
Vocabulary Review   1. complex fraction   **2.** LCD
3. whole numbers   **4.** simplify

Problems   1. 7   **3.** 3   **5.** 2   **7.** 35   **9.** $\frac{1}{6}$ **11.** $7\frac{1}{2}$
13. $3\frac{2}{3}$ **15.** $6\frac{3}{8}$ **17.** $4\frac{5}{12}$ **19.** $\frac{8}{9}$ **21.** $\frac{1}{2}$ **23.** $1\frac{1}{10}$
25. 5   **27.** $\frac{3}{5}$ **29.** $\frac{7}{11}$ **31.** 5   **33.** $\frac{17}{28}$ **35.** $\frac{13}{22}$

37. 14   **39.** $\frac{15}{16}$ **41.** $1\frac{5}{17}$ **43.** $\frac{3}{29}$ **45.** $1\frac{34}{67}$ **47.** $\frac{346}{441}$
49. $\frac{32}{33}$ **51.** $5\frac{2}{5}$ **53.** 8   **55.** $115\frac{2}{3}$ yd   **57.** $1\frac{3}{8}$
59. 3   **61.** $21x$ **63.** $6a - 16$ **65.** $3y - 9$
Find the Mistake   1. The first step in solving the problem $\frac{1}{4} - \left(2\frac{3}{8} - 1\frac{5}{8}\right)^2$ is to subtract the fractions inside the parentheses before evaluating the exponent.   **2.** To simplify $5\frac{2}{3} + \left(10\frac{1}{3} \cdot \frac{2}{3}\right)$ you must first change $10\frac{1}{3}$ into the improper fraction $\frac{31}{3}$ before multiplying by $\frac{2}{3}$.   **3.** A complex fraction is a fraction in which a fraction or combination of fractions appear in the numerator and/or the denominator of the original fraction.

4. To simplify the complex fraction $\dfrac{\frac{1}{6} + \frac{2}{3}}{\frac{5}{6} + \frac{5}{12}}$, multiply the top and bottom of the fraction by 12.

Exercise Set 4.8
Vocabulary Review   linear equations, LCD, subtraction, multiplication, original
Problems   1. $x = \frac{7}{8}$ **3.** $x = -\frac{3}{2}$ **5.** $x = -\frac{1}{15}$ **7.** $x = \frac{1}{10}$
9. $x = -\frac{21}{10}$ **11.** $x = -\frac{1}{11}$ **13.** $a = -1$ **15.** $x = \frac{7}{5}$
17. $x = 10$ **19.** $x = -5$ **21.** $x = -\frac{1}{12}$ **23.** $x = -3$
25. $x = 0$ **27.** $x = -10$ **29.** $x = \frac{17}{7}$ **31.** $x = 24$
33. $x = \frac{24}{19}$ **37.** Length: $16\frac{7}{8}$ feet, width: $5\frac{5}{8}$ feet   **39.** $x = 8$ cm
41. $x = 82$ **43.** no   **45.** yes   **47.** $x = \frac{15}{4}$ **49.** $x = 10$
51. $x = 4$
Find the Mistake   1. The first step to solving the linear equation $\frac{2}{3}(9x - 6) = 4(x - 2)$ is to distribute or eliminate the fractions.
2. In order to eliminate the fractions from the equation $3x - \frac{1}{3} = \frac{1}{6}$, we use the LCD, which is 6.   **3.** In order to eliminate the fractions from the equation $\frac{8}{3}x = -\frac{4}{5}$, we use the LCD, which is 15.   **4.** The solution to the equation $3x + \frac{1}{2} = \frac{1}{4}$ is $x = -\frac{1}{12}$.

Exercise Set 4.9
Vocabulary Review   1. x-coordinate   **2.** y-coordinate   **3.** ordered pair   **4.** x-axis, y-axis   **5.** quadrants   **6.** origin
Problems   1. $(0, -2)$ **3.** $(1, 5), (0, -2), (-2, -16)$
5. $(1, 6), (0, 0)$ **7.** $(2, -2)$ **9.** $(3, 0), (3, -3)$
11. $(0, 6), (3, 0), (6, -6)$ **13.** $(0, 3), (4, 0), (-4, 6)$
15. $(1, 1), (\frac{3}{4}, 0), (5, 17)$ **17.** $(2, 13), (1, 6), (0, -1)$
19. $(-5, 4), (-5, -3), (-5, 0)$

21.

x	y
1	3
-3	-9
4	12
6	18

23.

x	y
0	0
$-\frac{1}{2}$	-2
-3	-12
3	12

25.

x	y
2	3
3	2
5	0
9	-4

27.

x	y
2	0
3	2
1	-2
-3	-10

29.

x	y
0	-1
-1	-7
-3	-19
$\frac{3}{2}$	8

31.

x	y
0	3
-2	7
2	-1
5	-7

33–49.

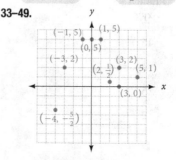

51. $(-4, 4)$; Q II **53.** $(-4, 2)$; Q II **55.** $(-3, 0)$; no quadrant, x-axis **57.** $(2, -2)$; Q IV **59.** $(-5, -5)$; Q III **61.** Yes
63. No **65.** Yes **67.** No **69.** Yes **71.** No **73.** No
75. No **77. a.** Answers may vary **b.** $320 **c.** 30 hours
d. No, if she works 35 hours, she would be paid $280
79. a. Yes **b.** No, she should earn $108 for working 9 hours
c. No, she should earn $84 for working 7 hours **d.** Yes
81. a. $375,000 **b.** At the end of 6 years **c.** No, the crane will
be worth $195,000 after 9 years **d.** $600,000 **83.** $(0, 70), (2, 73)$,
$(4, 68), (6, 75), (8, 80), (10, 73)$ **85.** $A = (1, 2), B = (6, 7)$
87. $A = (2, 2), B = (2,5), C = (7,5)$ **89. a.** -3 **b.** 6 **c.** 0 **d.** -4
91. a. 4 **b.** 2 **c.** -1 **d.** 9 **93.** -3 **95.** 2 **97.** 0
99. $y = -5x + 4$ **101.** $y = \frac{3}{2}x - 3$

Find the Mistake 1. A solution to a linear equation in two variables will
be an ordered pair that makes the equation a true statement. **2.** A solution to the equation $5x - 2y = 11$ is $(3, 2)$. **3.** An ordered pair is
not a solution to an equation if it satisfies the equation **4.** In the
ordered pair $(-3, 6)$, the x-coordinate is -3. **5.** To graph the ordered
pair $(7, 3)$, start at the origin, move 7 units to the right, and 3 units
up. **6.** The ordered pair $(-2, 5)$ appears in the second quadrant.

Exercise Set 4.10
Vocabulary Review 1. graphing **2.** linear **3.** ordered pairs
4. graph **5.** straight line **6.** horizontal, vertical

1. $(0, 4), (2, 2), (4, 0)$
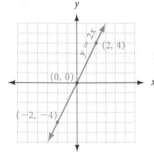

3. $(0, 3), (2, 1), (4, -1)$
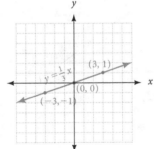

5. $(0, 0), (-2, -4), (2, 4)$
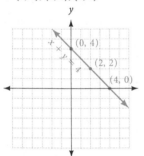

7. $(-3, -1), (0, 0), (3, 1)$
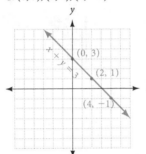

9. $(0, 1), (-1, -1), (1, 3)$
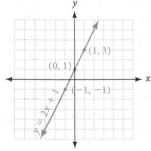

11. $(0, 4), (-1, 4), (2, 4)$
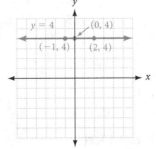

13. $(-2, 2), (0, 3), (2, 4)$
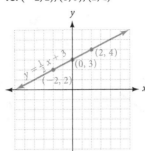

15. $(-3, 3), (0, 1), (3, -1)$
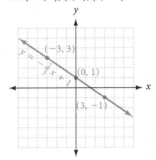

17. $y = -2x + 3$
$(-1, 5), (0, 3), (1, 1)$
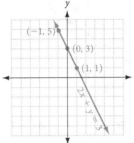

19. $y = -\frac{3}{2}x + 3$
$(0, 3), (2, 0), (4, -3)$
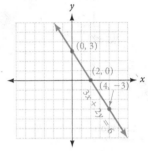

21. $y = \frac{1}{2}x + 3$
$(-2, 2), (0, 3), (2, 4)$
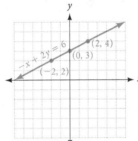

23.
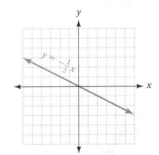

25.
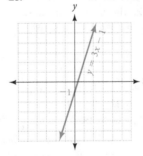

27.
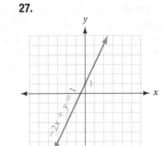

29.
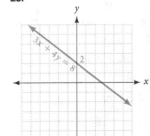

31.
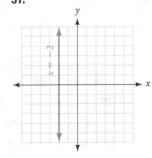

33.

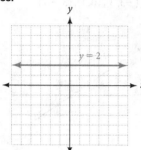

35.

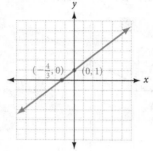

37.

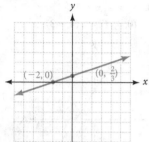

39.

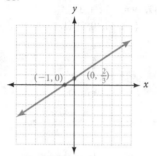

41.

Equation	H, V, and/or O
$x = 3$	V
$y = 3$	H
$y = 3x$	O
$y = 0$	O, H

43.

Equation	H, V, and/or O
$x = -\frac{3}{5}$	V
$y = -\frac{3}{5}$	H
$y = -\frac{3}{5}x$	O
$x = 0$	O, V

45.

x	y
-4	-3
-2	-2
0	-1
2	0
6	2

Find the Mistake   1. To graph a linear equation in two variables, you must find two or more solutions.   **2.** The line $y = \frac{1}{2}x$ intersects both axes.   **3.** A vertical line is given by the form $x = a$.   **4.** All lines require two points to define them.

Chapter 4 Review

1. $\frac{5}{7}$ **2.** $\frac{3}{8}$ **3.** $\frac{4}{13}$ **4.** $\frac{8}{15}$ **5.** $\frac{2}{7}$ **6.** $\frac{3}{20}$ **7.** $\frac{7}{2}$
8. $\frac{1}{6}$ **9.** $-\frac{4}{21}$ **10.** $-\frac{3}{4}$ **11.** 3   **12.** $\frac{6}{7}$ **13.** $\frac{7}{6}$
14. $\frac{12}{5}$ **15.** $-\frac{9}{4}$ **16.** $-\frac{1}{12}$ **17.** 25   **18.** 2   **19.** $\frac{4}{3}$
20. $\frac{10}{21}$ **21.** $\frac{3}{7}$ **22.** $\frac{1}{6}$ **23.** $\frac{14}{3}$ **24.** 2   **25.** $-\frac{5}{9}$
26. $-\frac{1}{3}$ **27.** $\frac{3}{7}$ **28.** $\frac{4}{7}$ **29.** $A = 26$ ft²   **30.** 8 dresses
31. $\frac{3}{8}$ **32.** $\frac{254}{1000}$ **33.** $\frac{4}{3}$ **34.** $\frac{1}{12}$ **35.** $4\frac{4}{5}$ **36.** $\frac{5}{8}$
37. $1\frac{7}{30}$ **38.** $12\frac{4}{15}$ **39.** $2\frac{1}{10}$ **40.** $8\frac{2}{5}$ **41.** $\frac{7}{16}$ **42.** $5\frac{5}{8}$
43. $\frac{1}{4}$ **44.** $-\frac{1}{2}$ **45.** $12\frac{1}{2}$ **46.** $\frac{1}{6}$ **47.** $4\frac{5}{24}$ **48.** $11\frac{7}{16}$
49. $17\frac{1}{2}$ **50.** $6\frac{7}{24}$ **51.** $19\frac{5}{8}$ in.   **52.** $P = 29\frac{1}{4}$ ft
53. $15\frac{2}{5}$ **54.** $1\frac{31}{32}$ **55.** $\frac{1}{2}$ **56.** $2\frac{3}{4}$ **57.** $13\frac{9}{32}$
58. $\frac{41}{48}$ **59.** $\frac{1}{2}$ **60.** $1\frac{21}{46}$ **61.** $\frac{7}{81}$ **62.** $\frac{1}{2}$ **63.** $x = \frac{5}{4}$
64. $x = \frac{13}{7}$ **65.** $x = \frac{26}{5}$ **66.** $x = -6$ **67.** $x = \frac{2}{3}$
68. $x = -4$ **69.** $\frac{8}{25}$ **70.** $\frac{16}{25}$

71–76.

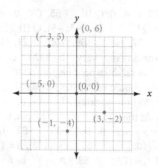

77. $\left(3, -\frac{4}{5}\right), \left(-2, -\frac{14}{5}\right), \left(\frac{20}{3}, \frac{2}{3}\right), \left(\frac{1}{2}, -\frac{9}{5}\right)$
78. $(0,1), (-1,3), (1,-1)$
79.

80.

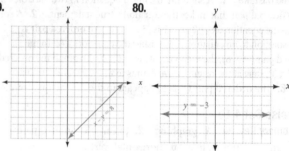

81.

82.

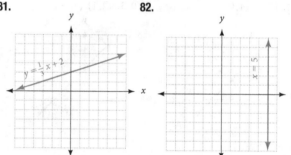

83.

84.

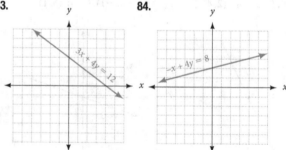

Chapter 4 Cumulative Review

1. $\frac{3}{4}$ **2.** $\frac{2}{3}$ **3.** $\frac{3}{4}$ **4.** $\frac{5}{8}$ **5.** $\frac{113}{19}$ **6.** $13\frac{20}{23}$
7. $\frac{1}{6}$ **8.** $16\frac{1}{42}$ **9.** $\frac{4}{15}$ **10.** 22   **11.** 12   **12.** 4   **13.** $3\frac{7}{13}$
14. $\frac{5}{9}$ **15.** 196   **16.** 18   **17.** $\frac{11}{15}$ **18.** 630,496   **19.** $\frac{2}{3}$
20. 11   **21.** $3\frac{4}{15}$ **22.** $\frac{32}{75}$ **23.** 6,888   **24.** $1\frac{1}{2}$ **25.** $\frac{19}{48}$
26. $4\frac{2}{3}$ **27.** $1\frac{47}{60}$ **28.** $\frac{28x}{60x}$ **29.** $1\frac{2}{21}$ **30.** 12
31. 12,850,361   **32.** 351,986   **33.** $\frac{14}{27}$ **34.** 113   **35.** $\frac{5}{8}$
36. 7   **37.** $12\frac{4}{5}$ **38.** $21\frac{1}{24}$ **39.** $1\frac{6}{11}$ **40.** $19\frac{3}{5}$

Chapter 4 Test

1. $\frac{3}{14}$ **2.** $\frac{3}{4}$ **3.** $\frac{10}{21}$ **4.** $\frac{15}{8}$ **5.** $-\frac{1}{10}$ **6.** $\frac{3}{20}$ **7.** 4
8. $-\frac{4}{5}$ **9.** $-\frac{1}{15}$ **10.** $\frac{4}{9}$ **11.** $\frac{2}{5}$ **12.** $\frac{3}{16}$ **13.** $-\frac{3}{8}$

14. $\frac{1}{5}$ **15.** $A = 15$ in.²   **16.** 10 dresses   **17.** $5\frac{5}{8}$ **18.** $1\frac{1}{2}$

19. $1\frac{7}{24}$ **20.** $9\frac{19}{20}$ **21.** $1\frac{5}{9}$ **22.** $3\frac{1}{8}$ **23.** $\frac{2}{9}$ **24.** $-\frac{5}{8}$

25. $9\frac{5}{6}$ **26.** $5\frac{25}{72}$ **27.** $13\frac{1}{8}$ **28.** $1\frac{2}{3}$ **29.** $\frac{17}{18}$ **30.** $\frac{3}{28}$

31. $x = \frac{1}{8}$ **32.** $x = -9$

33–36.

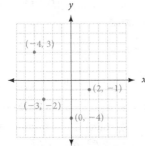

37. $(0, -3), (2, 0), (4, 3), (-2, -6)$ **38.** $(0, 7), (4, -5)$

39.   **40.**

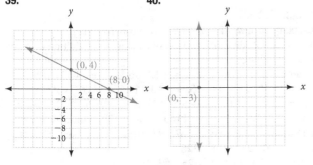

41. $\frac{3}{24}$ **42.** $\frac{12}{36}$

Chapter 5

Exercise Set 5.1

Vocabulary Review   **1.** fractional   **2.** decimal point   **3.** thousandths
4. tenths   **5.** hundredths   **6.** place value   **7.** left   **8.** right
Problems   **1.** Three tenths   **3.** Fifteen thousandths
5. Three and four tenths   **7.** Fifty-two and seven tenths
9. $405\frac{36}{100}$ **11.** $9\frac{9}{1,000}$ **13.** $1\frac{23}{1000}$ **15.** $14\frac{37}{10000}$ **17.** Tens
19. Tenths   **21.** Hundred thousandths   **23.** Ones   **25.** Hundreds
27. 0.55   **29.** 6.9   **31.** 11.11   **33.** 100.02   **35.** 3,000.003

	Rounded to the Nearest			
	Number	Whole	Tenth	Hundredth	Thousandth
37.	47.5479	48	47.5	47.55	47.548
39.	0.8175	1	0.8	0.82	0.818
41.	0.1562	0	0.2	0.16	0.156
43.	2,789.3241	2,789	2,789.3	2,789.32	2,789.324
45.	99.9999	100	100.0	100.00	100.000

47. 0.52   **49.** 0.04   **51.** 8.12   **53.** 12.87
55. $5 < 5.001 < 5.01 < 5.1$ **57.** $11.02 < 11.03 < 11.29 < 11.3$
59. $4 < 4.08 < 4.8 < 4.98$ **61.** $19.134 < 19.3 < 19.34 < 19.431$
63. Three and eleven hundredths; two and five tenths

65. Fifteen hundredths   **67.**

Price of 1 Gallon of Regular Gasoline	
Date	Price (Dollars)
3/21/11	3.526
3/28/11	3.596
4/4/11	3.684
4/11/11	3.791

69. 7.451 and 7.54   **71.** $\frac{1}{4}$ **73.** $\frac{1}{8}$ **75.** $\frac{5}{8}$ **77.** $\frac{7}{8}$
79. 9.99   **81.** 10.05   **83.** 0.05   **85.** 0.01   **87.** $6\frac{31}{100}$
89. $6\frac{23}{50}$ **91.** $18\frac{123}{1000}$
Find the Mistake   **1.** To move a place value from the tens column to the hundreds column, you must multiply by ten.   **2.** The decimal 0.09 can be written as the fraction $\frac{9}{100}$.   **3.** The decimal 142.9643 written as a mixed number is $142\frac{9,643}{10,000}$.   **4.** Rounding the decimal 0.06479 to the nearest thousandth gives us 0.065.

Exercise Set 5.2

Vocabulary Review   **1.** columns   **2.** decimal point   **3.** zeros
4. value
Problems   **1.** 6.19   **3.** 1.13   **5.** −1.49   **7.** 9.042   **9.** 8.021
11. 11.7843   **13.** 24.343   **15.** 24.111   **17.** 258.5414
19. 666.66   **21.** 11.11   **23.** 3.93   **25.** 4.22   **27.** 120.41
29. 44.933   **31.** 7.673   **33.** 530.865   **35.** 43.55   **37.** 5.918
39. 27.89   **41.** 35.64   **43.** 411.438   **45.** 6   **47.** 1
49. 3.1   **51.** 5.9   **53.** 3.3   **55.** 2.8   **57.** −11.41
59. −1.9   **61.** −17.5   **63.** 3.272   **65.** 4.001   **67.** $116.82
69. $1,571.10   **71.** 4.5 in.   **73.** $5.43
75. 1 minute, 2 seconds   **77. a.** $0.52 million   **b.** $1.26 million
c. $2,070,000; $1,550,000; $1,910,000; $810,000
79. 2 in.   **81.** $3.25; three $1 bills and a quarter   **83.** 3.25
85. $\frac{21}{100}$ **87.** $\frac{63}{10}$ **89.** 0.21   **91.** 6.3   **93.** 255   **95.** 156
Find the Mistake   **1.** To add 32.69 and 4.837, align the decimal point and add in columns.   **2.** To add 0.004 + 5.06 + 32 by first changing each decimal to a fraction would give us the problem
$\frac{4}{1,000} + 5\frac{6}{100} + 32$.   **3.** When subtracting 8.7 − 2.0163, we make sure to keep the digits in the correct columns by writing 8.7 as 8.7000.   **4.** Subtracting 4.367 from the sum of 12.1 and 0.036 gives us 7.769.

Exercise Set 5.3

Vocabulary Review   multiply, answer, digits, decimal points
Problems   **1.** 0.28   **3.** 0.028   **5.** 0.0027   **7.** −0.78   **9.** 0.792
11. 0.0156   **13.** 24.29821   **15.** 0.03   **17.** 187.85   **19.** 0.002
21. 27.96   **23.** 0.43   **25.** −49,940   **27.** −9,876,540
29. 1.89   **31.** 0.0025   **33.** 5.1106   **35.** 7.3485   **37.** 4.4
39. 2.074   **41.** 3.58   **43.** 187.4   **45.** 116.64   **47.** 20.75
49. 10.3   **51.** 8.4   **53.** 4.82   **55.** 14.36   **57.** $-11.4x + 7.8$
59. $5.64x - 17.86$ **61.** $-8.058x - 23.94$ **63.** $8.7x - 5.05$
65. 0.126   **67.** Moves it two places to the right   **69.** $1,381.38
71. $0.51   **73.** $44.40   **75.** $293.04   **77.** 8,509 mm²
79. 1.18 in.²   **81.** 1,879   **83.** 1,516 R 4   **85.** 298
87. 34.8   **89.** 49.896   **91.** 825   **93.** No
Find the Mistake   **1.** To multiply 18.05 by 3.5, multiply as if the numbers were whole numbers and then place the decimal in the answer with three digits to its right.   **2.** To estimate the answer for 24.9 × 7.3, round 24.9 to 25 and 7.3 to 7.   **3.** To simplify

$(8.43 + 1.002) - (0.05)(3.2)$, first work the operation inside the parentheses and find the product of 0.05 and 3.2 before subtracting.
4. Lucy pays $1.52 a pound for the first three pounds of candy she buys at a candy store, and pays $3.27 for each additional pound. To find how much she will pay if she buys 5.2 pounds of candy, we must solve the problem $1.52(3) + 3.27(2.2)$.

Exercise Set 5.4
Vocabulary Review   1. long division   **2.** above   **3.** last
4. divisor, right
Problems   1. 19.7   **3.** 6.2   **5.** 5.2   **7.** 11.04   **9.** 4.8
11. −9.7   **13.** 2.63   **15.** 4.24   **17.** 2.55   **19.** −1.35
21. 6.5   **23.** 9.9   **25.** 0.05   **27.** 9.79   **29.** 2.2   **31.** 63.2
33. 1.35   **35.** 16.97   **37.** 0.25   **39.** 2.71   **41.** 11.69
43. 3.98   **45.** 5.98   **47.** −4.24   **49.** $8.25/hr
51. 22.4 mi   **57.** 5 hr   **55.** 20 shares   **57.** 2.73   **59.** 0.13
61. 9.5   **63.** 5.3   **65.** 2.36x   **67.** 1.55x   **69.** 7.5 mi
71.

Rank	Name	Average per Tournament
1.	Ariya Jutanugarn	$91,105.25
2.	Lydia Ko	$103,877.46
3.	Brooke M. Henderson	$55,626.45
4.	In Gee Chun	$79,005.37
5.	Shanshan Feng	$69,456.14

73. 0.77778   **75.** 307.20607   **77.** 0.70945
79. $\frac{3}{4}$ **81.** $\frac{2}{3}$ **83.** $\frac{3}{8}$ **85.** $\frac{19}{50}$ **87.** $\frac{60}{100}$ **89.** $\frac{500}{100}$
91. $\frac{12}{15}$ **93.** $\frac{60}{15}$ **95.** $\frac{18}{15}$ **97.** 0.75   **99.** 0.875
Find the Mistake   1. The answer to the problem $25\overline{)70.75}$ will have a decimal point placed with two digits to its right.
2. To work the problem $27.468 \div 8.4$, multiply both numbers by 10 and then divide.   **3.** To divide 0.6778 by 0.54, multiply both numbers by 100 to move the decimal point two places to the right.
4. Samantha earns $10.16 an hour as a cashier. She received a paycheck for $309.88. To find out how many hours she worked, you must solve the problem $309.88 \div 10.16$.

Landmark Review   **1.** One and fifteen hundredths
2. Forty-five and eight hundredths   **3.** Five thousandths
4. Two hundred forty-five and one hundred fifty-seven thousandths
5. 0.0067   **6.** 5.6   **7.** 23.014   **8.** 2,013.15   **9.** 28.28
10. 9.150014   **11.** 124.15831   **12.** 11.799   **13.** 3.1
14. 7.07   **15.** 13.33   **16.** 78.37   **17.** 47.35   **18.** 0.00225
19. 20   **20.** 0.4   **21.** 5.16   **22.** 11.3505   **23.** 8.8
24. 33.46

Exercise Set 5.5
Vocabulary Review   1. division   **2.** repeats   **3.** place values, reduce
Problems   1. 0.125   **3.** 0.625
5.

Fraction	$\frac{1}{5}$	$\frac{2}{5}$	$\frac{3}{5}$	$\frac{4}{5}$	$\frac{5}{5}$
Decimal	0.2	0.4	0.6	0.8	1

7. 0.5   **9.** 0.56
11. −0.5625   **13.** −4.2
15. 0.92   **17.** −0.45
19. 0.11   **21.** −0.28
23.

Decimal	0.125	0.250	0.375	0.500	0.625	0.750	0.875
Fraction	$\frac{1}{8}$	$\frac{1}{4}$	$\frac{3}{8}$	$\frac{1}{2}$	$\frac{5}{8}$	$\frac{3}{4}$	$\frac{7}{8}$

25. $\frac{3}{20}$ **27.** $-\frac{2}{25}$ **29.** $\frac{3}{8}$ **31.** $5\frac{3}{5}$ **33.** $5\frac{3}{50}$
35. $-1\frac{11}{50}$ **37.** 2.4   **39.** 3.98   **41.** 3.02   **43.** 0.3
45. 0.072   **47.** 0.8   **49.** 1   **51.** 0.25   **53. a.** $\frac{13}{12}$ **b.** $-\frac{5}{12}$
c. $\frac{1}{4}$ **d.** $\frac{4}{9}$ **55.** $8.42   **57.** $43.02   **59.** 9 in.

61.

Change In Stock Price		
Date	Gain ($)	As a Decimal ($)
Monday	$\frac{3}{5}$	0.60
Tuesday	$\frac{1}{2}$	0.50
Wednesday	$\frac{1}{25}$	0.04
Thursday	$\frac{1}{5}$	0.20
Friday	$\frac{1}{10}$	0.10

63. 104.625 calories
65. $10.38
67. Yes   **69.** 12.2
71. 12.8
73. $118x + 24$
75. 90
77. 54.9

Find the Mistake   1. The correct way to write $\frac{6}{11}$ as a decimal is $0.\overline{54}$.
2. Writing 14.3 as a fraction gives us $14\frac{3}{10}$ or $1\frac{143}{10}$.   **3.** The simplified answer to the problem $\frac{12}{45(0.256 + 0.14)}$ contains only fractions or only decimals.   **4.** Simplifying the problem $\left(\frac{3}{2}\right)(0.5) + \left(\frac{1}{2}\right)^2(6.7)$ by first converting all decimals to fractions gives us $\left(\frac{3}{2}\right)\left(\frac{1}{2}\right) + \left(\frac{1}{2}\right)^2\left(\frac{67}{10}\right)$.

Exercise Set 5.6
Vocabulary Review   1. multiplication property of equality, multiplying   **2.** division property of equality   **3.** addition property of equality, adding
Problems   1. $x = 10.7$ **3.** $x = -1.1$ **5.** $n = -0.4$ **7.** $n = 3.8$
9. $x = 0.7$ **11.** $x = -18$ **13.** $y = 3.3$ **15.** $x = -2.6$ **17.** $x = 45$
19. $a = -1.1$ **21.** $y = 12.5$ **23.** $x = -5,000$ **25.** $x = 28.5$
27. $x = 4$ **29.** 87 mi   **31.** 147 mi   **33.** 8 nickels, 18 dimes
35. 16 dimes, 32 quarters   **37.** 300 megabytes   **39.** 5 hours
41. 36   **43.** 25   **45.** 125   **47.** 9   **49.** $\frac{1}{81}$ **51.** $\frac{25}{36}$
53. 0.25   **55.** 1.44   **57.** 25   **59.** 100
Find the Mistake   1. If you multiply the equation $0.23x = 1.2$ by 100, that would clear the decimals.   **2.** If you decide not to multiply by a power of 10 to solve the equation $0.23x = 12$, then you should divide both sides by 0.23 to find x.   **3.** When you use the distributive property $0.2(x + 5.2) = 0.2x + 1.04$.   **4.** To solve the equation $x - 5.15 = 2.3$, add 5.15 to 2.3 to get $x = 7.45$.

Exercise Set 5.7
Vocabulary Review   1. square root   **2.** radical sign
3. perfect squares   **4.** irrational   **5.** right   **6.** hypotenuse
7. Pythagorean theorem
Problems   1. 8   **3.** 9   **5.** 6   **7.** 5   **9.** 15   **11.** 48
13. 45   **15.** 48   **17.** 15   **19.** 1   **21.** 78   **23.** 9
25. $\frac{4}{7}$ **27.** $\frac{3}{4}$ **29.** $\frac{2}{3}$ **31.** $\frac{1}{4}$ **33.** False   **35.** True
37. 11.1803   **39.** 1.1180   **41.** 3.46   **43.** 11.18   **45.** 0.58
47. 0.58   **49.** 12.124   **51.** 9.327   **53.** 12.124   **55.** 12.124
57. 10 in.   **59.** 13 ft   **61.** 8.06 km   **63.** 17.49 m   **65.** 3 m
67. 12.12 in.   **69.** 12 yd   **71.** 30 ft   **73.** 25 ft
77.

Height h(feet)	Distance d(miles)
10	4
50	9
90	12
130	14
170	16
190	17

79. a. 120.4 million
b. 9.1 million
81. 3   **83.** 4
85. $3^2 \cdot 5$ **87.** $2^2 \cdot 3^2 \cdot 5$

Find the Mistake   1. The square root of a positive number x is the number we square to get x.   **2.** The square root of 225 is 15, and can be written in symbols as $\sqrt{225} = 15$.   **3.** Simplifying the radical $\sqrt{\frac{196}{25}}$ gives us $\frac{14}{5}$ because $\left(\frac{14}{5}\right)^2 = \frac{14}{5} \cdot \frac{14}{5} = \frac{196}{25}$.
4. The Pythagorean theorem states that $a^2 + b^2 = c^2$.

Exercise Set 5.8

Vocabulary Review   **1.** square root   **2.** simplified   **3.** factors
4. perfect square
Problems   **1.** $2\sqrt{3}$ **3.** $2\sqrt{5}$ **5.** $6\sqrt{2}$ **7.** $7\sqrt{2}$
9. $2\sqrt{7}$ **11.** $10\sqrt{2}$ **13.** $2x\sqrt{3}$ **15.** $5x\sqrt{2}$
17. $5x\sqrt{3}$ **19.** $5x\sqrt{2}$ **21.** $4xy\sqrt{2}$ **23.** $9x\sqrt{3}$
25. $6xy\sqrt{2}$ **27.** $2xy\sqrt{3}$ **29.** $3\sqrt{2}$ in.   **31.** $4\sqrt{2}$ in.
33. $x\sqrt{2}$ in.   **35.** 1.25 seconds   **37.** 8.485   **39.** 11.180
41. 55.902
43.

x	$\sqrt{x}$	$2\sqrt{x}$	$\sqrt{4x}$
1	1	2	2
2	1.414	2.828	2.828
3	1.732	3.464	3.464
4	2	4	4

45.

x	$\sqrt{x}$	$3\sqrt{x}$	$\sqrt{9x}$
1	1	3	3
2	1.414	4.243	4.243
3	1.732	5.196	5.196
4	2	6	6

47. $23x$ **49.** $27y$ **51.** $7ab$ **53.** $-7xy + 50x$
Find the Mistake   **1.** The simplified form of $\sqrt{300}$ is
$\sqrt{25 \cdot 4 \cdot 3} = 5 \cdot 2\sqrt{3} = 10\sqrt{3}$.   **2.** $5\sqrt{2}$ is in simplified
form.   **3.** The hypotenuse of an isosceles right triangle is always
$\sqrt{2}$ times the length of a leg.   **4.** To simplify a radical, we need
to factor using perfect squares.

Exercise Set 5.9

Vocabulary Review   **1.** radical expression   **2.** multiplied
3. like terms   **4.** distributive property
Problems   **1.** $10\sqrt{3}$ **3.** $4\sqrt{5}$ **5.** $7\sqrt{x}$ **7.** $9\sqrt{7}$
9. $6\sqrt{y}$ **11.** $7\sqrt{2}$ **13.** $8\sqrt{3}$ **15.** $-2\sqrt{3}$ **17.** $8\sqrt{10}$
19. $x\sqrt{2}$ **21.** $17x\sqrt{5}$ **23.** $7\sqrt{2}$ ft
25. $\sqrt{2} + \sqrt{3} \approx 3.1463$; $\sqrt{5} \approx 2.2361$.
27.   **29.**

x	$\sqrt{x^2 + 9}$	$x + 3$
1	3.162	4
2	3.606	5
3	4.243	6
4	5	7
5	5.831	8
6	6.708	9

x	$\sqrt{x + 3}$	$\sqrt{x} + \sqrt{3}$
1	2	2.732
2	2.236	3.146
3	2.449	3.464
4	2.646	3.732
5	2.828	3.968
6	3	4.181

Find the Mistake   **1.** $5\sqrt{2} + 3\sqrt{7}$ is already in simplified
form.   **2.** $5\sqrt{45} + 3\sqrt{20} = 15\sqrt{5} + 6\sqrt{5} = 21\sqrt{5}$.
3. $\sqrt{16 + 25}$ is not the same as $4 + 5$.   **4.** The notation $4\sqrt{5}$
assumes a multiplication symbol between the 4 and the $\sqrt{5}$, that is
$4 \cdot \sqrt{5}$.

Chapter 5 Review

1. Six and three hundred two thousandths
2. Two and four hundredths   **3.** $2\frac{106}{100,000}$

4. Thousandths   **5.** 23.5006   **6.** 0.0235   **7.** 75.00075
8. 72.20   **9.** 129, 128.9, 128.91, 128.912
10. $0.02 < 0.04 < 0.2 < 0.24 < 0.4 < 0.42$ **11.** $-\frac{3}{4}$ **12.** $\frac{3}{16}$
13. 12.02   **14.** -7.904 **15.** 10.5   **16.** 8.06
17. 671.3997   **18.** 247.569   **19.** 16.254   **20.** -2.482
21. 0.02814   **22.** 1,570,200   **23.** 14.59   **24.** 7.893
25. -3.069 **26.** 3.091   **27.** 26.866   **28.** 7.1
29. 15.23   **30.** 25.4   **31.** 6.097   **32.** $2.77   **33.** $23.81
34. $10.80   **35.** 0.85   **36.** -1.625 **37.** $\frac{31}{50}$ **38.** 29.036
39. 7.55   **40.** 16.882   **41.** 0.06   **42.** 23.68
43. 44.876   **44.** 0.45   **45.** 0.29   **46.** $\frac{3}{50}$ **47.** -0.192
48. 0.7   **49.** 2   **50.** 11   **51.** 3   **52.** -62 **53.** $\frac{5}{4}$
54. $\frac{1}{10}$ **55.** 36   **56.** 25   **57.** 12.65 in.   **58.** 9.22 in.
59. $2\sqrt{3}$ **60.** $5\sqrt{2}$ **61.** $2x\sqrt{5}$ **62.** $4x$
63. $3xy\sqrt{2}$ **64.** $5xy\sqrt{3}$ **65.** $10\sqrt{3}$ **66.** $17\sqrt{6}$
67. $5\sqrt{3}$ **68.** $10\sqrt{2}$ **69.** $5\sqrt{6}$ **70.** $5\sqrt{2}$
71. $-9\sqrt{3}$ **72.** $8\sqrt{5}$ **73.** $39.76 million per month
74. $2.23 million per month   **75.** $n = -0.85$
76. $y = -3.2$ **77.** $x = 0.42$ **78.** $a = 30$

Chapter 5 Cumulative Review

1. 5,291   **2.** 144   **3.** 17,670   **4.** 2.82   **5.** $153.568\overline{3}$
6. $\frac{53}{42} = 1\frac{11}{42}$ **7.** 100.373   **8.** 62   **9.** $\frac{15}{4} = 3\frac{3}{4}$ **10.** 0
11. $16\frac{1}{5}$ **12.** $\frac{31}{8}$ **13.** $25\frac{3}{8}$
14.

Decimal	Fraction
0.125	$\frac{1}{8}$
0.250	$\frac{1}{4}$
0.375	$\frac{3}{8}$
0.500	$\frac{1}{2}$
0.625	$\frac{5}{8}$
0.750	$\frac{3}{4}$
0.875	$\frac{7}{8}$
1	$\frac{8}{8}$

15. 4   **16.** $4(2 + 3) = 20$
17. $7(6 + 3) = 63$ **18.** $\frac{15}{26}$
19. False   **20.** 207   **21.** 2   **22.** 8
23. 1.02   **24.** $\frac{4}{81}$ **25.** $19\frac{49}{64}$
26. 86°F   **27.** $9\frac{1}{2}$ cups
28. $8.25

Chapter 5 Test

1. Eleven and eight hundred nineteen thousandths   **2.** Tenths
3. 73.0046   **4.** 100.91   **5.** 7.02   **6.** 11.724   **7.** 16.56
8. 5.84   **9.** 10.1   **10.** 7.89   **11.** -3.33 **12.** 0.22
13. $3.61   **14.** $18.10   **15.** $8.15   **16.** 0.68   **17.** $\frac{19}{50}$
18. 25.704   **19.** 2.38   **20.** 16.897   **21.** 0.47125   **22.** 8.92
23. 26.674   **24.** 10   **25.** 3   **26.** 15   **27.** 30
28. 11.18 in.   **29.** 17.86 yds.   **30.** $6\sqrt{2}$ **31.** $4x\sqrt{3}$
32. $8\sqrt{7}$ **33.** $-8\sqrt{3}$ **34.** $y = -4.1$ **35.** $y = 1.08$

Chapter 6

Exercise Set 6.1

Vocabulary Review   **1.** fraction   **2.** numerator, denominator
3. ratio   **4.** colon
Problems   **1.** $\frac{4}{3}$ **3.** $\frac{16}{3}$ **5.** $\frac{2}{5}$ **7.** $\frac{1}{2}$ **9.** $\frac{3}{1}$ **11.** $\frac{7}{6}$
13. $\frac{7}{5}$ **15.** $\frac{5}{7}$ **17.** $\frac{8}{5}$ **19.** $\frac{1}{3}$ **21.** $\frac{1}{10}$ **23.** $\frac{3}{25}$
25. a. $\frac{1}{2}$ b. $\frac{1}{3}$ c. $\frac{2}{3}$ **27.** a. $\frac{13}{8}$ b. $\frac{1}{4}$ c. $\frac{3}{8}$ d. $\frac{13}{3}$

29. a. $\frac{73}{14}$ **b.** $\frac{26}{51}$ **c.** $\frac{7}{13}$ **d.** $\frac{14}{51}$ **31. a.** $\frac{3}{4}$ **b.** 12 **c.** $\frac{3}{4}$

33. $\frac{2,408}{2,314} \approx 1.04$ **35.** $\frac{4,722}{2,408} \approx 1.96$ **37.** 40 **39.** 0.2

41. 0.695 **43.** 3.98 **45.** 36 **47.** 0.065 **49.** 0.025

Find the Mistake **1.** Writing the ratio of $\frac{2}{5}$ to $\frac{3}{8}$ is the same as writing

$\frac{2}{5} \cdot \frac{8}{3}$ or $\frac{\frac{2}{5}}{\frac{3}{8}}$. **2.** The ratio of 6 to 24 expressed in lowest terms is $\frac{1}{4}$.

3. To write the ratio of 0.04 to 0.20 as a fraction in lowest terms, you must first multiply 0.04 and 0.20 by 100 to rid the ratio of decimals. **4.** A cleaning solution of bleach and water contains 100 milliliters of bleach and 150 milliliters of water. To find the ratio of water to the whole solution in lowest terms, you must write the ratio as $\frac{150}{250} = \frac{3}{5}$.

Exercise Set 6.2

Vocabulary Review **1.** rate **2.** denominator **3.** division **4.** unit pricing

Problems **1.** 55 mi/hr **3.** 84 km/hr **5.** 0.2 gal/sec **7.** 12 L/min **9.** 19 mi/gal **11.** $4\frac{1}{3}$ mi/L **13.** 16¢ per ounce **15.** 4.95¢ per ounce **17.** Dry Baby: 34.7¢/diaper, Happy Baby: 31.6¢/diaper, Happy Baby is better buy **19.** 7.7 tons/year **21.** 10.8¢ per day **23.** 9.3 mi/gal **25.** $n = 6$ **27.** $n = 4$ **29.** $n = 4$ **31.** $n = 65$ **33.** 100 oz is the better value.

Wisk Laundry Detergent		
	Old	New
Size	100 Ounces	80 Ounces
Container Cost	$6.99	$5.75
Price per quart	$2.24	$2.30

Find the Mistake **1.** The rate in miles per hour for a plane traveling 3000 miles in 6 hours is 500 miles per hour. **2.** If a runner can run 16 miles in 2 hours, then her ratio of miles to hours is 8 miles per hour. **3.** If a supermarket sells a package of 20 cookies for $4.27, then the unit price for each cookie is $0.21. **4.** A supermarket sells 10 packages of oatmeal for $5.33. A wholesale store sells the same oatmeal for $8.86 for 24 packages of oatmeal. Given the information, we find that the wholesale store has the lowest unit price.

Exercise Set 6.3

Vocabulary Review **1.** proportion **2.** term **3.** first, fourth **4.** second, third **5.** product **6.** fundamental property of proportions

Problems **1.** Means: 3, 5; extremes: 1, 15; products: 15 **3.** Means: 25, 2; extremes: 10, 5; products: 50 **5.** Means: $\frac{1}{2}$, 4; extremes: $\frac{1}{3}$, 6; products: 2 **7.** Means: 5, 1; extremes: 0.5, 10; products: 5 **9.** $x = 10$ **11.** $y = \frac{12}{5}$ **13.** $x = \frac{3}{2}$ **15.** $x = \frac{10}{9}$ **17.** $x = 7$ **19.** $x = 14$ **21.** $y = 18$ **23.** $n = 6$ **25.** $n = 40$ **27.** $x = 50$ **29.** $y = 3$ **31.** $x = 3$ **33.** $n = 1$ **35.** $x = 0.1$ **37.** 20 **39.** 300 **41.** 297.5 **43.** 50.4 **45.** $x = 450$ **47.** $x = 5$

Find the Mistake **1.** A statement that two ratios are equal is called a proportion. **2.** For the proportion $\frac{5}{6} = \frac{10}{x}$, the extremes are 5 and x. **3.** To solve $\frac{7}{10} = \frac{n}{0.2}$, set the product of first and fourth terms equal to the product of the second and third terms. **4.** Solving the proportion $\frac{8}{5} = \frac{n}{\frac{3}{10}}$ gives us $n = \frac{12}{25}$.

5. 70 mi/hr **6.** 14.5 cents/ounce **7.** $x = 21$ **8.** $x = 72$ **9.** $x = 9$ **10.** $x = \frac{8}{5}$

Exercise Set 6.4

Vocabulary Review **1.** word problems **2.** proportion, quantities **3.** fundamental property of proportions

Problems **1.** 329 mi **3.** 360 points **5.** 15 pt **7.** 427.5 mi **9.** 900 eggs **11.** 435 in. = 36.25 ft **13.** $119.70 **15.** 265 g **17.** 91.3 liters **19.** 60,113 people **21.** 272 mg **23.** 37.4 mg **25.** 2 **27.** 147 **29.** $x = 20$ **31.** $x = 147$

Find the Mistake **1.** A basketball player scores 112 points in 8 games. The proportion to find how many points the player will score in 14 games is $\frac{112}{8} = \frac{x}{14}$. **2.** The scale of a map indicates that 2 inches corresponds to 250 miles in real life. If two cities on the map are 3.5 inches apart, they are 437.5 miles apart in real life. **3.** A jellybean company knows that for every 100 jellybeans, 4 will be misshapen. The proportion needed to find how many jelly beans were made if 36 misshapen jelly beans are found is $\frac{4}{100} = \frac{36}{x}$. **4.** If burning 1 gallon of gasoline produces 20.2 pounds of carbon dioxide, then burning 12 gallons of gasoline produces 242.4 pounds of carbon dioxide.

Exercise Set 6.5

Vocabulary Review **1.** similar **2.** proportional **3.** corresponding sides **4.** ratio

Problems **1.** $h = 9$ **3.** $y = 14$ **5.** $x = 12$ **7.** $a = 25$ **9.** $y = 32$

11. **13.**

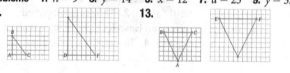

15. **17.**

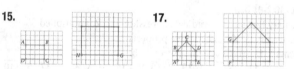

19. 250 in. **21.** 960 pixels **23.** 1,440 pixels **25.** 57 ft **27.** 4 ft **29. a.** $\frac{1}{2}$ **b.** Any 18 rectangles should be shaded. **c.** $\frac{1}{3}$ **31.** 442.5 **33.** 242.5 **35.** 181,723 **37.** 18,172

Find the Mistake **1.** The two triangles below are similar. The side x is equal to 12. **2.** The two triangles below are similar. We can find x by solving the proportion $\frac{12}{x} = \frac{8}{2}$ or $\frac{4}{1}$. **3.** The width of a rectangle on graph paper is 5 squares and the length is 7 squares. If a similar rectangle has a width of 10, then the length would be 14. **4.** A pocket dictionary is similar to a regular dictionary. The pocket dictionary is 4 inches wide by 6 inches long. The width of the regular dictionary is 16 inches. You must solve the proportion $\frac{6}{x} = \frac{4}{16}$ to find the remaining side length of the regular dictionary.

Exercise Set 6.6

Vocabulary Review **1.** average **2.** mean **3.** median **4.** mode **5.** range

Problems **1.** 3 **3.** 6 **5.** 16,194 **7.** 7.5 **9.** 11 **11.** 50 **13.** 900 **15.** 3.2 **17.** 18 **19.** 87 **21.** 1 **23.** 22 **25.** 2.9 **27.** 38 **29.** Mean = 79.5, median = 83 **31.** Both are $31,000 **33. a.** 78.5 **b.** 76 **c.** 76 **35.** Mean = $6,868.83; median = $6,993 **37.** Mean = $19,985, median = $19,788 **39.** 47 **41.** $3,190 **43.** $1,530

Find the Mistake **1.** Based on the list, the mean cost of lunch is $3.35. **2.** You would find the median by putting the list in order of shortest to longest, then finding half the sum of 2.7 and 3.0, which is 2.85 inches. **3.** The mode for the following list of numbers is 12. **4.** Suppose a basketball team scored 80 points during their highest scoring game, and 42 points during their lowest scoring game. The range of points scored is $80 - 42 = 38$.

Chapter 6 Review

1. $\frac{9}{4}$ **2.** $\frac{3}{16}$ **3.** $\frac{3}{1}$ **4.** $\frac{1}{7}$ **5.** $\frac{4}{3}$ **6.** $\frac{9}{11}$ **7.** $\frac{10}{7}$
8. $\frac{14}{19}$ **9.** $\frac{4}{3}$ **10.** $\frac{1}{7}$ **11.** $\frac{32}{71}$ **12.** $\frac{5}{11}$ **13.** $\frac{12}{7}$
14. $\frac{8}{1}$ **15.** $\frac{30}{1}$ **16.** $\frac{3}{98}$ **17.** $\frac{7}{5}$ **18.** $\frac{8}{3}$ **19.** $\frac{15}{64}$
20. $\frac{40}{7}$ **21.** $\frac{25}{8}$ **22.** $\frac{7}{3}$ **23.** $\frac{100}{157}$ **24.** 29 mpg
25. 25.75 mpg **26.** 72 mi/hr **27.** 700 km/hr
28. 54.03 mi/hr **29.** 41.1 mi/hr **30.** 70.1 mi/hr
31. 20-ounce cup: 19¢/ounce; 16-ounce cup: 22¢/ounce; 20-ounce cup is the better buy
32. $n = 3$ **33.** $a = 4$ **34.** $a = \frac{13}{8} = 1\frac{5}{8}$ **35.** $y = \frac{9}{11}$
36. $x = 4$ **37.** $b = 8$ **38.** Means $\frac{1}{4}$, 4; extremes: 2, $\frac{1}{2}$; products: 1 **39.** $x = 56$ **40.** $x = 2$ **41.** $n = 16$
42. $x = 107$ **43.** $h = 5$ **44.** $a = 32$ **45.** 36 hits
46. 9 hits **47.** 7.5 oz **48.** 96 ft **49.** 5 ft **50.** 850 mg
51. 288 mg **52. a.** 13 mpg **b.** 27.2 mpg **c.** 28 mpg
53. a. 2,947 ft **b.** 2,555 ft **c.** 2,150 ft **d.** 2,260 ft

Chapter 6 Cumulative Review

1. 13,372 **2.** 336 **3.** 17 **4.** 48 **5.** $516\frac{3}{8}$ or 516.375
6. 256 **7.** 63 **8.** 8 **9.** 91 **10.** 27 **11.** 144
12. 29.76 **13.** 42.6 **14.** 14.66 **15.** 6.6 **16.** $\frac{1}{432}$
17. 16 **18.** $\frac{19}{24}$ **19.** 1 **20.** $12\frac{2}{7}$ **21.** $x = 25$ **22.** $x = 24$
23. $P = 34$ in.; $A = 45$ in.^{2} **24.** $P = 74$ cm; $A = 144$ cm^2
25. $x = 78$ cm **26.** 20 women **27.** $83\frac{1}{4}$ in. or 6 ft, $11\frac{1}{4}$ in.
28. 69 sections **29.** $\frac{1511}{1189}$ **30.** $93.5 billion

Chapter 6 Test

1. $\frac{8}{3}$ **2.** $\frac{5}{6}$ **3.** $\frac{7}{3}$ **4.** $\frac{7}{20}$ **5.** $\frac{64}{15}$ **6.** $\frac{32}{157}$
7. 35 mpg **8.** 16-ounce cup: 22¢/ounce; 12-ounce cup: 23¢/ounce; 16-ounce cup is the better buy **9.** $x = 42$ **10.** $x = 3$
11. 39 hits **12.** 82.5 miles **13.** 540 mg **14.** 51.3 mg
15. $h = 9$ **16.** $\frac{111}{101}$ **17.** $\frac{347}{377}$
18. a. 300 min **b.** 3,343.6 min **c.** 3,342 min

Chapter 7

Exercise Set 7.1

Vocabulary Review **1.** percent **2.** ratio **3.** left **4.** right
5. % symbol **6.** decimal
Problems **1.** $\frac{20}{100}$ **3.** $\frac{60}{100}$ **5.** $\frac{24}{100}$ **7.** $\frac{65}{100}$ **9.** 0.23 **11.** 1.92
13. 0.09 **15.** 0.034 **17.** 0.00087 **19.** 0.009 **21.** 23%
23. 92.3% **25.** 45% **27.** 3% **29.** 60% **31.** 0.8%
33. 2700% **35.** 123% **37.** $\frac{3}{5}$ **39.** $\frac{3}{4}$ **41.** $\frac{1}{25}$
43. $2\frac{13}{20}$ **45.** $\frac{7,187}{10,000}$ **47.** $\frac{3}{400}$ **49.** $\frac{1}{16}$ **51.** $\frac{1}{3}$
53. 50% **55.** 75% **57.** $33\frac{1}{3}$% **59.** 80% **61.** 87.5%
63. 14% **65.** 325% **67.** 150% **69.** 48.8%
71. 0.50; 0.75 **73. a.** Nokia: $\frac{1}{50}$; Android: $\frac{3}{100}$; BlackBerry: $\frac{3}{50}$; Other: $\frac{3}{25}$; iPhone: $\frac{77}{100}$ **b.** Nokia: 0.02; Android: 0.03; BlackBerry: 0.06; Other: 0.12; iPhone: 0.77 **c.** About 2 times as likely.

75. 20% **77.** Liberal Arts: 15%, Science & Math: 15%, Engineering: 27.78%, Business: 11.11%, Architecture & Environmental Design: 11.11%, Agriculture: 22.22% **79.** 78.4% **81.** 11.8%
83. 72.2% **85.** 8.3%; 0.2% **87.** 18.5 **89.** 10.875
91. 0.5 **93.** 62.5 **95.** $n = 0.5$
Find the Mistake **1.** Writing 0.4% as a decimal gives us .004.
2. To write 3.21 as a percent, multiply the number by 100; that is, move the decimal two places to the right. **3.** Writing 25% as a fraction in lowest terms gives us $\frac{1}{4}$. **4.** To change $\frac{5}{8}$ to a percent, we change $\frac{5}{8}$ to 0.625 and then move the decimal two places to the right to get 62.5%.

Exercise Set 7.2

Vocabulary Review **1.** equals sign **2.** multiply **3.** variable
4. decimal **5.** fraction
Problems **1.** 8 **3.** 24 **5.** 20.52 **7.** 7.37 **9.** 50% **11.** 10%
13. 25% **15.** 75% **17.** 64 **19.** 50 **21.** 925 **23.** 400
25. 17.4 **27.** 120 **29.** 13.72 **31.** 22.5 **33.** 50%
35. 942.684 **37.** 97.8 **39.** What number is 25% of 350?
41. What percent of 24 is 16? **43.** 46 is 75% of what number?
45. 11.3% calories from fat; healthy **47.** 56.9% calories from fat; not healthy **49.** 0.80 **51.** 0.76 **53.** 48
55. Fewer than 175 to 280 gulls of breeding age
Find the Mistake **1.** The question, "What number is 28.5% of 30?" translates to $n = 0.285 \cdot 30$. **2.** Asking "75 is 30% of what number?" gives us 250. **3.** To answer the question, "What number is 45% of 90?", we can solve the proportion $\frac{x}{90} = \frac{45}{100}$. **4.** Using a proportion to answer the question, "What percent of 65 is 26?" will give us $n = 40\%$.

Landmark Review

1. $\frac{15}{100}$ **2.** $\frac{27}{100}$ **3.** $\frac{14}{100}$
4. $\frac{89}{100}$ **5.** 0.17 **6.** 0.28 **7.** 0.05 **8.** 0.0637 **9.** 38%
10. 98% **11.** 9% **12.** 487% **13.** 10% **14.** 33.3%
15. 14.3% **16.** 320% **17.** 5.25 **18.** 62.35% **19.** 237.84

Exercise Set 7.3

Vocabulary Review **1.** What number is y% of x?
2. What percent of x is z? **3.** z is y% of what number?
Problems **1.** 70% **3.** 40mL **5.** 45 mL
7. 18.2 acres for farming; 9.8 acres are not available for farming
9. 3,000 students **11.** 400 students **13.** 1,664 female students
15. 31.25% **17.** 50% **19.** 1,267 students **21.** 33 **23.** 8,685
25. 136 **27.** 0.05 **29.** 15,300 **31.** 0.15 **33.** 36.7%, to the nearest tenth of a percent **35.** 158 hits **37.** 19 hits
Find the Mistake **1.** On a test with 110 questions, a student answered 98 questions correctly. The percentage of questions the student answered correctly is 89.1%. **2.** A school track team consists of 12 boys and 10 girls. The total number of girls makes up 45.5% percent of the whole team. **3.** Suppose 39 students in a college class of 130 students received a B on their tests. To find what percent of students earned a B, solve the proportion $\frac{39}{130} = \frac{x}{100}$. **4.** Suppose a basketball player made 120 out of 150 free throws attempted. To find what percent of free throws the player made, solve the proportion $\frac{120}{150} = \frac{x}{100}$.

Exercise Set 7.4

Vocabulary Review **1.** D **2.** P **3.** P **4.** D
Problems **1.** $52.50 **3.** $2.70; $47.70 **5.** $150; $156 **7.** 5%
9. $2,820 **11.** $200 **13.** 14% **15.** $11.93 **17.** 4.5%
19. $3,995 **21.** 1,100 **23.** 75 **25.** 0.16 **27.** 4 **29.** 396
31. 415.8 **33.** Sales tax = $3,180; luxury tax = $2,300 **35.** $1,846
37. You saved $1,600 on the sticker price and $150 in luxury tax.

If you lived in a state with a 6% sales tax rate, you saved an additional 0.06($1600) = $96.

Find the Mistake   1. Suppose the sales tax rate on a new computer is 8%. If the computer cost $650, then the total price of purchase would be $702.   **2.** If a new shirt that costs $32 has sales tax equal to $1.92, then the sales tax rate is 6%.   **3.** A car salesman's commission rate is 7%. To find his commission on a $15,000 sale of a Ford truck, we would solve $15,000 \cdot 0.07 = n$.   **4.** A saleswoman makes a commission of $6.80 on a sale of $85 worth of clothing. To find the woman's commission rate, solve the equation $85n = 6.80$.

Exercise Set 7.5

Vocabulary Review   1. b   **2.** d   **3.** a   **4.** c

Problems   1. $24,610   **3.** $3,510   **5.** $13,200   **7.** 10%   **9.** 20%   **11.** 61%   **13.** $45; $255   **15.** $381.60   **17.** $46,595.88   **19. a.** 51.9% **b.** 7.8%   **21.** 140   **23.** 4   **25.** 152.25   **27.** 3,434.7   **29.** 10,150   **31.** 10,456.78   **33.** 2,140   **35.** 3,210

Find the Mistake   1. If a new model of a car increases 12% from and old model's price of $24,000, then the new selling price is $26,880.   **2.** A lawnmower goes on sale from $98 to $63.70. The percent decrease of the lawnmower's price is 35%.   **3.** A backpack that normally sells for $75 is on sale. The new price of $45 shows a percent decrease of 40%.   **4.** A designer pair of sunglasses is on sale from $125 for 20% off. If the sales tax is 6% of the sale price, then the total bill for the glasses would be $106.

Exercise Set 7.6

Vocabulary Review   1. principal   **2.** interest rate   **3.** simple   **4.** compound

Problems   1. $2,160   **3.** $665   **5.** $8,560   **7.** $2,160   **9.** $5   **11.** $813.33   **13.** $5,618   **15.** $8,407.56, Some answers may vary in the hundredths column depending on whether rounding is done in the intermediate steps.   **17.** $974.59   **19. a.** $13,468.55   **b.** $13,488.50   **c.** $12,820.37   **d.** $12,833.59   **21.** 50   **23.** 488   **25.** 25%

27. Percent increase in production costs: *Moonlight* to *Slumdog Millionaire*, 900%; *Slumdog Millionaire* to *The Hurt Locker*, 0%; *The Hurt Locker* to *Million Dollar Baby*, 100%; *Million Dollar Baby* to *The Departed*, 200%; *The Departed* to *Lord of the Rings*, 8%

Find the Mistake   1. A woman invests $1,500 into an account with a 6% annual interest rate. She will have $1,590 in her account by the end of one year.   **2.** A business man invests $2,750 into an account that has an 8% interest rate per year. To find out how much money will be in the man's account after 72 days, you must multiply the product of 2,750 and 0.08 by $\frac{72}{360}$.   **3.** If a person invests $10,000 into an account that is compounded annually at 6%, then after two years, the account will contain $11,236.   **4.** A woman deposits $4,000 into a savings account that pays 7% compounded quarterly. At the end of the year, the account contains $4,287.44.

Exercise Set 7.7

Vocabulary Review   percents, degrees, template, protractor

Problems   1. a. $\frac{103}{200}$ **b.** $\frac{12}{103}$ **c.** $\frac{47}{50}$ **d.** $\frac{47}{3}$
3. a. 64%   **b.** 15%   **c.** 36%
5. a. 540 people   **b.** 570 people   **c.** 840 people   **d.** 1,890 people
7.   **9.**

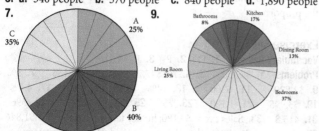

Find the Mistake   1. The percentage of people who live in their parents' home or on campus is 35%.   **2.** The percentage of people who live in a single bedroom apartment or studio, or in an apartment with friends can be found by adding 10% and 20%.   **3.** The number of people who live in a house with friends is 875.   **4.** To find the number of people who decided not to live off campus, multiply 2500 by 16%.

Chapter 7 Review

1. 0.56   **2.** 0.03   **3.** 0.004   **4.** 1.37   **5.** 20.04
6. 0.0006   **7.** 0.00008   **8.** 4.06   **9.** 0.2   **10.** 32%
11. 70%   **12.** 164%   **13.** 4%   **14.** 0.8%   **15.** 1057%
16. 500%   **17.** 13700%   **18.** 10.2%   **19.** $\frac{17}{20}$
20. $1\frac{7}{25}$ **21.** $\frac{21}{250}$ **22.** $\frac{2}{25}$ **23.** $\frac{51}{100}$ **24.** $\frac{3}{500}$
25. $\frac{3}{16}$ **26.** $\frac{41}{2000}$ **27.** $1\frac{73}{100}$ **28.** 52%   **29.** 62.5%
30. 145%   **31.** 175%   **32.** 33.3%   **33.** 6.25%
34. 9.375%   **35.** 162.5%   **36.** 0.07%   **37.** 12.8
38. 1.96   **39.** 60%   **40.** 20%   **41.** 80   **42.** 400
43. 20.7   **44.** 24   **45.** 508.712   **46.** Belgium: $\frac{24}{25}$; Sweden: $\frac{1}{4}$; United States: $\frac{3}{5}$ **47.** 56 is 85% of what number?   **48.** 84%
49. 375 students   **50.** $1,000   **51.** $6\frac{1}{4}$%, or 6.25%
52. $290.50; 35% off   **53.** $77.31   **54.** $750   **55.** $1,006.20
56. $320   **57.** $48   **58.** $5,310.52   **59.** $1,311.27
60. 130 million   **61.** 204 million   **62.** 24.82%   **63.** 1689 athletes
64.

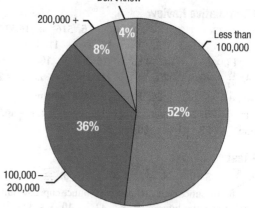

Chapter 7 Cumulative Review

1. 5,411   **2.** 1,091   **3.** 7,969   **4.** 53.4   **5.** 32   **6.** $\frac{4}{5}$
7. $\frac{27}{125}$ **8.** 9.502   **9.** 0.286   **10.** 1.19   **11.** $\frac{1}{9}$ **12.** 12
13. $\frac{29}{24} = 1\frac{5}{24}$ **14.** $\frac{23}{6} = 3\frac{5}{6}$ **15.** $\frac{29}{2} = 14\frac{1}{2}$ **16.** 6   **17.** 14
18. 3 (6 + 8) = 42   **19.** $\frac{1}{6}$ **20.** 19,008 feet   **21.** 1,134 in.²
22. 62.5%   **23.** $\frac{8}{25}$ **24.** 3.5   **25.** 38   **26.** 3.9   **27.** 35%
28. 95   **29.** $1.33   **30.** 91¢   **31.** 35°C   **32.** 9.5%
33. 375 miles   **34.** $3,187.50   **35.** $P = 24.8$ in.; $A = 38.44$ in.²
36. $8.50 per hour   **37.** 12.77 acres   **38.** 5.5 acres

Chapter 7 Test

1. 0.27   **2.** 0.06   **3.** 0.009   **4.** 64%   **5.** 30%   **6.** 149%
7. $\frac{9}{20}$ **8.** $1\frac{9}{25}$ **9.** $\frac{9}{125}$ **10.** 65%   **11.** 87.5%   **12.** 225%
13. 12   **14.** 35%   **15.** 75   **16.** 96%   **17.** $900
18. $145; 20% off   **19.** $135.32   **20.** $866.40   **21.** $140
22. $2,662.40   **23.** 20.52%   **24.** 19,048 finishers

25.

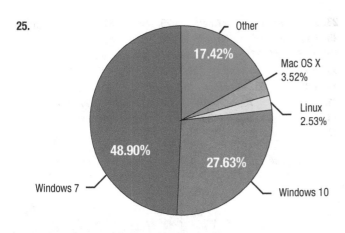

Pie chart labels: Other 17.42%, Mac OS X 3.52%, Linux 2.53%, Windows 10 27.63%, Windows 7 48.90%

Chapter 8

Exercise Set 8.1
Vocabulary Review   1. foot **2.** meter **3.** conversion factor
4. fraction bar **5.** unit analysis **6.** divide
Problems   1. 60 in.   **3.** 120 in.   **5.** 6 ft   **7.** 162 in.
9. $2\frac{1}{4}$ ft.   **11.** 13,200 ft   **13.** $1\frac{1}{3}$ yd   **15.** 1,800 cm
17. 4,800 m   **19.** 50 cm   **21.** 0.248 km   **23.** 670 mm
25. 34.98 m   **27.** 6.34 dm   **29.** 20 yd   **31.** 80 in.
33. 244 cm   **35.** 65 mm   **37.** 2,960 chains   **39.** 120,000 μm
41. 7,920 ft   **43.** 0.12 m, 0.35 m   **45.** 30.48 cm
47. $18,216   **49.** $157.50   **51.** 3,965,280 ft   **53.** 179,352 in.
55. 2.7 mi   **57.** 18,094,560 ft   **59.** 144   **61.** 6   **63.** 0.4
65. 405   **67.** 2,200   **69.** 607.5
Find the Mistake   1. The average length for a house cat is roughly
18 inches. To show how many feet this is, multiply by the conversion
factor $\frac{1 \text{ foot}}{12 \text{ inches}}$.   **2.** The length of a parking space is based on the
average car length, which measures approximately 15 feet. This
length converted to yards is 5 yards.   **3.** A cell phone measures 100
mm in length. To show how many meters this is, multiply 100 mm
by the conversion factor $\frac{1 \text{ m}}{1,000 \text{ mm}}$.   **4.** To complete a unit analysis
problem, make sure all units, except those you want to end up with,
will divide out.

Exercise Set 8.2
Vocabulary Review   1. area **2.** square inches **3.** multiply
4. U.S. system **5.** metric system **6.** volume
Problems   1. 432 in²   **3.** 2 ft²   **5.** 1,306,800 ft²
7. 1,280 acres   **9.** 3 mi²   **11.** 108 ft²   **13.** 1,700 mm²
15. 28,000 cm²   **17.** 0.0012 m²   **19.** 500 m²   **21.** 700 a
23. 3.42 ha   **25.** 102.6 ft³   **27.** 128 fl oz   **29.** 48 qt
31. 56 pt   **33.** 188.8 fl oz   **35.** 32 gal   **37.** 9 qt   **39.** 32 yd³
41. 9,600 mL   **43.** 0.0938 L   **45.** 3,000,000 mL
47. 4,710 L   **49.** Smallest: $A = 5,500$ sq yd = 1.1 acres;
Rose Bowl: $A = 8,352$ sq yd = 1.7 acres;
Largest: $A = 9,000$ sq yd = 1.9 acres
51. 2,400 tiles   **53.** 48 in   **55.** 16,200 dm²   **57.** 21,632 acres
59. 3.55 qt   **61.** 1.6 pints   **63.** 0.124 ft³   **65.** 3 glasses
67. 72 qt   **69.** 200 test tubes   **71.** 57.52 gal   **73.** 101,561,600 acres
75. 380.16 mi²   **77.** 0.25 ft³   **79.** 118,800,000 ft³   **81.** 240
83. 10,000   **85.** 500,000   **87.** 15,000   **89.** 15
Find the Mistake   1. A rectangular computer monitor is 24 inches
by 30 inches. To find the area of the computer monitor in square feet,
divide the product of 24 and 30 by 144.   **2.** A family bought 320
acres of land. The area of this land in square miles is 0.5 mi².
3. A 3-quart container of ice cream can hold 6 pints of ice cream.
4. To find how many milliliters four 2-liter soda bottles can hold, you
must find the product of 8 L and $\frac{1,000 \text{ mL}}{1 \text{ L}}$.

Exercise Set 8.3
Vocabulary Review   1. U.S. System **2.** pounds, ounces
3. metric system **4.** kilograms, metric tons
Problems   1. 128 oz   **3.** 4,000 lb   **5.** 12 lb   **7.** 0.9 T
9. 32,000 oz   **11.** 56 oz   **13.** 13,000 lb   **15.** 2,000 g
17. 40 mg   **19.** 200,000 cg   **21.** 508 cg   **23.** 4.5 g
25. 47.895 cg   **27.** 1.578 g   **29.** 0.42 kg   **31.** 48 g
33. 4 g   **35.** 9.72 g   **37.** 1,540 lbs   **39.** 1,400 g
41. 250 cg   **43.** 3 L   **45.** 1.5 L   **47.** 20.32   **49.** 6.36
51. 50   **53.** 56.82   **55.** 122   **57.** 248   **59.** 38.89
61. 0.000789 kg/cm³
Find the Mistake   1. Correct **2.** Incorrect, $\frac{2000 \text{ lbs}}{1 \text{ T}}$
3. Incorrect, $\frac{1 \text{kg}}{1000 \text{ g}}$ **4.** Correct

Landmark Review   1. 84 inches   **2.** 0.75 yards
3. 443,520 inches   **4.** 0.002841 miles   **5.** 3,800 centimeters
6. 1.43 decimeters   **7.** 4.3 meters   **8.** 1.15 meters
9. 1,152 square inches   **10.** 3.886 square miles   **11.** 8,960 acres
12. 45 square feet   **13.** 700 square meters
14. 0.00143 square meters   **15.** 3.5 square centimeters
16. 420 ares   **17.** 112 ounces   **18.** 0.9375 pounds
19. 64,000 ounces   **20.** 0.75 tons   **21.** 6,500 grams
22. 50 milligrams   **23.** 1.759 grams   **24.** 8.59 grams

Exercise Set 8.4
Vocabulary Review   1. centimeters   **2.** quarts
3. Celsius, Fahrenheit
Problems   1. 15.24 cm   **3.** 13.12 ft   **5.** 6.56 yd   **7.** 32,200 m
9. 5.98 yd²   **11.** 24.7 acres   **13.** 8,195 mL   **15.** 2.12 qt
17. 75.8 L   **19.** 339.6 g   **21.** 33 lb   **23.** 365°F   **25.** 30°C
27. 3.94 in.   **29.** 7.62 m   **31.** 46.23 L   **33.** 17.67 oz
35. Answers will vary.   **37.** 91.46 m   **39.** 20.90 m²
41. 88.55 km/hr   **43.** 2.03 m   **45.** 38.3°C   **47.** 75
49. 82   **51.** 3.25   **53.** 22   **55.** 41   **57.** 48   **59.** 195
61. 3.27   **63.** $90.00   **65.** 0.71 oz/in.³   **67.** 68.5 g
Find the Mistake   1. To convert 6 miles to km, multiply 6 miles
by $\frac{1.61 \text{ km}}{1 \text{ mi}}$.   **2.** Suppose a pasta recipe requires a half gallon of water,
but your measuring cup only measures milliliters. To find how many
milliliters are equal to a half gallon of water, multiply $\frac{1}{2}$ gal by
both conversion factors $\frac{3.79 \text{ L}}{1 \text{ gal}}$ and $\frac{1000 \text{ mL}}{1 \text{ L}}$.   **3.** To convert 25°
Celsius to Fahrenheit, use the formula $F = \frac{9}{5}C + 32$ to get 77° F.
4. A cookie recipe requires you to bake them at 325° F. This temperature in Celsius is 163° C (rounded to the nearest degree).

Exercise Set 8.5
Vocabulary Review   1. minutes, seconds **2.** columns
3. borrow
Problems   1. a. 270 min **b.** 4.5 hr   **3. a.** 320 min **b.** 5.33 hr
5. a. 390 sec **b.** 6.5 min   **7. a.** 320 sec **b.** 5.33 min
9. a. 40 oz **b.** 2.5 lb   **11. a.** 76 oz **b.** 4.75 lb
13. a. 54 in. **b.** 4.5 ft   **15. a.** 69 in. **b.** 5.75 ft
17. a. 9 qt **b.** 2.25 gal   **19.** 11 hr   **21.** 22 ft 4 in.
23. 11 lb   **25.** 5 hr 40 min   **27.** 3 hr 47 min   **29.** 52 min
31. 80.7 ft/sec   **33.** 19.5 mi/hr   **37.** 8:02:36; 8:05:25
39. 00:05:05   **41.** $104   **43.** 10 hr   **45.** $150
47. 356.79 grams   **49.** $29,293.60   **51.** 4.19 sec
Find the Mistake   1. Converting 6 feet 6 inches to inches gives us
78 inches.   **2.** The correct way to write the sum of 2 hours, 55 min
and 4 hours, 10 min is 7 hours and 5 minutes.   **3.** The correct way
to subtract 27 minutes from 6 hours and 12 minutes is to borrow 60
minutes from the 6 hours to get 5 hours and 45 minutes.   **4.** Jane
is buying two cups of frozen yogurt. One cup contains 3 ounces and

the other contains 11.9 grams. If each ounce cost \$1.50, then the total purchase price will be \$5.13.

Chapter 8 Review

1. 27 ft   **2.** 0.57 km   **3.** 7 ft   **4.** 360 in.   **5.** 198 in.
6. 35,640 ft   **7.** 6,200 m   **8.** 47 dm   **9.** 108,900 ft^2
10. 5.5 ft^2 **11.** 16,400 mL   **12.** 0.969 km   **13.** 25°C
14. 113°F   **15.** 92,000 lb   **16.** 8.5 lb   **17.** 84 oz
18. 5,000 g   **19.** 6.875 ft^2 **20.** 730 m^2 **21.** 180 ft^2
22. 1.5 cm^2 **23.** 56 pt   **24.** 9 qt   **25.** 6.2 yd^3
26. 149° F   **27.** 0.046 g   **28.** 0.00187 oz   **29.** 0.40 gal
30. 15.9 qt   **31.** 22,572 in.   **32.** 656 yd   **33.** 2.36 L
34. 8.05 km   **35.** 6.21 miles   **36.** 13.78 qt   **37.** 0.01 acres
38. 1.56 mi^2 **39.** 1,280 acres   **40.** 88.68 L   **41.** 151.83 m
42. 14.15 L   **43.** 14.57 in.   **44.** 67.62 km   **45.** 303.15 cm^2
46. 56.81 acres   **47.** 53.77 L   **48.** 21.36 kg   **49. a.** 435 min
b. 7.25 hr   **50. a.** 14 qt   **b.** 3.5 gal   **51.** 16 lb 2 oz
52. 24 ft 4 in.   **53.** 16 ft 11 in.   **54.** 1 hr 46 min   **55.** 0.02 ft^3
56. 20.90 m^2 **57.** 0.04 yd^2 **58.** 54 tiles   **59.** 8,889 yd^2
60. 72 glasses   **61.** 7.5 mi/hr   **62.** 1,076 km/hr
63. 1,193 mi/hr   **64.** 21,632 acres   **65.** 96.5 mi^2
66. 0.124 ft^3 **67.** 3 lbs   **68.** \$40   **69.** DiGiorno
12,246,222,000 pesos; Red Baron 6,907,661,000 pesos
70. Jack's 212,520,000 euros; Tombstone 238,128,000 euros

Chapter 8 Cumulative Review

1. 11,623   **2.** 1,001   **3.** 27   **4.** 162   **5.** $356\frac{7}{8} = 356.875$
6. 243   **7.** 34   **8.** 9   **9.** 56   **10.** 66   **11.** 15   **12.** 44.85
13. 21.65   **14.** 48.78   **15.** 13.5   **16.** $\frac{1}{576}$ **17.** 27   **18.** $\frac{9}{16}$
19. $2\frac{1}{4}$ **20.** $8\frac{1}{4}$ **21.** 2.1   **22.** 1.075   **23.** $14\frac{2}{3}$ **24.** $x = 4.25$
25. $y = 4.5$ **26.** $x = 21$ **27.** $P = 78$ in., $A = 228$ in.^{2} **28.** $3\frac{1}{20}$ cm
29. 18   **30.** 64 mi/hr   **31.** 2,064   **32.** $2 \cdot 3^2 \cdot 5 \cdot 7$ **33.** 54
34. 1.6 mi   **35.** 21.34 %   **36.** 39.59 %

Chapter 8 Test

1. 9 ft   **2.** 0.64 km   **3.** 174,240 ft^2 **4.** 6 ft^2 **5.** 12,000 mL
6. 4.83 km   **7.** 8.48 qt   **8.** 32.2° C   **9.** 5,200 lb   **10.** 7 lb
11. 4.5 ft^2 **12.** 630 m^2 **13.** 4.3 yd^3 **14.** 68° F   **15.** 0.53 gal
16. 13,032 in.   **17.** 0.22 ft^3 **18.** 61.32 L   **19.** 114.33 m
20. 10.38 L   **21.** 10.63 in.   **22.** 14.49 km   **23.** 187.05 cm^2
24. 41.99 acres   **25.** 33.96 L   **26.** 10.45 kg   **27.** 120 tiles
28. 192 glasses   **29. a.** 165 min **b.** 2.75 hr   **30.** 7 lb
31. Barq's 0.023 g; Coca-Cola Classic 0.035 g; Dr.Pepper 0.043 g; Mountain Dew 0.054 g; Pepsi 0.037; Vault 0.071 g
32. Barq's 0.0008127 oz; Coca-Cola Classic 0.001237 oz; Dr.Pepper 0.001519 oz; Mountain Dew 0.001908 oz; Pepsi 0.001307 oz; Vault 0.002509 oz

Chapter 9

Exercise Set 9.1

Vocabulary Review   **1.** base, exponent   **2.** product
3. power   **4.** distributive   **5.** scientific notation
Problems   **1.** 16; Base: 4; Exponent: 2
3. 0.09; Base: 0.03; Exponent: 2   **5.** 64; Base: 4; Exponent: 3
7. 25; Base: −5; Exponent: 2   **9.** −8; Base: 2; Exponent: 3
11. 81; Base: 3; Exponent: 4   **13.** $\frac{4}{9}$; Base: $\frac{2}{3}$; Exponent: 2
15. $\frac{1}{16}$; Base: $\frac{1}{2}$; Exponent: 4   **17.** $\frac{9}{16}$; Base: $-\frac{2}{3}$; Exponent: 2
19. $\frac{1}{36}$; Base: $\frac{1}{6}$; Exponent: 2

21. a.

Number x	1	2	3	4	5	6	7
Square x^2	1	4	9	16	25	36	49

b. Larger

23. x^9 **25.** y^{30} **27.** 2^{12} **29.** x^{28} **31.** x^{10} **33.** 5^{12}
35. y^9 **37.** 2^{50} **39.** a^{3x} **41.** b^{xy} **43.** $16x^2$
45. $32y^5$ **47.** $81x^4$ **49.** $0.25a^2b^2$ **51.** $64x^3y^3z^3$
53. $-64x^3y^3$ **55.** $8x^{12}$ **57.** $16a^6$ **59.** x^{14} **61.** a^{11}
63. $128x^7$ **65.** $432x^{10}$ **67.** $16x^4y^6$ **69.** $\frac{8}{27}a^{12}b^{15}$
71. 4.32×10^4 **73.** 5.7×10^2 **75.** 2.38×10^5 **77.** 1.0×10^{10}
79. 2,490   **81.** 352   **83.** 28,000   **85.** −310,000
87.

Number x	−3	−2	−1	0	1	2	3
Square x^2	9	4	1	0	1	4	9

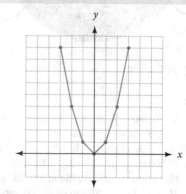

89.

Number x	−2.5	−1.5	−0.5	0	0.5	1.5	2.5
Square x^2	6.25	2.25	0.25	0	0.25	2.25	6.25

91.

Name	Location	Area (sq. mi.)	Scientific Notation
Caspian Sea	5 countries	152,239	1.52×10^5
Superior	US, Canada	31,820	3.18×10^4
Victoria	Tanzania, Uganda	26,828	2.68×10^4
Huron	US, Canada	23,010	2.30×10^4
Michigan	US	22,400	2.24×10^4

93. 27 inches^3 **95.** 15.6 inches^3 **97.** x^{10} **99.** $2xy\sqrt{5xy}$
101. $6x\sqrt{2x}$ **103.** 6.5×10^8 seconds   **105.** \$740,000
107. \$180,000   **109.** \$30,957.48   **111.** 219 inches^3
113. 182 inches^3 **115.** −3   **117.** 11   **119.** −5
121. 5   **123.** 2   **125.** 6   **127.** 4   **129.** 3
Find the Mistake   **1.** Simplifying the expression $\left(-\frac{12}{32}\right)^2$ will give a negative answer.   **2.** You would use the product property for exponents to simplify the expression $x^8 \cdot x^4 \cdot x^{10}$.   **3.** To simplify the expression $(x^3 \cdot y)^4 (y \cdot z^2)^8$, we must first use the distributive property of exponents.   **4.** 5.83×10^5 in an example of a number written in scientific notation.

Exercise Set 9.2

Vocabulary Review   **1.** negative   **2.** quotient   **3.** expanded
4. exponents
Problems   **1.** $\frac{1}{9}$ **3.** $\frac{1}{36}$ **5.** $\frac{1}{64}$ **7.** $\frac{1}{125}$ **9.** $-\frac{1}{9}$
11. $-\frac{1}{8}$ **13.** $\frac{2}{x^3}$ **15.** $\frac{1}{8x^3}$ **17.** $\frac{1}{25y^2}$
19. $\frac{1}{100}$

21.

Number x	Square x^2	Power of 2 2^x
−3	9	$\frac{1}{8}$
−2	4	$\frac{1}{4}$
−1	1	$\frac{1}{2}$
0	0	1
1	1	2
2	4	4
3	9	8

23. $\frac{1}{25}$ **25.** x^6 **27.** 64   **29.** $8x^3$ **31.** 6^{10} **33.** $\frac{1}{6^{10}}$ **35.** $\frac{1}{2^8}$
37. 2^8 **39.** $27x^3$ **41.** $16x^2$ **43.** $\frac{x^3}{27}$ **45.** $\frac{16}{y^2}$ **47.** $-\frac{125}{x^3}$
49. $\frac{64}{y^2}$ **51.** 1   **53.** $-2y$ **55.** $-3ab^2$ **57.** 1   **59.** $81x^4y^4$
61. 1   **63.** $2a^2b$ **65.** $\frac{1}{49y^6}$ **67.** $\frac{1}{x^8}$ **69.** $\frac{1}{y^3}$ **71.** x^2
73. a^6 **75.** $\frac{1}{y^9}$ **77.** y^{40} **79.** $\frac{1}{x}$ **81.** x^9 **83.** $\frac{4b^8}{a^4}$
85. a^{16} **87.** $\frac{1}{a^4}$ **89.** $\frac{27}{16x^2y^4}$ **91.** 4.8×10^{-3} **93.** 2.5×10^1
95. -9×10^{-6} **97.** -8.7×10^{-5} **99.** 0.00423   **101.** 0.000 08
103. −4.2   **105.** −0.0036
107.

Expanded Form	Scientific Notation $n \times 10^r$
0.000357	3.57×10^{-4}
0.00357	3.57×10^{-3}
0.0357	3.57×10^{-2}
0.357	3.57×10^{-1}
3.57	3.57×10^{0}
35.7	3.57×10^{1}
357	3.57×10^{2}
3,570	3.57×10^{3}
35,700	3.57×10^{4}

109.

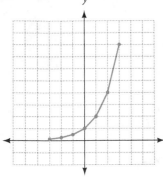

Number x	Power of x 2^x
−3	$\frac{1}{8}$
−2	$\frac{1}{4}$
−1	$\frac{1}{2}$
0	1
1	2
2	4
3	8

111. 0.002   **113.** Mercury 5.7×10^7 km; Earth 1.5×10^8 km; Jupiter 7.79×10^8 km; Neptune 4.5×10^9 km   **115.** 2.5×10^4
117. 2.35×10^5 **119.** 8.2×10^{-4} **117.** 100 inches^2, 400 inches^2; 4   **123.** x^2; $4x^2$; 4   **125.** 216 inches^3; 1,728 inches^3; 8
127. x^3; $8x^3$; 8   **129.** 1,407   **131.** 13.5   **133.** 8
135. 26.52   **137.** 12   **139.** x^8 **141.** x **143.** $\frac{1}{y^2}$
145. 1   **147.** 340   **149.** 0.000035
Find the Mistake   1. The negative exponent property says that

$x^{-y} = \left(\frac{1}{x}\right)^y$.   **2.** When using the quotient property of exponents to simplify the expression $\frac{y^{12}}{y^8}$, we get y^4.   **3.** When using the expanded distributive property of exponents to simplify the expression $\left(\frac{x}{3}\right)^4$, we get $\frac{x^4}{81}$.   **4.** The number 0.00238 written in scientific notation is 2.38×10^{-3}.

Exercise Set 9.3
Vocabulary Review   1. monomial   **2.** terms   **3.** coefficient
4. variable   **5.** subtraction
Problems   1. $12x^7$ **3.** $-16y^{11}$ **5.** $32x^2$ **7.** $200a^6$
9. $-24a^3b^3$ **11.** $24x^6y^8$ **13.** $3x$ **15.** $\frac{6}{y^3}$ **17.** $\frac{1}{2a}$
19. $-\frac{3a}{b^2}$ **21.** $\frac{x^2}{9z^2}$ **23.** $-\frac{y^2}{4x^3z}$
25.

a	b	ab	$\frac{a}{b}$	$\frac{b}{a}$
10	$5x$	$50x$	$\frac{2}{x}$	$\frac{x}{2}$
$20x^3$	$6x^2$	$120x^5$	$\frac{10x}{3}$	$\frac{3}{10x}$
$25x^5$	$5x^4$	$125x^9$	$5x$	$\frac{1}{5x}$
$3x^{-2}$	$3x^2$	9	$\frac{1}{x^4}$	x^4
$-2y^4$	$8y^7$	$-16y^{11}$	$-\frac{1}{4y^3}$	$-4y^3$

27. $4x^3$ **29.** $\frac{1}{b^2}$ **31.** $\frac{6y^{10}}{x^4}$ **33.** $-\frac{4x^2}{3y}$ **35.** 6×10^8
37. 1.75×10^{-1} **39.** 1.21×10^{-6} **41.** 4.2×10^3
43. 3×10^{10} **45.** 5×10^{-3} **47.** -5×10^{-4} **49.** 2×10^6
51. 1×10^1 **53.** 4.2×10^{-6} **55.** $8x^2$ **57.** $-11x^5$
59. 0   **61.** $4x^3$ **63.** $31ab^2$ **65.** $-11x^2y$
67.

a	b	ab	$a + b$
$5x$	$3x$	$15x^2$	$8x$
$4x^2$	$2x^2$	$8x^4$	$6x^2$
$3x^3$	$6x^3$	$18x^6$	$9x^3$
$2x^4$	$-3x^4$	$-6x^8$	$-x^4$
x^5	$7x^5$	$7x^{10}$	$8x^5$

69. $x^2y + x$ **71.** $x + y$ **73.** $x^2 - 4$ **75.** $x^2 - x - 6$
77. $x^2 - 5x$ **79.** $x^2 - 8x$ **81.** $9x^3$ **83.** $-20a^2$
85. $6x^5y^2$ **87.** −5   **89.** 6   **91.** 76   **93.** $6x^2$ **95.** $2x$
97. $-2x - 9$ **99.** 11   **101.** 36
Find the Mistake   1. The coefficient of the monomial $12x^4y^2z$ is 12.
2. Multiplying the monomials $-15x^3y$ and $2x^2$ gives us $-30x^5y$.
3. When dividing $28x^6y^2$ by $4x^2y$, write the problem as the separate fractions $\frac{28}{4} \cdot \frac{x^6}{x^2} \cdot \frac{y^2}{y}$.   **4.** Monomials with similar terms have the same variable parts, but coefficients may differ.

Landmark Review   1. −49   2. x^8 3. x^6 4. $27a^3$
5. $256y^5$ **6.** 25   **7.** $27x^3$ **8.** $\frac{3}{x^7}$ **9.** $\frac{1}{4}$ **10.** $\frac{1}{a^2}$
11. $4xy$ **12.** 1   **13.** 3×10^2 **14.** 2×10^3 **15.** $18x^5y^4$
16. $\frac{a^2b}{2c^3}$ **17.** $5x^2$ **18.** $9y^2$ **19.** $2x^2 - 10x$ **20.** $-11y^6$

Exercise Set 9.4
Vocabulary Review   1. polynomial   **2.** degree   **3.** like
4. opposite
Problems   1. Trinomial, 3   **3.** Trinomial, 3   **5.** Binomial, 1
7. Binomial, 2   **9.** Monomial, 2   **11.** Monomial, 0
13. $5x^2 + 5x + 9$ **15.** $5a^2 - 9a + 7$ **17.** $x^2 + 6x + 8$
19. $6x^2 - 13x + 5$ **21.** $x^2 - 9$ **23.** $3y^2 - 11y + 10$
25. $6x^3 + 5x^2 - 4x + 3$ **27.** $2x^2 - x + 1$ **29.** $2a^2 - 2a - 2$

31. $-\frac{1}{9}x^3 - \frac{2}{3}x^2 - \frac{5}{2}x + \frac{7}{4}$ **33.** $-4y^2 + 15y - 22$

35. $x^2 - 33x + 63$ **37.** $8y^2 + 4y + 26$ **39.** $75x^2 - 150x - 75$

41. $12x + 2$ **43.** 4   **45.** -4 **47.** 25   **49.** 3

51. 18π inches^3 **53.** 5   **55.** -6 **57.** $-20x^2$ **59.** $-21x$

61. $2x$ **63.** $-8x$ **65.** $6x - 18$ **67.** $-3xy + 12$

Find the Mistake   1. The degree of the polynomial $x^2 + 6 + 4x - x^7$
is 7.   **2.** Adding $x^3 + 4x^2 - 8 + x^2$ gives us $x^3 + 5x^2 - 8$.
3. Subtracting $2x^2 + 3x - 2$ from $4x^2 + 5x - 9$ gives us
$2x^2 + 2x - 7$.   **4.** The value of the polynomial $7a^2 + 5a - 10$
when a is 4 is 122.

Exercise Set 9.5
Vocabulary Review   1. distributive   **2.** term   **3.** binomials
4. products   **5.** column

Problems   1. $6x^2 + 2x$ **3.** $6x^4 - 4x^3 + 2x^2$ **5.** $2a^3b - 2a^2b^2 + 2ab$
7. $3y^4 + 9y^3 + 12y^2$ **9.** $8x^5y^2 + 12x^4y^3 + 32x^2y^4$
11. $-4x^2y^2 + 6xy^3 - 14xy^2$ **13.** $x^2 + 7x + 12$
15. $x^2 + 7x + 6$ **17.** $a^2 + 2a - 15$ **19.** $3a^2 - 16a - 12$
21. $xy + bx - ay - ab$ **23.** $x^2 + x + \frac{6}{25}$ **25.** $y^2 - \frac{16}{49}$
27. $3x^2 - 11x + 10$ **29.** $6x^2 + 9x - 6$
31. $2ax - 8x - 3a + 12$ **33.** $36x^2 - 25$ **35.** $4x^2 + \frac{1}{2}x - \frac{3}{4}$
37. $3 - 7a - 6a^2$ **39.** $a^2 + 6a + 9$ **41.** $x^2 - 4x + 4$
43. $x^2 - 8x + 16$ **45.** $a^2 + a + \frac{1}{4}$ **47.** $a^2 - 0.8a + 0.16$
49. $9x^2 + 12x + 4$ **51.** $9x^2 - 12x + 4$
53. $25x^2 + 40xy + 16y^2$ **55.** $36x^2 - 120xy + 100y^2$
57. $a^2 - 36$ **59.** $y^2 - 4$ **61.** $100 - x^2$ **63.** $9x^2 - 25$
65. $(x + 4)(x + 5) = x^2 + 4x + 5x + 20$
$\qquad\qquad\qquad\quad = x^2 + 9x + 20$
67. $(2x + 1)(2x + 2) = 4x^2 + 6x + 2$
69. $a^3 + 7a^2 + 13a + 15$ **71.** $x^3 + 27$
73. $3x^3 - 23x^2 + 38x - 16$
75. $2x^4 - 7x^3 + 3x^2 - x + 3$ **77.** $28a^7 - 42a^4 - 32a^3 + 48$
79. $x^3 - 12x^2 + 47x - 60$ **81.** $6x^2 - 11x - 14$
83. $15x^2 + 19x - 4$ **85.** $x^2 - x - 20$ **87.** $6x + 19$
89. $x^2 + 4x$ **91.** $2x^2 - 8x + 6$
93. $A = x(3x + 2) = 3x^2 + 2x$ **95.** $R = 1{,}300p - 100p^2$
97. $A = x(x + 2) = x^2 + 2x$
99. a. $A = \pi(r + 2)^2 = \pi r^2 + 4\pi r + 4\pi$
  b. $A = 4\pi(r + 1) = 4\pi r + 4\pi$

Find the Mistake   1. To find the product of two binomials, multiply
each term in the first by each term in the second.
2. When using the FOIL method to multiply the binomials $(9x - 2)$
and $(5x + 3)$, the product of the two outside terms is $27x$.
3. For the problem $(x^2 - 4)(3x^2 + 6)$, adding the products of the two
outside terms with the two inside terms gives us $-6x^2$.
4. For the problem $4x^2(3x^2 + 4x + 9)$, the degree of the answer is 4.

Chapter 9 Review
1. -25, base: 5, exponent: 2   **2.** 16, base: -2, exponent: 4
3. -343 **4.** $-\frac{1}{4}$ **5.** $\frac{8}{27}$ **6.** $\frac{-1}{25}$ **7.** y^{60} **8.** x^{10}
9. $-27x^3$ **10.** $0.25x^2y^2$ **11.** $36b^4$ **12.** x^{26}
13. $81x^6y^{10}$ **14.** $\frac{27}{64}a^3b^{21}$ **15.** $256x^{19}$ **16.** 4.78×10^6
17. 3.0×10^1 **18.** -7.18×10^{-6} **19.** 3.478×10^{-2}
20. 34,700   **21.** -0.000205 **22.** 3.98×10^1 **23.** $\frac{1}{49}$
24. $\frac{8}{x^2}$ **25.** $-\frac{1}{27}$ **26.** 1   **27.** $\frac{1}{a^2}$ **28.** $\frac{1}{8x^3}$ **29.** $8x^3$
30. $\frac{32}{x^5}$ **31.** $\frac{49}{y^2}$ **32.** $\frac{1}{y^4}$ **33.** $\frac{27a^9b^3}{8}$ **34.** x
35. $80a^{10}$ **36.** $-30a^5b^9$ **37.** $\frac{3}{y^3}$ **38.** $4a^4b$ **39.** $5xz$
40. $\frac{18a^3}{b^2}$ **41.** $5x^3$ **42.** 0.00012   **43.** $xy^2 + y$ **44.** $3y - 2x$
45. $x^2 - 9$ **46.** $x^2 - 5x + 6$ **47.** $8x^2 - x - 2$
48. $2x^2 - 7x + 11$ **49.** $x - 14$ **50.** $-x^2 - 6x - 2$

51. $-5x + 1$ **52.** 24   **53.** 7   **54.** $8a^4 + 10a^3 + 14a^2$
55. $x^2 + x - 6$ **56.** $12x^2 - 24x + 12$
57. $x^3 + 6x^2 + 18x + 27$ **58.** $x^2 + x + \frac{6}{25}$ **59.** $y^2 - \frac{25}{36}$
60. $x^3 + 3x^2 + 3x + 1$
61. $9a^2 - 12a + 4$ **45.** $x^2 - 9$ **63.** $4x^2 - b^2$
64. $V = 3.375$ mi^3 **65.** $V = 2w^3$
66. McLaren: $\$3.7 \times 10^6$, Lykan: $\$3.4 \times 10^6$, Lamborghini: $\$3.3 \times 10^6$,
  Aston Martin: $\$3 \times 10^6$, Pagani: $\$2.8 \times 10^6$
67. Clement/Mucheru: 5×10^{-2} sec, Ibarguen/Rojas: 1.9×10^{-1} sec,
  Drouin/Barshim: 2×10^{-2} sec, Thompson/Bowie: 1.2×10^{-1} sec

Chapter 9 Cumulative Review
1. 5,044   **2.** $\frac{23}{28}$ **3.** 10.519   **4.** $2\frac{1}{2}$ **5.** 2,026,794
6. 0.84   **7.** 36   **8.** $\frac{9}{14}$ **9.** 540,000   **10.** $\frac{9}{25}$ **11.** $7\frac{5}{8}$
12. 0.265   **13.** 37%   **14.** 19.8 lb   **15.** $1\frac{9}{25}$ **16.** 35%
17. $\frac{5}{64}$ **18.** $12x + 3$ **19.** -9 **20.** $-\frac{1}{3}$ **21.** 5   **22.** -3
23. $y = 42$ **24.** $x = -\frac{47}{18} = -2\frac{11}{18}$ **25.** 13   **26.** $x = 6$
27. $-2x^2 - 10x - 3$ **28.** $25x^2 + 10x + 1$ **29.** $x^3 - 8$
30. Ben is 31, Ryan is 26   **31.** 23 mpg   **32.** $\$140$, 25%
33. 5 m   **34.** $\$11.04$ **35.** $\$32$ **36.** 60   **37.** $\$468$
38. 128   **39.** 11.9 million; 15.3%   **40.** 78 million; 90 million; $\frac{13}{15}$

Chapter 9 Test
1. -243 **2.** $\frac{4}{25}$ **3.** $72x^{10}$ **4.** 247,000   **5.** $-\frac{1}{9}$
6. $7a^2b^2$ **7.** $\frac{1}{a^3}$ **8.** $\frac{1}{x^3}$ **9.** 2.78×10^1 **10.** $\frac{5x^2y^2}{z^2}$
11. $9a^3$ **12.** $5x$ **13.** 1.6×10^4 **14.** $8x^2 - x - 12$
15. $x^2 + 7x$ **16.** $-6x - 10$ **17.** 11   **18.** $6a^4 + 10a^3 - 8a^2$
19. $x^2 - x - \frac{3}{4}$ **20.** $8x^2 - 2x - 6$ **21.** $x^2 - 9$
22. $\$7.83 \times 10^8$ **23.** $\$5.55 \times 10^8$ **24.** 2×10^{-2} **25.** 4×10^{-2}

INDEX ....

PHOTO CREDITS ....